Jon Holder
Shine RM 622

Introduction to Ordinary Differential Equations

Second Enlarged Edition with Applications

Introduction to Ordinary Differential Equations

Second Enlarged Edition with Applications

ALBERT L. RABENSTEIN
MACALESTER COLLEGE

ACADEMIC PRESS   New York and London

ACADEMIC PRESS, INC.
111 Fifth Avenue, New York, New York 10003

United Kingdom Edition published by
ACADEMIC PRESS, INC. (LONDON) LTD.
24/28 Oval Road, London NW1 7DD

LIBRARY OF CONGRESS CATALOG CARD NUMBER: 78-185031

AMS(MOS) 1970 Subject Classification: 34-01

Second Printing, 1972

PRINTED IN THE UNITED STATES OF AMERICA

CONTENTS

PREFACE

This book is intended to provide an introduction to differential equations. The topics considered are those important in applications, but the stress is on the mathematical techniques. Applications from various branches of science are presented for purposes of motivation. Standard elementary methods for finding solutions are described. The book also treats a number of special topics that are useful in applications. These include Laplace transforms, special functions, eigenvalue problems, and Fourier series. A chapter on partial differential equations and boundary value problems has been included to provide applications of these topics. The final two chapters deal with more theoretical topics that are not directly concerned with finding solutions. The material in these chapters is not, however, without importance in applications.

The reader is assumed to have a knowledge of elementary but not advanced calculus. Because of this, several basic theorems have been stated without proof. Properties of determinants and results concerning the consistency of systems of linear algebraic equations are used fairly often. The necessary facts are derived in an appendix. More difficult theoretical topics have been arranged so that they may be taken up after the more elementary material. For example, the theory of linear equations is discussed at the end of Chapter II, and convergence of series solutions at the end of Chapter III. General existence and uniqueness theory has been postponed until the final chapter. These sections can be omitted without loss of continuity.

The first three chapters are concerned with methods for solving single differential equations; Chapter VIII deals with systems of equations. The material in these chapters is basic. Chapters IV–VI, IX, XI, and XII are almost entirely independent of one another (except for Section 6.5) and can be taken up in any order. Chapter X depends on Chapter VII, which in turn depends on Chapters IV–VI. Answers to approximately half of the computational exercises have been placed at the end of the book.

A number of changes in the revised edition are intended to make the book more suitable for a first course in differential equations. A new introductory chapter provides a more leisurely treatment of first-order equations. The number of exercises has been greatly increased. The applications and examples have been expanded, and now include problems in biology, chemistry, and economics as well as mechanics and electric circuits. Some topics in complex variables and eigenvalue problems have been dropped. Other sections have been rewritten wherever it seemed that clarity or usefulness could be improved.

I

Introduction
to Differential Equations

1.1   INTRODUCTION

An ordinary differential equation may be defined as an equation that involves a single unknown function of a single variable and some finite number of its derivatives. For example, 'a simple problem from calculus is that of finding all functions f for which

$$f'(x) = 3x^2 - 4x + 5 \tag{1.1}$$

for all x. Clearly a function f satisfies the condition (1.1) if and only if it is of the form

$$f(x) = x^3 - 2x^2 + 5x + c,$$

where c is an arbitrary number. A more difficult problem is that of finding all functions g for which

$$g'(x) + 2[g(x)]^2 = 3x^2 - 4x + 5. \tag{1.2}$$

Another difficult problem is that of finding all functions y for which (we use the abbreviation y for $y(x)$)

$$x^2 \frac{d^2 y}{dx^2} - 3x \left(\frac{dy}{dx}\right)^2 + 4y = \sin x. \tag{1.3}$$

In each of the problems (1.1), (1.2), and (1.3), we are asked to find all functions that satisfy a certain condition where the condition involves one or more *derivatives* of the function. We can reformulate our definition of a differential equation as follows. Let F be a function of $n + 2$ variables. Then the equation

$$F[x, y, y', y'', \ldots, y^{(n)}] = 0 \tag{1.4}$$

is called an ordinary differential equation of order n for the unknown function y. The *order* of the equation is the order of the highest order derivative that appears in the equation. Thus, Eqs. (1.1) and (1.2) are first-order equations, while Eq. (1.3) is of second order.

A *partial* differential equation (as distinguished from an *ordinary* differential equation) is an equation that involves an unknown function of more than one independent variable, together with partial derivatives of the function. An example of a partial differential equation for an unknown function $u(x, t)$ of two variables is

$$\frac{\partial^2 u}{\partial x^2} = \frac{\partial u}{\partial t} + u.$$

Except in Chapter X, almost all the differential equations that we shall consider will be ordinary.

By a *solution* of an ordinary differential equation of order n, we mean a function that, on some interval,† possesses at least n derivatives and satisfies the equation. For example, a solution of the equation

$$\frac{dy}{dx} - 2y = 6$$

is given by the formula

$$y = e^{2x} - 3 \qquad \text{for all } x,$$

because

$$\frac{d}{dx}(e^{2x} - 3) - 2(e^{2x} - 3) = 2e^{2x} - 2e^{2x} + 6 = 6$$

for all x. The set of all solutions of a differential equation is called the *general solution* of the equation. For instance, the general solution of the equation

$$\frac{dy}{dx} = 3x^2 - 4x$$

---

† We shall use the notations (a, b), $[a, b]$, $(a, b]$, $[a, b)$, (a, ∞), $[a, \infty]$, $(-\infty, a)$, $(-\infty, a]$, $(-\infty, \infty)$ for intervals. Here (a, b) is the set of all real numbers x such that $a < x < b$; $[a, b]$ is the set of all real numbers x such that $a \leq x \leq b$; $[a, b)$ is the set of all real numbers x such that $a \leq x < b$; and so on.

consists of all functions that are of the form

$$y = x^3 - 2x^2 + c, \qquad x \text{ in } \mathcal{I},$$

where c is an arbitrary constant and $\mathcal{I}$ is an arbitrary interval. To *solve* a differential equation is to find its general solution.

Let us now solve the second-order equation

$$\frac{d^2 y}{dx^2} = 12x + 8.$$

Integrating, we find that

$$\frac{dy}{dx} = 6x^2 + 8x + c_1,$$

where c_1 is an arbitrary constant. A second integration yields

$$y = 2x^3 + 4x^2 + c_1 x + c_2$$

for the general solution. Here c_2 is a second arbitrary constant.

The general solution of the third-order equation

$$y''' = 16e^{-2x}$$

can be found by three successive integrations. We find easily that

$$y'' = -8e^{-2x} + c_1',$$
$$y' = 4e^{-2x} + c_1' x + c_2,$$

and

$$y = -2e^{-2x} + \tfrac{1}{2}c_1' x^2 + c_2 x + c_3,$$

where c_1', c_2, and c_3 are arbitrary constants. If we replace the constant c_1' in the last formula by $2c_1$, it becomes

$$y = -2e^{-2x} + c_1 x^2 + c_2 x + c_3.$$

This last formula is slightly simpler in appearance. The two formulas describe the same set of functions since the coefficient of x^2 is completely arbitrary in both cases. Since $c_1' = 2c_1$, we see that to any arbitrarily assigned value for c_1, there corresponds a value for c_1' and vice versa.

If a formula can be found that describes the general solution of an nth-order equation, it usually involves n arbitrary constants. We note that this principle has been borne out in the last three examples, which admittedly are rather simple. Actually it is possible to find a simple formula that describes the general solution only for relatively few types of differential equations. Several such classes of first-order equations are discussed in the following three sections. In cases where it is not possible to find explicit formulas for the solutions, it still may be possible to discover certain properties of the solutions. For instance, it may be possible to show that a solution is bounded (or unbounded), to find its limiting value as the independent variable becomes infinite, or to establish that it is a periodic function. Much advanced work in differential equations is concerned with such matters.

Perhaps some reasons should now be given as to why we want to solve differential equations. Briefly, many experimentally discovered laws of science can be formulated as relations that involve not only magnitudes of quantities but also rates of change (usually with respect to time) of these magnitudes. Thus, the laws can be formulated as differential equations. A number of examples of problems that give rise to differential equations are presented in this book. Some applications will be described in Sections 1.6, 1.7, and 1.8 after we have learned how to solve several kinds of first-order equations.

We have seen that ordinary differential equations can be classified as to order. We shall also categorize them in one more way. An equation of order n is said to be a *linear* equation if it is of the special form

$$a_0(x)y^{(n)} + a_1(x)y^{(n-1)} + \cdots + a_{n-1}(x)y' + a_n(x)y = f(x),$$

where $a_0, a_1, \ldots, a_n$ and f are given functions that are defined on an interval $\mathcal{I}$. Thus the general nth-order equation (1.4) is linear if the function F is a first-degree polynomial in $y, y', \ldots, y^{(n)}$. An equation that is not linear is said to be a *nonlinear* equation. For example, each of the equations

$$y' + (\cos x)y = e^x,$$
$$xy'' + y' = x^2,$$
$$xy''' - e^x y' + (\sin x)y = 0,$$

is linear, while each of the equations

$$y' + y^2 = 1,$$
$$y'' + (\cos x)yy' = \sin x,$$
$$y''' - x(y')^3 + y = 0,$$

is nonlinear. Because linear equations possess special properties, they will be treated in a separate chapter, Chapter II.

In most applications that involve differential equations, the unknown function is required not only to satisfy the differential equation but also to satisfy certain other auxiliary conditions. These auxiliary conditions often specify the values of the function and some of its derivatives at one or more points. As an example, suppose we are asked to find a solution of the equation

$$\frac{dy}{dx} = 3x^2$$

that satisfies the auxiliary condition $y = 1$ when $x = 2$, or

$$y(2) = 1.$$

Thus, we require the graph of our solution (which is called a *solution curve* or *integral curve*) to pass through the point $(2, 1)$ in the xy plane. The general solution of the equation is

$$y = x^3 + c,$$

where c is an arbitrary constant. In order to find a specific solution that satisfies the initial condition, we set $x = 2$ and $y = 1$ in the last formula, finding that $1 = 8 + c$ or $c = -7$. Thus, there is only one value of c for which the condition is satisfied. The equation possesses one and only one solution (defined for all x) that satisfies the condition, namely,

$$y = x^3 - 7.$$

For an nth-order equation of the form

$$y^{(n)} = G[x, y, y', y'', \ldots, y^{(n-1)}], \tag{1.5}$$

auxiliary conditions of the type

$$y(x_0) = k_0, \quad y'(x_0) = k_1, \quad y''(x_0) = k_2, \ldots, \quad y^{(n-1)}(x_0) = k_{n-1}, \tag{1.6}$$

where the k_i are given numbers, are common. We note that there are n conditions for the nth-order equation. These conditions specify the values of the unknown function and its first $n - 1$ derivatives at a single point x_0. For a first-order equation,

$$y' = H(x, y),$$

we would have only one condition,

$$y(x_0) = k_0,$$

specifying the value of the unknown function itself at x_0. In the case of a second-order equation,

$$y'' = K(x, y, y'),$$

we would have two conditions

$$y(x_0) = k_0, \qquad y'(x_0) = k_1.$$

A set of auxiliary conditions of the form (1.6) is called a set of *initial conditions* for the Eq. (1.5). The equation (1.5) together with the conditions (1.6) constitute an *initial value problem*. The reason for this terminology is that in many applications the independent variable x represents time and the conditions are specified at the instant x_0 at which some process begins.

In specifying the values of the first $n - 1$ derivatives of a solution of Eq. (1.5) at x_0, we have essentially specified the values of any higher derivatives that might exist. The values of these higher derivatives can be found from the differential equation itself. For example, let us consider the initial value problem

$$y'' = x^2 - y^3$$
$$y(1) = 2, \qquad y'(1) = -1.$$

From the differential equation we see that

$$y''(1) = 1 - 8 = -7.$$

By differentiating through in the differential equation, we find that

$$y''' = 2x - 3y^2y'$$

and hence

$$y'''(1) = 2 - (3)(4)(-1) = 14.$$

The values of higher derivatives at $x = 1$ can be found by repeated differentiation.

If a function can be expanded in a power series about a point x_0, a knowledge of the values of the function and its derivatives at x_0 completely determines the function. This discussion suggests that the initial value problem (1.5) and (1.6) can have but one solution if the function G is infinitely differentiable with respect to all variables. Actually it can be shown that, under rather mild restrictions on G, the initial value problem possesses a solution and that it has only one solution. A fuller discussion of questions of existence and uniqueness of solutions is given in Chapter XII. In most of the problems and examples of this chapter, it is possible to actually find all the solutions of the differential equation at hand. In cases where this is impossible, it is comforting to know that the problem being considered actually has a solution and that there is only one solution. An initial value problem purporting to describe some physical process would not be very valuable without these two properties.

Exercises for Section 1.1

1. Find the order of the differential equation and determine whether it is linear or nonlinear.

   (a) $y' = e^x$

   (b) $y'' + xy = \sin x$

   (c) $y' + e^y = 0$

   (d) $y'' + 2y' + y = \cos x$

   (e) $y'' + xyy' + y = 2$

   (f) $y^{(4)} + 3(\cos x)y''' + y' = 0$

   (g) $y''' = 0$

   (h) $yy'' + y' = 0$

2. Find the general solution of the differential equation.

   (a) $y' = 2x - 3$

   (b) $y' = 3x^2 \sin x^3$

   (c) $y' = \dfrac{4}{x(x-4)}$

   (d) $y'' = 12e^{-2x} + 4$

   (e) $y'' = \sec^2 x$

   (f) $y'' = 8e^{-2x} + e^x$

   (g) $y''' = 24x - 6$

   (h) $y^{(4)} = 32 \sin 2x$

3. Find a solution of the differential equation that satisfies the specified conditions.

   (a) $y' = 0, \quad y(2) = -5$

   (b) $y' = x, \quad y(2) = 9$

   (c) $y' = 4x - 3, \quad y(4) = 3$

   (d) $y' = 3x^2 - 6x + 1, \quad y(-2) = 0$

   (e) $y'' = 0, \quad y(2) = 1, \quad y'(2) = -1$

   (f) $y'' = 9e^{-3x}, \quad y(0) = 1, \quad y'(0) = 2$

   (g) $y'' = \cos x, \quad y(\pi) = 2, \quad y'(\pi) = 0$

   (h) $y''' = e^{-x}, \quad y(0) = -1, \quad y'(0) = 1, \quad y''(0) = 3$

4. Show that a function is a solution of the equation $y' + ay = 0$, where a is a constant, if and only if it is a solution of the equation $(e^{ax}y)' = 0$. Hence show that the general solution of the equation is described by the formula $y = ce^{-ax}$, where c is an arbitrary constant.

5. Use the result of Exercise 4 to find the general solution of the given differential equation.

   (a) $y' + 3y = 0$

   (b) $y' - 3y = 0$

   (c) $3y' - y = 0$

   (d) $3y' + 2y = 0$

6. Verify that every function of the form $y = x^2 + c/x$, where c is a constant, is a solution of the equation $xy' + y = 3x^2$ on any interval that does not contain $x = 0$.

7. Verify that each of the functions $y = e^{-x}$ and $y = e^{3x}$ is a solution of the equation $y'' - 2y' - 3y = 0$ on any interval. Then show that $c_1 e^{-x} + c_2 e^{3x}$ is a solution for every choice of the constants c_1 and c_2.

8. Suppose that a function f is a solution of the initial value problem $y' = x^2 + y^2, y(1) = 2$. Find $f'(1), f''(1)$, and $f'''(1)$.

9. If the function g is a solution of the initial value problem
$$y'' + yy' - x^3 = 0, \quad y(-1) = 1, \quad y'(-1) = 2,$$
find $g''(-1)$ and $g'''(-1)$.

10. Show that the problem $y' = 2x$, $y(0) = 0$, $y(1) = 100$, has no solution. Is this an initial value problem?

1.2   SEPARABLE EQUATIONS

A first-order differential equation that can be written in the form

$$p(y)\frac{dy}{dx} = q(x),\tag{1.7}$$

where p and q are given functions, is called a *separable* equation. Examples of such equations are

$$y^{-2}\frac{dy}{dx} = 2x, \qquad y^{-1}\frac{dy}{dx} = (x+1)^{-1}, \qquad (3y^2 + e^y)\frac{dy}{dx} = \cos x.$$

If a function f is a solution of Eq. (1.7) on an interval $\mathscr{I}$, then

$$p[f(x)]f'(x) = q(x)$$

for x in $\mathscr{I}$. Taking antiderivatives, we have

$$\int p[f(x)]f'(x)\,dx = \int q(x)\,dx + c$$

or

$$\int p(y)\,dy = \int q(x)\,dx + c.$$

If P and Q are functions such that $P'(y) = p(y)$ and $Q'(x) = q(x)$, then the solution f must satisfy the equation

$$P(y) = Q(x) + c,\tag{1.8}$$

where c is a constant. That is,

$$P[f(x)] = Q(x) + c$$

for x in $\mathscr{I}$. Conversely, if y is any differentiable function that satisfies Eq. (1.8), we see by implicit differentiation that

$$P'(y)\frac{dy}{dx} = Q'(x)$$

or

$$p(y)\frac{dy}{dx} = q(x).$$

Thus, a function is a solution of Eq. (1.7) if and only if it satisfies an equation of the form (1.8) for some choice of the constant c. It may not be possible to find an explicit formula for y in terms of x from Eq. (1.8). However, we say that Eq. (1.8) determines the solutions of the differential equation *implicitly*. Let us now consider some examples of separable equations.

Example 1

$$\frac{dy}{dx} = 2xy^2. \tag{1.9}$$

"Separating the variables," we have

$$y^{-2}\frac{dy}{dx} = 2x$$

or

$$y^{-2}\, dy = 2x\, dx.$$

Taking antiderivatives, we have

$$\int y^{-2}\, dy = \int 2x\, dx + c$$

or

$$-\frac{1}{y} = x^2 + c.$$

Thus, the functions defined by the formula

$$y = \frac{-1}{x^2 + c} \tag{1.10}$$

are solutions of Eq. (1.9). Note, however, that the identically zero function $(y = 0)$ is also a solution. In arriving at formula (1.10), we started out by dividing both sides of the original equation by y^2, and this procedure is not valid when $y = 0$.

Suppose that it is desired to find the solution curve that passes through the point $(2, -1)$ in the xy plane. Then our initial condition is

$$y(2) = -1.$$

Setting $x = 2$ and $y = -1$ in formula (1.10), we see that

$$-1 = \frac{-1}{4 + c}$$

or $c = -3$. Then the desired solution is given by the formula

$$y = \frac{1}{3 - x^2}.$$

Example 2

$$(x + 1)\frac{dy}{dx} = 2y.$$

Here we have

$$\frac{dy}{y} = 2\frac{dx}{x + 1}$$

or

$$\ln|y| = \ln(x + 1)^2 + c'.$$

Then

$$|y| = e^{c'}(x + 1)^2$$

and

$$y = \pm e^{c'}(x + 1)^2, \tag{1.11}$$

where c' is an arbitrary constant. But $\pm e^{c'}$ can have any value except zero, so the set of functions described by formula (1.11) is also described by the simpler formula

$$y = c(x + 1)^2, \tag{1.12}$$

where c is a constant different from zero but otherwise is arbitrary. However, since $y = 0$ is obviously a solution of the differential equation, formula (1.12) also describes a solution when $c = 0$. This formula, with c completely arbitrary, gives the general solution of the equation.

Example 3   Consider the initial value problem

$$\frac{dy}{dx} = \frac{\cos x}{3y^2 + e^y}, \qquad y(0) = 2.$$

From the differential equation we have

$$(3y^2 + e^y)\,dy = \cos x\,dx$$

or

$$y^3 + e^y = \sin x + c.$$

Setting $x = 0$ and $y = 2$ (these values come from the initial condition) we find that

$$8 + e^2 = c.$$

Hence, the desired solution (if such a solution exists) is implicitly determined by the equation

$$y^3 + e^y = \sin x + 8 + e^2.$$

Some differential equations that are not separable as they stand become separable after a change of variable. One such class of equations consists of those that can be written in the form

$$\frac{dy}{dx} = F\left(\frac{y}{x}\right). \tag{1.13}$$

An example of such an equation is

$$(x^4 + y^4)\frac{dy}{dx} = x^3 y,$$

which may be rewritten as

$$\frac{dy}{dx} = \frac{x^3 y}{x^4 + y^4}$$

or

$$\frac{dy}{dx} = \frac{y/x}{1 + (y/x)^4}.$$

An equation of the form (1.13) can be made separable by introducing a new independent variable v where

$$v = \frac{y}{x}.$$

For then

$$y = vx, \qquad \frac{dy}{dx} = x\frac{dv}{dx} + v,$$

and Eq. (1.13) becomes

$$x\frac{dv}{dx} + v = F(v)$$

or

$$\frac{1}{F(v) - v}\frac{dv}{dx} = \frac{1}{x},$$

which is separable.

As an example we consider the equation

$$2x^2 \frac{dy}{dx} = x^2 + y^2.$$

This equation can be put in the form (1.21) since

$$\frac{dy}{dx} = \frac{x^2 + y^2}{2x^2} = \frac{1}{2}\left[1 + \left(\frac{y}{x}\right)^2\right].$$

Setting $y = vx$, we have

$$x\frac{dv}{dx} + v = \tfrac{1}{2}(1 + v^2),$$

or

$$2x\frac{dv}{dx} = v^2 - 2v + 1,$$

or

$$\frac{dv}{(v-1)^2} = \frac{1}{2}\frac{1}{x}dx.$$

Then

$$\frac{-1}{v-1} = \tfrac{1}{2}\ln|x| + c'$$

or

$$v = 1 - \frac{2}{\ln|x| + 2c'}.$$

Replacing v by y/x and setting $c = 2c'$, we have

$$y = x - \frac{2x}{\ln|x| + c}.$$

In determining if a given first-order equation can be written in the form (1.13), the following criterion is often useful. An equation

$$M(x, y) + N(x, y)\frac{dy}{dx} = 0 \qquad\qquad (1.14)$$

can be put in the form (1.13) if the functions M and N are *homogeneous of the same degree*. A function $g(x, y)$ (defined for all (x, y)) is said to be *homogeneous of degree m* if

$$g(tx, ty) = t^m g(x, y)$$

for all t.† For example, if

$$g(x, y) = x^3y^2 - 3x^5,$$

we see that

$$g(tx, ty) = t^5(x^3y^2 - 3x^5) = t^5g(x, y).$$

Thus, g is homogeneous of degree 5. However, the function h, where

$$h(x, y) = x^3y - 3x^2,$$

is not homogeneous.

Let us write Eq. (1.14) as

$$\frac{dy}{dx} = -\frac{M(x, y)}{N(x, y)}.$$

If M and N are both homogeneous of degree m, then

$$M(x, y) = t^{-m}M(tx, ty), \qquad N(x, y) = t^{-m}N(tx, ty).$$

Setting $t = x^{-1}$, we have

$$M(x, y) = x^mM(1, y/x), \qquad N(x, y) = x^mN(1, y/x)$$

and

$$\frac{dy}{dx} = -\frac{M(1, y/x)}{N(1, y/x)}.$$

This equation is of the form (1.13).

In the example

$$x^2 + y^2 - 2x^2\frac{dy}{dx} = 0,$$

where

$$M(x, y) = x^2 + y^2, \qquad N(x, y) = -2x^2,$$

it is clear that M and N are both homogeneous of degree 2. Hence the equation can be written in the form (1.13). Other examples of equations that can be put in the form (1.13) are

$$x^2\frac{dy}{dx} = y^2 - x^2$$

and

$$(xy + x^2)\sin\frac{y}{x} + y^2\frac{dy}{dx} = 0.$$

---

† Some restriction must be placed on the possible values of t if g is not defined everywhere.

Exercises for Section 1.2

In Exercises 1–20, find the general solution, if possible. Otherwise find a relation that defines the solutions implicitly. If an initial condition is specified, also find the particular solution that satisfies the condition.

1. $yy' = 4x$, $y(1) = -3$

2. $xy' = 4y$, $y(1) = -3$

3. $y' = 2xy^2$, $y(2) = 1$

4. $y' = e^x(1 - y^2)^{1/2}$, $y(0) = \frac{1}{2}$

5. $y' = \dfrac{1 + y^2}{1 + x^2}$, $y(2) = 3$

6. $e^y y' = 4$, $y(0) = 2$

7. $2(y - 1)y' = e^x$, $y(0) = -2$

8. $2y' = y(y - 2)$

9. $3y^2 y' = (1 + y^3) \cos x$

10. $(\cos^2 x)y' = y^2(y - 1) \sin x$

11. $(\cos y)y' = 1$

12. $(\cos^2 x)y' = (1 + y^2)^{1/2}$

13. $x^2 y' = xy - y^2$

14. $x^2 y' = y^2 + 2xy$

15. $xyy' = 2y^2 - x^2$

16. $xy' = y - xe^{y/x}$

17. $e^{y/x}y' = 2(e^{y/x} - 1) + \dfrac{y}{x}e^{y/x}$

18. $y' = \dfrac{y}{x} - 3\left(\dfrac{y}{x}\right)^{4/3}$

19. $xy' = y + (x^2 + y^2)^{1/2}$

20. $3xy^2 y' = 4y^3 - x^3$

21. Show that an equation of the form $y' = F(ay + bx + c)$, $a \neq 0$, becomes separable under the change of dependent variable $v = ay + bx + k$ where k is any number.

22. Use the result of Exercise 21 to solve the differential equation.

   (a) $y' = (y + 4x - 1)^2$

   (b) $(y - x + 1)y' = y - x$

   (c) $(y - 3x)y' = 3(y - 3x + 2)$

   (d) $(y - 2x)y' = 3y - 6x + 1$

23. Consider a first-order differential equation of the form

$$(a_1 x + b_1 y + c_1)y' = a_2 x + b_2 y + c_2.$$

   (a) If $a_1 b_2 - b_1 a_2 = 0$, show that the equation is of the type considered in Exercise 21.

   (b) If $a_1 b_2 - b_1 a_2 \neq 0$ introduce new variables u and v, where

$$u = x + p, \qquad v = y + q.$$

Show that the constants p and q can be chosen in such a way that the equation takes on the form

$$(a_1 u + b_1 v)\frac{dv}{du} = a_2 u + b_2 v.$$

Hence

$$\frac{dv}{du} = F\left(\frac{v}{u}\right).$$

24. Use the results of Exercise 23 to solve the equation.

(a) $(x + y + 1)y' = y + 2$

(b) $(3x - y + 1)y' = -x + 3y + 5$

1.3 EXACT EQUATIONS

The first-order equation

$$M(x, y) + N(x, y)\frac{dy}{dx} = 0 \qquad (1.15)$$

is said to be *exact* (in some region of the xy plane) if there exists a function ϕ with continuous first partial derivatives such that

$$\frac{\partial \phi(x, y)}{\partial x} = M(x, y), \qquad \frac{\partial \phi(x, y)}{\partial y} = N(x, y). \qquad (1.16)$$

The relationship between the function ϕ and the solutions of the differential equation is described in the following theorem.

Theorem 1.1   If the differential equation (1.15) is exact and if the function ϕ has the properties (1.16) then a function f, with $y = f(x)$, is a solution of the differential equation if and only if it satisfies an equation of the form

$$\phi(x, y) = c,$$

where c is a constant.

PROOF   Suppose that the function f is a solution of Eq. (1.15). If $y = f(x)$ we have

$$\frac{\partial \phi(x, y)}{\partial x} + \frac{\partial \phi(x, y)}{\partial y}\frac{dy}{dx} = 0$$

or

$$\frac{d\phi(x,\ y)}{dx} = 0.$$

Hence $\phi(x,\ y) = c$. Conversely, suppose that a (differentiable) function f satisfies the equation $\phi(x,\ y) = c$. Then by implicit differentiation we have

$$\frac{\partial\phi(x,\ y)}{\partial x} + \frac{\partial\phi(x,\ y)}{\partial y}\frac{dy}{dx} = 0$$

or

$$M(x,\ y) + N(x,\ y)\frac{dy}{dx} = 0.$$

Hence the function is a solution of the differential equation.

Notice that if Eq. (1.15) is exact, then the total differential of ϕ is

$$d\phi = \frac{\partial\phi}{\partial x}\ dx + \frac{\partial\phi}{\partial y}\ dy = M\ dx + N\ dy.$$

Along any solution curve, $d\phi = 0$, and the solutions satisfy equations of the form $\phi(x,\ y) = c$.

We need a criterion for determining whether or not an equation is exact. We also need a method for finding the function ϕ when it is exact. In what follows we assume that the functions M and N are continuous together with their first partial derivatives in some region.

Suppose that Eq. (1.15) is exact. Then there exists a function ϕ such that $M = \partial\phi/\partial x$ and $N = \partial\phi/\partial y$. Hence

$$\frac{\partial M}{\partial y} = \frac{\partial^2\phi}{\partial y\ \partial x},\qquad \frac{\partial N}{\partial y} = \frac{\partial^2\phi}{\partial x\ \partial y},$$

and because the mixed second partial derivatives of ϕ are equal (since ϕ, ϕ_x, ϕ_y, ϕ_{xy}, and ϕ_{yx} are continuous), we have

$$\frac{\partial M}{\partial y} = \frac{\partial N}{\partial x}. \tag{1.17}$$

Thus if the equation is exact, the condition (1.17) is satisfied.

It can be shown that if M and N satisfy the condition (1.17) in a *simply connected region* then the differential equation is exact. A simply connected region is such that every simple closed curve† in the region contains only

_____

† A *simple* closed curve does not cross itself. A circle is a simple closed curve. A figure eight is closed but not simple.

points of the region inside it. The interior of an ellipse or a rectangle is a simply connected region but the region bounded by two concentric circles is not simply connected. We shall prove that the condition (1.17) is sufficient for exactness in the special case of a rectangle. Let D be the rectangle

$$\{(x, y): a < x < b, \quad c < y < d\},$$

where any or all of a, b, c, and d may be infinite. Such a region is simply connected.

Theorem 1.2 Let M and N satisfy the condition (1.17) in the rectangle D. Then the equation $M + Ny' = 0$ is exact.

PROOF Let (x_0, y_0) be any fixed point in D. We define a function ϕ of two variables by means of the formula

$$\phi(x, y) = \int_{x_0}^{x} M(s, y_0)\, ds + \int_{y_0}^{y} N(x, t)\, dt \tag{1.18}$$

for (x, y) in D. See Fig. 1.1. We need to verify that $\partial\phi/\partial x = M$ and $\partial\phi/\partial y = N$.

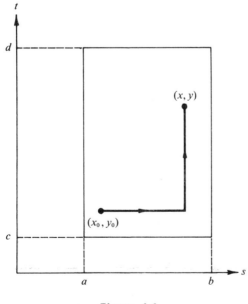

Figure 1.1

Differentiating with respect to x, we have†

$$\frac{\partial \phi(x, y)}{\partial x} = M(x, y_0) + \int_{y_0}^{y} \frac{\partial N(x, t)}{\partial x} \, dt.$$

Since the condition (1.17) is satisfied, $\partial N(x, t)/\partial x = \partial M(x, t)/\partial t$. Hence

$$\frac{\partial \phi(x, y)}{\partial x} = M(x, y_0) + \int_{y_0}^{y} \frac{\partial M(x, t)}{\partial t} \, dt$$

$$= M(x, y_0) + M(x, y) - M(x, y_0)$$

$$= M(x, y).$$

In similar fashion it can be shown (Exercise 1) that $\partial \phi/\partial y = N$. Since the function ϕ has the property (1.16) the differential equation is exact.

Formula (1.18) can be used to find a function ϕ when the equation (1.15) is exact. However, the function can usually be found by means of a simpler procedure which does not necessitate memorizing the formula. We shall illustrate the method with an example.

The equation

$$3x^2 - 2y^2 + (1 - 4xy)\frac{dy}{dx} = 0 \qquad\qquad (1.19)$$

is exact, since

$$M(x, y) = 3x^2 - 2y^2, \qquad N(x, y) = 1 - 4xy,$$

and

$$\frac{\partial M(x, y)}{\partial y} = -4y = \frac{\partial N(x, y)}{\partial x}$$

for all (x, y). Hence, by Theorem 1.2, there exists a function ϕ such that

$$\frac{\partial \phi(x, y)}{\partial x} = 3x^2 - 2y^2, \qquad \frac{\partial \phi(x, y)}{\partial y} = 1 - 4xy. \qquad (1.20)$$

Integrating with respect to x in the first of these relations, we see that ϕ is of the form

$$\phi(x, y) = x^3 - 2xy^2 + f(y), \qquad\qquad (1.21)$$

---

† We have differentiated with respect to x under the integral sign, a procedure that requires justification. This situation is covered by *Leibnitz's rule*, which is discussed in most advanced calculus books.

where f can be any function of y only since $\partial f(y)/\partial x = 0$. We must choose f so that the second of the conditions (1.20) is satisfied. We require that

$$\frac{\partial \phi(x, y)}{\partial y} = -4xy + f'(y) = 1 - 4xy$$

or

$$f'(y) = 1.$$

One possible choice for f is $f(y) = y$. Then from Eq. (1.21) we have

$$\phi(x, y) = x^3 - 2xy^2 + y.$$

The solutions of Eq. (1.19) are those differentiable functions that satisfy equations of the form

$$x^3 - 2xy^2 + y = c.$$

If the equation $M + Ny' = 0$ is not exact, it may be possible to make it exact by multiplying through by some function. That is, we may be able to find a function ρ such that

$$\rho(x, y)M(x, y) + \rho(x, y)N(x, y)y' = 0$$

is an exact equation. If such a function ρ exists, it is called an *integrating factor* for the original equation. As an example, let us consider the equation

$$1 + x^2y^2 + y + xy' = 0. \tag{1.22}$$

This equation is not exact since

$$\frac{\partial M(x, y)}{\partial y} = 2x^2y + 1, \qquad \frac{\partial N(x, y)}{\partial x} = 1.$$

However, if we multiply through in Eq. (1.22) by

$$\rho(x, y) = \frac{1}{1 + x^2y^2},$$

it becomes

$$\left(1 + \frac{y}{1 + x^2y^2}\right) + \frac{x}{1 + x^2y^2} y' = 0. \tag{1.23}$$

This equation is exact, since

$$\frac{\partial}{\partial y}\left(1 + \frac{y}{1 + x^2y^2}\right) = \frac{\partial}{\partial x}\left(\frac{x}{1 + x^2y^2}\right) = \frac{1 - x^2y^2}{(1 + x^2y^2)^2}.$$

Since

$$d(\tan^{-1} xy) = \frac{y}{1 + x^2y^2} dx + \frac{x}{1 + x^2y^2} dy,$$

we see from Eq. (1.23) that

$$d(x + \tan^{-1} xy) = 0$$

along a solution curve. Hence the solutions satisfy the relation

$$x + \tan^{-1} xy = c$$

and the solutions themselves are given by the formula

$$y = \frac{1}{x} \tan(c - x).$$

There is no general rule for finding integrating factors. If the solver has in mind the formula for $d(\tan^{-1} xy)$, he might be led to an integrating factor in the above example. Usually the procedure is one of trial and error, with educated guessing.

Exercises for Section 1.3

1. Show that $\partial\phi(x, y)/\partial y = N(x, y)$, where ϕ is defined as in Eq. (1.18).

In Exercises 2–13, first determine if the equation is exact. If it is exact, find the general solution, or at least a relation that defines the solutions implicitly.

2. $3x^3y^2y' + 3x^2y^3 - 5x^4 = 0$

3. $(3x^2y^2 - 4xy)y' + 2xy^3 - 2y^2 = 0$

4. $xe^{xy}y' + ye^{xy} - 4x^3 = 0$

5. $(x + y^2)y' + 2x^2 - y = 0$

6. $[\cos(x^2 + y) - 3xy^2]y' + 2x\cos(x^2 + y) - y^3 = 0$

7. $(x^2 - y)y' + 2x^3 + 2xy = 0$

8. $(x + y \sin x)y' + y + x \sin y = 0$

9. $(y^3 - x^2y)y' - xy^2 = 0$

10. $(y^{-1/3} - y^{-2/3}e^x)y' - 3(e^xy^{1/3} + e^{2x}) = 0$

11. $(e^{2y} - xe^y)y' - e^y - x = 0$

12. $y^2(x^6 + y^3)^{1/3}y' + 2x^5[(x^6 + y^3)^{1/3} - x^2] = 0$

13. $(y^{-3} - y^{-2} \sin x)y' + y^{-1} \cos x = 0$

14. Show that the separable equation $p(y)y' - q(x) = 0$ is exact.

15. Show that the function ρ is an integrating factor for the equation $M + Ny' = 0$ if it satisfies the partial differential equation

$$N\frac{\partial\rho}{\partial x} - M\frac{\partial\rho}{\partial y} = \rho\left(\frac{\partial M}{\partial y} - \frac{\partial N}{\partial x}\right).$$

16. Show that an integrating factor for the equation $y' - F(y/x) = 0$ is

$$\rho(x, y) = \frac{1}{xF(y/x) - y}.$$

In Exercises 17–20, determine if the equation has an integrating factor of the form $\rho(x, y) = x^m y^n$. If it does, solve the equation.

17. $(1 - xy)y' + y^2 + 3xy^3 = 0$

18. $(3x^2 + 5xy^2)y' + 3xy + 2y^3 = 0$

19. $(x^2 + xy^2)y' - 3xy + 2y^3 = 0$

20. $3xy' + xy^3 + y^2 = 0$

In Exercises 21–24 find an integrating factor by inspection and solve the equation. The following formulas may be helpful:

$$\frac{x\,dx + y\,dy}{x^2 + y^2} = \tfrac{1}{2}d\ln(x^2 + y^2)$$

$$\frac{-y\,dx + x\,dy}{x^2 + y^2} = d\left(\tan^{-1}\frac{y}{x}\right)$$

$$y\,dx + x\,dy = d(xy)$$

$$\frac{-y\,dx + x\,dy}{x^2} = d\left(\frac{y}{x}\right)$$

$$\frac{y\,dx - x\,dy}{y^2} = d\left(\frac{x}{y}\right)$$

21. $(x - 4x^2y^3)y' + 3x^4 - y = 0$

22. $(x - 2x^2y - 2y^3)y' - y = 0$

23. $(2y^3 - x)y' + 3x^2y^2 + y = 0$

24. $yy' + x - x^2 - y^2 = 0$

25. Let $P(x) = \int p(x)\,dx$. Show that $e^{P(x)}$ is an integrating factor for the linear equation $y' + p(x)y - q(x) = 0$.

1.4   FIRST-ORDER LINEAR EQUATIONS

As defined in Section 1.1, a *linear* differential equation of order n has the form

$$a_0(x)y^{(n)} + a_1(x)y^{(n-1)} + \cdots + a_{n-1}(x)y' + a_n(x)y = f(x),$$

where the functions a_i and f are specified on some interval. We assume that $a_0(x) \neq 0$ for all x in this interval. (A solution may not exist throughout an interval on which a_0 vanishes. The discussion in Sections 2.13 and 12.4 explains this point more fully.)

A first-order linear equation is of the form

$$a_0(x)y' + a_1(x)y = f(x).$$

Since $a_0(x)$ is never zero, we can divide through by a_0 and write this Eq. in the form

$$y' + p(x)y = q(x), \tag{1.24}$$

where $p = a_1/a_0$ and $q = f/a_0$. A formula for the solutions of Eq. (1.24) is given in the following theorem.

Theorem 1.3   Let P be any function such that $P'(x) = p(x)$; that is,

$$P(x) = \int p(x)\, dx,$$

and let ρ be specified by the relation

$$\rho(x) = \pm e^{P(x)}, \tag{1.25}$$

where either the plus or the minus sign may be chosen. Then the solutions of Eq. (1.24) are given by the formula

$$\rho(x)y = \int \rho(x)q(x)\, dx + c, \tag{1.26}$$

where c is an arbitrary constant.

PROOF   We treat the case where the plus sign is chosen. The other case is similar. If Eq. (1.24) is multiplied through by $e^{P(x)}$, it becomes

$$[y' + p(x)y]e^{P(x)} = e^{P(x)}q(x)$$

or, since $P'(x) = p(x)$,

$$\frac{d[ye^{P(x)}]}{dx} = e^{P(x)}q(x).$$

Taking antiderivatives, we have the relation

$$e^{P(x)}y = \int e^{P(x)}q(x)\,dx + c, \tag{1.27}$$

which is the same as formula (1.26). Thus if a solution of the differential equation (1.24) exists, it must be of the form (1.27). Conversely, any function defined by Eq. (1.27) is a solution of the Eq. (1.24), as can be verified by starting with formula (1.27) and retracing steps.

The trick in solving Eq. (1.24) was to multiply through first by $\pm e^{P(x)}$. Some motivation for doing this is provided by the following reasoning. Suppose we attempt to find an integrating factor for equation (1.24) that depends on x only. Multiplying through in the equation by $\rho(x)$ and collecting all terms on one side of the equals sign, we have

$$[p(x)y - q(x)]\rho(x) + \rho(x)y' = 0.$$

For this equation to be exact we must have

$$p(x)\rho(x) = \rho'(x).$$

This is a separable equation for ρ. We find that

$$\frac{\rho'(x)}{\rho(x)} = p(x), \qquad \ln|\rho(x)| = \int p(x)\,dx,$$

and

$$\rho(x) = \pm\exp\left(\int p(x)\,dx\right) = \pm\,e^{P(x)}.$$

An example of a first-order linear equation is

$$(x + 1)y' - y = x. \tag{1.28}$$

Dividing through by $x + 1$ to put it in the form (1.24), we have

$$y' + \frac{-1}{x + 1}y = \frac{x}{x + 1}.$$

Here

$$p(x) = \frac{-1}{x + 1}, \qquad q(x) = \frac{x}{x + 1},$$

and

$$P(x) = \int p(x)\,dx = -\ln|x + 1| + c.$$

Our integrating factors are of the form

$$p(x) = \pm e^{P(x)} = \pm \frac{e^c}{|x + 1|}.$$

For simplicity we may as well choose $c = 0$. Then

$$p(x) = \pm \frac{1}{|x + 1|}. \tag{1.29}$$

This function is not defined when $x = -1$. (Notice that the coefficient $a_0(x) = x + 1$ in Eq. (1.28) vanishes when $x = -1$.) We may consider the two intervals $(-\infty, -1)$ and $(-1, \infty)$ separately. If we choose the minus sign for the first interval in Eq. (1.29) and the plus sign for the second interval, we obtain the simple formula

$$p(x) = \frac{1}{x + 1}, \qquad x \neq -1$$

for our integrating factor. From formula (1.26) we have

$$\frac{y}{x + 1} = \int \frac{x}{(x + 1)^2}\, dx + c.$$

Partial fractions can be used to evaluate the interval. We find that

$$\frac{y}{x + 1} = \int \left[\frac{1}{x + 1} - \frac{1}{(x + 1)^2} \right] dx + c,$$

$$\frac{y}{x + 1} = \ln|x + 1| + \frac{1}{x + 1} + c,$$

or

$$y = c(x + 1) + 1 + (x + 1) \ln|x + 1|.$$

Sometimes a nonlinear equation can be put in the form (1.24) by means of a change of variable. One set of equations for which this can always be accomplished is the class of *Bernoulli equations*. These are of the form

$$y' + p(x)y = q(x)y^n,$$

where n is any number other than 0 or 1. Division by y^n yields the equation

$$y^{-n}y' + p(x)y^{1-n} = q(x).$$

If we let $u = y^{1-n}$, then $u' = (1 - n)y^{-n}y'$ and this equation becomes

$$\frac{1}{1 - n} u' + p(x)u = q(x).$$

This is a linear equation that can be solved by the method described earlier in this section.

An example of a Bernoulli equation is

$$y' + \frac{3}{x}y = x^2 y^2.$$

Dividing through by y^2, we have

$$y^{-2}y' + \frac{3}{x}y^{-1} = x^2.$$

If we set $u = y^{-1}$, then $u' = -y^{-2}y'$ and the equation becomes

$$u' - \frac{3}{x}u = -x^2.$$

An integrating factor is

$$\pm\exp\left(-3\int x^{-1}\, dx\right) = \pm|x|^{-3}.$$

If we choose the plus sign for $x > 0$ and the minus sign for $x < 0$, then

$$\rho(x) = x^{-3}.$$

Using formula (1.26), we find that

$$ux^{-3} = -\int x^{-1}\, dx = -\ln|x| + c$$

and

$$u = x^3(c - \ln|x|).$$

Since $u = y^{-1}$ we have

$$y = x^{-3}(c - \ln|x|)^{-1}.$$

It should be noted that $y = 0$ is also a solution of the original equation. In dividing through by y^2 we tacitly assumed that y was never zero.

Exercises for Section 1.4

In Exercises 1–12, find the general solution of the equation. If an initial condition is given, also find the solution that satisfies the condition.

1. $xy' + 2y = 4x^2,\quad y(1) = 4$ 2. $xy' - 3y = x^3,\quad y(1) = 0$

3. $xy' + (x - 2)y = 3x^3 e^{-x}$ 4. $y' - 2y = 4x,\quad y(0) = 1$

5. $y' - 2xy = 1$, $y(a) = b$ 6. $y' + (\cos x)y = \cos x$, $y(\pi) = 0$

7. $x(\ln x)y' + y = 2 \ln x$ 8. $(x^2 + 1)y' - 2xy = x^2 + 1$, $y(1) = \pi$

9. $y' + 2xy = 2x$ 10. $y' + (\cot x)y = 3 \sin x \cos x$

11. $x(x + 1)y' - y = 2x^2(x + 1)$ 12. $xy' - y = x \sin x$

13. Show that the solution of the initial value problem

$$y' + p(x)y = q(x), \qquad y(a) = b$$

is given by the formula

$$y = be^{-P(x)} + \int_a^x e^{-[P(x) - P(t)]} q(t)\, dt,$$

where

$$P(x) = \int_a^x p(t)\, dt.$$

Suggestion: Integrate from a to x in the equation preceding (1.27).

14. A function f is said to be *bounded* on an interval I if there exists a number M such that $|f(x)| \le M$ for x in I. Let the function q be continuous and bounded on the interval $[0, \infty)$. Let k be a positive constant.

    (a) Show that every solution of the equation $y' + ky = q(x)$ is bounded on the interval $[0, \infty)$.

    (b) Show that the equation $y' - ky = q(x)$ possesses solutions that are not bounded on $[0, \infty)$.

15. Let q be continuous on $[0, \infty)$ and let $\lim_{x \to \infty} q(x) = L$. If k is a positive number, show that every solution of the equation $y' + ky = q(x)$ tends to the limit L/k as x becomes infinite. *Suggestion*: Given $\varepsilon > 0$ there is a positive number x_0 such that $|q(x) - L| < \varepsilon$ if $x \ge x_0$. Let $h(x) = q(x) - L$ and use the result of Exercise 13, with $a = x_0$.

In Exercises 16–21, solve the differential equation.

16. $xy' + y + x^2 y^2 e^x = 0$

17. $xy' - (3x + 6)y = -9xe^{-x}y^{4/3}$

18. $3xy^2 y' - 3y^3 = x^4 \cos x$

19. $xyy' = y^2 - x^2$

20. $y' - 2(\sin x)y = -2y^{3/2} \sin x$

21. $2y' + \dfrac{1}{x + 1}y + 2(x^2 - 1)y^3 = 0$

In Exercises 22–24 find a new dependent variable such that the equation becomes linear in that variable. Then solve the equation.

22. $xe^y y' - e^y = 3x^2$ (*Suggestion:* Let $u = e^y$)

23. $\dfrac{1}{y^2 + 1} y' + \dfrac{2}{x} \tan^{-1} y = \dfrac{2}{x}$

24. $y' - \dfrac{1}{x+1} y \ln y = (x+1)y$

1.5 ORTHOGONAL TRAJECTORIES

If c is an arbitrary constant, the equation

$$y = cx^2 \tag{1.30}$$

describes a family of parabolas. Some of these are shown by the solid curves in Fig. 1.2. Through every point (x_0, y_0) in the plane, except those points on the y-axis, there passes exactly one curve of the family. For if we specify (x_0, y_0) with $x_0 \neq 0$, then c is determined by the condition $y_0 = cx_0^2$ or $c = y_0/x_0^2$.

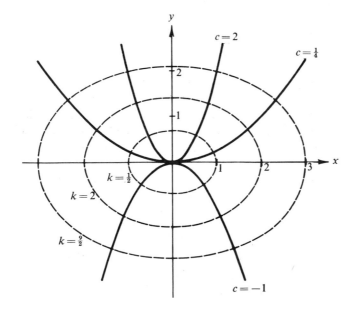

Figure 1.2

The slope of the curve through the point (x, y) is

$$y' = 2cx.$$

But since $c = y/x^2$, we have the formula

$$y' = 2\frac{y}{x} \qquad (1.31)$$

for the slope of the curve of the family (1.30) that passes through the point (x, y) at the point (x, y).

Suppose now that we wish to find a second family of curves, with exactly one curve of the family passing through each point (x, y) and such that at each point the curve of this second family is orthogonal or perpendicular to the curve of the original family (1.30) that passes through the point. The slope of the curve of the second family must be the negative reciprocal of the slope of the curve of the first family. In view of formula (1.31), we must find a family of curves for which

$$y' = -\frac{x}{2y}.$$

This is a separable equation. We have

$$2y\, dy = -x\, dx$$

and hence

$$y^2 = -\tfrac{1}{2}x^2 + k$$

or

$$\frac{x^2}{2k} + \frac{y^2}{k} = 1.$$

(Here k must be positive constant, otherwise there is no curve.) This is a family of ellipses, a few of which are shown by the dotted curves in Fig. 1.2.

To consider a slightly different problem, suppose we wish to find a third family of curves, with one curve of the family through each point, such that at (x, y) the curve of the third family makes an angle of $\pi/4$ with the curve of the first family (1.30). The angle is to be measured counterclockwise from the curve of the third family to the curve of the first family, as shown in Fig. 1.3. Using the notation shown in the figure, we must have

$$\frac{\tan \phi_2 - \tan \phi_1}{1 + \tan \phi_2 \tan \phi_1} = \tan \frac{\pi}{4}.$$

But $\tan \phi_2 = 2y/x$, and if we set $\tan \phi_1 = y'$, we require that

$$\frac{(2y/x) - y'}{1 + (2y/x)y'} = 1.$$

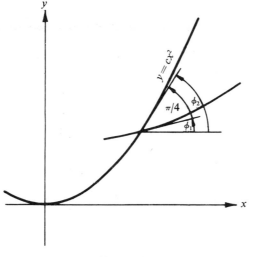

Figure 1.3

Simplification yields the differential equation

$$(2y + x)y' = 2y - x.$$

This equation can be written in the form $y' = F(y/x)$. The change of variable $y = vx$ leads to the separable equation

$$\frac{4v + 2}{2v^2 - v + 1} v' = -\frac{2}{x}.$$

Integration yields the relation

$$\ln(2v^2 - v + 1) + \frac{6}{\sqrt{7}} \tan^{-1}\left(\frac{4v - 1}{\sqrt{7}}\right) = -\ln x^2 + k.$$

In terms of x and y this relation is

$$\ln(2y^2 - xy + x^2) + \frac{6}{\sqrt{7}} \tan^{-1}\left(\frac{4y - x}{\sqrt{7}x}\right) = k.$$

Exercises for Section 1.5

In Exercises 1–10 find the orthogonal trajectories of the family of curves. In Exercises 1–6, also sketch several curves of each family.

1. $y = e^x + c$ 2. $y = ce^x$

3. $y = cx$ 4. $y = \tan^{-1} x + c$

5. $x^2 + \dfrac{y^2}{4} = c^2$ 6. $x^2 + (y - c)^2 = c^2$

7. $x^2 - y^2 = 2cx$ 8. $y = x \ln cx$

9. $y = \dfrac{x}{cx + 1}$ 10. $y = \dfrac{1 + cx}{1 - cx}$

In Exercises 11–14, find a family of curves making an angle of $\pi/4$ with the curves of the given family. The angle is to be measured counterclockwise *to* the curve of the given family.

11. $y = cx^{-1}$ 12. $y = \dfrac{1}{x + c}$

13. $y = \dfrac{x^3}{3} + c$ 14. $y = \sin x + c$

15. Find a family of curves that cuts the family $y = x^2 + c$ at an angle of $\pi/6$. The angle is to be measured counterclockwise toward the curve of the given family.

16. Find a family of curves that cuts the family $y = x^3 + c$ at an angle of $\pi/3$. The angle is to be measured counterclockwise toward the curve of the given family.

17. Let (r, θ) be polar coordinates. If ψ is the positive angle measured counterclockwise from the radius vector to the tangent line to a curve $r = f(\theta)$, then it is shown in calculus that

$$\tan \psi = \frac{r}{dr/d\theta}.$$

Show that two curves $r = f_1(\theta)$ and $r = f_2(\theta)$ are orthogonal at a point if the corresponding values of $r/(dr/d\theta)$ are negative reciprocals, provided that the same coordinates (r, θ) are used to describe the same point on both curves.

Use the results of Exercise 17 to find the orthogonal trajectories of the family of curves in Exercises 18–21. Sketch a few curves of each family.

18. $r = c(1 + \cos \theta), \quad c > 0$ 19. $r = c \sin \theta$

20. $r = c \sin 2\theta$ 21. $r^2 = c \cos 2\theta$

1.6   DECAY AND MIXING PROBLEMS

In Section 1.1, we stated that many natural laws of science could be formulated as differential equations. In this and the next three sections we consider some phenomena whose mathematical description leads to first-order equations.

Our first example concerns the rate of decay of a radioactive substance. It is to be expected that the more of the undecayed substance present, the greater will be the rate of decay. Experiment indicates that a radioactive substance decays at a rate directly proportional to the amount of undecayed matter remaining. Thus if $x(t)$ is the amount (mass) of undecayed substance present at time t, we have

$$\frac{dx}{dt} = -kx, \tag{1.32}$$

where k is a positive constant of proportionality. The minus sign occurs because x is a decreasing function, and dx/dt is negative.

Suppose that at time t_0 the amount of undecayed substance is x_0 and that at some later time t_1 it is x_1. Thus we have the auxiliary conditions

$$x(t_0) = x_0, \qquad x(t_1) = x_1. \tag{1.33}$$

Separating the variables in Eq. (1.32) we have

$$\frac{dx}{x} = -k \, dt. \tag{1.34}$$

Integrating, we have

$$\ln x = -kt + \ln c$$

(here $x > 0$ and $\ln c$ is an arbitrary constant for $c > 0$) or

$$x = ce^{-kt}.$$

We could now use the two conditions (1.33) to determine the numbers c and k in this formula. However, let us proceed in another way. Starting with Eq. (1.34) and using definite integrals, we may write

$$\int_{x_0}^{x_1} \frac{dx}{x} = -k \int_{t_0}^{t_1} dt.$$

Then

$$\ln \frac{x_1}{x_0} = -k(t_1 - t_0)$$

and so

$$k = \frac{1}{t_1 - t_0} \ln \frac{x_0}{x_1}. \tag{1.35}$$

Having determined k, we go back to Eq. (1.34) and write

$$\int_{x_0}^{x} \frac{dx}{x} = -k \int_{t_0}^{t} dt.$$

(We could have used t_1 and x_1 in place of t_0 and x_0, respectively.) Carrying out the integration, we find that

$$\ln \frac{x}{x_0} = -k(t - t_0)$$

or

$$x = x_0 e^{-k(t - t_0)}.$$

The use of the value (1.35) for k yields the result

$$x = x_0 \exp \left[-\frac{t - t_0}{t_1 - t_0} \ln \frac{x_0}{x_1} \right].$$

As a second example of a situation that leads to a first-order equation, we consider a mixing problem. Suppose that we start with a tank that contains 20 gal of a solution of a certain chemical and that 10 lb of the chemical are in the solution. Starting at a certain instant, a solution of the same chemical, with a concentration of 2 lb/gal, is allowed to flow into the tank at the rate of 3 gal/min. The mixture is drained off at the same rate so that the volume of solution in the tank remains constant. (We make the simplifying assumption that the concentration of the solution in the tank is kept uniform, perhaps by stirring.) The problem we wish to solve is this. How many gallons of the solution should be pumped into the tank to raise the amount of dissolved chemical to 15 lb?

It is true that each gallon of the solution coming in brings with it 2 lb of the chemical, but the mixture leaving takes some of the chemical with it. We can solve our problem if we can obtain a formula for the amount of chemical in the tank at time t. If $x(t)$ is the amount in the tank at time t, then the rate of change of x, dx/dt, is given by the following rule: dx/dt is equal to the rate at which the chemical enters the tank minus the rate at which the chemical leaves the tank. The rate at which the chemical enters is $2 \times 3 = 6$ lb/min, since 3 gal of solution flow in per minute and each gallon contains 2 lb of the chemical. At time t the concentration of the solution in the tank is $x(t)/20$, since the volume of solution in the tank is always 20 gal. Hence the rate at which the chemical is leaving the tank is $3 \times x/20$ gal/min. Thus we arrive at the differential equation

$$\frac{dx}{dt} = 6 - \frac{3}{20}x.$$

This is a linear equation. It is also separable. The general solution is

$$x = ce^{-3t/20} + 40.$$

Using the fact that $x = 10$ when $t = 0$, we have $10 = c + 40$ or $c = -30$. Then

$$x = 40 - 30e^{-3t/20}.$$

We want to find the value of t when x is 15. Setting $x = 15$ in the above equation, we have

$$15 = 40 - 30e^{-3t/20},$$

$$e^{-3t/20} = \frac{25}{30} = \frac{5}{6},$$

or

$$t = \frac{20}{3} \ln \frac{6}{5}.$$

Using a table of natural logarithms we find that $\ln 6/5 = 1.8232$ and that $t = 12.15$ min. Since 3 gal of solution enter the tank per minute, we must pump in 36.45 gal to bring the concentration up to the desired value.

Exercises for Section 1.6

1. Let x_0 be the amount of radioactive substance present at $t = 0$ and let T be the time required for one-half of the substance to decay. Show that T is independent of x_0. The time T is called the *half-life* of the radioactive substance.

2. Let $x(t)$ be the amount of a radioactive substance present at time t and let $x(0) = x_0$. If T is the half-life (see Exercise 1) show that
$$x(t) = x_0 2^{-t/T}.$$

3. At a certain instant 100 gm of a radioactive substance are present. After 4 yr, 20 gm remain. How much of the substance remains after 8 years?

4. After 6 hr, 60 gm of a radioactive substance are present. After 8 hr (2 hr later) 50 gm are present. How much of the substance was present initially?

5. If the half-life (see Exercise 1) of a radioactive substance is 10 yr, when does 25 percent of the substance remain? Think!

6. Let $N(t)$ denote the number of bacteria in a culture at time t. Assuming that N increases at a rate proportional to the number of bacteria present, find a formula for N in terms of t.

7. A conical tank of height 12 ft and radius 4 ft is initially filled with fluid. After 6 hr the height of the fluid is 10.5 ft. If the fluid evaporates at a rate proportional to the surface area exposed to the air, find a formula for the volume of fluid in the tank as a function of time.

8. A tank initially contains 100 gal of a solution that holds 30 lb of a chemical. Water runs into the tank at the rate of 2 gal/min and the solution runs out at the same rate. How much of the chemical remains in the tank after 20 min?

9. A tank initially contains 50 gal of a solution that holds 30 lb of a chemical. Water runs into the tank at the rate of 3 gal/min and the mixture runs out at the rate of 2 gal/min. After how long will there be 25 lb of the chemical in the tank?

10. A tank initially contains 100 gal of a solution that holds 40 lb of a chemical. A solution containing 2 lb/gal of the chemical runs into the tank at the rate of 2 gal/min and the mixture runs out at the rate of 3 gal/min. How much chemical is in the tank after 50 min?

11. A tank initially holds 100 liters of a solution in which is dissolved 200 gm of a radioactive substance. Assume that the substance decays at a rate equal to k times the amount present. If water flows in at the rate of 2 liters/min and the solution flows out at the same rate, find a formula for the amount of radioactive substance in the tank after t min.

1.7 POPULATION GROWTH

The applications of this section involve mathematical models for the population growth of a biological species. We shall consider models in which the rate of change of the population at any time depends only on the population at that time. Thus, if $N(t)$ is the population at time t, our mathematical formulation of the problem is a differential equation of the form

$$\frac{dN}{dt} = f(N).\qquad(1.36)$$

In general, such a model will exclude the effects of immigration, emigration, competition with other species, changes in climate, and environmental changes other than those caused by the change of the population itself. The time interval over which the model is valid may be short.

If the birth rate is higher than the death rate, dN/dt should increase with N. Then, in Eq. (1.36), f should be an increasing function. The simplest model is

$$\frac{dN}{dt} = kN,\qquad(1.37)$$

where k is a positive constant. The solution,

$$N(t) = N_0\, e^{kt},$$

where $N_0 = N(0)$, is an increasing function of time. In fact, as t becomes infinite, so does $N(t)$.

We might consider models in which $f(N) = kN^\alpha$, where α is a positive constant. Then f will be an increasing function and $f(0) = 0$. This last condition is desirable because the growth rate dN/dt should be zero when the population is zero. We leave a discussion of these models to the exercises.

The model (1.37) cannot be valid over a long time interval because a real population cannot increase indefinitely. Instead, we expect the population to level off at a certain value, called the *saturation value*. At this point the growth rate will be zero. We therefore consider the equation

$$\frac{dN}{dt} = kN(a - N)\qquad(1.38)$$

in which k and a are positive constants. If $N_0 = N(0)$ is less than a, dN/dt is positive so long as N remains less than a. If N should ever exceed the value a, then dN/dt will be negative and N will decrease. The solution of this separable equation is found to be

$$N(t) = \frac{a}{1 + \left(\dfrac{a}{N_0} - 1\right)e^{-akt}}.\qquad(1.39)$$

Notice that as t increases, $N(t)$ approaches the limiting value a, regardless of the value of N_0.

Problems involving the growth of the populations of two species in competition will be considered in Chapter VIII, which deals with systems of differential equations.

Exercises for Section 1.7

1.   The population of a certain species is initially 2000. After two hours it is 2500. Find a formula for the population as a function of time, assuming that the model (1.37) applies.

2.   Using the data of Exercise 1, find the population as a function of time, assuming that the model $dN/dt = kN^{1/2}$ applies.

3.   (a) Find a formula for $N(t)$ if $N(0) = N_0$ and

$$\frac{dN}{dt} = kN^\alpha,$$

where α is a positive constant, $\alpha \neq 1$.

(b) If $0 < \alpha < 1$ in part (a), what happens to $N(t)$ as t becomes infinite?

(c) If $\alpha > 1$ in part (a), show that $N(t)$ becomes infinite after a finite time.

4.   Derive the solution (1.39) of Eq. (1.38).

5.   Initially the population of a species is 5000. After 10 days it is 8000. After a very long time the population stabilizes at 15000. Find a formula for the population as a function of time, assuming that a model of the form (1.38) applies.

6.   What is $N(t)$ if $N_0 = 0$ in the problem (1.38)?

7.   Let us assume that the function f in the equation $N' = f(N)$ is continuous everywhere. If $N(t)$ exists for all $t \geq 0$ and if $N(t)$ tends to the limit a as t becomes infinite, then we see from the equation $N'(t) = f[N(t)]$ that $N'(t)$ tends to $f(a)$. It can be shown (Exercise 8) that $f(a)$ must be zero. Using this fact, show that if $N(0) > 0$ and $f(N) > 0$ for $N > 0$, then $N(t)$ becomes infinite as t becomes infinite.

8.   If the function g is such that $g(t)$ and $g'(t)$ exist for $t > 0$ and both functions have finite limits as t becomes infinite, show that $g'(t)$ approaches zero. *Suggestion*: Consider first the case where g' has constant sign after some time t_1.

1.8   AN ECONOMIC MODEL

Let us assume that the price P, the supply S, and the demand D of a commodity can be represented by continuously varying functions of time t. In the model to be considered here, we assume that dP/dt is directly proportional to the difference between demand and supply. Thus

$$\frac{dP}{dt} = k(D - S),$$

where k is a positive constant. If demand exceeds supply, dP/dt is positive and the price increases. If supply exceeds demand, dP/dt is negative and the price decreases.

We must now determine the supply and demand functions. In this example, we shall assume that the supply is seasonal and periodic. To obtain a specific model, let us take

$$S(t) = c(1 - \cos \alpha t),$$

where c and α are positive constants.† Then S is periodic and nonnegative. (A negative value for $S(t)$ is unreasonable.) We shall assume that the demand depends on the price only. We expect the demand to be a decreasing function of price. The simplest such function is a linear function,

$$D = a - bP,$$

where a and b are positive constants. This is reasonable only as long as $0 < P < a/b$, since the demand should not be negative.

Insertion of the expressions for S and D into the formula for dP/dt yields the differential equation

$$\frac{dP}{dt} = k[a - bP - c(1 - \cos \alpha t)]$$

for P. This is a first-order linear equation, solvable by the method of Section 1.4. Its solution is found to be

$$P(t) = \left[P(0) - \frac{a - c}{b} - \frac{k^2 bc}{k^2 b^2 + \alpha^2} \right] e^{-kbt}$$

$$+ \frac{a - c}{b} + \frac{kc}{k^2 b^2 + \alpha^2} (kb \cos \alpha t + \alpha \sin \alpha t) .$$

† Actually the supply should also depend on the price. See Exercises 1 and 2.

After a long time, $P(t)$ is approximately equal to

$$\frac{a - c}{b} - \frac{kc}{(k^2b^2 + \alpha^2)^{1/2}} \sin(\alpha t + \theta),$$

where $\theta = \tan^{-1}(kb/\alpha)$. Thus P fluctuates about the value $(a - c)/b$. We notice that the supply $S(t)$ is a minimum when t is an integral multiple of $2\pi/\alpha$. However, the price $P(t)$ is not a maximum at these times. It is a maximum when $t = [2n\pi - (\pi/2 + \theta)]/\alpha$, where n is an integer.

Exercises for Section 1.8

1. In the equation $dP/dt = k(D - S)$ let $D = a - bP$ as before, but assume that S is an increasing function of P, namely $S = c + dP$ where c and d are positive constants. Find $P(t)$ and discuss its behavior as t becomes infinite.

2. In the equation $dP/dt = k(D - S)$, let $D = a - bP$ and $S = c + dP$ $+ h \sin \alpha t$, where a, b, c, d, h, and α are positive constants. Find $P(t)$ and discuss its behavior as t becomes infinite.

3. Assume that the rate of change of the supply of a commodity is proportional to the difference between demand and supply, so that

    $$\frac{dS}{dt} = k(D - S).$$

    Find a formula for $S(t)$ if D is constant.

4. Work Exercise 3 in the case where $D(t) = c(1 - \cos \alpha t)$.

5. For a country, let I and Y denote investment and national income per year, respectively. We assume that $I = aY$, where a is a positive constant. (Thus a constant fraction of income is invested.) The productive capacity Q of the country is assumed to be a function of capital K; in particular we assume that $Q = bK$, where b is a positive constant. Since rate of investment is equal to the rate of change of capital, we have $dK/dt = I$. In the *Domar growth model* it is assumed that $Y = Q$; that is, productive capacity is equal to national income, or supply is equal to demand. Show that K must satisfy the differential equation $dK/dt = abK$ and find a formula for $K(t)$.

6. In this exercise we assume that the productive capacity Q of a country depends on both capital K and labor L, so that $Q = F(K, L)$. The function F is assumed to be positive valued and to be an increasing function of each

variable when the other is fixed. Furthermore, F is assumed to be homo-
geneous† of degree 1, so that $F(cK, cL) = cF(K, L)$ for every positive
constant c. Thus when capital and labor are both changed by the same
factor, productivity is also changed by that factor. In the *Solow growth
model*, it is assumed that $dL/dt = aL$ and $dK/dt = bQ$, where a and b are
positive constants.

(a) If $k = K/L$ is the ratio of capital to labor, show that k satisfies the
differential equation

$$\frac{dk}{dt} = bf(k) - ak,$$

where $f(k) = F(k, 1)$.

(b) Verify that the function

$$F(K, L) = AK^\alpha L^{1-\alpha}, \qquad A > 0, \qquad 0 < \alpha < 1,$$

satisfies the conditions described earlier for the production function.

(c) If F is as in part (b), find a formula for the quantity k in part (a).

1.9   COOLING: THE RATE OF A CHEMICAL REACTION

The first problem that we consider in this section has to do with the change
in temperature in a cooling body. If a body cools in a surrounding medium
(such as air or water) it might be expected that the rate of change of the temperature of the body would depend on the difference between the temperature
of the body and that of the surrounding medium. *Newton's law of cooling*
asserts that the rate of change is directly proportional to the difference of the
temperatures. Thus if $u(t)$ is the temperature of the body at time t and if u_0
is the (constant) temperature of the surrounding medium, we have

$$\frac{du}{dt} = -k(u - u_0,)$$

where k is a positive constant. The minus sign occurs because du/dt will be
negative when $u > u_0$.

As an example, suppose that an object is heated to $300°F$ and allowed to
cool in a room whose air temperature is $80°F$. If after 10 min the temperature

† Homogeneous functions were defined in Section 1.3.

of the body is 250°, what will be its temperature after 20 min? The differential equation becomes

$$\frac{du}{dt} = -k(u - 80)$$

and the initial condition is $u(0) = 300$. We also know that $u(10) = 250$.

This equation is linear; it is also separable. Treating it as a separable equation, we write

$$\frac{du}{u - 80} = -k\, dt . \tag{1.40}$$

Using the specified conditions to determine k, we have

$$\int_{300}^{250} \frac{du}{u - 80} = -k \int_{0}^{10} dt .$$

From this equation we find that

$$k = \frac{1}{10} \ln \frac{220}{170} = 0.0258 .$$

To determine u when $t = 20$, we go back to Eq. (1.40) and write

$$\int_{300}^{u} \frac{du}{u - 80} = -k \int_{0}^{20} dt .$$

We find that

$$\ln \frac{u - 80}{220} = -20k$$

or

$$u = 220e^{-20k} + 80 .$$

Since $e^{-20k} = e^{-0.516} = 0.60$, we have

$$u(20) = 212° .$$

Our next application of differential equations concerns the rate of a chemical reaction. Suppose that A and B are two chemicals that react in solution. Let $x(t)$ and $y(t)$ denote the concentrations (in moles† per liter) at time t of A and B, respectively.

In our first example, we shall assume that one molecule of A combines with one molecule of B to form a new product or products. Then x and y

---

† If the molecular weight of a chemical is w, then one mole of that chemical consists of w grams.

decrease at the same rate, so that $dx/dt = dy/dt$. Let $z(t)$ be the amount by which x and y have decreased in time t. If a and b are the initial concentrations of A and B, respectively, then

$$x(t) = a - z(t), \qquad y(t) = b - z(t) \tag{1.41}$$

and

$$\frac{dz}{dt} = -\frac{dx}{dt} = -\frac{dy}{dt}.$$

The quantity dz/dt is called the *rate of reaction*. For many reactions of this type (one molecule of A combining with one molecule of B), it is found that† under conditions of constant temperature

$$\frac{dz}{dt} = kxy \tag{1.42}$$

or

$$\frac{dz}{dt} = k(a - z)(b - z), \tag{1.43}$$

where k is a positive constant of proportionality. Thus the rate of reaction is directly proportional to the concentration of each reactant.

The differential equation (1.43) is nonlinear, but separable. Separating the variables and using the fact that $z(0) = 0$, we have

$$\int_0^z \frac{dz}{(a - z)(b - z)} = k \int_0^t dt.$$

The integral on the left can be evaluated by the use of partial fractions. We find that

$$\frac{1}{a - b} \int_0^z \left(\frac{-1}{a - z} + \frac{1}{b - z} \right) dz = kt$$

or

$$\frac{1}{a - b} \ln \frac{b(a - z)}{a(b - z)} = kt.$$

The value of k can be determined by experiment, in which z is measured for various values of t. From the above relation we obtain the formula

$$z = ab \frac{e^{k(a-b)t} + 1}{a e^{k(a-b)t} - b}$$

for z. The concentrations of A and B can be found from Eq. (1.41).

---

† The formula (1.43) does not always apply. In some cases nonreacting substances (catalysts) influence the rate of reaction. In any case the rate of reaction must ultimately be determined by experiment.

Let us next consider a reaction in which two molecules of chemical B combine with one molecule of chemical A to form new products. Then two moles of B are used up for every mole of A, so that

$$\frac{dy}{dt} = 2\frac{dx}{dt}.$$

If $z(t)$ is the decrease in chemical A in time t, then

$$x = a - z, \qquad y = b - 2z. \tag{1.44}$$

In this case (two molecules of B combining with one of A), it is found that†

$$\frac{dz}{dt} = kxy^2 \tag{1.45}$$

or

$$\frac{dz}{dt} = k(a - z)(b - 2z)^2. \tag{1.46}$$

Here dz/dt is directly proportional to x and to the square of y. The integration of Eq. (1.46) is left to the exercises.

In the general case where m molecules of A combine with n molecules of B, we have

$$n\frac{dx}{dt} = m\frac{dy}{dt}.$$

If we set

$$z = \frac{1}{m}(a - x) = \frac{1}{n}(b - y),$$

then $z(0) = 0$ and

$$\frac{dz}{dt} = -\frac{1}{m}\frac{dx}{dt} = -\frac{1}{n}\frac{dy}{dt}.$$

The equation for z is found to be

$$\frac{dz}{dt} = kx^m y^n$$

or

$$\frac{dz}{dt} = k(a - mz)^m(b - nz)^n.$$

The exponents m and n are often called the *orders* of the reaction with respect to the concentrations of A and B.

† See the footnote on p. 41.

Exercises for Section 1.9

1. An object whose initial temperature is 150°F is allowed to cool in a room where the temperature of the air is 75°F. After 10 min the temperature of the object is 125°. When will its temperature be 100°?

2. A heated object is allowed to cool in air whose temperature is 20°C. After 5 min its temperature is 200°C. After 10 min (5 min later) its temperature is 160°. What was the temperature of the object initially?

3. An object whose temperature is 220°F is placed in a room where the temperature is 60°F. After 10 min the temperature of the object is 200°. At this point refrigeration equipment, which lowers the temperature of the room at the rate of 1°F/min, is turned on. What is the temperature of the object t min after the equipment is turned on?

4. An object with a temperature of 10°F is placed in a room where the temperature is 80°F. After 10 min the temperature of the object is 30°. What will be the temperature of the object after it has been in the room for 30 min?

5. Suppose that in a chemical reaction where one molecule of A combines with one molecule of B, the rule (1.42) applies. Assume that A and B have the same initial concentration a.

    (a) Find a formula for the concentrations of A and B at time t.

    (b) Find a formula for the half-life of the reaction, which is the time required for the concentrations of the reactants to be halved.

6. Suppose that in a chemical reaction where 2 molecules of B combine with one of A, the rule (1.45) applies. Find a formula that expresses k in terms of z and t in the case where

    (a) $b \neq 2a$ (b) $b = 2a$.

7. A chemical A breaks down when heated, with n molecules of A reacting to form new products. The law of reaction is

$$\frac{dx}{dt} = -kx^n,$$

where $x(t)$ is the amount of the chemical remaining at time t. If half the chemical decomposes after T min, find a formula for x in terms of t. Let a denote the initial amount of the chemical.

1.10   TWO SPECIAL TYPES OF SECOND-ORDER EQUATIONS

A second-order differential equation is of the form

$$F\left(t, x, \frac{dx}{dt}, \frac{d^2x}{dt^2}\right) = 0.$$

In this section we shall consider two classes of second-order equations that can be solved by successively solving two first-order equations. Thus the methods of solution for first-order equations that were presented earlier in this chapter may be used.

We consider first the class of second-order equations in which the dependent variable x is absent. Such an equation is of the form

$$G\left(t, \frac{dx}{dt}, \frac{d^2x}{dt^2}\right) = 0.$$

Suppose that x is a solution of this equation. If we set $v = dx/dt$, then v must be a solution of the first-order equation

$$G\left(t, v, \frac{dv}{dt}\right) = 0.$$

If we can solve this equation for v, then the solutions of the original equation can be found from the relation

$$\frac{dx}{dt} = v(t)$$

by integration.

As an example, let us consider the equation

$$t\frac{d^2x}{dt^2} = 2\left[\left(\frac{dx}{dt}\right)^2 - \frac{dx}{dt}\right]. \tag{1.47}$$

Note that x itself is absent. Setting $v = dx/dt$, we obtain the first-order equation

$$t\frac{dv}{dt} = 2(v^2 - v) \tag{1.48}$$

for v. This equation is separable and we have

$$\frac{dv}{v^2 - v} = 2\frac{dt}{t}$$

or

$$\left(\frac{1}{v-1}-\frac{1}{v}\right)dv = 2\frac{dt}{t}.$$

Integrating, we find that

$$\ln\left|\frac{v-1}{1}\right| = 2\ln|t| = c_1'$$

or

$$\frac{v-1}{v} = c_1 t^2.$$

Then

$$v = \frac{dx}{dt} = \frac{1}{1-c_1 t^2}.$$

If c_1 is positive, say $c_1 = a^2$, we have

$$\frac{dx}{dt} = \frac{1}{1-a^2 t^2},$$

so that

$$x = \frac{1}{2a}\ln\left|\frac{1+at}{1-at}\right| + c_2.$$

If c_1 is negative, say $c_1 = -b^2$, then

$$\frac{dx}{dt} = \frac{1}{1+b^2 t^2}$$

and

$$x = \frac{1}{b}\tan^{-1} bt + c_2.$$

Finally, we observe that since the constant functions $v = 0$ and $v = 1$ are solutions of Eq. (1.48), the functions

$$x = c, \qquad x = t + c$$

are solutions of Eq. (1.47).

The second class of second-order equations that we shall consider are those in which the independent variable t is missing. Such equations are of the form

$$H\left(x, \frac{dx}{dt}, \frac{d^2 x}{dt^2}\right) = 0.$$

Suppose that x is a solution and let $v = dx/dt$. On an interval where x is a strictly increasing, or decreasing, function, t can be regarded as a function of x and we can write

$$\frac{d^2x}{dt^2} = \frac{dv}{dt} = \frac{dv}{dx}\frac{dx}{dt} = v\frac{dv}{dx}.$$

Then the equation becomes

$$H\left(x, v, v\frac{dv}{dx}\right) = 0$$

and this is a first-order equation for v. If we can solve it, finding a solution v, then a solution of the original equation can be found by solving the first-order equation

$$\frac{dx}{dt} = v(x).$$

As an illustration, we consider the equation

$$x\frac{d^2x}{dt^2} = \left(\frac{dx}{dt}\right)^2 + 2\frac{dx}{dt}, \tag{1.49}$$

in which t is missing. Setting

$$\frac{dx}{dt} = v, \qquad \frac{d^2x}{dt^2} = v\frac{dv}{dx},$$

we have

$$xv\frac{dv}{dx} = v^2 + 2v. \tag{1.50}$$

By inspection we see that $v = 0$ and $v = -2$ are solutions of this equation, so that

$$x = c, \qquad x = -2t + c$$

are solutions of Eq. (1.49). To find the remaining solutions, we divide through by v in Eq. (1.50), obtaining the separable equation

$$x\frac{dv}{dx} = v + 2.$$

We easily find that

$$v = c_1x - 2.$$

Now we must solve the equation

$$\frac{dx}{dt} = c_1x - 2.$$

For $c_1 \neq 0$ we find that

$$x = \frac{1}{c_1}(c_2\, e^{c_1 t} + 2).$$

(When $c_1 = 0$ we have $v = -2$, which was considered previously.)

Some applications that give rise to the types of differential equations discussed here are presented in the next section.

Exercises for Section 1.10

1. If v_0 is a zero of the function f, show that the differential equation

$$\frac{d^2x}{dt^2} = f\left(\frac{dx}{dt}\right) g(t).$$

possesses the solutions $x = v_0\, t + c$.

In Exercises 2–21, find the general solution.

2. $\dfrac{d^2x}{dt^2} = \dfrac{dx}{dt} + 2t$

3. $2t\,\dfrac{dx}{dt}\dfrac{d^2x}{dt^2} = \left(\dfrac{dx}{dt}\right)^2 + 1$

4. $\dfrac{d^2x}{dt^2} = -2t\left(\dfrac{dx}{dt}\right)^2$

5. $2t\,\dfrac{d^2x}{dt^2} = \left(\dfrac{dx}{dt}\right)^2 - 1$

6. $t^2\,\dfrac{d^2x}{dt^2} + \left(\dfrac{dx}{dt}\right)^2 = 2t\,\dfrac{dx}{dt}$

7. $\left(\dfrac{dx}{dt} - t\right)\dfrac{d^2x}{dt^2} - \dfrac{dx}{dt} = 0$

8. $t\exp\left(\dfrac{dx}{dt}\right)\dfrac{d^2x}{dt^2} = \exp\left(\dfrac{dx}{dt}\right) - 1$

9. $t\,\dfrac{d^2x}{dt^2} = \dfrac{dx}{dt} + 2\sqrt{t^2 + \left(\dfrac{dx}{dt}\right)^2}$

10. $\dfrac{d^2x}{dt^2} = \dfrac{1}{t}\dfrac{dx}{dt} + \tanh\left(\dfrac{dx}{dt}\Big/ t\right)$

11. $\dfrac{d^2x}{dt^2} + x^{-3} = 0$

12. $x\,\dfrac{d^2x}{dt^2} = \left(\dfrac{dx}{dt}\right)^2$

13. $\dfrac{d^2x}{dt^2} + \left(\dfrac{dx}{dt}\right)^3 = 0$

14. $3x\,\dfrac{dx}{dt}\dfrac{d^2x}{dt^2} = \left(\dfrac{dx}{dt}\right)^3 - 1$

15. $\dfrac{d^2x}{dt^2} + e^{-x}\dfrac{dx}{dt} = 0$

16. $(x^2 + 1)\dfrac{d^2x}{dt^2} = 2x\left(\dfrac{dx}{dt}\right)^2$

17. $x^3\,\dfrac{d^2x}{dt^2} = 2\left(\dfrac{dx}{dt}\right)^3$

18. $\dfrac{d^2x}{dt^2} = \left(\dfrac{dx}{dt}\right)^2 \tanh x$

19. $x\,\dfrac{d^2x}{dt^2} = \dfrac{dx}{dt}\left(\dfrac{dx}{dt} + 2\right)$

20. $\dfrac{d^2x}{dt^2} + 2\left(\dfrac{dx}{dt}\right)^2 \tan x = 0$

21. $\dfrac{d^2x}{dt^2}\exp\left(\dfrac{dx}{dt}\right) = 1$

1.11 FALLING BODIES

The applications in this section involve the motion of a solid body whose center of mass moves in a straight line. Let us denote by x the directed distance of the center of mass from some fixed point on the line of motion. Then x depends on time t. The velocity and acceleration of the center of mass are dx/dt and d^2x/dt^2, respectively. The notations

$$\dot{x} = \frac{dx}{dt}, \qquad \ddot{x} = \frac{d^2x}{dt^2}$$

are commonly used.

According to *Newton's second law of motion*, the mass of the body times the acceleration of the center of mass is proportional to the force acting on the body. Actually, the commonly used systems of units for measuring mass, distance, time, and force are arranged so that the constant of proportionality may be taken as unity. Thus

$$m \frac{d^2x}{dt^2} = F, \tag{1.51}$$

where m is the mass of the body and F is the force. When F depends on t, x, and dx/dt, Eq. (1.51) is a second-order differential equation for x. The units in Eq. (1.51) must be chosen appropriately. Equation (1.51) is sometimes called the *equation of motion* of the body.

In the *centimeter-gram-second* system of units (cgs), distance is in *centimeters*, time is in *seconds*, mass is in *grams*, and force is in *dynes*. In the *British* system of units, distance is in *feet*, time is in *seconds*, mass is in *slugs*, and force is in *pounds*.

In the examples of this section we shall examine the motion of falling (and rising) bodies. One of the forces present is that of gravity. The *weight* of a body is very nearly† the force exerted on the body by the earth's gravitational field. Near the surface of the earth the force due to gravity is mg, where g is approximately 980 cm/sec^2 or 32 ft/sec^2. Actually the value of g (the acceleration due to gravity) varies slightly over the surface of the earth, being slightly larger at the poles than at the equator. If the weight of a body is w lb, then the mass m of the body in slugs is given by the formula

$$m = \frac{w}{g}.$$

† The rotation of the earth complicates an exact definition of weight, but for most practical considerations the weight of a body may be taken to be the force due to gravity.

In our first example let us suppose that an object is thrown directly upward from the surface of the earth, with an initial velocity v_0. Let x denote the directed distance upward of the object from the surface of the earth. If we assume that the only force acting on the object is that due to gravity, then Eq. (1.51) becomes

$$m\ddot{x} = -mg. \tag{1.52}$$

The minus sign occurs because the force acts in the direction of decreasing x. The initial conditions are

$$x(0) = 0, \qquad \dot{x}(0) = v_0,$$

assuming that $t = 0$ is the time at which the object is thrown.

A first integration of Eq. (1.52) yields the relation

$$\dot{x} = -gt + c_1,$$

where c_1 is a constant. The condition $x(0) = v_0$ tells us that $c_1 = v_0$, so we have

$$\dot{x} = -gt + v_0. \tag{1.53}$$

Integrating again, we have

$$x = -\tfrac{1}{2}gt^2 + v_0 t + c_2.$$

Since $x(0) = 0$ we must have $c_2 = 0$ and

$$x = -\tfrac{1}{2}gt^2 + v_0 t. \tag{1.54}$$

Formulas (1.53) and (1.54) describe the velocity and position of the object at time t, $t \ge 0$. From formula (1.53) we see that the velocity is positive until $t = v_0/g$, after which time it becomes negative, with the object descending. Thus the time required for the object to reach its maximum height is v_0/g and the maximum height, as found from formula (1.54), is

$$h = \frac{v_0^2}{2g}.$$

The time when the object returns to earth can be found by setting $x = 0$ in Eq. (1.54) and solving for t. We find that the time is $2v_0/g$ so that the time that it takes the object to fall back to earth is the same as the time going up. The velocity with which the object strikes the earth is found by setting $t = 2v_0/g$ in formula (1.53). This velocity is found to be $-v_0$. The magnitude of the final velocity is therefore the same as that of the initial velocity. The symmetry that occurs in this problem (time going up equals time coming down, and final velocity equals initial velocity) does not always arise when forces other than gravity are considered. Examples are presented in the exercises.

If an object is dropped from a specified height h above the earth, it is probably more convenient to let x denote the directed distance *downward* from the point of release. Then the equation of motion becomes

$$m\ddot{x} = mg. \tag{1.55}$$

Here the force acts in the direction of increasing x, and there is no minus sign. The initial conditions are

$$x(0) = 0, \qquad \dot{x}(0) = 0.$$

Two integrations of Eq. (1.55) yield the formula

$$x = \tfrac{1}{2}gt^2 \tag{1.56}$$

for the distance through which the object falls in time t. If a stone is dropped from a bridge and 2 sec elapse before it hits the water below, we can estimate the height of the bridge above the water from formula (1.56). Using the value $g = 32$ ft/sec^2, we have

$$h = \tfrac{1}{2}(32)(3^2) = 144 \text{ ft.}$$

Actually, when a body moves through the air (or other surrounding medium) the air exerts a damping force F_d on the body. This force depends on the velocity of the body (and on the shape of the body and the nature of the surrounding medium). In some situations the damping force is proportional to the velocity. In others it is more nearly proportional to the square or cube of the velocity.

Let us now reexamine the problem of a falling object that is released from a height h above the earth. Let x be the directed distance downward from the point of release. If the damping force F_d is proportional to the velocity, then

$$F_d = -c\dot{x},$$

where c is a positive constant of proportionality called the *damping constant*. The minus sign indicates that the force acts in a direction opposite to that of the velocity vector. The resultant force F is the sum of the forces acting, and in this case is

$$F = -c\dot{x} + mg.$$

The equation of motion becomes

$$m\ddot{x} = -c\dot{x} + mg \tag{1.57}$$

and the initial conditions are

$$x(0) = 0, \qquad \dot{x}(0) = 0.$$

In the second-order equation (1.57) both x and t are absent. Setting $\dot{x} = v$ and $\ddot{x} = \dot{v}$, we obtain the first-order linear equation

$$m\dot{v} + cv = mg \tag{1.58}$$

for v. Solving, and using the initial condition $v(0) = 0$, we find that

$$v = \dot{x} = \frac{mg}{c}(1 - e^{-ct/m}). \tag{1.59}$$

An integration yields the formula

$$x = \frac{mg}{c}\left(t + \frac{m}{c}e^{-ct/m}\right) - g\left(\frac{m}{c}\right)^2 \tag{1.60}$$

for x.

We notice from formula (1.59) that as t becomes infinite the velocity tends to the limiting value

$$v_\infty = \frac{mg}{c}.$$

Given that there is a limiting velocity, its value could have been found from the equation of motion (1.58). As the velocity of the falling object increases, the damping force increases in magnitude until it balances the force due to gravity. The acceleration thus tends to zero. Setting $\dot{v} = 0$ in Eq. (1.58), we find that $cv = mg$ or $v = mg/c$, which is the value given in the last formula.

When the damping constant c is small, we might expect the formula (1.60) to agree closely with the formula (1.56), at least when the time interval is short. The latter formula was derived in the absence of a damping force ($c = 0$). To make a comparison, we expand the exponential function that appears in formula (1.60) in a Maclaurin series,

$$e^{-ct/m} = 1 - \frac{ct/m}{1!} + \frac{(ct/m)^2}{2!} - \frac{(ct/m)^3}{3!} + \cdots.$$

Formula (1.60) becomes

$$x = g\left(\frac{m}{c}\right)^2\left[\frac{1}{2}\left(\frac{ct}{m}\right)^2 - \frac{1}{6}\left(\frac{ct}{m}\right)^3 + \cdots\right]$$

or

$$x = \frac{1}{2}gt^2 - \frac{1}{6}\frac{cg}{m}t^3 + \cdots.$$

When ct/m is small compared with unity, we see that formula (1.56) is a good approximation to the more complicated formula (1.60).

In the case of a body falling from a great height we can no longer assume that the force due to gravity is constant. Instead we must use the more accurate "inverse square law" of Newton. This implies that the force of attraction between any two spherically symmetric bodies is directly proportional to the product of their masses and inversely proportional to the square of the distance between their centers of mass. Consider the case of a body of mass m falling toward the earth. We assume that the earth is a sphere of mass M and radius R. If r is the distance from the center of the earth to the center of mass of the falling body, then the force is

$$F = k \frac{mM}{r^2}, \tag{1.61}$$

where k is a constant of proportionality. To determine k we use the fact that, when $r = R$, F has the value mg. Setting $r = R$ in formula (1.61) we have

$$mg = k \frac{mM}{R^2}$$

or

$$k = \frac{gR^2}{M}.$$

Substituting this value for k into Eq. (1.61), we obtain the formula

$$F = \frac{mgR^2}{r^2}.$$

As we check we observe that $F = mg$ when $r = R$.

Let us denote by x the directed distance from the center of the earth to the center of mass of the falling body. Then the equation of motion of the body is

$$m\ddot{x} = -\frac{mgR^2}{x^2}, \tag{1.62}$$

neglecting air resistance and other forces.

As an example, suppose that a projectile is fired directly upward from the surface of the earth with a velocity v_0. Then the initial conditions are

$$x(0) = R, \qquad \dot{x}(0) = v_0.$$

In the second-order equation (1.62), the independent variable t is missing. Setting $\dot{x} = v$ we have

$$x = \frac{dv}{dt} = \frac{dv}{dx}\frac{dx}{dt} = v\frac{dv}{dx}$$

and the equation becomes

$$v \frac{dv}{dx} = -\frac{gR^2}{x^2}.$$

Then

$$\int_{v_0}^{v} v \, dv = -gR^2 \int_{R}^{x} \frac{dx}{x^2},$$

$$\tfrac{1}{2}(v^2 - v_0^2) = gR^2 \left(\frac{1}{x} - \frac{1}{R} \right),$$

or

$$v^2 = v_0^2 + 2gR^2 \left(\frac{1}{x} - \frac{1}{R} \right).$$

Initially v is positive and must be the positive square root of the right-hand side of this equation. Thus

$$v = \frac{dx}{dt} = \left[v_0^2 - 2gR + \frac{2gR^2}{x} \right]^{1/2}. \tag{1.63}$$

As x increases we see that the velocity decreases. If the quantity in brackets in Eq. (1.63) vanishes, the velocity becomes negative and the body starts to fall back to earth. However, if $v_0^2 - 2gR \geq 0$, v can never become negative no matter how large x becomes. The critical value $v_0 = \sqrt{2gR}$ is called the *escape velocity* of the earth. Unless v_0 is greater than, or equal to, this value, the projectile will ultimately fall back to earth. The value of the escape velocity is approximately 7 m/sec. It should be pointed out that we have ignored a number of forces acting on the body, such as air resistance and the attractive forces of other celestial bodies.

Exercises for Section 1.11

1. Suppose that a particle of mass m moves along a straight line. Let $x(t)$ denote the directed distance of the particle from a fixed-point on the line of motion at time t. Suppose that the force acting on the particle depends only on x (and not on t or $\dot{x}$), so that the equation of motion has the form $m\ddot{x} = F(x)$. If

$$T = \tfrac{1}{2}m\dot{x}^2, \qquad V(x) = -\int_{0}^{x} F(s) \, ds,$$

show that $T + V$ is constant during the motion. (Here T and V are the kinetic and potential energies, respectively, of the particle.)

2. An object of mass m is thrown directly upward from the surface of the earth with velocity v_0. Assume that the acceleration due to gravity has the constant value g and that the air resists the motion of the object with a force equal to a constant c times the velocity.

(a) Find the equation of motion.

(b) Find the velocity and position of the object as functions of time.

(c) Find the maximum height h attained by the object and the time t_1 required to reach this height.

(d) Show that the velocity of impact (the velocity when the object returns to earth) is less in magnitude than the initial velocity v_0. *Suggestion:* Show that

$$\int_{t'}^{t''} (\dot{x}\ddot{x} + g\dot{x})\, dt < 0$$

if $t' < t''$. Note that $2\dot{x}\ddot{x} = (d/dt)\dot{x}^2$.

(e) Show that the time t_1 required for the object to attain its maximum height is less than the time required for the object to fall back to earth from this height. *Suggestion:* Show that $x(2t_1) > 0$.

3. An object of mass m is thrown directly upward from the surface of the earth with velocity v_0. Assume that the acceleration due to gravity has the constant value g and that the air resists the motion with a force equal to c times the square of the velocity.

(a) Find the equation of motion. *Suggestion:* Treat the time intervals when the object is going up and when it is coming down separately.

(b) Find the maximum height h attained by the object and the time t_1 required to reach this height.

(c) Find the time T required for the object to fall back to earth from its maximum height and find the velocity of impact.

4. An object of mass m is thrown directly upward from the surface of the earth with velocity v_0, where $v_0 < (2gR)^{1/2}$, R being the radius of the earth. Assume that Newton's inverse square law applies and neglect air resistance.

(a) Find the maximum height h attained by the object.

(b) Find the time t_1 required for the object to attain its maximum height.

(c) Show that the time required for the object to fall back to earth from its maximum height is the same as the time required for it to reach this height. Also show that the velocity of impact is the same in magnitude as the initial velocity.

5. A body of mass m falls from a height h above the earth. Assuming that the acceleration due to gravity has the constant value g and that the force due to air resistance is equal to c times the nth power of the velocity, find:

    (a) the equation of motion,

    (b) the limiting value of the velocity of the body.

6. A ship of mass m traveling in a straight line with speed v_0 shuts off its engines and coasts. Assume that the water resistance is equal to c times the α power of the velocity.

    (a) Show that the ship travels a finite distance before coming to rest if $0 < \alpha < 2$ and find this distance.

    (b) What is the time required for the ship to come to rest?

7. An object of mass m is thrown directly upward from the surface of the earth with velocity v_0. Assume that the acceleration due to gravity has the constant value g and that the force due to air resistance is equal to c times the fourth power of the velocity.

    (a) Find the maximum height attained by the object.

    (b) From what height must an object of mass m be dropped in order to achieve an impact velocity of v_0?

8. A particle of mass m moves along a straight line, with $x(t)$ its directed distance from a fixed point on the line of motion at time t. The particle is repelled from the point $x = 0$ by a force of magnitude m/x^2. It starts at $x = 1$ with a speed v_0 toward $x = 0$.

    (a) How close does the particle come to the origin?

    (b) What is the time required for the particle to reach the position where it is closest to the origin?

9. A simple pendulum consists of an object of mass m attached to the end of a massless rod of length L. The other end of the rod is connected to a frictionless pivot, as in Fig. 1.4. Assume that the acceleration due to gravity has the constant value g and that air resistance is negligible.

    (a) By equating $m\ddot{s}$ to the tangential component of force, derive the equation of motion

    $$\ddot{\theta} + \frac{g}{L}\sin\theta = 0.$$

    (b) To what physical situations do the constant solutions $\theta = n\pi$, n an integer, of the equation in part (a) correspond?

    (c) Suppose that the pendulum is released from rest at time $t = 0$ from the

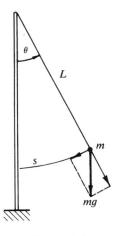

Figure 1.4

position $\theta = -\alpha$, where $0 < \alpha < \pi$. Show that on the first half-swing of the pendulum (θ increasing)

$$t = \left(\frac{L}{2g}\right)^{1/2} \int_{-\alpha}^{\theta} (\cos \theta - \cos \alpha)^{-1/2} \, d\theta.$$

(d) Show that the formula in part (c) can be written as

$$t = \left(\frac{L}{g}\right)^{1/2} \int_{-\pi/2}^{\psi} (1 - k^2 \sin^2 z)^{-1/2} \, dz,$$

where $k = \sin \alpha/2$ and $\psi = \sin^{-1}(k^{-1} \sin \theta/2)$. *Suggestion:* Let $k \sin z = \sin \theta/2$.

(e) The function F, where

$$F(\phi, k) = \int_0^\phi (1 - k^2 \sin^2 z)^{-1/2} \, dz,$$

is called an elliptic integral of the first kind. It has been tabulated for various values of ϕ and k. By using the result of part (d), show that the period of the pendulum is

$$4\left(\frac{L}{g}\right)^{1/2} F\left(\frac{\pi}{2}, k\right).$$

REFERENCES

1. Kaplan, W., *Ordinary Differential Equations*. Addison-Wesley, Reading, Massachusetts, 1958.
2. Martin, W. T., and Reissner, E., *Elementary Differential Equations*, 2nd ed. Addison-Wesley, Reading, Massachusetts, 1961.
3. Murphy, G. M., *Ordinary Differential Equations and Their Solutions*. Van Nostrand–Reinhold, Princeton, New Jersey, 1960.
4. Spiegel, M. R., *Applied Differential Equations*, 2nd ed. Prentice-Hall, Englewood Cliffs, New Jersey, 1967.
5. Symon, K. R., *Mechanics*, 2nd ed. Addison-Wesley, Reading, Massachusetts, 1960.

homogeneous up to 2.8 then nonhomogeneous

II

Linear
Differential Equations

2.1 INTRODUCTION

In Section 1.1, a linear differential equation of order n was defined to be an equation of the form

$$a_0 y^{(n)} + a_1 y^{(n-1)} + \cdots + y' + a_n y = F, \tag{2.1}$$

where the functions a_i and F are specified on some interval $\mathscr{I}$. If F is the zero function, the linear equation is said to be *homogeneous*; otherwise it is called *nonhomogeneous*. The zero function is always a solution of a homogeneous equation. It is called the *trivial solution*.

In Section 1.4 a method was presented for solving a first-order linear equation,

$$a_0 y' + a_1 y = F.$$

Our concern in this chapter is with higher-order linear equations. Even for second-order linear equations, no general method of solution is available as there was for first-order equations. Formulas for general solutions can be found only for certain special classes of higher-order equations. However, there are known important basic properties of solutions of linear differential equations in general, and we shall describe some of them in this section. We shall consider here only homogeneous equations. A theory for nonhomogeneous equations, based on that for homogeneous equations, is described in Section 2.8.

58

For the sake of convenience we now introduce some new notation. We introduce first the symbol D for the derivative operator, writing

$$Df = f', \qquad Df(x) = f'(x)$$

for any differentiable function f. Positive integral powers of D are defined by the formulas

$$D^2f = D(Df) = Df' = f'',$$
$$D^3f = D(D^2f) = Df'' = f''',$$
$$\vdots$$
$$D^mf = D(D^{m-1}f) = Df^{(m-1)} = f^{(m)}.$$

The zeroth power of D is defined as

$$D^0f = f.$$

We now consider a more general class of operators. To begin with, let a_0, a_1, and a_2 be functions defined on a common interval. We define an operator L by means of the relation

$$Lf = a_0 D^2f + a_1 Df + a_2 f,$$

where f is any twice differentiable function. We write

$$L = a_0 D^2 + a_1 D + a_2$$

and call L a second-order differential operator.

More generally, if $a_0, a_1, \ldots, a_n$ are functions defined on an interval $\mathscr{I}$, we define an nth-order differential operator

$$L = a_0 D^n + a_1 D^{n-1} + \cdots + a_{n-1}D + a_n$$

by means of the relation

$$Lf = a_0 D^nf + a_1 D^{n-1}f + \cdots + a_{n-1}Df + a_n f$$

or

$$Lf = a_0 f^{(n)} + a_1 f^{(n-1)} + \cdots + a_{n-1}f' + a_n f,$$

where f is any function that possesses at least n derivatives on $\mathscr{I}$. With this notation the differential equation (2.1) may be written as

$$Ly = F.$$

The operator L transforms a sufficiently differentiable function f into a function Lf. A solution of Eq. (2.1) is a function that is transformed into the function F. For example, the equation

$$y'' - (x + 1)y + xy = 0$$

may be written as $Ly = 0$, where

$$L = D^2 - (x + 1)D + x.$$

The function f, where $f(x) = e^x$, is a solution because

$$L(e^x) = (e^x)'' - (x + 1)(e^x)' + xe^x$$
$$= e^x - (x + 1)e^x + xe^x = 0$$

for all x.

A linear differential operator L possesses the following basic general properties.

Theorem 2.1 If u and v are functions that possess at least n derivatives on the interval $\mathscr{I}$ and if c is any constant, then

$$L(cu) = cLu$$

and

$$L(u + v) = Lu + Lv.$$

PROOF. We consider only the second-order case, leaving a proof in the general case as an exercise. Since $L = a_0 D^2 + a_1 D + a_2$, we have

$$L(cu) = a_0(cu)'' + a_1(cu)' + a_2(cu)$$
$$= c(a_0 u'' + a_1 u' + a_2 u)$$
$$= cLu$$

and

$$L(u + v) = a_0(u + v)'' + a_1(u + v)' + a_2(u + v)$$
$$= (a_0 u'' + a_1 u' + a_2 u) + (a_0 v'' + a_1 v' + a_2 v)$$
$$= Lu + Lv.$$

If u_1 and u_2 are functions and c_1 and c_2 constants, then

$$L(c_1 u_1 + c_2 u_2) = c_1 Lu_1 + c_2 Lu_2.$$

This follows from two applications of Theorem 2.1 since

$$L(c_1 u_1 + c_2 u_2) = L(c_1 u_1) + L(c_2 u_2) = c_1 Lu_1 + c_2 Lu_2.$$

Also,

$$L(c_1 u_1 + c_2 u_2 + c_3 u_3) = L[(c_1 u_1 + c_2 u_2) + c_3 u_3]$$
$$= L(c_1 u_1 + c_2 u_2) + L(c_3 u_3)$$
$$= c_1 Lu_1 + c_2 Lu_2 + c_3 Lu_3.$$

In general, if m is any positive integer,

$$L(c_1 u_1 + c_2 u_2 + \cdots + c_m u_m) = c_1 L u_1 + c_2 L u_2 + \cdots + c_m L u_m. \quad (2.2)$$

This fact may be established by mathematical induction.

A function u is a solution of the homogeneous differential equation $Ly = 0$ if and only if it is transformed into the zero function by L. The following results are almost immediate consequences of Theorem 2.1 and property (2.2). *know*

Theorem 2.2 If u and v are solutions of the homogeneous equation $Ly = 0$ and if c is any constant, then cu and $u + v$ are also solutions. If $u_1, u_2, \ldots, u_m$ are solutions and if $c_1, c_2, \ldots, c_m$ are constants, then $c_1 u_1 + c_2 u_2 + \cdots + c_m u_m$ is a solution.

PROOF Since $Lu = 0$ and $Lv = 0$, we have

$$L(cu) = cLu = c \cdot 0 = 0$$

and

$$L(u + v) = Lu + Lv + 0 + 0 = 0.$$

Hence cu and $u + v$ are solutions. Next, since $Lu_i = 0$ for $1 \leq i \leq m$, we have

$$L(c_1 u_1 + c_2 u_2 + \cdots + c_m u_m) = c_1 L u_1 + c_2 L u_2 + \cdots + c_m L u_m$$
$$= 0 + 0 + \cdots + 0$$
$$= 0.$$

Hence $c_1 u_1 + c_2 u_2 + \cdots + c_m u_m$ is a solution.

We shall now give an application of Theorem 2.2, using it to solve the initial value problem

$$y'' - 3y' + 2y = 0, \qquad y(0) = 2, \qquad y'(0) = -1.$$

The reader may verify that each of the functions $u_1(x) = e^x$ and $u_2(x) = e^{2x}$ is a solution of the linear homogeneous equation $Ly = 0$, where $L = D^2 - 3D + 2$. By Theorem 2.2, any function of the form

$$y(x) = c_1 e^x + c_2 e^{2x},$$

where c_1 and c_2 are arbitrary constants, is also a solution. We attempt to choose the constants so that the initial conditions are satisfied. Since

$$y'(x) = c_1 e^x + 2c_2 e^{2x},$$

the initial conditions require that

$$c_1 + c_2 = 2, \qquad c_1 + 2c_2 = -1.$$

Solving for c_1 and c_2, we find that $c_1 = 5$ and $c_2 = -3$. Hence the function

$$y(x) = 5e^x - 3e^{2x}$$

is the solution of the initial-value problem.

More generally, let us consider the nth order initial-value problem

$$a_0 y^{(n)} + a_1 y^{(n-1)} + \cdots + a_{n-1} y' + a_n y = 0,$$
$$y^{(i)}(x_0) = k_i, \qquad 0 \le i \le n - 1.$$

Suppose that $u_1, u_2, \ldots, u_n$ are solutions of the differential equation. Then $c_1 u_1 + c_2 u_2 + \cdots + c_n u_n$ is also a solution, for every choice of the constants c_i. We attempt to choose these n constants so that the n initial conditions are satisfied. The problem that faces us is how to find the n solutions $u_1, u_2, \ldots, u_n$. These solutions must be distinct, in a sense to be explained in the next section.

Exercises for Section 2.1

1. Find at least one solution of the equation $y'' + x^2 y' + y = 0$.

2. Let $a_0(x) = 1$ and $a_1(x) = 2x$ for all x. If $L = a_0 D + a_1$, find $Lf(x)$, where f is as given.

    (a) $f(x) = e^{2x}$ (b) $f(x) = x^2$ (c) $f(x) = e^{-x^2}$

3. Let $a_0(x) = x$, $a_1(x) = -2$, and $a_2(x) = 3x$ for all x. If $L = a_0 D^2 + a_1 D + a_2$, find $Lf(x)$, where f is as given.

    (a) $f(x) = x$ (b) $f(x) = e^{2x}$ (c) $f(x) = \sin x$

4. Let $L = D^2 + D - 6$. Which of the following functions are solutions of the homogeneous differential equation $Ly = 0$?

    (a) $f(x) = e^x$ (b) $g(x) = e^{-3x}$ (c) $h(x) = e^{-3x} + 4e^{2x}$

5. Let L_1 and L_2 be the operators $L_1 = D + 2x$, $L_2 = D - 1$. Find $L_1(L_2 f)$ and $L_2(L_1 f)$ and show that $L_1(L_2 f) \ne L_2(L_1 f)$ in general.

6. Verify that the functions $u_1(x) = e^{-x}$ and $u_2(x) = e^{-3x}$ are solutions of the equation $y'' + 4y' + 3y = 0$. Then find the solution for which $y(0) = 1$ and $y'(0) = 5$.

7. Verify that the functions $u_1(x) = x^4$ and $u_2(x) = x^{-2}$ are solutions of the equation $x^2 y'' - xy' - 8y = 0$ on the interval $(0, \infty)$. Then find the solution that satisfies the initial conditions $y(1) = 3$, $y'(1) = 0$.

8. Verify that the functions $u_1(x) = e^x$, $u_2(x) = e^{-x}$, and $u_3(x) = xe^x$ are solutions of the equation $(D^3 - D^2 - D + 1)y = 0$. Then find the solution for which $y(0) = 1$, $y'(0) = -1$, $y''(0) = 5$.

9. Find a solution of the equation

$$y''' - xy'' + (\sin x)y' + y = 0$$

for which $y(2) = y'(2) = y''(2) = 0$.

10. Prove Theorem 2.1 for an operator (a) of order 1 (b) of arbitrary order n.

11. Use induction to establish the relation (2.2).

12. If u and v are both solutions of the equation $Ly = F$, show that $u - v$ is a solution of the equation $Ly = 0$.

13. Let $a_0, a_1, \ldots, a_n$, and F be functions that possess derivatives of all orders on an interval $\mathscr{I}$ with a_0 never zero. Show that every solution of Eq. (2.1) must then possess derivatives of all orders on $\mathscr{I}$. *Suggestion:* Write the equation as

$$y^{(n)} = -\frac{1}{a_0} [a_1 y^{(n-1)} + \cdots + a_{n-1} y' + a_n y].$$

2.2 LINEAR DEPENDENCE

Let $f_1, f_2, \ldots, f_m$ be functions defined on an interval $\mathscr{I}$. The set of functions $\{f_1, f_2, \ldots, f_m\}$ is said to be *linearly dependent* (we also say that the functions of the set are linearly dependent) if there exist constants $c_1, c_2, \ldots, c_m$, not all zero, such that

$$c_1 f_1 + c_2 f_2 + \cdots + c_m f_m = 0; \tag{2.3}$$

that is,

$$c_1 f_1(x) + c_2 f_2(x) + \cdots + c_m f_m(x) = 0$$

for all x in $\mathscr{I}$. If the constants c_i could all be zero, the relation (2.3) would hold no matter what the functions f_i were. Thus the restriction that the constants not all be zero is essential. A set of functions that is not linearly dependent is said to be *linearly independent*.

If $g_1, g_2, \ldots, g_k$ are functions and if $a_1, a_2, \ldots, a_k$ are constants, a function of the form

$$a_1 g_1 + a_2 g_2 + \cdots + a_k g_k$$

is called a *linear combination* of the functions $g_1, g_2, \ldots, g_k$. Thus a set of functions is linearly dependent if some linear combination of them, in which the constants are not all zero, is the zero function.

The linear dependence of a set of functions may be characterized in the following way.

Theorem 2.3   The set of functions $\{f_1, f_2, \ldots, f_m\}$ is linearly dependent if and only if at least one of the functions is a linear combination of the others.

PROOF   Suppose first that the set is linearly dependent. Then

$$c_1 f_1 + c_2 f_2 + \cdots + c_m f_m = 0$$

and at least one of the constants, say c_k, is not zero. Then we may write

$$f_k = -\frac{c_1}{c_k} f_1 - \cdots - \frac{c_{k-1}}{c_k} f_{k-1} - \frac{c_{k+1}}{c_k} f_{k+1} - \cdots - \frac{c_m}{c_k} f_m,$$

so that f_k is a linear combination of the other functions.

Next suppose that one of the functions, say f_j, is a linear combination of the other functions. Then

$$f_j = a_1 f_1 + \cdots + a_{j-1} f_{j-1} + a_{j+1} f_{j+1} + \cdots + a_m f_m$$

or

$$a_1 f_1 + \cdots + a_{j-1} f_{j-1} - f_j + a_{j+1} f_{j+1} + \cdots + a_m f_m = 0.$$

The coefficient of f_j is not zero, therefore the functions are linearly dependent.

Example 1   Let $f_1(x) = x^2 - x$, $f_2(x) = 2x^2$, and $f_3(x) = 3x$ for all x. We see that

$$f_1(x) = \tfrac{1}{2} f_2(x) - \tfrac{1}{3} f_3(x);$$

therefore, by Theorem 2.3 the functions are linearly dependent.

Example 2   Let $f_1(x) = x^2$ and $f_2(x) = 2/x$ for $x > 0$. If $c_1 f_1 + c_2 f_2 = 0$, then

$$c_1 x^2 + 2c_2 \frac{1}{x} = 0$$

for $x > 0$. Taking $x = 1$ and $x = 2$, we see that

$$c_1 + 2c_2 = 0, \qquad 4c_1 + c_2 = 0.$$

These equations imply that $c_1 = c_2 = 0$; therefore, the functions are linearly independent.

We shall now see why the notion of linear dependence is important in the study of linear differential equations. We consider a linear homogeneous equation

$$a_0 y^{(n)} + a_1 y^{(n-1)} + \cdots + a_{n-1} y' + a_n y = 0. \tag{2.4}$$

If $u_1, u_2, \ldots, u_m$ are solutions, any linear combinations of these functions is again a solution according to Theorem 2.2. In order to determine whether we have found all the solutions, we may use the following criterion.

Theorem 2.4 Let the functions $a_0, a_1, \ldots, a_n$ be continuous on an interval $\mathscr{I}$, with a_0 never zero on $\mathscr{I}$. Let $u_1, u_2, \ldots, u_n$ be n solutions of the nth-order equation (2.4). If the set $\{u_1, u_2, \ldots, u_n\}$ is linearly independent, then every solution of Eq. (2.4) on $\mathscr{I}$† is of the form

$$y = c_1 u_1 + c_2 u_2 + \cdots + c_n u_n,$$

where $c_1, c_2, \ldots, c_n$ are constants. Furthermore, a set of n linearly independent solutions of Eq. (2.4) always exists.

We defer a discussion of the proof of this theorem until Section 2.13. However, the next several examples show how the theorem may be applied.

Example 3 Consider the second-order equation

$$y'' - 3y' + 2y = 0.$$

It is easily seen that the functions $u_1(x) = e^x$ and $u_2(x) = e^{2x}$ are solutions. They are linearly independent since if

$$c_1 e^x + c_2 e^{2x} = 0$$

for all x, then upon setting $x = 0$ and $x = 1$, we arrive at the conditions

$$c_1 + c_2 = 0, \qquad c_1 e + c_2 e^2 = 0,$$

which imply that $c_1 = c_2 = 0$. By Theorem 2.4, the general solution of the equation is

$$y(x) = c_1 e^x + c_2 e^{2x},$$

where c_1 and c_2 are arbitrary constants. Every solution is of this form.

The functions $v_1(x) = e^x + e^{2x}$ and $v_2(x) = e^x - e^{2x}$ are also solutions of the differential equation since they are linear combinations of the solutions u_1 and u_2. It is not hard to show that they are linearly independent. Hence the general solution can also be described by the formula

$$y(x) = a_1(e^x + e^{2x}) + a_2(e^x - e^{2x}),$$

where a_1 and a_2 are arbitrary constants. Knowledge of *any two* linearly independent solutions of the second-order equation enables us to describe the general solution.

† If the function u is a solution of Eq. (2.4) on an interval $\mathscr{J}$ that is contained in $\mathscr{I}$, it can be shown that there exists a solution v on $\mathscr{I}$ such that $u(x) = v(x)$ for x in $\mathscr{J}$. For this reason we consider only solutions on $\mathscr{I}$.

Example 4   For this example we take the equation

$$x^2 y'' - 2y = 0$$

on the interval $(0, \infty)$. The functions $u_1(x) = x^2$ and $u_2(x) = 1/x$ are solutions, as the reader may verify. If

$$c_1 x^2 + c_2 \frac{1}{x} = 0$$

for $x > 0$, then the cases $x = 1$ and $x = 2$ lead to the conditions

$$c_1 + c_2 = 0, \qquad 4c_1 + \tfrac{1}{2}c_2 = 0.$$

Hence $c_1 = c_2 = 0$ and the two solutions are linearly independent. The general solution of the equation is

$$y(x) = c_1 x^2 + c_2 \frac{1}{x}.$$

Example 5   In order to describe the general solution of the third-order equation

$$y''' - 3y'' + 2y' = 0,$$

we need three linearly independent solutions. Three such solutions are

$$u_1(x) = 1, \qquad u_2(x) = e^x, \qquad u_3(x) = e^{2x}.$$

Every solution is, therefore, of the form

$$y(x) = c_1 + c_2 e^x + c_3 e^{2x}.$$

One obvious problem that confronts us in solving an nth-order linear differential equation is how to find a set of n linearly independent solutions. Methods for doing this in certain special cases are discussed in Sections 2.4–2.7. We also need a general criterion for determining whether a set of n solutions is linearly independent. Such a criterion is developed in the next section.

Exercises for Section 2.2

1.   Determine whether the given functions are linearly dependent or independent. (The domain of each function is the set of all real numbers.)

(a) $2x;\ x^2 + 1$ (b) $2x - 1;\ x + 3;\ x$

(c) $x^2 - x;\ x^2 + x;\ 2x^2 + 3x$ (d) $\cos x;\ \sin x$

(e) $x;\ |x|$ (f) $e^{ax};\ e^{bx};\ a \neq b$

(g) $\sin x;\ \cos x; \cos\left(x - \dfrac{\pi}{3}\right)$ (h) $e^x;\ xe^x;\ (2x - 1)e^x$

(i) $e^x + e^{-x}; e^x - e^{-x}$ (j) $1; x; x^2$

2. Show that any set of functions that contains the zero function is linearly dependent.

3. If a set with one function as its only element is linearly dependent, what can be said about the function?

4. Let $\{u_1, u_2\}$ be a linearly independent set. Let $v_1 = Au_1 + Bu_2$ and $v_2 = Cu_1 + Du_2$, where A, B, C, and D are constants. Show that $\{v_1, v_2\}$ is linearly independent if and only if $AD - BC \neq 0$.

5. Let $\{u_1, u_2, \ldots, u_m\}$ be a linearly independent set of functions. If the function f can be expressed as

$$f = \sum_{i=1}^{m} a_i u_i \quad \text{and as} \quad f = \sum_{i=1}^{m} b_i u_i,$$

where the a_i and b_i are constants, show that $a_i = b_i$, $1 \leq i \leq m$.

6. Let $\{u_1, u_2, \ldots, u_m\}$ be a linearly dependent set of functions. If a function f can be expressed as a linear combination of the functions of this set, show that f is actually a linear combination of fewer than m of the functions.

7. Let $\{u_1, u_2, \ldots, u_m\}$ be a set of functions.

(a) If the set is linearly independent, is every subset linearly independent?

(b) If the set is linearly dependent, is every subset linearly dependent?

8. Two functions f and g defined on $[a, b]$ are said to be *orthogonal* if $\int_a^b f(x)g(x)\, dx = 0$. Let $\{f_1, f_2, \ldots, f_m\}$ be a set of continuous functions on $[a, b]$, none of which is the zero function. If every pair of the functions is orthogonal, show that the set is linearly independent. *Suggestion:* If f is continuous and is not the zero function, then $\int_a^b [f(x)]^2\, dx > 0$.

9. Use Theorem 2.4 to show that the general solution of the given linear differential equation is as indicated.

(a) $y'' - y = 0$; $y = c_1 e^x + c_2 e^{-x}$

(b) $y'' - y = 0$; $y = c_1 \cosh x + c_2 \sinh x$

(c) $y'' + y = 0$; $y = c_1 \cos x + c_2 \sin x$

(d) $x^2 y'' - 2xy' + 2y = 0$; $y = c_1 x + c_2 x^2$ $(x > 0)$

(e) $2x^2 y'' + 3xy' - y = 0$; $y = c_1 x^{-1} + c_2 x^{1/2}$ $(x > 0)$

(f) $y''' = 0$; $y = c_1 + c_2 x + c_3 x^2$

(g) $y''' - 6y'' + 11y' - 6y = 0$; $y = c_1 e^x + c_2 e^{2x} + c_3 e^{3x}$

2.3 WRONSKIANS

Let $f_1(x) = e^x$ and $f_2(x) = e^{2x}$ for all x. In Example 3 of the previous section we showed that these functions are linearly independent. We shall now reestablish their linear independence by the use of another method that is of general importance.

If

$$c_1 f_1 + c_2 f_2 = 0,$$

differentiation shows that

$$c_1 f_1' + c_2 f_2' = 0,$$

Thus we have the two equations

$$c_1 e^x + c_2 e^{2x} = 0$$

$$c_1 e^x + 2c_2 e^{2x} = 0,$$

which hold for all x. If c_1 and c_2 are not both zero, the determinant

$$\begin{vmatrix} e^x & e^{2x} \\ e^x & 2e^{2x} \end{vmatrix}$$

must be zero for every x. Since the value of the determinant is e^{3x}, which is never zero, we conclude that c_1 and c_2 must both be zero. Hence the functions are linearly independent.

We now generalize this procedure. Let $f_1, f_2, \ldots, f_m$ be functions that are defined and possess at least $m - 1$ derivatives on an interval $\mathcal{I}$. The determinant

$$\begin{vmatrix} f_1(x) & f_2(x) & \cdots & f_m(x) \\ f_1'(x) & f_2'(x) & \cdots & f_m'(x) \\ f_1''(x) & f_2''(x) & \cdots & f_m''(x) \\ \vdots & \vdots & & \vdots \\ f_1^{(m-1)}(x) & f_2^{(m-1)}(x) & \cdots & f_m^{(m-1)}(x) \end{vmatrix}$$

is called the *Wronskian* of the functions $f_1, f_2, \ldots, f_m$ at the point x. We denote it by $W(x: f_1, f_2, \ldots, f_m)$, or sometimes simply by $W(x)$ when it is clear what functions are involved. For example, if $f_1(x) = x^2$ and $f_2(x) = 3x - 1$ for all x, then

$$W(x; f_1, f_2) = \begin{vmatrix} x^2 & 3x - 1 \\ 2x & 3 \end{vmatrix} = -3x^2 + 2x.$$

The next theorem shows how the Wronskian can sometimes be used to establish the linear independence of a set of functions.

Theorem 2.5 Let $f_1, f_2, \ldots, f_m$ be defined and possess at least $m - 1$ derivatives on an interval $\mathcal{I}$. If the functions are linearly dependent, their Wronskian is zero at every point of $\mathcal{I}$. Hence if the Wronskian is not zero at even one point of $\mathcal{I}$, the functions are linearly independent.

PROOF If the functions are linearly dependent, there exist constants $c_1, c_2, \ldots, c_m$, not all zero, such that $c_1 f_1 + c_2 f_2 + \cdots + c_m f_m$ is the zero function. The derivatives of this function must also be the zero function. Differentiating repeatedly, $m - 1$ times, we obtain the relations

$$c_1 f_1(x) + c_2 f_2(x) + \cdots + c_m f_m(x) = 0$$

$$c_1 f_1'(x) + c_2 f_2'(x) + \cdots + c_m f_m'(x) = 0$$

$$\vdots$$

$$c_1 f_1^{(m-1)}(x) + c_2 f_2^{(m-1)}(x) + \cdots + c_m f_m^{(m-1)}(x) = 0.$$

For each fixed x in $\mathcal{I}$ this is a homogeneous linear system of equations for $c_1, c_2, \ldots, c_m$. Since the constants are not all zero, the determinant of the system must be zero. But this determinant is the Wronskian. Thus $W(x) = 0$ for every x in $\mathcal{I}$. If the Wronskian is not zero at some point, the functions cannot be linearly dependent. Hence they must be linearly independent.

We shall use Theorem 2.5 to show that a set of exponential functions,

$$f_1(x) = e^{r_1 x}, \quad f_2(x) = e^{r_2 x}, \quad \ldots, \quad f_n(x) = e^{r_n x}$$

for all x, where $r_i \neq r_j$ when $i \neq j$, is linearly independent. This fact will be important later on in our study of linear differential equations. The Wronskian of the exponential functions is

$$W(x) = e^{(r_1 + r_2 + \cdots + r_n)x} D_n,$$

where

$$D_n = \begin{vmatrix} 1 & 1 & \cdots & 1 \\ r_1 & r_2 & \cdots & r_n \\ r_1^2 & r_2^2 & \cdots & r_n^2 \\ \vdots & \vdots & & \vdots \\ r_1^{n-1} & r_2^{n-1} & \cdots & r_n^{n-1} \end{vmatrix}$$

This determinant is known as *Vandermonde's determinant*. When $n = 2$, we have

$$D_2 = \begin{vmatrix} 1 & 1 \\ r_1 & r_2 \end{vmatrix} = r_2 - r_1.$$

We leave it as an exercise to show that

$$D_3 = \begin{vmatrix} 1 & 1 & 1 \\ r_1 & r_2 & r_3 \\ r_1^2 & r_2^2 & r_3^2 \end{vmatrix} = (r_2 - r_1)(r_3 - r_1)(r_3 - r_2). \tag{2.5}$$

In general, it can be shown (Exercise 5) that

$$D_n = (r_2 - r_1)[(r_3 - r_1)(r_3 - r_2)][(r_4 - r_1)(r_4 - r_2)(r_4 - r_3)] \cdots$$
$$\times [(r_n - r_1)(r_n - r_2) \cdots (r_n - r_{n-1})]. \tag{2.6}$$

Hence $D_n \neq 0$ and the exponential functions are linearly independent.

One final observation about Wronskians should be made. Theorem 2.5 says that if a set of functions is linearly dependent, the Wronskian is identically zero. The converse is not true. If the Wronskian is identically zero, the functions may still be linearly independent. An example is provided by the functions

$$f_1(x) = x^2, \qquad f_2(x) = x|x|,$$

for all x. When $x \geq 0$ we have $f_2(x) = x^2$ and

$$W(x) = \begin{vmatrix} x^2 & x^2 \\ 2x & 2x \end{vmatrix} = 0.$$

When $x < 0$, $f_2(x) = -x^2$ and

$$W(x) = \begin{vmatrix} x^2 & -x^2 \\ 2x & -2x \end{vmatrix} = 0.$$

Hence $W(x) = 0$ for all x. However, f_1 and f_2 are linearly independent. If we set $x = 1$ and $x = -1$ in the equation

$$c_1 x^2 + c_2 x|x| = 0$$

we obtain the conditions

$$c_1 + c_2 = 0, \qquad c_1 - c_2 = 0$$

for c_1 and c_2. Hence $c_1 = c_2 = 0$ and the functions are linearly independent, even though their Wronskian is identically zero.

Exercises for Section 2.3

1. Compute the Wronskian of the given set of functions. Then determine whether the functions are linearly dependent or linearly independent.

    (a) e^{ax}, e^{bx}, $a \neq b$, x in any interval

    (b) $\cos ax$, $\sin ax$, $a \neq 0$, x in any interval

    (c) 1, x, x^2, x in any interval

    (d) $x + 1$, $x + 2$ $x + 3$,   all x

    (e) 1, x^{-1}, x^{-2}, $x > 0$

    (f) e^x, xe^x, $x^2 e^x$, x in any interval

    (g) x^m, $|x|^m$, m a positive integer,   all x

    (h) $x^2 - x$, $x^2 + x$, x^2,   all x

2. (a) If the Wronskian of a set of functions is identically zero, the functions must be linearly dependent. True or false?

    (b) If a set of functions is linearly dependent, the Wronskian must be identically zero. True or false?

    (c) If the Wronskian of a set of functions is zero at some points and not zero at some points, the functions are linearly independent. True or false?

3. Derive formula (2.5).

4. Use formula (2.6) to find the Wronskian of the functions e^x, e^{2x}, e^{3x}, e^{-x}.

5. Use mathematical induction to prove formula (2.6). *Suggestion:* If

$$P(r) = \begin{vmatrix} 1 & 1 & \cdots & 1 & 1 \\ r_1 & r_2 & \cdots & r_k & r \\ \vdots & \vdots & & \vdots & \vdots \\ r_1^k & r_2^k & \cdots & r_k^k & r^k \end{vmatrix},$$

then P is a polynomial of degree k with zeros $r_1, r_2, \ldots, r_k$; also $P(r_{k+1}) = D_{k+1}$.

6. Let $f_m(x) = x^m$ for all x and m a nonnegative integer. Find $W(x; f_0, f_1, \ldots, f_n)$ and show that the set $\{f_0, f_1, \ldots, f_n\}$ is linearly independent for every positive integer n.

7. Use the result of Exercise 6 to show that a polynomial is the zero function if and only if all its coefficients are zero.

8. Let u_1 and u_2 be solutions of the second-order linear differential equation $a_0 y'' + a_1 y' + a_2 y = 0$ on an interval where a_0 is never zero. Show that the Wronskian W of u_1 and u_2 satisfies the equation

$$a_0 W' + a_1 W = 0$$

and hence that

$$W(x) = C \exp\left\{-\int \frac{a_1(x)}{a_0(x)} \, dx\right\}.$$

This formula is known as *Abel's formula*. It shows that W is either identically zero or never zero.

9. Let u and v be twice differentiable functions defined on an interval. Show that the equation $W(x; u, v, y) = 0$ is a differential equation for an unknown function y that has u and v as solutions.

10. Use the result of Exercise 9 to construct a second-order differential equation that has $u(x) = e^x$ and $v(x) = x + 1$, all x, as solutions.

2.4 POLYNOMIAL OPERATORS

In order to describe the general solution of the nth order linear equation

$$a_0 y^{(n)} + a_1 y^{(n-1)} + \cdots + a_{n-1} y' + a_n y = 0, \tag{2.7}$$

we must find a set of n linearly independent solutions. This can be done easily only in special cases. One such case is when the coefficient functions a_i are all *constant* functions. Examples of equations with constant coefficients are

$$y'' - 3y' + 2y = 0, \qquad y''' - 2y'' - y' + 2y = 0.$$

The equations

$$xy' - 3y = 0, \qquad y'' + xy' + e^x y = 0$$

do *not* have constant coefficients.

Eq. (2.7) may be written as $Ly = 0$, where L is the operator

$$L = a_0 D^n + a_1 D^{n-1} + \cdots + a_{n-1} D + a_0.$$

Associated with this operator is the polynomial P, where

$$P(r) = a_0 r^n + a_1 r^{n-1} + \cdots + a_{n-1} r + a_n.$$

We shall write

$$P(D) = a_0 D^n + a_1 D^{n-1} + \cdots + a_{n-1} D + a_n,$$

and call $P(D)$ a *polynomial operator*. Equation (2.7) may be written as $P(D)y = 0$.

Any two operators L_1 and L_2 are said to be *equal*, written $L_1 = L_2$, if and only if $L_1 f = L_2 f$ for every function f for which both operations are defined. The *sum* $L_1 + L_2$ and the *product* L_1L_2 of two operators are defined according to the rules

$$(L_1 + L_2)u = L_1u + L_2u,$$
$$(L_1L_2)v = L_1(L_2v),$$

where u and v are any functions such that the indicated operations on the right are defined.

Example 1   Let $P(D) = D^2 - D + 2$ and $Q(D) = D + 1$. Then

$$[P(D) + Q(D)]u = P(D)u + Q(D)u$$
$$= (u'' - u' + 2u) + (u' + u)$$
$$= u'' + 3u.$$

Thus $P(D) + Q(D) = D^2 + 3$. Since

$$P(r) + Q(r) = (r^2 - r + 2) + (r + 1) = r^2 + 3,$$

we see that $P(D) + Q(D)$ is the polynomial operator whose associated polynomial is $P + Q$.

Next we have

$$[P(D)Q(D)]v = (D^2 - D + 2)(v' + v)$$
$$= v''' + v'' - v'' - v' + 2v' + 2v$$
$$= v''' + v' + 2v.$$

Hence

$$P(D)Q(D) = D^3 + D + 2.$$

Since

$$P(r)Q(r) = (r^2 - r + 2)(r + 1) = r^3 + r + 2,$$

we see that $P(D)Q(D)$ is the polynomial operator whose associated polynomial is PQ.

This example illustrates the following general principles.

Theorem 2.6   Let P and Q be polynomials. Then $P(D) + Q(D)$ and $P(D)Q(D)$ are polynomial operators whose associated polynomials are $P + Q$ and PQ, respectively.

The proof is omitted.

Since ordinary polynomials commute, that is, $P(r)Q(r) = Q(r)P(r)$ for all r, it follows that polynomial operators commute. Thus

$$P(D)Q(D) = Q(D)P(D).$$

Also, in view of the associative property $P(r)[Q(r)R(r)] = [P(r)Q(r)]R(r)$ for polynomials, we have

$$P(D)[Q(D)R(D)] = [P(D)Q(D)]R(D).$$

If P is any polynomial that can be written in the factored form

$$P(r) = P_1(r)P_2(r) \cdots P_k(r),$$

it follows that

$$P(D) = P_1(D)P_2(D) \cdots P_k(D).$$

Because of the commutative and associative properties of polynomial operators under multiplication, the order and manner of grouping of the operators in this product do not matter.

If P is any polynomial,

$$P(r) = a_0 r^n + a_1 r^{n-1} + \cdots + a_{n-1}r + a_n,$$

then P can be written as the product of linear factors,

$$P(r) = a_0(r - r_1)(r - r_2) \cdots (r - r_n).$$

The numbers $r_1, r_2, \ldots, r_n$, which may not be distinct, are the zeros of P and the roots of the equation $P(r) = 0$. Some of these roots may be complex. If P has real coefficients and if $r_1 = a + ib$, $b \neq 0$, is a complex root, then $r_2 = a - ib$ is also a root. The second-degree polynomial

$$(r - r_1)(r - r_2) = [r - (a + ib)][r - (a - ib)] = (r - a)^2 + b^2$$

has real coefficients. Therefore any polynomial operator $P(D)$ with real coefficients can be written as the product of first- and second-order polynomial operators with real coefficients. For example, let

$$P(D) = D^3 - 5D^2 + 9D - 5.$$

Since

$$P(r) = (r - 1)(r - 2 - i)(r - 2 + i) = (r - 1)(r^2 - 4r + 5),$$

we may write

$$P(D) = (D - 1)(D^2 - 4D + 5) = (D^2 - 4D + 5)(D - 1).$$

If a function is to be a solution of the equation

$$P(D)y = 0, \tag{2.8}$$

where

$$P(D) = a_0 D^n + a_1 D^{n-1} + \cdots + a_n,$$

a certain linear combination of that function and its first n derivatives must vanish. If f is an exponential function, of the form $f(x) = e^{rx}$, the derivatives of f are multiples of f itself. We have

$$D^m e^{rx} = r^m e^{rx} \tag{2.9}$$

for every nonnegative integer m. We therefore attempt to find solutions of Eq. (2.8) that are of this form. In view of formula (2.9) we have

$$(a_0 D^n + a_1 D^{n-1} + \cdots + a_n)e^{rx} = (a_0 r^n + a_1 r^{n-1} + \cdots + a_n)e^{rx}$$

or

$$P(D)e^{rx} = P(r)e^{rx}.$$

The polynomial P is called the *auxiliary polynomial* associated with the differential equation (2.8). We may write

$$P(D)e^{rx} = a_0(r - r_1)(r - r_2) \cdots (r - r_n)e^{rx}.$$

If r_i is a real zero of P, the function $e^{r_i x}$ is a solution of Eq. (2.8). If $r_1, r_2, \ldots, r_n$ are real and distinct, each of the functions

$$e^{r_1 x}, e^{r_2 x}, \ldots, e^{r_n x}$$

is a solution. These solutions are linearly independent, as was shown in Section 2.3. In this case the general solution of Eq. (2.8) is

$$y(x) = c_1 e^{r_1 x} + c_2 e^{r_2 x} + \cdots + c_n e^{r_n x}.$$

Example 2   Consider the equation

$$y'' - y' - 2y = 0,$$

which may be written as

$$(D^2 - D - 2)y = 0.$$

The auxiliary polynomial is

$$r^2 - r - 2 = (r + 1)(r - 2).$$

The zeros are $r_1 = -1$ and $r_2 = 2$. Hence e^{-x} and e^{2x} are linearly independent solutions and the general solution is

$$y(x) = c_1 e^{-x} + c_2 e^{2x}.$$

In the general case of Eq. (2.8), the polynomial P may not have n distinct zeros. Even if it does, some of the zeros may be complex. The next two examples illustrate these possibilities.

Example 3

$$y'' - 4y' + 4y = 0.$$

Here the auxiliary polynomial

$$r^2 - 4r + 4 = (r - 2)^2$$

has only one distinct zero, $r_1 = 2$. Thus e^{2x} is a solution, but we need still another solution to be able to describe the general solution.

Example 4

$$y'' - 2y' + 5y = 0.$$

The auxiliary polynomial equation

$$r^2 - 2r + 5 = 0$$

has the complex roots $r_1 = 1 + 2i$ and $r_2 = 1 - 2i$. Thus we are unable (as yet) to write down any nontrivial solution.

The difficulties caused by the appearance of complex zeros of the auxiliary polynomial will be removed in the next section.

Exercises for Section 2.4

1.   Write the differential equation in the form $P(D)y = 0$.

    (a) $y'' - 3y' + 2y = 0$ (b) $y' + 4y = 0$

    (c) $y''' - 3y'' - y' + y = 0$ (d) $y^{(4)} - y'' + y = 0$

2.   Write the differential equation in factored form, in terms of real polynomial operators of first- and second-order.

    (a) $(D^2 + D - 2)y = 0$ (b) $(D^4 - 1)y = 0$

    (c) $(D^3 - 3D + 2)y = 0$ (d) $(D^3 + D^2 - 4D + 6)y = 0$

3.   Find a differential equation of the form $P(D)y = 0$, with real coefficients, whose associated polynomial P has the given numbers among its zeros. The order of P should be as low as possible.

    (a) $r_1 = 2, \ r_2 = -1$ (b) $r_1 = 3 - 2i$

    (c) $r_1 = r_2 = 2, \ r_3 = 0$ (d) $r_1 = 2i, \ r_2 = -1, \ r_3 = 2$

4.   If the function u is a solution of the equation $P(D)y = 0$ and v is a solution of the equation $Q(D)y = 0$, show that u and v are both solutions of the equation $P(D)Q(D)y = 0$.

In Exercises 5–10, express the general solution of the given differential equation in terms of exponential functions, if possible.

5. $y'' - 5y' + 6y = 0$ 6. $2y'' + 5y' - 3y = 0$

7. $y''' + 5y'' - y' - 5y = 0$ 8. $y'' + 4y = 0$

9. $y'' - 6y' + 9y = 0$ 10. $y''' - 4y' = 0$

11. Show that no differential equation of the form $P(D)y = 0$ has the function f, where $f(x) = 1/x$, $x > 0$, as a solution.

12. If $L_1 = D$ and $L_2 = xD$, show that $L_1 L_2 \neq L_2 L_1$. In general, operators with nonconstant coefficients do not commute.

2.5 COMPLEX SOLUTIONS

In applications that give rise to differential equations, we are almost always concerned with real solutions of the equations. However, it is sometimes convenient to extract a desired real solution from a complex solution, as will be seen later on.

A complex function w of a real variable can be regarded as an ordered pair of real functions (u, v). We write

$$w(x) = u(x) + iv(x),$$

where i is the imaginary unit with the property that $i^2 = -1$. We call u the real part and v the imaginary part of w. The derivative of the complex function w is defined by the relation

$$w'(x) = u'(x) + iv'(x),$$

provided that $u'(x)$ and $v'(x)$ both exist.

In this chapter we are concerned with linear differential equations with *real* coefficients. Let

$$L = a_0 D^n + a_1 D^{n-1} + \cdots + a_{n-1} D + a_n,$$

where the functions a_i are real valued. Since

$$a_k D^{n-k} w = a_k D^{n-k} u + i a_k D^{n-k} v$$

for $k = 0, 1, \ldots, n$, it follows that

$$Lw = Lu + iLv,$$

where Lu and Lv are both real functions. If w is a complex solution of the homogeneous equation $Ly = 0$, then

$$Lu + iLv = 0.$$

Since a complex number can be zero only if its real and imaginary parts are both zero, it follows that $Lu = 0$ and $Lv = 0$. Consequently the real and imaginary parts, u and v, of a complex solution w are real solutions of the differential equation.

We shall also be interested in nonhomogeneous linear equations of the form

$$Ly = F, \tag{2.10}$$

where F is a complex function,

$$F(x) = f(x) + ig(x).$$

If $w = u + iv$ is a solution of Eq. (2.10), then

$$Lw = F$$

or

$$Lu + iLv = f + ig.$$

But this means that

$$Lu = f, \qquad Lv = g.$$

Thus by finding a complex solution of Eq. (2.10) we obtain real solutions for the two equations

$$Ly = f, \qquad Ly = g.$$

We shall be particularly concerned with a class of complex functions known as complex exponential functions. In order to define these functions, we first define the complex number e^{a+ib}, where e is the base of natural logarithms, as

$$e^{a+ib} = e^a \cos b + i e^a \sin b. \tag{2.11}$$

When $a + ib$ happens to be real ($b = 0$) we see that e^a has its usual real value. Other special cases of interest are

$$e^{ib} = \cos b + i \sin b, \qquad e^{-ib} = \cos b - i \sin b. \tag{2.12}$$

From these relations, we obtain the formulas

$$\cos b = \frac{1}{2}(e^{ib} + e^{-ib}), \qquad \sin b = \frac{1}{2i}(e^{ib} - e^{-ib}). \tag{2.13}$$

The laws of exponents

$$e^{z_1} \cdot e^{z_2} = e^{z_1 + z_2}, \tag{2.14a}$$

$$\frac{e^{z_1}}{e^{z_2}} = e^{z_1 - z_2}, \tag{2.14b}$$

where z_1 and z_2 are arbitrary complex numbers, can be derived from the definition (2.11). We shall consider the rule (2.14a) here, leaving the second to the exercises. Writing $z_1 = a_1 + ib_1$ and $z_2 = a_2 + ib_2$, we have

$$e^{z_1} \cdot e^{z_2} = e^{a_1}(\cos b_1 + i \sin b_1) \cdot e^{a_2}(\cos b_2 + i \sin b_2)$$
$$= e^{a_1 + a_2}[(\cos b_1 \cos b_2 - \sin b_1 \sin b_2)$$
$$+ i(\cos b_1 \sin b_2 + \sin b_1 \cos b_2)]$$
$$= e^{a_1 + a_2}[\cos(b_1 + b_2) + i \sin(b_1 + b_2)]$$
$$= e^{(a_1 + a_2) + i(b_1 + b_2)}$$
$$= e^{z_1 + z_2}.$$

We now consider a complex function F of the form

$$F(x) = e^{h(x)},$$

where $h(x) = u(x) + iv(x)$. We seek a formula for the derivative of this function. Writing

$$F(x) = e^{u(x)} \cos v(x) + i e^{u(x)} \sin v(x)$$

we see that

$$F' = u'(e^u \cos v + i e^u \sin v) + v'(-e^u \sin v + i e^u \cos v)$$
$$= (u' + iv')(e^u \cos v + i e^u \sin v).$$

Hence

$$\frac{de^{h(x)}}{dx} = h'(x)e^{h(x)}. \tag{2.15}$$

A function w of the form

$$w(x) = e^{cx},$$

where $c = a + ib$ is a complex constant, is called a *complex exponential function*. Using the rule (2.15), we see that

$$\frac{de^{cx}}{dx} = ce^{cx}$$

for all x. From Eqs. (2.12) and (2.13) we obtain the formulas

$$e^{ibx} = \cos bx + i \sin bx,$$
$$e^{-ibx} = \cos bx - i \sin bx, \tag{2.16}$$

and

$$\cos bx = \frac{1}{2}(e^{ibx} + e^{-ibx}),$$

$$\sin bx = \frac{1}{2i}(e^{ibx} - e^{-ibx}), \tag{2.17}$$

which relate the real trigonometric functions and the complex exponential functions. As an example of their use, let us consider the homogeneous differential equation $(D^2 + 4)y = 0$. Seeking a solution of the form $y = e^{cx}$, we find that

$$(D^2 + 4)e^{cx} = (c^2 + 4)e^{cx} = (c + 2i)(c - 2i)e^{cx}.$$

Since this is identically zero when $c = \pm 2i$ the functions e^{2ix} and e^{-2ix} are complex solutions. But then the real and imaginary parts, $\cos 2x$ and $\sin 2x$, are real solutions.

Next we consider the nonhomogeneous differential equation

$$Ly = Ae^{ibx}, \qquad\qquad\qquad (2.18)$$

where L has real coefficients and A is a real constant. According to the formulas (2.16),

$$Ae^{ibx} = A \cos bx + iA \sin bx.$$

If we can find a complex solution of Eq. (2.18), then the real and imaginary parts of this solution will be real solutions of the equations

$$Ly = A \cos bx, \qquad Ly = A \sin bx,$$

respectively. The reason for preferring to deal with complex exponential functions rather than real trigonometric functions is that the differentiation formulas for the former are simpler. A number of examples are presented in Section 2.6 and 2.9.

If $c = a + ib$ is any complex number, and if α is any positive real number, we define

$$\alpha^c = e^{c \ln \alpha}. \qquad\qquad\qquad (2.19)$$

Notice that when c is real $(b = 0)$ this formula agrees with the definition of α^c given in calculus. The laws of exponents

$$\alpha^{z_1} \cdot \alpha^{z_2} = \alpha^{z_1 + z_2}, \qquad\qquad\qquad (2.20a)$$

$$\frac{\alpha^{z_1}}{\alpha^{z_2}} = \alpha^{z_1 - z_2}, \qquad\qquad\qquad (2.20b)$$

follow easily from the laws (2.14). Their derivations are left to the exercises.

If x is a positive real number we have

$$x^c = e^{c \ln x} \qquad\qquad\qquad (2.21)$$

according to the definition (2.19). Application of the differentiation formula (2.15) yields

$$\frac{dx^c}{dx} = \frac{c}{x}e^{c \ln x} = \frac{c}{x}x^c$$

or

$$\frac{dx^c}{dx} = cx^{c-1}, \qquad x > 0.$$

Notice that we have not defined α^β when α and β are both complex, or even when α is real and negative. To give proper definitions would take us further into the theory of complex variables than is necessary for our study of linear differential equations.

Exercises for Section 2.5

1. (a) If $w = u + iv$ is a complex function and $c = a + ib$ is a complex constant, show that

    $$\frac{d[cw(x)]}{dx} = c\frac{dw(x)}{dx}.$$

    (b) If $w_1 = u_1 + iv_1$ and $w_2 = u_2 + iv_2$ are complex functions, show that $(w_1 + w_2)' = w_1' + w_2'$.

2. Let $w_1 = u_1 + iv_1$ and $w_2 = u_2 + iv_2$ be complex functions. Show that
    (a) $(w_1 w_2)' = w_1' w_2 + w_1 w_2'$
    (b) $(w_1/w_2)' = (w_1' w_2 - w_1 w_2')/w_2^2$

3. Express each complex exponential function in terms of trigonometric functions and express each trigonometric function in terms of complex exponential functions.
    (a) e^{3ix} (b) e^{-2ix} (c) $e^{(2-3i)x}$ (d) $e^{(-2+i)x}$
    (e) $\cos 2x$ (f) $\sin 5x$ (g) $\sin x$ (h) $\cos 5x$

4. Show that $e^{z_1}/e^{z_2} = e^{z_1 - z_2}$ when z_1 and z_2 are arbitrary complex numbers.

5. The *modulus* of a complex number $c = a + ib$, written $|c|$, is defined to be $|c| = (a^2 + b^2)^{1/2}$. Show that $|e^{a+ib}| = e^a$.

6. For every real number θ and every integer m show that

    $$(e^{i\theta})^m = e^{im\theta}$$

    and hence that

    $$(\cos \theta + i \sin \theta)^m = \cos m\theta + i \sin m\theta.$$

This is known as DeMoivre's formula. *Suggestion:* First let m be non-negative and use induction.

7. Show that the complex function $e^{(-1+2i)x}$ is a solution of the differential equation

$$(D^2 + 2D + 5)y = 0.$$

Use this fact to find two linearly independent real solutions.

8. For each of the following differential equations find all numbers r, real and complex, such that e^{rx} is a solution. Find two linearly independent real solutions.

(a) $(D^2 + 9)y = 0$ (b) $(D^2 - 3D + 2)y = 0$

(c) $(D^2 - 4D + 5)y = 0$ (d) $(D^2 + 4D + 5)y = 0$

9. Let $P(D) = D^2 - D + 5$. Find a complex solution of the equation

$$P(D)y = 10e^{2ix}$$

of the form $y = Ae^{2ix}$, where A is a complex constant. Use your answer to find a real solution of each of the equations

$$P(D)y = 10 \cos 2x, \qquad P(D)y = 10 \sin 2x.$$

10. Derive the laws of exponents (2.20) from the laws (2.14).

11. Find all solutions of the differential equation

$$x^2 y'' + xy' + 4y = 0$$

on the interval $(0, \infty)$ that are of the form $y = x^c$, where c may be complex. Use your answer to find two linearly independent real solutions.

2.6 EQUATIONS WITH CONSTANT COEFFICIENTS

By making use of complex exponential functions we can now solve any differential equation of the type

$$P(D)y = 0, \tag{2.22}$$

provided that the auxiliary polynomial P does not have multiple zeros. If $a + ib$ and $a - ib$ are complex zeros of P, then

$$e^{(a+ib)x} = e^{ax}(\cos bx + i \sin bx),$$
$$e^{(a-ib)x} = e^{ax}(\cos bx - i \sin bx)$$

are complex solutions of Eq. (2.22). The real and imaginary parts

$$e^{ax} \cos bx, \qquad e^{ax} \sin bx$$

are real solutions. Thus, to every pair of complex conjugate zeros of P there corresponds a pair of real solutions of Eq. (2.22), and to each real zero c of P there corresponds a real solution e^{cx}. It will be shown in this section later on that the set of all real solutions so obtained is linearly independent. First we consider some examples.

Example 1

$$y'' + a^2 y = 0. \tag{2.23}$$

The polynomial equation, $r^2 + a^2 = 0$, has the roots ai and $-ai$. Hence

$$e^{iax} = \cos ax + i \sin ax$$

is a complex solution. The real and imaginary parts, $\cos ax$ and $\sin ax$, are real solutions. The general solution is

$$y(x) = c_1 \cos ax + c_2 \sin ax. \tag{2.24}$$

Equation (2.23) is important for many applications. We rewrite formula (2.24) as

$$y = (c_1^2 + c_2^2)^{1/2}[p \cos ax + q \sin ax],$$

where

$$p = \frac{c_1}{(c_1^2 + c_2^2)^{1/2}}, \qquad q = \frac{c_2}{(c_1^2 + c_2^2)^{1/2}}.$$

Since $p^2 + q^2 = 1$, there exist angles α and β such that

$$\cos \alpha = p, \qquad \sin \alpha = -q,$$
$$\sin \beta = p, \qquad \cos \beta = q.$$

Consequently the general solution is also described by either of the formulas

$$y(x) = A \cos(ax + \alpha), \qquad y(x) = B \sin(ax + \beta), \tag{2.25}$$

where A, B, α, and β are arbitrary constants. (See Exercise 28.)

Example 2

$$(D^3 - 5D^2 + 9D - 5)y = 0.$$

The polynomial

$$P(r) = r^3 - 5r^2 + 9r - 5 = (r - 1)(r^2 - 4r + 5)$$

has the zeros $r_1 = 1$, $r_2 = 2 + i$, and $r_3 = 2 - i$. Thus

$$e^{(2+i)x} = e^{2x}(\cos x + i \sin x)$$

is a complex solution and $e^{2x} \cos x$, $e^{2x} \sin x$ are real solutions. The general solution is

$$y(x) = c_1 e^x + c_2 e^{2x} \cos x + c_3 e^{2x} \sin x.$$

Let us now consider the general case of an nth-order equation (2.22) where the polynomial P,

$$P(r) = a_0(r - r_1)(r - r_2) \cdots (r - r_n),$$

has n distinct zeros. The functions

$$e^{r_1 x}, e^{r_2 x}, \ldots, e^{r_n x},$$

some of which may be complex, are solutions of Eq. (2.22) on $(-\infty, \infty)$. These solutions are linearly independent *with respect to the set of complex numbers*,† as follows from a consideration of their Wronskian. We shall now show that the corresponding set of n real solutions is a linearly independent set of elements of the space of real functions that are defined on $(-\infty, \infty)$. Suppose that $c_1, c_2, \ldots, c_n$ are real numbers such that

$$c_1 e^{ax} \cos bx + c_2 e^{ax} \sin bx + \cdots = 0$$

for all x. Then

$$c_1' e^{(a+ib)x} + c_2' e^{(a-ib)x} + \cdots = 0$$

for all x, where

$$c_1 = c_1' + c_2', \qquad c_2 = i(c_1' - c_2').$$

But then $c_1' = c_2' = \cdots = 0$ so $c_1 = c_2 = \cdots = 0$. Hence the n real solutions are linearly independent.

In order to treat the case where the polynomial P has multiple zeros, we need the following result.

Lemma   If r is any number, real or complex, and if the function w, which may be complex, has at least m derivatives, then

$$(D - r)^m [e^{rx} w(x)] = e^{rx} D^m w(x). \tag{2.26}$$

---

† A set of (complex) functions is said to be linearly dependent with respect to the set of complex numbers if the constants in Eq. (2.3) are permitted to be complex. The set is linearly independent if it is not linearly dependent.

This formula evidently holds when $m = 0$. It also holds for $m = 1$, because

$$(D - r)[e^{rx}w(x)] = e^{rx}w'(x) + re^{rx}w(x) - re^{rx}w(x)$$
$$= e^{rx}Dw(x).$$

The reader who understands mathematical induction should be able to establish that formula (2.26) holds for every nonnegative integer m.

Now suppose that r_1 is a zero of P of multiplicity k, so that

$$P(r) = a_0(r - r_1)^k(r - r_2) \cdots (r - r_{n-k+1}).$$

Then

$$P(D) = Q(D)(D - r_1)^k,$$

where $Q(D)$ is a polynomial operator of order $n - k$. We shall show that each of the k functions

$$x^{r_1 x}, \ xe^{r_1 x}, \ x^2 e^{r_1 x}, \ \ldots, \ x^{k-1}e^{r_1 x}$$

is a solution of the equation $P(D)y = 0$. Using the lemma, we have

$$P(D)(x^j e^{r_1 x}) = Q(D)(D - r_1)^k x_j e^{r_1 x}$$
$$= Q(D)e^{r_1 x}D^k x^j$$
$$= 0$$

since $D^k x^j = 0$ when $j < k$. This proves our assertion. Of course if r_1 is complex, the functions will be complex.

If $r_1 = a + ib$ is a complex zero of P of multiplicity k, then $r_1 = a - ib$ is also a zero of multiplicity k. Then each of the $2k$ functions

$$x^j e^{(a+ib)x}, \qquad x^j e^{(a-ib)x}, \qquad 0 \le j \le k - 1$$

is a complex solution of the differential equation $P(D)y = 0$. But since the real and imaginary parts of a complex solution are both real solutions, we know that each of the $2k$ real functions

$$x^j e^{ax} \cos bx, \qquad x^j e^{ax} \sin bx, \qquad 0 \le j \le k - 1$$

is a real solution.

Thus even when P has complex and multiple zeros, we can still find n seemingly distinct real solutions of the nth-order equation $P(D)y = 0$. Proofs that these n solutions are linearly independent are given by Coddington [1], and Kaplan [3]. We summarize our results as follows.

Theorem 2.7 If r_1 is a real root of multiplicity k of the nth-degree polynomial equation $P(r) = 0$, then each of the k functions

$$x^j e^{r_1 x}, \qquad 0 \le j \le k - 1$$

is a solution of the nth-order differential equation $P(D)y = 0$. If $a + ib$, $b \neq 0$, is a complex root of multiplicity k (in which case $a - ib$ is also a root of multiplicity k), then each of the $2k$ real functions

$$x^j e^{ax} \cos bx, \qquad x^j e^{ax} \sin bx, \qquad 0 \leq j \leq k - 1$$

is a solution. The n real solutions of the differential equation (corresponding to the n zeros of the polynomial) that are described here are linearly independent on every interval.

Example 3

$$y'' + 4y' + 4y = 0.$$

Since $r^2 + 4r + 4 = (r + 2)^2$, we have $r_1 = r_2 = -2$. Accordingly, e^{-2x} and xe^{-2x} are solutions. The general solution is

$$y(x) = c_1 e^{-2x} + c_2 xe^{-2x}.$$

Example 4

$$D^2(D + 2)^3(D - 3)y = 0.$$

The polynomial equation $r^2(r + 2)^3(r - 3) = 0$ has roots $0, 0, -2, -2, -2$, and 3. Each of the functions

$$1, \quad x, \quad e^{-2x}, \quad xe^{-2x}, \quad x^2 e^{-2x}, \quad e^{3x}$$

is a solution of the differential equation. (Remember that $e^{0x} = 1$.) The general solution is

$$y(x) = c_1 + c_2 x + (c_3 + c_4 x + c_5 x^2)e^{-2x} + c_6 e^{3x}.$$

Example 5

$$(D^4 + 8D^2 + 16)y = 0.$$

The auxiliary polynomial equation is

$$r^4 + 8r^2 + 16 = (r^2 + 4)^2 = 0,$$

with roots $2i, 2i, -2i$, and $-2i$. Thus

$$e^{2ix}, \quad xe^{2ix}, \quad e^{-2ix}, \quad xe^{-2ix}$$

are complex solutions. The functions

$$\cos 2x, \quad x \cos 2x, \quad \sin 2x, \quad x \sin 2x$$

are real solutions and the general solution is

$$y(x) = (c_1 + c_2 x) \cos 2x + (c_3 + c_4 x) \sin 2x.$$

Differential equations of certain classes can be transformed into equations with constant coefficients by means of a change of variable. One such class is considered in the next section.

Exercises for Section 2.6

In Exercises 1–20, find the general solution of the differential equation.

1. $y'' - y' - 6y = 0$

2. $2y'' - 5y' + 2y = 0$

3. $y'' + 2y' = 0$

4. $y''' + 2y'' - y' - 2y = 0$

5. $y''' + 3y'' - 4y' = 0$

6. $y^{(4)} - 10y'' + 9y = 0$

7. $y'' + 2y' + y = 0$

8. $y'' - 6y' + 9y = 0$

9. $y''' - 6y'' + 12y' - 8y = 0$

10. $y''' + 5y'' + 3y' - 9y = 0$

11. $y''' + y'' = 0$

12. $(D - 1)^3(D + 2)^2 y = 0$

13. $y' + 9y = 0$

14. $y'' + 2y' + 10y = 0$

15. $y'' - 6y' + 13y = 0$

16. $y''' + 2y'' + y' + 2y = 0$

17. $y^{(4)} + 2y'' + y = 0$

18. $(D^2 - 2D + 5)^2 y = 0$

19. $(D - 2)^2(D^2 + 2)y = 0$

20. $y^{(5)} + 4y''' = 0$

In Exercises 21–25, find the solution of the initial value problem.

21. $y'' - 4y' + 3y = 0$, $y(0) = -1$, $y'(0) = 3$

22. $y'' - 4y' + 4y = 0$, $y(0) = 2$, $y'(0) = 1$

23. $y'' + 4y = 0$, $y(\pi) = 1$, $y'(\pi) = -4$

24. $y'' + 2y' + 2y = 0$, $y(0) = 2$, $y'(0) = -3$

25. $y''' + y'' = 0$, $y(0) = 2$, $y'(0) = 1$, $y''(0) = -1$

26. Show that every solution of the differential equation $P(D)y = 0$ tends to zero as x becomes infinite if and only if all the roots of the polynomial equation $P(r) = 0$ have negative real parts.

27. Show that the general solution of the equation $y'' - a^2 y = 0$, where a is a constant, can be written either as

$$y(x) = c_1 e^{ax} + c_2 e^{-ax}$$

or as

$$y(x) = C_1 \cosh ax + C_2 \sinh ax.$$

28. Show that the general solution of the equation $y'' + a^2y = 0$, where a is a constant, can be written in the forms (2.25).

29. Find a linear homogeneous differential equation with real constant coefficients, whose order is as low as possible, that has the given function as a solution.

(a) xe^{-2x} (b) $x - e^{3x}$
(c) $\cos 2x$ (d) $e^x \sin 2x$
(e) $x \sin 3x$ (f) $\cos 2x + 3e^{-x}$

2.7 CAUCHY–EULER EQUATIONS

A linear differential equation of the form

$$(b_0 x^n D^n + b_1 x^{n-1} D^{n-1} + \cdots + b_{n-1} x D + b_n)y = 0, \qquad (2.27)$$

where $b_0, b_1, \ldots, b_n$ are constants, is known as a *Cauchy–Euler equation*, or as an *equidimensional equation*. Examples of Cauchy–Euler equations are

$$x^2 y'' - 3xy' + 4y = 0, \qquad x^3 y''' + 2xy' = 0.$$

Equations of this type can be transformed into equations with constant coefficients by means of a change of independent variable.

Let

$$x = e^t, \qquad t = \ln x,$$

where as t varies over the set of all real numbers, x varies over the interval $(0, \infty)$. In what follows we assume that $x > 0$. The case $x < 0$ is treated in Exercise 19.

Let us write

$$y(e^t) = Y(t).$$

Then, by the chain rule for differentiation,

$$x\,Dy(x) = x\,\frac{dy(x)}{dx} = e^t\,\frac{dY(t)}{dt}\frac{dt}{dx}.$$

Since $dt/dx = 1/x = e^{-t}$ we have

$$x\,Dy(x) = DY(t).$$

Next, using the chain rule again,

$$x^2 \, D^2 y(x) = x^2 \, \frac{d}{dx} \left[\frac{dy(x)}{dx} \right]$$

$$= e^{2t} \frac{dt}{dx} \frac{d}{dt} \left[e^{-t} \frac{dY(t)}{dt} \right]$$

$$= e^t \left[e^{-t} \frac{d^2 Y(t)}{dt^2} - e^{-t} \frac{dY(t)}{dt} \right]$$

$$= \frac{d^2 Y(t)}{dt^2} - \frac{dY(t)}{dt}.$$

Thus

$$x^2 \, D^2 y(x) = (D^2 - D)Y(t) = D(D - 1)Y(t).$$

By the use of mathematical induction, it can be shown that

$$x^m D^m y(x) = D(D - 1)(D - 2) \cdots (D - m + 1) Y(t) \qquad (2.28)$$

for every positive integer m.

Using formula (2.28) we see that the original equation (2.27) becomes

$$[b_0 \, D(D - 1) \cdots (D - n + 1) + b_1 D(D - 1) \cdots (D - n + 2)$$
$$+ \cdots + b_{n-1} D + b_n] Y = 0. \qquad (2.29)$$

This equation with constant coefficients has the auxiliary polynomial Q, where

$$Q(r) = b_0 \, r(r - 1) \cdots (r - n + 1) + b_1 r(r - 1) \cdots (r - n + 2)$$
$$+ \cdots + b_{n-1} r + b_n. \qquad (2.30)$$

This polynomial is of degree n. If r_1 is a real zero of multiplicity k, then each of the k functions

$$t^j e^{r_1 t}, \qquad 0 \leq j \leq k - 1$$

is a solution of Eq. (2.29) and each of the functions

$$(\ln x)^j x^{r_1}, \qquad 0 \leq j \leq k - 1$$

is a solution of the original equation (2.27). If $a + ib$ and $a - ib$ are zeros of Q of multiplicity k, the functions

$$t^j e^{at} \cos bt, \qquad t^j e^{at} \sin bt, \qquad 0 \leq j \leq k - 1,$$

are solutions of Eq. (2.29). The corresponding solutions of the original equation are

$$x^a (\ln x)^j \cos(b \ln x), \qquad x^a (\ln x)^j \sin(b \ln x), \qquad 0 \leq j \leq k - 1.$$

Example 1

$$2x^2y'' - 5xy' + 3y = 0.$$

The change of variable $x = e^t$ leads to the equation

$$[2D(D - 1) - 5D + 3]Y = 0$$

or

$$(2D - 1)(D - 3)Y = 0.$$

Hence

$$Y(t) = c_1 e^{t/2} + c_2 e^{3t}$$

or

$$y(x) = c_1 x^{1/2} + c_2 x^3, \qquad x > 0.$$

Example 2

$$x^2y'' - xy' + 5y = 0.$$

This equation becomes

$$[D(D - 1) - D + 5]Y = 0$$

or

$$(D^2 - 2D + 5)Y = 0.$$

The roots of the auxiliary equation are $1 + 2i$ and $1 - 2i$. Thus

$$Y(t) = c_1 e^t \cos 2t + c_2 e^t \sin 2t$$

or

$$y(x) = c_1 x \cos(2 \ln x) + c_2 x \sin(2 \ln x).$$

The equation

$$Ly \equiv (b_0 x^n D^n + b_1 x^{n-1} D^{n-1} + \cdots + b_{n-1} xD + b_n)y = 0$$

can be solved more directly by attempting to find solutions of the form $y = x^r$, without any change of variable. Observing that

$$D^k x^r = r(r - 1)(r - 2) \cdots (r - k + 1)x^{r-k}$$

and

$$x^k D^k x^r = r(r - 1)(r - 2) \cdots (r - k + 1)x^r,$$

we have

$$L(x^r) = [b_0(r - 1) \cdots (r - n + 1) + b_1 r(r - 1) \cdots (r - n + 2) \\ + \cdots + b_{n-1} r + b_n]x^r$$

or

$$L(x^r) = Q(r)x^r,$$

where Q is the polynomial (2.30). If r_1 is a real zero of Q of multiplicity k, the functions

$$x^{r_1}(\ln x)^j, \qquad 0 \le j \le k - 1$$

are solutions. If $a + ib$ and $a - ib$ are zeros of multiplicity k, then the functions

$$x^a(\ln x)^j \cos(b \ln x), \qquad x^a(\ln x)^j \sin(b \ln x), \qquad 0 \le j \le k - 1$$

are solutions.

Example 3

$$x^3 y''' - x^2 y'' + xy' = 0.$$

Setting $y = x^r$, we must have

$$r(r - 1)(r - 2) - r(r - 1) + r = 0$$

or

$$r(r - 2)^2 = 0.$$

The general solution is

$$y(x) = c_1 + (c_2 + c_3 \ln x)x^2.$$

Exercises for Section 2.7

In Exercises 1–12, find the general solution of the differential equation if x is restricted to the interval $(0, \infty)$.

1. $x^2 y'' - 2y = 0$
2. $x^2 y'' + 3xy' - 3y = 0$
3. $3xy'' + 2y' = 0$
4. $x^3 y''' + x^2 y'' - 2xy' + 2y = 0$
5. $4x^2 y'' + y = 0$
6. $x^2 y'' - 3xy' + 4y = 0$
7. $xy''' + 2y'' = 0$
8. $x^3 y''' + 6x^2 y'' + 7xy' + y = 0$
9. $x^2 y'' + xy' + 4y = 0$
10. $x^2 y'' - 5xy' + 13y = 0$
11. $x^3 y''' + 2x^2 y'' + xy' - y = 0$
12. $x^4 y^{(4)} + 6x^3 y''' + 15x^2 y'' + 9xy' + 16y = 0$

In Exercises 13–15, find the solution of the initial value problem on the interval $(0, \infty)$.

13. $x^2 y'' + 4xy' + 2y = 0, \qquad y(1) = 1, \quad y'(1) = 2$
14. $x^2 y'' - 3xy' + 4y = 0, \qquad y(1) = 2, \quad y'(1) = 1$
15. $x^2 y'' + xy' + 4y = 0, \qquad y(1) = 1, \quad y'(1) = 4$

In Exercises 16–18, find all solutions on the interval $(0, \infty)$ that have a finite limit as x tends to zero.

16. $4x^2y'' + 4xy' - y = 0$ 17. $x^2y'' + 2xy' - 2y = 0$

18. $x^2y'' + 6xy' + 6y = 0$

19. If the function f is a solution of Eq. (2.27) on the interval $(0, \infty)$ show that the function g, where $g(x) = f(-x)$, is a solution on $(-\infty, 0)$.

20. Show that the change of variable $t = ax + b$ transforms the equation
$$b_0(ax + b)^2y'' + b_1(ax + b)y' + b_2 y = 0$$
into a Cauchy–Euler equation.

21. Use the result of Exercise 20 to find the general solution of the given equation.

   (a) $(x - 3)^2y'' + 3(x - 3)y' + y = 0, \quad x > 3$

   (b) $(2x + 1)^2y'' + 4(2x + 1)y' - 24y = 0, \quad x > -1/2$

22. What conditions must the zeros of the polynomial Q satisfy in order that every solution of Eq. (2.27) tend to zero as

   (a) x approaches zero through positive values?

   (b) x becomes positively infinite?

23. If the functions $f_1, f_2, \ldots, f_n$ are linearly independent on the set of all real numbers and if $g_i(x) = f_i(\ln x)$ for $x > 0$, show that the functions g_i are linearly independent on $(0, \infty)$.

2.8 NONHOMOGENEOUS EQUATIONS

The linear equation
$$Ly = F, \tag{2.31}$$
where
$$L = a_0 D^n + a_1 D^{n-1} + \cdots + a_{n-1}D + a_n$$
(the functions a_i need not be constants) is called *nonhomogeneous* if F is not the zero function. Associated with the nonhomogeneous equation is the homogeneous equation
$$Ly = 0. \tag{2.32}$$

It turns out that we can solve the nonhomogeneous equation if we can solve the homogeneous equation and if we can also find just one particular solution of the nonhomogeneous equation.

Theorem 2.8   Let $u_1, u_2, \ldots, u_n$ be linearly independent solutions of the homogeneous equation (2.32) on an interval $\mathscr{I}$† and let u_p be any particular solution of the nonhomogeneous equation (2.31) on $\mathscr{I}$. Then the set of all solutions of equation (2.31) on $\mathscr{I}$ consists of all functions of the form

$$c_1 u_1 + c_2 u_2 + \cdots + c_n u_n + u_p, \tag{2.33}$$

where $c_1, c_2, \ldots, c_n$ are constants.

PROOF   First let us verify that every function of the form (2.33) is a solution of Eq. (2.31). Since $Lu_i = 0, 1 \le i \le n$, and $Lu_p = F$, we have

$$L(c_1 u_1 + c_2 u_2 + \cdots + c_n u_n + u_p) = c_1 Lu_1 + c_2 Lu_2 + \cdots + c_n Lu_n + Lu_p$$
$$= 0 + 0 + \cdots + 0 + F$$
$$= F,$$

which we wished to show. Next we must show that every solution of Eq. (2.31) is of the form (2.33). Let u be any solution. Then $Lu = F$. Since also $Lu_p = F$ we have

$$L(u - u_p) = Lu - Lu_p = F - F = 0.$$

Thus the function $u - u_p$ is a solution of the homogeneous equation $Ly = 0$. By Theorem 2.4, $u - u_p$ must be of the form

$$u - u_p = c_1 u_1 + c_2 u_2 + \cdots + c_n u_n.$$

Then

$$u = c_1 u_1 + c_2 u_2 + \cdots + c_n u_n + u_p,$$

which we wished to show.

To illustrate the use of this theorem, let us consider the equation

$$y'' - 4y' + 4y = 9e^{-x}.$$

It is easy to verify that a particular solution is $u_p(x) = e^{-x}$. The associated homogeneous equation has e^{2x} and xe^{2x} as linearly independent solutions. Hence the general solution of the nonhomogeneous equation is

$$y(x) = (c_1 + c_2 x)e^{2x} + e^{-x}.$$

† The functions a_i and F are assumed to be continuous on $\mathscr{I}$ with a_0 never zero on $\mathscr{I}$.

In case the associated homogeneous equation has constant coefficients, or is of the Cauchy–Euler type, we can solve it. There remains the problem of finding one solution u_p of the nonhomogeneous equation. A method that applies in certain cases is described in the next section. A more general method is discussed in Section 2.10. In finding particular solutions, the following result is often useful.

Theorem 2.9 If u_p and v_p are solutions of the equations $Ly = f$ and $Ly = g$, respectively, then $u_p + v_p$ is a solution of the equation $Ly = f + g$.

PROOF Since $Lu_p = f$ and $Lv_p = g$, we have

$$L(u_p + v_p) = Lu_p + Lv_p = f + g.$$

For example, suppose that u_p and v_p are solutions of the equations

$$Ly = 3e^x, \qquad Ly = -2\sin x,$$

respectively. Then $u_p + v_p$ is a solution of the equation

$$Ly = 3e^x - 2\sin x.$$

Exercises for Section 2.8

1. Verify that u_p, where $u_p(x) = \sin 2x$, is a solution of the differential equation

    $$y'' - y = -5\sin 2x.$$

    Use this fact to find the general solution of the equation.

2. Show that the nonhomogeneous equation $P(D)y = ce^{ax}$ has a solution of the form $y = Ae^{ax}$ if and only if $P(a) \neq 0$. Show that in this case the solution is $y = ce^{ax}/P(a)$.

3. Use the result of Exercise 2 to find the general solution of the given differential equation.

    (a) $y' - 2y = 6e^{5x}$ (b) $y'' - 2y' + y = -9e^{-2x}$

    (c) $y'' + y = 4e^x$ (d) $(D + 1)(D + 2)(D + 3)y = 6e^{-4x}$

4. If a_n is a nonzero constant and c is a constant, show that a solution of the equation

    $$a_0 y^{(n)} + a_1 y^{(n-1)} + \cdots + a_n y = c$$

    is $y = c/a_n$.

5. Show that the equation

$$b_0 x^2 y'' + b_1 x y' + b_2 y = c x^a$$

has a solution of the form $y = A x^a$ provided that

$$b_0 a(a - 1) + b_1 a + b_2 \neq 0.$$

6. If F is a solution of the equation $Q(D)y = 0$, show that every solution of the nonhomogeneous equation $P(D)y = F$ is a solution of the homogeneous equation $Q(D)P(D)y = 0$.

7. Use the result of Exercise 2 and Theorem 2.9 to solve the given differential equation.

    (a) $y'' - 4y' + 3y = -2e^{2x} + 8e^{-x}$ (b) $y'' + 3y' = 4e^{-x} - 2e^{-2x}$

2.9 THE METHOD OF UNDETERMINED COEFFICIENTS

In this section we describe a method that yields a particular solution of the nonhomogeneous equation $Ly = F$ when the following two conditions are both met.

(a) The operator L has constant coefficients.
(b) The function F is itself a solution of some linear homogeneous differential equation with constant coefficients.

Here F must consist of a linear combination of functions of the types

$$x^j, \qquad x^j e^{cx}, \qquad x^j e^{ax} \cos bx, \qquad x^j e^{ax} \sin bx. \qquad (2.34)$$

Actually, according to Theorem 2.9, we can concentrate on the case where F is a constant multiple of just *one* of these functions. For instance, to find a solution of the equation

$$Ly = 5e^x \sin 2x - 4x^2 e^{-x} \qquad (2.35)$$

we first find solutions u and v of the equations

$$Ly = 5e^x \sin 2x, \qquad Ly = -4x^2 e^{-x},$$

respectively. Then $u + v$ will be a solution of Eq. (2.35).

Also, if $w = u + iv$ is a complex solution of the equation

$$Ly = A x^j e^{(a + ib)x},$$

then u and v will be solutions of the equations

$$Ly = Ax^j e^{ax} \cos bx, \qquad Ly = Ax^j e^{ax} \sin bx,$$

respectively.

We therefore consider an nth-order equation

$$P(D)y = F, \tag{2.36}$$

where F is of the form

$$F(x) = Ax^j e^{cx},$$

and where c may be real or complex. (In particular, c may be zero.) Then there exists a polynomial operator $Q(D)$, with real coefficients, such that

$$Q(D)F = 0.$$

We say that the operator $Q(D)$ *annihilates* F. If c is real, we may take

$$Q(D) = (D - c)^{j+1}.$$

If $c = a + ib$, $b \neq 0$, we may take

$$Q(D) = [(D - c)(D - \bar{c})]^{j+1} = [(D - a)^2 + b^2]^{j+1}.$$

With these choices, the order of $Q(D)$ is as low as possible.

Suppose that the order of $Q(D)$ is m. If we operate on both members of Eq. (2.36) with $Q(D)$† we see that every solution of Eq. (2.36) is also a solution of the homogeneous equation

$$Q(D)P(D)y = 0. \tag{2.37}$$

[However, not every solution of Eq. (2.37) need be a solution of Eq. (2.36).] The order of this equation is $m + n$. Every solution of the equation

$$P(D)y = 0 \tag{2.38}$$

is a solution of Eq. (2.37), but the latter equation also possesses additional solutions. Let the general solution of Eq. (2.37) be

$$A_1 u_1 + \cdots + A_m u_m + B_1 v_1 + \cdots + B_n v_n,$$

where the functions u_i and v_i are of the types (2.34) and the functions v_i are linearly independent solutions of Eq. (2.38).

Since every solution of the nonhomogeneous equation (2.36) is also of the

---

† Every solution of Eq. (2.36) possesses derivatives of all orders, so the derivatives of y in $Q(D)P(D)y$ all exist.

above form, it must be possible to choose the constants A_i and B_i in such a way that

$$P(D)(A_1 u_1 + \cdots + A_m u_m + B_1 v_1 + \cdots + B_n v_n) = F.$$

Since

$$P(D)(B_1 v_1 + \cdots + B_n v_n) = 0$$

for every choice of the B_i, it must be possible to find constants A_i such that

$$A_1 u_1 + \cdots + A_m u_m \qquad\qquad (2.39)$$

is a solution of Eq. (2.36). If the functions u_i are known, the constants A_i can be determined by substituting the expression (2.39) into the differential equation (2.36) and requiring that the latter be satisfied identically. The expression (2.39) is called a *trial solution* for Eq. (2.36).

Let us pause to consider some specific cases.

Example 1

$$y'' - y' - 2y = 20e^{4x}.$$

This equation may be written as

$$(D + 1)(D - 2)y = 20e^{4x}. \qquad\qquad (2.40)$$

The operator $D - 4$ annihilates e^{4x}. Operating on both sides of this equation with $D - 4$, we see that every solution is also a solution of the homogeneous equation

$$(D - 4)(D + 1)(D - 2)y = 0.$$

The solutions of this equation are of the form

$$y(x) = Ae^{4x} + B_1 e^{-x} + B_2 e^{2x},$$

and hence every solution of Eq. (2.40) is of this form. Thus there exist constants A, B_1, and B_2 such that

$$(D + 1)(D - 2)(Ae^{4x} + B_1 e^{-x} + B_2 e^{2x}) = 20^{4x}.$$

Since e^{-x} and e^{2x} are solutions of the homogeneous equation

$$(D + 1)(D - 2)y = 0,$$

it must be possible to choose A so that

$$(D + 1)(D - 2)(Ae^{4x}) = 20e^{4x}.$$

This yields the requirement

$$(D^2 - D - 2)(Ae^{4x}) = 20e^{4x},$$

$$10Ae^{4x} = 20e^{4x},$$

or

$$A = 2.$$

Hence a particular solution of Eq. (2.40) is $y_p(x) = 2e^{4x}$. The general solution is

$$y(x) = c_1 e^{-x} + c_2 e^{2x} + 2e^{4x},$$

where c_1 and c_2 are arbitrary constants.

Example 2

$$y'' - 2y' + y = 6 \sin x. \tag{2.41}$$

We consider instead the equation

$$(D - 1)^2 y = 6e^{ix}. \tag{2.42}$$

The operator $(D - i)(D + i) = D^2 + 1$ annihilates e^{ix}. Operating on both sides of Eq. (2.42) with $D^2 + 1$, we see that every solution of Eq. (2.42) is also a solution of the equation

$$(D^2 + 1)(D - 1)^2 y = 0.$$

The solutions of this equation that are not solutions of the homogeneous equation $(D - 1)^2 y = 0$ are e^{ix} and e^{-ix}. Hence Eq. (2.42) has a solution of the form $Ae^{ix} + Be^{-ix}$. But B is destined to be zero (since e^{ix} and e^{-ix} are linearly independent complex functions) so we take as our trial solution

$$y_p(x) = Ae^{ix}.$$

Substituting in Eq. (2.42), we obtain the requirement

$$(D^2 - 2D + 1)(Ae^{ix}) = 6e^{ix},$$

$$-2Aie^{ix} = 6e^{ix},$$

or

$$A = 3i.$$

Since the imaginary part of

$$y_p(x) = 3ie^{ix} = 3i(\cos x + i \sin x)$$

is $3 \cos x$, a particular solution of the original equation (2.41) is $3 \cos x$. The general solution is

$$y(x) = (c_1 + c_2 x)e^x + 3 \cos x.$$

We now return to the general case and seek to determine the nature of the functions u_i in the trial solution (2.39). These functions are the solutions of equation $Q(D)P(D)y = 0$ that are not solutions of the equation $P(D)y = 0$. If P and Q have no common zeros, the functions u_i are simply the solutions of the equation $Q(D)y = 0$. Hence our trial solution for the equation

$$P(D)y = Ax^j e^{cx} \qquad (2.43)$$

is of the form†

$$y_r(x) = (A_0 + A_1 x + \cdots + A_j x^j) e^{cx}. \qquad (2.44)$$

Next, suppose that c is a zero of P, of multiplicity m. Then

$$e^{cx}, xe^{cx}, \ldots, x^{m-1}e^{cx} \qquad (2.45)$$

are solutions of the equation $P(D)y = 0$. Since c is a zero of QP of multiplicity $m + j + 1$, the functions

$$e^{cx}, xe^{cx}, \ldots, x^{m+j}e^{cx} \qquad (2.46)$$

are solutions of the equation $Q(D)P(D)y = 0$. Selecting those functions in the set (2.46) that are not in the set (2.45), we see that our trial solution takes the form

$$y_p(x) = x^m (A_0 + A_1 x + \cdots + A_j x^j) e^{cx}. \qquad (2.47)$$

We may formulate the following rule for finding a particular solution of Eq. (2.43). Our tentative trial solution is given by formula (2.44). But if $x^{m-1}e^{cx}$ is a solution of the homogeneous equation $P(D)y = 0$, and m is the largest integer for which this is true, then this tentative trial solution must be modified by multiplying each term by x^m, as in formula (2.47). In any case, the constants in the expression (2.44) or (2.47) are determined by substituting in Eq. (2.43) and requiring that it be satisfied identically.

We now consider several more examples.

Example 3

$$y'' - 3y' + 2y = 6e^{3x}.$$

The general solution of the associated homogeneous equation

$$y'' - 3y' + 2y = 0$$

is

$$c_1 e^x + c_2 e^{2x}.$$

The tentative trial solution is

$$y_p(x) = Ae^{3x}.$$

† If c is not real, it can be shown that no function of the form $x^m e^{\bar{c}x}$ is a solution of Eq. (2.43).

Since no function of the form $x^m e^{3x}$ is a solution of the homogeneous equation, the trial solution need not be modified. The constant A is determined by the requirement that

$$(D^2 - 3D + 2)(Ae^{3x}) = 6e^{3x}$$

or

$$2Ae^{3x} = 6e^{3x}.$$

Thus $A = 3$ and a particular solution of the nonhomogeneous equation is

$$y_p(x) = 3e^{3x}.$$

The general solution of the nonhomogeneous equation is

$$y(x) = c_1 e^x + c_2 e^{2x} + 3e^{3x}.$$

Example 4

$$y'' - 4y' + 4y = 12xe^{2x}.$$

The general solution of the associated homogeneous equation is

$$c_1 e^{2x} + c_2 xe^{2x}.$$

The tentative trial solution is

$$y_p(x) = (A + Bx)e^{2x}.$$

But since xe^{2x} is a solution of the homogeneous equation, we must take

$$y_p(x) = (Ax^2 + Bx^3)e^{2x}.$$

Differentiation shows that

$$y_p'(x) = [2Ax + (2A + 3B)x^2 + 2Bx^3]e^{2x},$$
$$y_p''(x) = [2A + (8A + 6B)x + (4A + 12B)x^2 + 4Bx^3]e^{2x}.$$

Calculation shows that

$$(D^2 - 4D + 4)y_p(x) = (2A + 6Bx)e^{2x}$$

and this must be equal to $12xe^{2x}$ if y_p is to be a solution of the original equation. Hence we take $A = 0$ and $B = 2$. Then

$$y_p(x) = 2x^3 e^{2x}$$

and the general solution is

$$y(x) = (c_1 + c_2 x)e^{2x} + 2x^3 e^{2x}.$$

Example 5

$$y'' + y' - 2y = 4 \sin 2x.$$

We consider instead the equation

$$y'' + y' - 2y = 4e^{2ix}.$$

By taking the imaginary part of a solution of this equation, we obtain a real solution of the original equation. The general solution of the homogeneous equation is $c_1 e^x + c_2 e^{-2x}$. Our tentative trial solution is

$$y_p(x) = Ae^{2x}.$$

Since the homogeneous equation has no solution of the form $x^m e^{2ix}$, this is correct as is. We have

$$y_p'(x) = 2iAe^{2ix}, \qquad y_p''(x) = -4Ae^{2ix},$$

and

$$(D^2 + D - 2)y_p(x) = (-6 + 2i)Ae^{2ix}.$$

We require that

$$(-6 + 2i)Ae^{2ix} = 4e^{2ix}$$

or

$$A = \frac{-2}{3-i} = -\frac{3+i}{5}.$$

Then

$$y_p(x) = -\frac{3+i}{5}e^{2ix} = -\frac{3+i}{5}(\cos 2x + i \sin 2x).$$

The real and imaginary parts of y_p are

$$u_p(x) = -\tfrac{3}{5}\cos 2x + \tfrac{1}{5}\sin 2x,$$
$$v_p(x) = -\tfrac{1}{5}\cos 2x - \tfrac{3}{5}\sin 2x,$$

respectively. The general solution of the equation

$$(D^2 + D - 2)y = 4 \sin 2x$$

is

$$y(x) = c_1 e^x + c_2 e^{-2x} - \tfrac{1}{5}\cos 2x - \tfrac{3}{5}\sin 2x.$$

As a by-product, we have also found that the general solution of the equation

$$(D^2 + D - 2)y = 4 \cos 2x$$

is

$$y(x) = c_1 e^x + c_2 e^{-2x} - \tfrac{3}{5}\cos 2x + \tfrac{1}{5}\sin 2x.$$

Example 6

$$y''' + y' = 4 \cos x.$$

We consider the equation

$$y''' + y' = 4e^{ix}$$

and take the real part of a particular solution. The general solution of the homogeneous equation is

$$c_1 + c_2 \cos x + c_3 \sin x.$$

Since e^{ix} is a solution of the homogeneous equaton, we take

$$y_p(x) = Axe^{ix}$$

as our trial solution. We find that

$$y_p'(x) = A(ix + 1)e^{ix},$$
$$y_p''(x) = A(-x + 2i)e^{ix},$$
$$y_p'''(x) = A(-ix - 3)e^{ix}$$

and

$$(D^3 + D)y_p(x) = -2Ae^{ix}.$$

Taking $A = -2$, we have

$$y_p(x) = -2xe^{ix} = -2x(\cos x + i \sin x).$$

Then $-2x \cos x$ is a real solution of our original equation. The general solution is

$$y(x) = c_1 + c_2 \cos x + c_3 \sin x - 2x \cos x.$$

Example 7

$$x^2y'' - 2xy' + 2y = 6 \ln x, \qquad x > 0.$$

The change of variable $x = e^t$ leads to the equation

$$(D - 1)(D - 2)Y = 6t,$$

where $Y(t) = y(e^t)$. The general solution of the homogeneous equation with constant coefficients is

$$Y(t) = c_1 e^t + c_2 e^{2t}.$$

The tentative trial solution is

$$Y_p(t) = A + Bt.$$

Since the homogeneous equation has no solution of the form t^m, this is correct as it stands. Calculation shows that $A = \frac{9}{2}$, $B = 3$. The general solution of the equation with constant coefficients is

$$Y(t) = c_1 e^t + c_2 e^{2t} + 3t + \tfrac{9}{2}.$$

The general solution of the original equation, obtained by setting $t = \ln x$, is

$$y(x) = c_1 x + c_2 x^2 + 3 \ln x + \tfrac{9}{2}.$$

Exercises for Section 2.9

In Exercises 1–20, find the general solution of the differential equation. If initial conditions are given, also find the solution that satisfies those conditions.

1. $y'' + 2y' - 3y = 5e^{2x}$, $y(0) = 5$, $y'(0) = 2$

2. $y'' + 4y' + 4y = 3e^{-x}$, $y(0) = 3$, $y(0) = 1$

3. $y'' + 3y' + 2y = 36xe^x$

4. $y'' + y' - 2y = 6e^{-x} + 4e^{-3x}$, $y(0) = -1$, $y'(0) = 1$

5. $y'' + 3y' + 2y = 20 \cos 2x$, $y(0) = -1$, $y'(0) = 6$

6. $y'' + y = 5e^x \sin x$ 7. $y'' - y' - 6y = 2$

8. $y'' + 3y' + 2y = 4x^2$ 9. $(D-1)^2(D+1)y = 10 \cos 2x$

10. $y'' + 2y' + y = -4e^{-3x} \sin 2x$ 11. $y'' + 3y' + 2y = 5e^{-2x}$

12. $y'' - y = 4e^x - 3e^{2x}$ 13. $y'' - y' - 2y = -6xe^{-x}$

14. $y'' + 4y' + 4y = 4e^{-2x}$ 15. $y'' + 4y' + 3y = 6x^2 e^{-x}$

16. $y'' + 2y' = -4$ 17. $y'' + y' = 3x^2$

18. $y'' + y = 4 \sin x$ 19. $y'' + 2y' + 5y = 4e^{-x} \cos 2x$

20. $y'' + 4y = 16x \sin 2x$

21. Show that a particular solution of the nonhomogeneous equation

$$P(D)y = Ae^{cx}$$

is

$$y_p(x) = \frac{A}{P(c)} e^{cx}$$

provided that c is not a root of the equation $P(r) = 0$.

22. Use the result of Exercise 21 to find the general solutions of the differential equations:

(a) $y'' - 3y' + 2y = 6e^{-x}$ (b) $y'' - 2y' + y = -3e^{2x}$

(c) $y'' - y' - 2y = 10 \cos x$ (d) $y'' - 3y' + 2y = 4e^{3x} + 6e^{-x}$

(e) $(D - 1)^2(D + 1)y = 9e^{2x}$ (f) $y'' + y' = 6 \sin 2x$

23. If the number c is an m-fold root of the polynomial equation $P(r) = 0$, then $P(r) = Q(r)(r - c)^m$, where $Q(c) \neq 0$. Show that in this case the differential equation

$$P(D)y = Ae^{cx}$$

possesses the solution

$$y(x) = \frac{A}{m!\, Q(c)}\, x^m e^{cx}.$$

24. Use the result of Exercise 23 to find the general solutions of the differential equations:

(a) $y'' - y' - 2y = 6e^{2x}$ (b) $y'' - 4y' + 4y = 4e^{2x}$

(c) $y'' + y = 4 \cos x$ (d) $(D + 1)(D - 2)^3y = 6e^{2x}$

In Exercises 25–30, find the general solution of the differential equation. Assume that the independent variable is restricted to the interval $(0, \infty)$.

25. $x^2y'' - 6y = 6x^4$ **26.** $x^2y'' + xy' - y = 9x^2 \ln x$

27. $x^2y'' - 3xy' + 3y = -6$ **28.** $x^2y'' - xy' = -4$

29. $x^2y'' + 2xy' - 2y = 6x$ **30.** $x^2y'' - xy' + y = 6x \ln x$

2.10 VARIATION OF PARAMETERS

The method of undetermined coefficients discussed in the last section allows us to find a particular solution of the nonhomogeneous equation $Ly = F$ only in special cases. The operator L must have constant coefficients, and F must belong to a certain class of functions. The method of variation of parameters is more general. It gives a formula for a particular solution provided only that the general solution of the homogeneous equation $Ly = 0$ is known. The operator L need not have constant coefficients and there is no restriction (other than continuity) on F. However, the method of undetermined coefficients is usually easier to use when that method applies. The

method of variation of parameters is valuable for theoretical purposes, as
well as for actually finding solutions of equations. Some examples of its
use are given in the exercises at the end of this section, and also in those at
the end of Section 2.13.

In the method of variation of parameters, we assume that n linearly
independent solutions $u_1, u_2, \ldots, u_n$ of the homogeneous equation

$$a_0(x)y^{(n)} + a_1(x)y^{(n-1)} + \cdots + a_{n-1}(x)y' + a_n(x)y = 0 \qquad (2.48)$$

are known. We attempt to find a solution of the nonhomogeneous equation

$$a_0(x)y^{(n)} + a_1(x)y^{(n-1)} + \cdots + a_{n-1}(x)y' + a_n(x)y = F(x) \qquad (2.49)$$

that is of the form

$$y(x) = C_1(x)u_1(x) + C_2(x)u_2(x) + \cdots + C_n(x)u_n(x), \qquad (2.50)$$

where the functions $C_1, C_2, \ldots, C_n$ are to be determined. If we simply calculate the first n derivatives of the expression (2.50) and substitute them into
the differential equation (2.49), we shall obtain one condition to be satisfied
by the n functions. We shall impose $n - 1$ other conditions *en route*. Differentiating once, we have

$$y' = (C_1u_1' + \cdots + C_nu_n') + (C_1'u_1 + \cdots + C_n'u_n). \qquad (2.51)$$

We now impose the requirement

$$C_1'u_1 + \cdots + C_n'u_n = 0. \qquad (2.52)$$

This simplifies expression (2.51) for the first derivative since it now becomes

$$y' = C_1u_1' + \cdots + C_nu_n'. \qquad (2.53)$$

We have also obtained one condition to be satisfied by the functions C_i.
Differentiating again, we have

$$y'' = (C_1u_1'' + \cdots + C_nu_n'') + (C_1'u_1' + \cdots + C_n'u_n'). \qquad (2.54)$$

This time we require that

$$C_1'u_1' + \cdots + C_n'u_n' = 0. \qquad (2.55)$$

The second derivative then simplifies to

$$y'' = C_1u_1'' + \cdots + C_nu_n''. \qquad (2.56)$$

We have now imposed two conditions, (2.52) and (2.55), on the functions C_i.
Continuing in this way through $n - 1$ differentiations, we impose the $n - 1$
conditions

$$C_1'u_1^{(k)} + C_2'u_2^{(k)} + \cdots + C_n'u_n^{(k)} = 0, \qquad 0 \le k \le n - 2, \qquad (2.57)$$

on the functions C_i, and the derivatives of y are given by the formula

$$y^{(k)} = C_1 u_1^{(k)} + C_2 u_2^{(k)} + \cdots + C_n u_n^{(k)}, \qquad 0 \le k \le n-1. \qquad (2.58)$$

Then

$$y^{(n)} = C_1 u_1^{(n)} + \cdots + C_n u_n^{(n)} + C_1' u_1^{(n-1)} + \cdots + C_n' u_n^{(n-1)}. \qquad (2.59)$$

To obtain a final nth condition on the functions C_i, we substitute the expressions (2.58) and (2.59) into the differential equation (2.49). We find that

$$a_0[C_1 u_1^{(n)} + \cdots + C_n u_n^{(n)} + C_1' u_1^{(n-1)} + \cdots + C_n' u_n^{(n-1)}]$$
$$+ a_1[C_1 u_1^{(n-1)} + \cdots + C_n u_n^{(n-1)}] + \cdots + a_n[C_1 u_1 + \cdots + C_n u_n] = F,$$

or, upon regrouping terms,

$$a_0[C_1' u_1^{(n-1)} + \cdots + C_n' u_n^{(n-1)}] + C_1[a_0 u_1^{(n)} + \cdots + a_n u_1]$$
$$+ \cdots + C_n[a_0 u_n^{(n)} + \cdots + a_n u_n] = F.$$

This reduces to

$$C_1' u_1^{(n-1)} + \cdots + C_n' u_n^{(n-1)} = F/a_0$$

since the functions u_i are solutions of the homogeneous equation (2.48). We have now obtained the n conditions

$$\begin{aligned}
C_1' u_1 + \cdots + C_n' u_n &= 0, \\
C_1' u_1' + \cdots + C_n' u_n' &= 0, \\
C_1' u_1'' + \cdots + C_n' u_n'' &= 0, \\
&\vdots \\
C_1' u_1^{(n-2)} + \cdots + C_n' u_n^{(n-2)} &= 0, \\
C_1' u_1^{(n-1)} + \cdots + C_n' u_n^{(n-1)} &= F/a_0
\end{aligned} \qquad (2.60)$$

for $C_1', C_2', \ldots, C_n'$. The determinant of this system is the Wronskian of the functions $u_1, u_2, \ldots, u_n$. It will be shown in Section 2.13 that this Wronskian is never zero on an interval where a_0 does not vanish. Consequently the system (2.60) possesses a unique solution. If we solve for the quantities C_i', the functions C_i can be found by integration.

In arriving at the conditions (2.60), we proceeded under the assumption that the Eq. (2.49) had a solution of the form (2.50). To make our argument rigorous, let the functions C_i be functions which satisfy the conditions (2.60). Then the corresponding function (2.50) has derivatives given by the formulas (2.58) and (2.59). It can now be verified that the function (2.50) is indeed a solution of the differential equation. We sum up our results as follows.

Theorem 2.10 Let the functions a_i and F be continuous on an interval I, with a_0 never zero on I. Let $u_1, u_2, \ldots, u_n$ be linearly independent solutions of the homogeneous equation (2.48) on I. If the functions C_i are such that their derivatives C_i' satisfy the system of equations (2.60), then the function

$$y_p = C_1 u_1 + C_2 u_2 + \cdots + C_n u_n$$

is a solution of the nonhomogeneous equation (2.49).

Example 1

$$y'' - 3y' + 2y = -\frac{e^{2x}}{e^x + 1}.$$

The functions u_1 and u_2, where

$$u_1(x) = e^x, \qquad u_2(x) = e^{2x},$$

are linearly independent solutions of the associated homogeneous equation

$$y'' - 3y' + 2y = 0.$$

We seek a solution of the nonhomogeneous equation of the form

$$y_p(x) = C_1 e^x + C_2 e^{2x}.$$

The conditions (2.60) in this case are

$$C_1' e^x + C_2' e^{2x} = 0,$$

$$C_1' e^x + 2C_2' e^{2x} = -\frac{e^{2x}}{e^x + 1}$$

or, upon dividing through in each equation by e^x,

$$C_1' + C_2' e^x = 0,$$

$$C_1' + 2C_2' e^x = -\frac{e^x}{e^x + 1}.$$

Solving, we find that

$$C_1' = \frac{e^x}{e^x + 1}, \qquad C_2' = \frac{-1}{e^x + 1} = -\frac{e^{-x}}{1 + e^{-x}}.$$

Then we may take

$$C_1 = \ln(e^x + 1), \qquad C_2 = \ln(1 + e^{-x}).$$

A particular solution of the nonhomogeneous equation is

$$y_p(x) = e^x \ln(e^x + 1) + e^{2x} \ln(1 + e^{-x}).$$

The general solution is

$$y(x) = c_1 e^x + c_2 e^{2x} + e^x \ln(e^x + 1) + e^{2x} \ln(1 + e^{-x}).$$

Example 2

$$x^2 y'' + xy' - y = -2x^2 e^x, \qquad x > 0.$$

Notice that if we make the change of variable $x = e^t$, the equation becomes

$$[D(D - 1) + D - 1]Y = -2e^{2t} \exp(e^t).$$

The nonhomogeneous term is one for which the method of undertermined coefficients does not apply; therefore, we must use the method of variation of parameters. The homogeneous equation

$$x^2 y'' + xy' - y = 0$$

possesses the solutions $u_1(x) = x$ and $u_2(x) = x^{-1}$. We seek a solution of the original equation that is of the form

$$y_p(x) = C_1(x)x + C_2(x)x^{-1}.$$

Conditions (2.60) become

$$C_1' x + C_2' x^{-1} = 0,$$
$$C_1' - C_2' x^{-2} = -2e^x.$$

(Here $a_0(x) = x^2$, therefore $F(x)/a_0(x) = -2e^x$.) We find that

$$C_1' = -e^x, \qquad C_2' = x^2 e^x,$$

so we may take

$$C_1 = -e^x, \qquad C_2 = (x^2 e^x - 2x + 2).$$

Our general solution is

$$y(x) = c_1 x + c_2 x^{-1} - xe^x + x^{-1}e^x(x^2 - 2x + 2)$$

or

$$y(x) = c_1 x + c_2 x^{-1} + 2(x^{-1} - 1)e^x.$$

The method of variation of parameters requires that the associated homogeneous equation can be solved. Thus far we are able to do this when the homogeneous equation

(a) has constant coefficients,
(b) is of the Cauchy–Euler type,
(c) is a second-order equation with dependent or independent variable absent (Section 1.8).

One other situation might be mentioned here. If one nontrivial solution of the homogeneous equation is known, the problem of solving the equation can be reduced to that of solving an equation whose order is one less. If the original equation is of second order, we arrive at a first-order linear equation that can be treated by the method of Section 1.4. (first order linear)

Suppose that the function u_1 is a nontrivial solution of the equation

$$a_0(x)y'' + a_1(x)y' + a_2(x)y = 0,$$

and that we wish to solve the equation

$$a_0(x)y'' + a_1(x)y' + a_2(x)y = F(x), \qquad (2.61)$$

where F may or may not be the zero function. We introduce a new dependent variable v, where $y = u_1 v$. Then

$$y' = u_1 v' + u_1' v, \qquad y'' = u_1 v'' + 2u_1' v' + u_1'' v.$$

Substituting into Eq. (2.61), we have

$$a_0(u_1 v'' + 2u_1' v' + u_1'' v) + a_1(u_1 v' + u_1' v) + a_2 u_1 v = F$$

or

$$a_0 u_1 v'' + (2a_0 u_1' + a_1 u_1)v' + (a_0 u_1'' + a_1 u_1' + a_2 u_1)v = F.$$

Here the coefficient of V is zero since u_1 is a solution of the homogeneous equation. The equation

$$a_0 u_1 v'' + (2a_0 u_1' + a_1 u_1)v' = F$$

has the dependent variable missing. Setting $w = v'$, we obtain the first-order equation

$$a_0 u_1 w' + (2a_0 u_1' + a_1 u_1)w = F.$$

We solve this equation for w, find v by integration, and then multiply v by u_1 to obtain the solutions of the original equation (2.61).

Example 3

$$x^2(x + 1)y'' - 2xy' + 2y = 0.$$

We observe that a solution is $u_1(x) = x$. Setting $y = vx$, we have

$$x^2(x + 1)(xv'' + 2v') - 2x(xv' + v) + 2xv = 0$$

or

$$(x + 1)v'' + 2v' = 0.$$

This first-order equation for v' has the solutions

$$v'(x) = -\frac{c_1}{(x + 1)^2};$$

therefore

$$v(x) = \frac{c_1}{x + 1} + c_2.$$

The general solution of the original equation is

$$y(x) = v(x)x = c_1 \frac{x}{x+1} + c_2 x.$$

Example 4

$$xy'' + 2(1 - x)y' + (x - 2)y = 2e^x.$$

It is easy to verify that $u_1(x) = e^x$ is a solution of the associated homogeneous equation. Setting $y = ve^x$, we find that

$$[x(v'' + 2v' + v) + (2 - 2x)(v' + v) + (x - 2)v]e^x = 2e^x$$

or

$$xv'' + 2v' = 2.$$

Then

$$v'(x) = -\frac{c_1}{x^2} + 1$$

and

$$v(x) = \frac{c_1}{x} + c_2 + x.$$

The general solution of the original equation is

$$y(x) = [(c_1/x) + c_2 + x]e^x.$$

Exercises for Section 2.10

In Exercises 1–10, find the general solution of the differential equation.

1. $y'' - y = \dfrac{2}{e^x + 1}$
2. $y'' - 2y' + y = \dfrac{e^x}{x}$
3. $y'' + 2y' + y = 4e^{-x} \ln x$
4. $y'' + 2y' + y = e^{-x} \sec^2 x$
5. $y'' + y = \csc x$
6. $y'' + y = \tan x \sec x$
7. $y'' + 2y' + 2y = 2e^{-x} \tan^2 x$
8. $x^2 y'' - 2xy' + 2y = x^3 e^x$
9. $(D - 1)^3 y = 2\dfrac{e^x}{x^2}$
10. $(D - 1)(D + 1)(D + 2)y = \dfrac{6}{e^x + 1}$

11. Let F be defined and continuous on the interval $[0, \infty)$.
    (a) Show that the general solution of the equation

$$y'' + k^2 y = F(x)$$

may be written as

$$y(x) = A \sin (kx + \alpha) - \frac{1}{k} \int_{x_0}^{x} \sin k(t - x)F(t) \, dt,$$

where A and α are arbitrary constants and x_0 is any nonnegative number.

(b) Suppose that there exist numbers M, x_1, and a, $a > 1$, such that

$$|F(x)| \le Mx^{-a}, \qquad x \ge x_1.$$

Show that every solution of the equation in part (a) is bounded on the interval $[0, \infty)$.

(c) If $\int_0^\infty |F(x)| \, dx$ converges, show that every solution of the equation in part (a) is bounded on $[0, \infty)$.

12. Let a and b be positive real numbers with $a \ne b$. Let the function F be defined and continuous on $[0, \infty)$.

(a) Show that the general solution of the equation

$$(D + a)(D + b)y = F(x)$$

may be written as

$$y(x) = c_1 e^{-ax} + c_2 e^{-bx} + \frac{1}{b - a} \int_{x_0}^{x} [e^{-a(x-t)} - e^{-b(x-t)}]F(t) \, dt,$$

where x_0 is any nonnegative number.

(b) If F is bounded (that is, $|F(x)| \le M$ for some number M and $x \ge 0$), show that every solution of the equation in part (a) is bounded on $[0, \infty)$.

(c) If $\int_0^\infty |F(x)| \, dx$ converges, show that every solution of the equation in part (a) is bounded.

(d) If $\lim_{x \to \infty} F(x) = L$, show that every solution of the equation in part (a) tends to the limit $L/(ab)$ as x becomes infinite.

(Reduction of Order)

In Exercises 13–16, find the general solution of the differential equation, given one solution of the homogeneous equation.

13. $x^3 y'' + xy' - y = 0, \quad y = x$ ← homogeneous eq

14. $xy'' + (1 - 2x)y' + (x - 1)y = 0, \quad y = e^x$

15. $2xy'' + (1 - 4x)y' + (2x - 1)y = e^x, \quad y = e^x$

16. $x^2(x + 2)y'' + 2xy' - 2y = (x + 2)^2, \quad y = x$

17. Suppose that u_1 and u_2 are linearly independent solutions of the third-order equation

$$a_0 y''' + a_1 y'' + a_2 y' + a_3 y = 0.$$

Show that the change of variable $y = u_1 v$ leads to a second-order equation for $v' = w$. Find a solution of this equation, in terms of u_2, and use it to reduce the equation to one of first order.

2.11 SIMPLE HARMONIC MOTION

Suppose that a spring hangs vertically from a support, as in Fig. 2.1a.

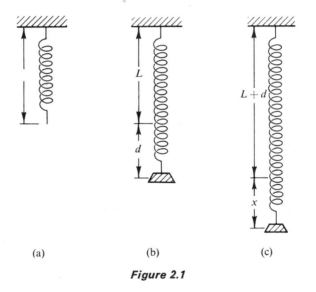

(a)   (b)   (c)

Figure 2.1

Let L denote the length of the spring when it is at rest. When the spring is stretched or compressed a distance s by a force F applied at the ends, it is found by experiment that the magnitude of the force is approximately proportional to the distance s, at least when s is not too large. Thus

$$F = ks,$$

where k is a positive constant of proportionality known as the *spring constant*. For example, if a force of 30 lb is required to stretch a spring 2 in., then

$$30 = 2k;$$

therefore $k = 15$ lb/in.

When a body of mass m, and weight mg, is attached to the free end of the spring, the body will remain at rest in a position such that the spring has length $L + d$ (Fig. 2.1b), where $mg = kd$. The downward force mg due to gravity is balanced by the restoring force kd of the spring. Let us denote by x the directed distance downward of the center of mass of the body from its position of rest, or equilibrium (Fig. 2.1c). Then the equation of motion $m\ddot{x} = F$ becomes

$$m\ddot{x} = mg - k(x + d)$$

or

$$m\ddot{x} + kx = 0.$$

The general solution of this equation is

$$x(t) = c_1 \cos \omega t + c_2 \sin \omega t, \qquad (2.62)$$

where

$$\omega = (k/m)^{1/2}.$$

If the body is held in the position $x = x_0$ and released from rest at time $t = 0$, the initial conditions are

$$x(0) = x_0, \qquad \dot{x}(0) = 0.$$

Using these conditions to determine the constants c_1 and c_2 in the formula (2.62), we find that

$$x(t) = x_0 \cos \omega t. \qquad (2.63)$$

Thus the body oscillates about the equilibrium position $x = 0$ between the points $x = \pm |x_0|$ without ever coming to rest.

If the body is struck sharply when it is in the equilibrium position, giving it a velocity v_0, the initial conditions become

$$x(0) = 0, \qquad \dot{x}(0) = v_0.$$

This time we find that

$$x(t) = \frac{v_0}{\omega} \sin \omega t. \qquad (2.64)$$

In the more general case where

$$x(0) = x_0, \qquad \dot{x}(0) = v_0,$$

the solution is the sum of the solutions (2.63) and (2.64). We have

$$x(t) = x_0 \cos \omega t + \frac{v_0}{\omega} \sin \omega t. \qquad (2.65)$$

Let us write
$$A = [x_0^2 + (v_0/\omega)^2]^{1/2}.$$

Then there is an angle θ_1 such that
$$\cos \theta_1 = x_0/A, \qquad \sin \theta_1 = -v_0/(\omega A),$$

and formula (2.65) can be written
$$x(t) = A \cos (\omega t + \theta_1).$$

If we put
$$\sin \theta_2 = x_0/A, \qquad \cos \theta_2 = v_0/(\omega A),$$

it becomes
$$x(t) = A \sin (\omega t + \theta_2).$$

Straight line motion that can be described by a function of the form
$$x(t) = A \cos (\omega t + \theta) \qquad \text{or} \qquad x(t) = A \sin (\omega t + \theta)$$

is called *simple harmonic motion*. The number $|A|$ is called the *amplitude* of the motion. Notice that x fluctuates between $-|A|$ and $|A|$ periodically. The period P of the motion is given by the formula $P = 2\pi/\omega$. This is the time required for the body to move through one cycle. The frequency f is the number of cycles per unit time. Thus $f = 1/P = \omega/(2\pi)$.

The presence of a damping force equal to c times the velocity may be indicated by means of a *dashpot*, as shown in Fig. 2.2. In this case, the

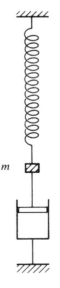

m

Figure 2.2

body is said to exhibit *damped harmonic motion*. The equation of motion becomes

$$m\ddot{x} + c\dot{x} + kx = 0. \tag{2.66}$$

The auxiliary polynomial equation is

$$mr^2 + cr + k = 0,$$

with roots

$$r = \frac{1}{2m}[-c \pm (c^2 - 4mk)^{1/2}].$$

We consider separately the following cases:

(1) $c^2 < 4mk$ (two complex roots);
(2) $c^2 > 4mk$ (two distinct real roots);
(3) $c^2 = 4mk$ (equal real roots).

These cases are called the *underdamped, overdamped,* and *critically damped* cases, respectively.

For case 1, we may write the general solution of the equation of motion as

$$x(t) = c_1 e^{-\alpha t} \cos \omega t + c_2 e^{-\alpha t} \sin \omega t,$$

where

$$\alpha = \frac{c}{2m}, \qquad \omega = \frac{1}{2m}(4mk - c^2)^{1/2}.$$

The solution that satisfies the initial conditions

$$x(0) = x_0, \qquad x(0) = 0$$

is

$$x(t) = x_0 e^{-\alpha t}\left(\cos \omega t + \frac{\alpha}{\omega}\sin \omega t\right).$$

This may be written

$$x(t) = x_0\left[1 + \left(\frac{\alpha}{\omega}\right)^2\right]^{1/2} e^{-\alpha t} \sin(\omega t + \theta_1),$$

where

$$\theta_1 = \tan^{-1}\frac{\omega}{\alpha}$$

or

$$x(t) = x_0\left[1 + \left(\frac{\alpha}{\omega}\right)^2\right]^{1/2} e^{-\alpha t} \cos(\omega t + \theta_2),$$

where

$$\theta_2 = -\tan^{-1}\frac{\alpha}{\omega}.$$

In this case the body still oscillates back and forth across the equilibrium position, but the amplitude decreases exponentially with time. The situation is illustrated in Fig. 2.3. In the overdamped and critically damped cases, the

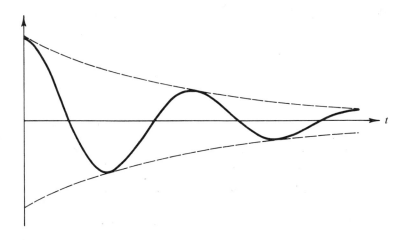

Figure 2.3

body no longer exhibits this oscillatory behavior. The derivations of the exact forms of the solutions in these cases are left as exercises.

If an external force $F(t)$ is applied to the body on the spring, the equation becomes

$$m\ddot{x} + c\dot{x} + kx = F(t). \tag{2.67}$$

We shall consider the case where F is a periodic force of the form

$$F(t) = A \sin \omega_1 t$$

and where damping is absent ($c = 0$). Then Eq. (2.67) becomes

$$m\ddot{x} + kx = A \sin \omega_1 t. \tag{2.68}$$

In order to obtain a particular solution, we consider the equation

$$m\ddot{x} + kx = Ae^{i\omega_1 t}. \tag{2.69}$$

If $x(t) = Ce^{i\omega_1 t}$, then $\ddot{x}(t) = -C\omega_1^2 e^{i\omega_1 t}$ and we require that

$$(-Cm\omega_1^2 + kC)e^{i\omega_1 t} = Ae^{i\omega_1 t}$$

or

$$C = \frac{A}{k - m\omega_1^2}.$$

Using the notation $\omega = (k/m)^{1/2}$, we have

$$C = \frac{A}{m(\omega^2 - \omega_1^2)}$$

provided that $\omega_1 \neq \omega$. The general solution of Eq. (2.68) is

$$x(t) = c_1 \cos \omega t + c_2 \sin \omega t + \frac{A}{m(\omega^2 - \omega_1^2)} \sin \omega_1 t.$$

However, if $\omega_1 = \omega$, we must seek a particular solution of Eq. (2.69) that is of the form

$$x(t) = Cte^{i\omega t}.$$

A particular solution turns out to be

$$x(t) = -\frac{Ai}{2\omega m} te^{i\omega t}.$$

We take the imaginary part to obtain a real solution of Eq. (2.68). The general solution of this equation is

$$x(t) = c_1 \cos \omega t + c_2 \sin \omega t - \frac{A}{2\omega m} t \cos \omega t.$$

In this case, $\omega_1 = \omega$, the magnitude of the oscillations increases indefinitely because of the presence of the term $t \cos \omega t$. This phenomena is called *resonance*. Actually, when the oscillations become sufficiently large the law $|F| = ks$ does not hold and our mathematical model no longer applies.

Exercises for Section 2.11

1. (a) Find the general solution of the equation of motion (2.66) in the overdamped case $c^2 > 4mk$. Show that every solution tends to zero as t become infinite. For convenience, let

$$\alpha = -\frac{1}{2m}[-c + (c^2 - 4mk)^{1/2}],$$

$$\beta = -\frac{1}{2m}[-c - (c^2 - 4mk)^{1/2}].$$

(b) Find the solution for which $x(0) = x_0$, $\dot{x}(0) = 0$. Draw a graph of the solution for $t \geq 0$.

(c) Find the solution for which $x(0) = 0$, $\dot{x}(0) = v_0$. Draw a graph of the solution for $t \geq 0$.

2. (a) Find the general solution of the equation of motion (2.66) in the critically damped case $c^2 = 4mk$. Show that every solution tends to zero as t becomes infinite. For convenience let $\gamma = c/(2m)$.

(b) Find the solution for which $x(0) = x_0$, $\dot{x}(0) = 0$ and draw its graph.

(c) Find the solution for which $x(0) = 0$, $\dot{x}(0) = v_0$ and draw its graph.

3. If an external force $F(t)$ is applied to the body on the spring, its equation of motion becomes

$$m\ddot{x} + c\dot{x} + kx = F(t).$$

Assume that $c \neq 0$ and that F is a periodic function of the form

$$F(t) = A \sin \omega_1 t.$$

(a) When t is large, show that every solution is approximately equal to

$$x_p(t) = B \sin(\omega_1 t - \theta),$$

where

$$B = \frac{A}{D}, \qquad D = [(k - m\omega_1^2)^2 + c^2\omega_1^2]^{1/2}, \qquad \theta = \cos^{-1}\frac{k - m\omega_1^2}{D},$$

This is called the *steady-state solution* of the equation.

(b) If $c^2 \geq 4mk$ (overdamping or critical damping), show that the amplitude $|B|$ is a strictly decreasing function of ω_1.

(c) If $c^2 < 4mk$ (underdamping), the homogeneous equation has damped oscillatory solutions of the form

$$x(t) = e^{-\alpha t}(c_1 \cos \omega t + c_2 \sin \omega t),$$

where

$$\alpha = \frac{c}{2m}, \qquad \omega = \frac{1}{2m}(4mk - c^2)^{1/2}.$$

Show that the amplitude $|B|$ of the steady-state solution, considered as a function of k, is largest when $k = m\omega_1^2$, in which case $\omega = (\omega_1^2 - \alpha^2)^{1/2}$.

4. If the applied force F is constant, $F(t) = F_0$, find the limiting position of the body on the spring.

5. The equation of motion of a particle that moves in a straight line is

$$m\ddot{x} + 2\dot{x} + x = 0.$$

For what values of m is the motion oscillatory?

2.12 ELECTRIC CIRCUITS

Let us consider an electric circuit in which a resistance, capacitance, and inductance are connected in series with a voltage source, as in Fig. 2.4. When the switch is closed at $t = 0$, a current will flow in the loop. We denote the value of the current at time t by $I(t)$. The arrow in the figure gives the loop a direction. We understand that I is positive when the flow is in the direction of the arrow and negative when in the opposite direction. In Fig. 2.5 we

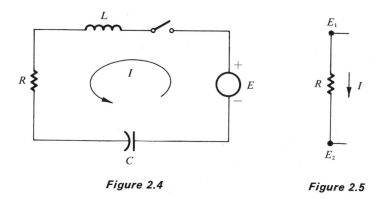

Figure 2.4   Figure 2.5

have isolated one circuit element, the resistance. The voltages at the terminals are denoted by E_1 and E_2. When the current is positive, in the direction of the arrow, $E_1 < E_2$ and the *voltage drop* across the element is $E_1 - E_2$, a positive quantity. Thus a positive current flows in the direction of decreasing voltage. This is a matter of convention, and the term "current" as used here should not be identified with a flow of electrons. Actually it may help the reader to think of the current as a flow of positively charged particles.

We shall use the following system of units: *amperes* for the current I, *volts* for the voltage, *ohms* for the resistance R, *henrys* for the inductance L, *farads* for the capacitance C, *coulombs* for the charge on the capacitance, and *seconds* for the time t. Using this system of units, the voltage drop across the resistance is RI and that across the inductance is $L \, dI/dt$. The voltage drop across the capacitance is Q/C, where Q is the charge on the capacitance. The charge and current are related by the equations

$$I = \frac{dQ}{dt}, \qquad Q(t) = \int_0^t I(s) \, ds + Q_0,\qquad (2.70)$$

where Q_0 is the charge on the capacitance at $t = 0$.

According to one of Kirchhoff's two laws (the other will be considered presently) the sum of the voltage drops around the loop must be equal to the applied voltage. Therefore the equality

$$L\frac{dI}{dt} + RI + \frac{1}{C}Q = E(t) \tag{2.71}$$

must hold for $t \geq 0$, provided that the sign of $E(t)$ is chosen in accordance with the $+$ and $-$ signs in Fig. 2.4. Upon differentiating with respect to t, and using relations (2.70), we arrive at the second-order differential equation

$$L\frac{d^2I}{dt^2} + R\frac{dI}{dt} + \frac{1}{C}I = E'(t) \tag{2.72}$$

for I. We notice the resemblance of this equation to that for a harmonic oscillator,

$$m\frac{d^2x}{dt^2} + c\frac{dx}{dt} + kx = F(t).$$

In particular, the term Ld^2I/dt^2 in the circuit equation corresponds to the inertia term $m\, d^2x/dt^2$ in this equation. This means that the current passing through the inductance must be the same immediately before and after a sudden change† or jump in the voltage drop across it. Since the current was zero before the switch was closed we must have

$$I(0) = 0.$$

Using this fact we can find the initial value of dI/dt from Eq. (2.71). Assuming that the initial charge on the capacitance is zero, we have

$$LI'(0) + RI(0) = E(0)$$

or

$$I'(0) = \frac{E(0)}{L}.$$

In many applications, the applied voltage is approximately constant, as in the case of a battery, or sinusoidal, as in the case of an alternating current generator. Let us consider the cases where the applied voltage has the constant value E_0. Then $E'(t) = 0$ and Eq. (2.72) becomes

$$L\frac{d^2I}{dt^2} + R\frac{dI}{dt} + \frac{1}{C}I = 0.$$

† Unless the change is infinite, as can happen in some idealized situations.

The initial conditions are

$$I(0) = 0, \qquad I'(0) = \frac{E_0}{L}.$$

The form of the solution depends on whether the quantity $R^2 - 4L/C$ is positive, negative, or zero. We consider here only the case where $R^2 - 4L/C > 0$. The solution of the initial value problem, as found by routine methods, is

$$I(t) = \frac{E_0}{(R^2 - 4L/C)^{1/2}} (e^{-\alpha t} - e^{-\beta t}),$$

where

$$\alpha = \frac{1}{2L} [R - (R^2 - 4L/C)^{1/2}], \qquad \beta = \frac{1}{2L} [R + (R^2 - 4L/C)^{1/2}].$$

Since α and β are both positive, $I(t)$ tends to zero as t becomes infinite.

We next consider the circuit of Fig. 2.6, in which the applied voltage is

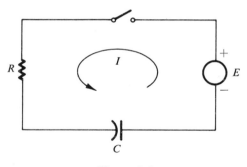

Figure 2.6

sinusoidal, of the form $E(t) = E_0 \cos \omega t$. No inductance is present. Kirchhoff's law leads to the equation

$$RI + \frac{1}{C} Q = E_0 \cos \omega t \qquad (2.73)$$

or

$$R \frac{dI}{dt} + \frac{1}{C} I = \omega E_0 \sin \omega t. \qquad (2.74)$$

From Eq. (2.73) we obtain the initial condition

$$I(0) = \frac{E_0}{R},$$

again assuming that the initial charge on the capacitance is zero. The solution
of the first-order equation (2.74) that satisfies the initial condition is found
to be

$$I(t) = I_1(t) + I_2(t),$$

where

$$I_1(t) = \frac{E_0}{R}\left[1 + \frac{\omega^2}{(RC)^{-2} + \omega^2}\right]e^{-t/(RC)}$$

and

$$I_2(t) = \frac{E_0\,\omega}{R[(RC)^{-2} + \omega^2]}\left(\frac{1}{RC}\sin\omega t - \omega\cos\omega t\right).$$

The function I_1 dies out as t becomes infinite. It is called the *transient solution*
of the initial-value problem. When t is large the solution I is very nearly equal
to I_2; this is called the *steady-state* solution.

We next examine a circuit that consists of a resistance, inductance, and
capacitance connected in parallel with a current source. Such a circuit is
shown in Fig. 2.7. The switch is opened at $t = 0$. The circuit has three loops

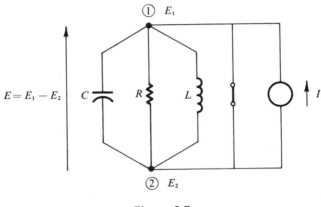

Figure 2.7

(once the switch is opened) and two junctures, or nodes. Here it is advan-
tageous to use Kirchhoff's other law, which says that the current entering
a node must be equal to the current leaving it. If $E(t)$ is the increase in voltage
from node 2 to node 1 (or the voltage drop from node 1 to node 2), then the
current flowing from node 1 to node 2 is

$$\frac{1}{R}E \quad \text{through the resistance,}$$

$$C\frac{dE}{dt} \quad \text{through the capacitance,}$$

and

$$\frac{1}{L}\int_0^t E(s)\, ds \quad \text{through the inductance.}$$

If $I(t)$ is the applied current, we must then have

$$C\frac{dE}{dt} + \frac{1}{R}E + \frac{1}{L}\int_0^t E(s)\, ds = I(t). \tag{2.75}$$

Differentiation with respect to t yields the second-order equation

$$C\frac{d^2E}{dt^2} + \frac{1}{R}\frac{dE}{dt} + \frac{1}{L}E = I'(t)$$

for the voltage E.

It can be shown that the voltage drop across a capacitance is the same immediately before and after a sudden change in the current through it. Consequently $E(0) = 0$. From Eq. (2.75), we find that

$$C\, E'(0) + 0 + 0 = I(0)$$

or

$$E'(0) = \frac{1}{C}I(0).$$

Thus our initial conditions are

$$E(0) = 0, \qquad E'(0) = \frac{1}{C}I(0).$$

The mathematics of this problem is similar to that for problems considered earlier in this section, and we shall proceed no further.

Electric circuits that involve more than one loop and more than one pair of nodes will be considered in Chapter VIII, which deals with systems of differential equations.

Exercises for Section 2.12

1. A resistance and an inductance are connected in series with a battery of constant voltage E_0, as shown in Fig. 2.8. The switch is closed at $t = 0$.

    (a) Find a formula for the current as a function of t.

    (b) Find the voltage drop across the resistance and that across the inductance.

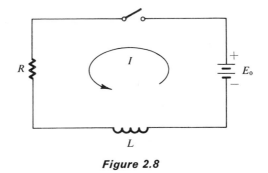

Figure 2.8

2. In the circuit of Fig. 2.4, suppose that $E(t) = E_0$ and that $Q_0 = 0$.

    (a) Find the current in the loop for the case $R^2 = 4L/C$.

    (b) Find the current if $R^2 < 4L/C$.

    (c) Show that the current tends to zero as t becomes infinite regardless of whether $R^2 - 4L/C$ is positive, negative, or zero so long as $R \neq 0$.

    (d) Show that the charge $Q(t)$ on the capacitance tends to the value $E_0 C$ regardless of whether $R^2 - 4L/C$ is positive, negative, or zero. *Suggestion:* Look at Eq. (2.71).

3. In the circuit of Fig. 2.4 suppose that the applied-voltage is sinusoidal of the form

$$E(t) = A \sin(\omega_1 t + \alpha),$$

    where A, ω_1, and α are constants. Find the steady-state solution. *Suggestion:* Look for a particular solution of the form

$$ae^{i(\omega_1 t + \alpha)}.$$

4. In the circuit of Fig. 2.9 suppose that

$$E(t) = A \sin \omega_1 t.$$

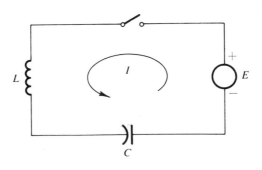

Figure 2.9

Let $\omega = (LC)^{-1/2}$. Find a formula for the current if

(a) $\omega_1 \neq \omega$ (b) $\omega_1 = \omega$

5.   In the circuit of Fig. 2.10, a charge Q_0 has been placed on the capacitance. If the switch is closed at $t = 0$, find a formula for the current.

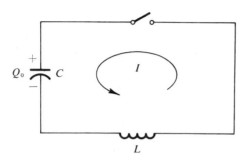

Figure 2.10

6.   A current source is connected in parallel with an inductance and a resistance, as shown in Fig. 2.11. The switch is opened at $t = 0$. If $I(t)$ has the constant value I_0, find

(a) the voltage $E(t)$;

(b) the current through the resistance;

(c) the current through the inductance.

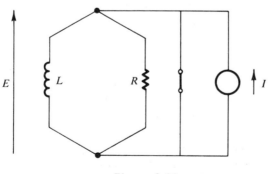

Figure 2.11

7.   In the circuit of Fig. 2.12 the switch is opened at $t = 0$. If $I(t) = A \sin \omega t$ find

(a) the voltage $E(t)$;

(b) the steady-state current through the resistance;

(c) the steady-state current through the capacitance.

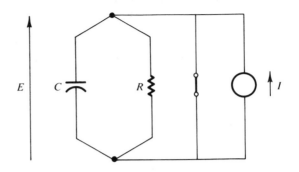

Figure 2.12

2.13   THEORY OF LINEAR DIFFERENTIAL EQUATIONS

Let us consider the initial value problem

$$a_0(x)y^{(n)} + a_1(x)y^{(n-1)} + \cdots + a_{n-1}(x)y' + a_n(x)y = F(x),$$
$$y^{(i)}(x_0) = k_i, \qquad 0 \le i \le n-1,$$

(2.76)

where the k_i are constants and the functions a_i and F are continuous on an interval $\mathscr{I}$ that contains the point x_0. We assume that a_0 is never zero on $\mathscr{I}$. The most basic result in the theory of linear differential equations is given by the following theorem.

Theorem 2.11   The initial value problem (2.76) possesses a solution that exists throughout the interval $\mathscr{I}$. Furthermore, any two solutions that exist on an interval that contains x_0 are identical on that interval.

This theorem is an *existence* theorem because it says that the initial value problem has a solution. It is also a *uniqueness* theorem because it says that the problem has essentially only one solution.

In the case of an initial value problem that involves an equation with constant coefficients, such as

$$y'' - y' - 2y = 0,$$
$$y(0) = k_0, \qquad y'(0) = k_1,$$

we can actually exhibit the solution. Any function of the form

$$y(x) = c_1 e^{-x} + c_2 e^{2x}$$

is a solution of the equation for all x, and if we require that

$$y(0) = c_1 = c_2 = k_0,$$
$$y'(0) = -c_1 + 2c_2 = k_1,$$

then

$$c_1 = \tfrac{1}{3}(2k_0 - k_1), \qquad c_2 = \tfrac{1}{3}(k_0 + k_1).$$

Hence the solution of the problem is

$$y(x) = \tfrac{1}{3}[(2k_0 - k_1)e^{-x} + (k_0 + k_1 e)^{2x}].$$

However, for an initial value problem such as

$$y'' + (\sin x)y' - e^x y = x^2,$$
$$y(1) = k_0, \qquad y'(1) = k_1,$$

we can no longer find a simple formula for the solution. Nevertheless, Theorem 2.11 assures us that a solution does exist for all x, and that there is only one solution.

One important consequence of Theorem 2.11 is that there exists a set of n linearly independent solutions for the nth-order equation $Ly = 0$. To see this, let $u_1, u_2, \ldots, u_n$ be the solutions for which

$$u_i^{(j-1)}(x_0) = \delta_{ij},$$

i and j varying from 1 to n. (Theorem 2.11 guarantees that these solutions exist.) The Wronskian of these functions at x_0 is one and hence is not equal to zero. Thus the solutions u_i are linearly independent.

A proof of the existence of a solution to the problem (2.76) is deferred until Chapter XII. We only remark here that the proof involves the construction of a sequence of functions that can be shown to converge to a function that is a solution of the problem. The functions of the sequence are expressed in terms of integrals and it is seldom possible to find a simple formula for the limit of the sequence.

The restriction that a_0, the coefficient of the highest derivative in the differential equation of problem (2.76), is never zero should be emphasized. Let us consider the example

$$xy' + y = 2x, \qquad y(0) = 1,$$

where $a_0(x) = x$. Obviously a_0 does vanish at $x = 0$. If the problem has a solution it must satisfy the relation

$$(xy)' = 2x$$

or

$$xy = x^2 + c.$$

Setting $x = 0$ and $y = 1$, we see that $c = 0$. Hence $xy = x^2$ or $y = x$. But then the initial condition $y(0) = 1$ is not satisfied. We conclude that the problem can have no solution.

The uniqueness part of Theorem 2.11 is not so difficult to prove. The proof that we shall present here is based on the following lemma:

Lemma In an interval $\mathcal{I}$ containing the point x_0 let the function w be continuous and nonnegative, and satisfy the inequality

$$w(x) \le M \left| \int_{x_0}^x w(s)\, ds \right|, \qquad (2.77)$$

where M is a positive constant. Then w is identically zero on $\mathcal{I}$.

PROOF   We define the function W by means of the formulas

$$W(x) = \int_{x_0}^x w(s)\, ds, \qquad x \ge x_0,$$

$$W(x) = -\int_{x_0}^x w(s)\, ds, \qquad x < x_0.$$

Notice that W is nonnegative and that $W(x_0) = 0$.

We consider first the case where $x \ge x_0$. Then $W'(x) = w(x)$ and the inequality (2.77) can be written as

$$W'(x) - MW(x) \le 0, \qquad x \ge x_0.$$

If we multiply through in this inequality by $\exp[-M(x - x_0)]$, which is always positive, we find that

$$\frac{d}{dx}[W(x)e^{-M(x-x_0)}] \le 0, \qquad x \ge x_0.$$

Integrating from x_0 to x, we have

$$W(x)e^{-M(x-x_0)} - W(x_0) \le 0$$

or

$$W(x) \le W(x_0)e^{M(x-x_0)}, \qquad x \ge x_0.$$

Since $W(x_0) = 0$ we must have $W(x) = 0$ for $x \geq x_0$. From the inequality (2.77) we see that $w(x) = 0$ for $x \geq x_0$. The case where $x < x_0$ can be treated similarly. The details are left as an exercise.

We can now prove that a solution of the initial value problem (2.76) is unique. Since a_0 is never zero, we shall first divide through by a_0 in the differential equation and consider the problem

$$Ly = y^{(n)} + b_1(x)y^{(n-1)} + \cdots + b_{n-1}(x)y' + b_n(x)y = G(x),$$
$$y^{(i)}(x_0) = k_i, \qquad 0 \leq i \leq n-1, \tag{2.78}$$

where $b_i = a_i/a_0$ and $G = F/a_0$. The functions b_i and G are continuous on an interval $\mathscr{I}$ that contains x_0.

Theorem 2.12   Suppose that the functions u and v are both solutions of the initial value problem (2.78) on an interval $\mathscr{J}$ that is contained in $\mathscr{I}$ and which contains x_0. Then $u(x) = v(x)$ for all x in $\mathscr{J}$.

PROOF   Let $w = u - v$. Since $Lu = G$ and $Lv = G$ we have $Lw = Lu - Lv = 0$. Thus w is a solution of the homogeneous equation $Ly = 0$, so that

$$w^{(n)} = -[b_1 w^{(n-1)} + \cdots + b_{n-1}w' + b_n w] \tag{2.79}$$

on $\mathscr{J}$. Also,

$$w^{(i)}(x_0) = 0, \qquad 0 \leq i \leq n-1.$$

Let us write

$$w_1 = w, \qquad w_2 = w', \qquad w_3 = w'', \ldots, \qquad w_n = w^{(n-1)}.$$

Then

$$w_1(x) = \int_{x_0}^{x} w_2(s)\, ds,$$

$$w_2(x) = \int_{x_0}^{x} w_3(s)\, ds, \tag{2.80}$$

$$\cdots$$

$$w_{n-1}(x) = \int_{x_0}^{x} w_n(s)\, ds,$$

and, from Eq. (2.79),

$$w_n(x) = -\int_{x_0}^{x} [b_n(s)w_1(s) + \cdots + b_1(s)w_n(s)]\, ds. \tag{2.81}$$

Let $\mathscr{K}$ be a bounded closed interval that contains x_0 and is contained in $\mathscr{J}$. Each point of $\mathscr{J}$ belongs to such an interval. Since the functions b_i are continuous on $\mathscr{K}$ there is a constant M such that $|b_i(x)| \le M$ for x in $\mathscr{K}$, $1 \le i \le n$. From Eq. (2.81), we have

$$|w_n(x)| \le M \left| \int_{x_0}^x [|w_1(s)| + \cdots + |w_n(s)|] \, ds \right|. \tag{2.82}$$

From Eqs. (2.80), we have

$$|w_i(x)| \le \left| \int_{x_0}^x |w_{i+1}(s)| \, ds \right|, \qquad 1 \le i \le n-1. \tag{2.83}$$

Adding the n inequalities (2.82) and (2.83), and considering the case $x \ge x_0$ and $x < x_0$ separately, we find that

$$|w_1(x)| + \cdots + |w_n(x)| \le (M+1) \left| \int_{x_0}^x [|w_1(s)| + \cdots + |w_n(s)|] \, ds \right|.$$

By the lemma, $|w_1| + |w_2| + \cdots + |w_n| = 0$. In particular $w_1 = w$ is zero on $\mathscr{K}$. But this means that $u = v$ on $\mathscr{K}$. Hence $u = v$ on $\mathscr{J}$, which we wished to show.

Theorem 2.12 has several important consequences. We recall that in Section 2.3 we showed that the Wronskian of a set of linearly dependent functions was identically zero. However, it was possible for a set of linearly independent functions to have a Wronskian that vanished identically also. In the case of n functions that are all solutions of the same nth order linear homogeneous differential equation this is no longer true, as we shall now show.

Theorem 2.13   Let the functions $u_1, u_2, \ldots, u_n$ be solutions of the differential equation

$$y^{(n)} + b_1(x)y^{(n-1)} + \cdots + b_{n-1}(x)y' + b_n(x)y = 0 \tag{2.84}$$

on an interval $\mathscr{J}$ where the functions b_i are continuous. If the functions are linearly dependent their Wronskian is identically zero on $\mathscr{J}$, but if they are linearly independent their Wronskian never vanishes on $\mathscr{J}$. Thus the functions are linearly dependent if and only if their Wronskian is identically zero.

PROOF   When the functions u_i are linearly dependent we know that their Wronskian vanishes identically by the results of Section 2.3. We shall now show that if the functions are linearly independent their Wronskian can never vanish.

Suppose that the Wronskian does vanish at a point x_0. Then there exist constants $c_1, c_2, \ldots, c_n$, not all zero, such that

$$c_1 u_1(x_0) + \cdots + c_n u_n(x_0) = 0,$$
$$c_1 u_1'(x_0) + \cdots + c_n u_n'(x_0) = 0, \qquad (2.85)$$
$$\vdots$$
$$c_1 u_1^{(n-1)}(x_0) + \cdots + c_n u_n^{(n-1)}(x_0) = 0.$$

This is because the determinant of the system of equations for the c_i is zero. Let us define the function w by means of the formula

$$w(x) = c_1 u_1(x) + \cdots + c_n u_n(x).$$

Then w is a solution of the homogeneous equation (2.84) on $\mathscr{I}$ and $w^{(i)}(x_0) = 0$ for $0 \le i \le n - 1$, according to Eqs. (2.85). By Theorem 2.12, w must be identically zero on $\mathscr{I}$. Hence

$$c_1 u_1(x) + \cdots + c_n u_n(x) = 0$$

for x in $\mathscr{I}$ and the constants c_i are not all zero. But this is impossible since the functions u_i are linearly independent. Consequently the Wronskian cannot vanish at any point of $\mathscr{I}$.

The result of Theorem 2.13 was used in Section 2.10 in finding a particular solution of a nonhomogeneous equation by the method of variation of parameters. The next result was stated without proof in Section 2.2.

Theorem 2.14 Let $u_1, u_2, \ldots, u_n$ be linearly independent solutions of the equation

$$y^{(n)} + b_1(x)y^{(n-1)} + \cdots + b_{n-1}(x)y' + b_n(x)y = 0 \qquad (2.86)$$

on an interval $\mathscr{I}$ where the b_i are continuous. Then every solution that exists on $\mathscr{I}$ is of the form $c_1 u_1 + c_2 u_2 + \cdots + c_n u_n$, where the c_i are constants.

PROOF Let v be a solution of Eq. (2.86) on $\mathscr{I}$. Let x_0 be any fixed point of $\mathscr{I}$. Since the Wronskian of the functions u_i is not zero at x_0 (or at any other point) there exist numbers $c_1, c_2, \ldots, c_n$ such that

$$c_1 u_1(x_0) + \cdots + c_n u_n(x_0) = v(x_0),$$
$$c_1 u_1'(x_0) + \cdots + c_n u_n'(x_0) = v'(x_0),$$
$$\vdots$$
$$c_1 u_1^{(n-1)}(x_0) + \cdots + c_n u_n^{(n-1)}(x_0) = v^{(n-1)}(x_0).$$

Let $w(x) = c_1 u_1(x) + c_2 u_2(x) + \cdots + c_n u_n(x)$. Then w is also a solution of Eq. (2.86) and $w^{(i)}(x_0) = v^{(i)}(x_0)$ for $0 \le i \le n - 1$. By Theorem 2.12, $v(x) = w(x)$ for x in $\mathscr{I}$. That is,

$$v(x) = c_1 u_1(x) + c_2 u_2(x) + \cdots + c_n u_n(x),$$

which we wished to show.

Exercises for Section 2.13

1. This problem furnishes a proof of the uniqueness of solutions for the initial value problem (2.76) when the differential equation has constant coefficients. Let the function f be a solution of the equation

$$P(D)y = 0, \tag{1}$$

where

$$P(D) = D^n + a_1 D^{n-1} + \cdots + a_{n-1}D + a_n$$

on a closed bounded interval I.

(a) Show that f possesses derivatives of all orders at every point of I.

(b) Since f and its derivatives are continuous on I, there exist constants K_i such that

$$|f^{(i)}(x)| \le K_i, \qquad 0 \le i \le n-1,$$

for x in I. If

$$K = \max(K_0, K_1, \ldots, K_{n-1})$$

and

$$M = \max(1, |a_1|, |a_2|, \ldots, |a_n|),$$

show that

$$|f^{(m)}(x)| \le K(nM)^m, \qquad m = 0, 1, 2, \ldots$$

for x in I.

(c) Show that the Taylor series for f about any point x_0 in I converges to f throughout I.

(d) If the function g is a solution of Eq. (1) on an interval J and satisfies the initial conditions $y^{(i)}(x_0) = 0, 0 \le i \le n-1$, show that $g(x) = 0$ for all x in J.

(e) If f_1 and f_2 are both solutions of the equation $P(D)y = F(x)$ on an interval J, and if both functions satisfy the same set of initial conditions $y^{(i)}(x_0) = k_i$, $0 \le i \le n-1$, show that $f_1(x) = f_2(x)$ for all x in J.

2. Prove the lemma in this section for the case when $x < x_0$.

3. Let u and v be nonnegative continuous functions defined on an interval $[a, b]$ and let c be a nonnegative constant. If

$$u(x) \le c + \int_a^x u(t)v(t)\, dt, \qquad a \le x \le b,$$

show that

$$u(x) \le c\left[\exp \int_a^x v(t)\, dt\right], \qquad a \le x \le b.$$

Suggestion: Let $W(x) = c + \int_a^x u(t)v(t)\, dt$. Then $W'(x) - v(x)W(x) \leq 0$.

4. Let the function f be a solution of the equation

$$y'' + [k^2 + a(x)]y = 0 \tag{2}$$

for $x \geq x_0$. The function a is assumed to be continuous for $x \geq x_0$.

(a) Show that f is a solution of the nonhomogeneous equation

$$y'' + k^2 y = -a(x)f(x)$$

for $x \geq x_0$, and hence that

$$f(x) = A \sin(kx + \alpha) + \int_{x_0}^x \sin k(t - x)a(t)f(t)\, dt,$$

where A and α are constants.

(b) If $\int_{x_0}^\infty |a(t)|\, dt$ converges, show that every solution of Eq. (2) is bounded on $[x_0, \infty)$. *Suggestion:* Use the result of Exercise 3.

5. Let α and β be positive real numbers, with $\alpha \neq \beta$. Let the function a be continuous on $[x_0, \infty)$. If $\int_{x_0}^\infty |a(t)|\, dt$ converges, show that every solution of the equation

$$[(D + \alpha)(D + \beta) + a(x)]y = 0$$

is bounded on $[x_0, \infty)$. *Suggestion:* Follow the procedure used in Exercise 4.

6. Consider the equation

$$y'' + a_1(x)y' + a_2(x)y = 0. \tag{3}$$

(a) Making the change of variable $y = uF$, where F is to be determined, show that Eq. (3) becomes

$$Fu'' + (2F' + a_1 F)u' + (F'' + a_1 F' + a_2 F)u = 0. \tag{4}$$

(b) If the function F in part (a) is chosen as

$$F(x) = \exp[-\tfrac{1}{2}\int a_1(x)\, dx],$$

show that Eq. (4) assumes the form

$$u'' + g(x)u = 0, \tag{5}$$

in which the first derivative is missing.

(c) Put the equation

$$xy'' + y' + xy = 0$$

in the form (5).

7. If the function f is a solution of the equation

$$xy'' + y' + xy = 0$$

on the interval $(0, \infty)$ show that $x^{1/2}f(x)$ is bounded as x becomes infinite and hence that $f(x)$ tends to zero. Use the results of Exercises 4 and 6.

REFERENCES

1. Coddington, E. A., *An Introduction to Ordinary Differential Equations*. Prentice-Hall, Englewood Cliffs, New Jersey, 1961.
2. Desoer, C. A., and Kuh, E. S., *Basic Circuit Theory*. McGraw-Hill, New York, 1969.
3. Kaplan, W., *Ordinary Differential Equations*. Addison-Wesley, Reading, Massachusetts, 1958.
4. Spiegel, M. R., *Applied Differential Equations*, 2nd ed. Prentice-Hall, Englewood Cliffs, New Jersey, 1967.
5. Symon, K. R., *Mechanics*, 2nd ed. Addison-Wesley, Reading, Massachusetts, 1960.

III

Series Solutions

3.1 POWER SERIES

The simplest functions in calculus are the polynomials, and those functions "built" from polynomials by a finite number of operations. These operations include the four arithmetic operations, raising to a positive integral power, and root-taking. Functions of this class are known as *algebraic functions*. Examples of such functions are f and g, where

$$f(x) = \left(\frac{x^2 - 3x + 1}{2x + 5}\right)^3, \qquad g(x) = \sqrt{x^3 + 1}.$$

Still other functions are too complicated to be defined by the procedures described above. Some can be defined in terms of integrals of simpler functions. For instance, the formulas

$$\ln x = \int_0^x \frac{1}{t}\, dt, \qquad x > 0,$$

$$\sin^{-1} x = \int_0^x (1 - t^2)^{-1/2}\, dt, \qquad |x| \leq 1$$

can be used to define the natural logarithm and inverse sine functions. Other functions can be defined by infinite sequences or series of simpler functions. Thus we may define

$$e^x = \sum_{n=0}^{\infty} \frac{x^n}{n!}, \qquad \sin x = \sum_{n=1}^{\infty} (-1)^n \frac{x^{2n-1}}{(2n-1)!}$$

for all x. In doing computational work manually with any of these functions, or even with the square-root function, a table of values of the functions would be convenient. A knowledge of the basic properties of the function is also useful. For instance, we know that the exponential function is nonnegative and increasing. The sine function is periodic with period 2π and its values vary between -1 and 1. Actually we may feel more comfortable in working with some of these functions than with many of the more complicated algebraic functions.

Even simple differential equations can have complicated solutions. Thus the solutions of the equation $y' = y$ are not algebraic functions but are multiples of the exponential function. The solutions of the equation $y'' = xy$ are not algebraic functions, nor can they be expressed in a simple way in terms of the standard exponential and trigonometric functions of our library of functions. Rather, they become new functions that can be added to our library if we find them sufficiently important.

In this chapter we consider the possibility of representing the solutions of certain linear differential equations in terms of power series. These "series solutions" form a starting point for the investigation of the general properties of the solutions and for the computation of their values. We begin with a review of power series.

A *power series* is a series of functions which at every real number x has the form

$$\sum_{n=0}^{\infty} a_n(x - x_0)^n. \tag{3.1}$$

Here x_0 is a fixed number, called the *center of expansion* (we speak of a power series *about the point* x_0) and the numbers a_i are the *coefficients* of the power series. The series (3.1) always converges at $x = x_0$ to the sum a_0. It may converge only at this point. It may converge for all values of x. If neither of these extreme situations occurs, there is a positive number R such that the series converges absolutely for $|x - x_0| < R$ and diverges when $|x - x_0| > R$. The number R is called the *radius of convergence* of the series. (If the series converges only at x_0 we set $R = 0$; if it converges everywhere we write $R = \infty$.) The interval $(x_0 - R, x_0 + R)$ is called the *interval of convergence* of the series.

The radius of convergence of a power series can sometimes be found by the following method, which is based on the ratio test for convergence of series. We leave the proof as an exercise.

Theorem 3.1   The radius of convergence of the series (3.1) is given by

$$R = \lim_{n \to \infty} \left| \frac{a_n}{a_{n+1}} \right|,$$

provided that the limit exists. (If $|a_n/a_{n+1}| \to \infty$, then $R = \infty$.)

Example 1   For the series

$$\sum_{n=0}^{\infty} \frac{2^n(x-1)^n}{n!}$$

we have $a_n = 2^n/n!$ and $a_{n+1} = 2^{n+1}/(n+1)!$ so $a_n/a_{n+1} = (n+1)/2$. Since this ratio becomes infinite as n increases, we have $R = \infty$. The series converges everywhere.

Example 2   The series

$$\sum_{n=1}^{\infty} \frac{n}{n+1} x^n$$

converges for $|x| < 1$ and diverges for $|x| > 1$ because

$$R = \lim_{n \to \infty} \left| \frac{a_n}{a_{n+1}} \right| = \lim_{n \to \infty} \frac{n(n+2)}{(n+1)^2} = 1.$$

A power series defines a function f whose domain is the interval of convergence (plus perhaps one or both endpoints of the interval). The value $f(x)$ of the function f at each point x in this interval is the sum of the series at the point x.

In the next two theorems we state, without proof, some facts about functions defined by power series. Proofs are given in most books on advanced calculus. See, for example, Taylor [4].

Theorem 3.2   Let

$$f(x) = \sum_{n=0}^{\infty} a_n(x - x_0)^n, \qquad g(x) = \sum_{n=0}^{\infty} b_n(x - x_0)^n$$

for $|x - x_0| < r$. Then for $|x - x_0| < r$,

$$cf(x) = \sum_{n=0}^{\infty} ca_n(x - x_0)^n$$

for every real number c,

$$f(x) + g(x) = \sum_{n=0}^{\infty} (a_n + b_n)(x - x_0)^n,$$

and

$$f(x)g(x) = \sum_{n=0}^{\infty} c_n(x - x_0)^n,$$

where

$$c_n = a_0 b_n + a_1 b_{n-1} + \cdots + a_n b_0 = \sum_{k=0}^{n} a_k b_{n-k} = \sum_{k=0}^{n} a_{n-k} b_k.$$

Example 3   Let

$$f(x) = \sum_{n=0}^{\infty} (n+1)x^n, \qquad g(x) = \sum_{n=0}^{\infty} x^n$$

for $|x| < 1$. Then

$$f(x)g(x) = \sum_{n=0}^{\infty} c_n x^n,$$

where

$$c_n = \sum_{k=0}^{n} (k+1)(1) = 1 + 2 + \cdots + (n+1) = \frac{(n+1)(n+2)}{2}.$$

The next theorem concerns facts about differentiation and integration of power series.

Theorem 3.3   Let

$$f(x) = \sum_{n=0}^{\infty} a_n (x - x_0)^n$$

for $|x - x_0| < R$. Then f is differentiable on the interval $(x_0 - R, x_0 + R)$, and

$$f'(x) = \sum_{n=1}^{\infty} n a_n (x - x_0)^{n-1}$$

for $|x - x_0| < R$.

If a and b are any points in $(x_0 - R, x_0 + R)$, then

$$\int_a^b f(x) \, dx = \sum_{n=0}^{\infty} \frac{a_n}{n+1} [(b - x_0)^{n+1} - (a - x_0)^{n+1}].$$

In particular,

$$\int_{x_0}^{x} f(t) \, dt = \sum_{n=0}^{\infty} \frac{a_n}{n+1} (x - x_0)^{n+1}, \qquad |x - x_0| < R.$$

The first part of the theorem says, roughly speaking, that the derivative of the sum of a power series is equal to the series of derivatives. Since the series of derivatives is again a power series, we may differentiate termwise again to find the second derivative. For instance, if

$$f(x) = \sum_{n=0}^{\infty} \frac{n+1}{n+2} x^n, \qquad |x| < 1,$$

then

$$f'(x) = \sum_{n=1}^{\infty} \frac{n(n+1)}{n+2} x^{n-1}, \qquad |x| < 1,$$

$$f''(x) = \sum_{n=2}^{\infty} \frac{n(n+1)(n-1)}{n+2} x^{n-2}, \qquad |x| < 1,$$

and so on. The series for f' (and the one for f'') can be written in the form (3.1) by making a shift in the index of summation. If we set

$$k = n - 1 \qquad n = k+1$$

then as n runs over the sequence $(1, 2, 3, \ldots)$, k varies over $(0, 1, 2, \ldots)$. Thus

$$\sum_{n=1}^{\infty} \frac{n(n+1)}{n+2} x^{n-1} = \sum_{k=0}^{\infty} \frac{(k+1)(k+2)}{(k+3)} x^k.$$

This is also the same as

$$\sum_{n=0}^{\infty} \frac{(n+1)(n+2)}{n+3} x^n,$$

since the sum of the series depends only on x, and not on either the index of summation k or the index n. The procedure is much like making a "change of variable" in an integral. If in the series for f'' we set $n = k + 2$, we see that

$$\sum_{n=2}^{\infty} \frac{n(n+1)(n-1)}{n+2} x^{n-2} = \sum_{k=0}^{\infty} \frac{(k+2)(k+3)(k+1)}{k+4} x^k.$$

In working with power series with a center of expansion x_0 different from zero, it is often convenient to make a change of variable $z = x - x_0$. Then

$$\sum_{n=0}^{\infty} a_n(x - x_0)^n = \sum_{n=0}^{\infty} a_n z^n.$$

Exercises for Section 3.1

In Exercises 1–8, find the interval of convergence of the power series.

1. $\displaystyle\sum_{n=0}^{\infty} \frac{n+2}{n+1} (x-1)^n$

2. $\displaystyle\sum_{n=0}^{\infty} \frac{n+1}{2^n} (x+3)^n$

3. $\displaystyle\sum_{n=1}^{\infty} n^3 (x-2)^n$

4. $\displaystyle\sum_{n=0}^{\infty} \frac{(n!)^2}{(2n)!} x^n$

5. $\displaystyle\sum_{n=0}^{\infty} \frac{1 \cdot 3 \cdot 5 \cdots (2n+1)}{(2n)!} x^n$

6. $\displaystyle\sum_{n=1}^{\infty} n^n (x+5)^n$

7. $\displaystyle\sum_{n=1}^{\infty} (-1)^n \frac{n}{\ln (n+1)} x^n$

8. $\displaystyle\sum_{n=1}^{\infty} \frac{n!}{n^n} x^n$

In Exercises 9–12, let f and g be defined by the indicated power series. Find power series expansions for $f + g$ and fg.

9. $f(x) = \sum_{n=0}^{\infty} (n + 1)(x - 2)^n, \qquad g(x) = \sum_{n=0}^{\infty} (x - 2)^n$

10. $f(x) = \sum_{n=0}^{\infty} \frac{x^n}{n!}, \qquad g(x) = \sum_{n=1}^{\infty} nx^n$

11. $f(x) = \sum_{n=0}^{\infty} (n + 1)x^n, \qquad g(x) = \sum_{n=0}^{\infty} \frac{x^n}{n + 1}$

12. $f(x) = \sum_{n=0}^{\infty} \frac{n + 1}{n + 2} x^n, \qquad g(x) = \sum_{n=0}^{\infty} \frac{n + 2}{n + 3} x^n$

In Exercises 13–16, write the series in the form

$$\sum_{n=n_0}^{\infty} a_n x^n,$$

where n_0 and a_n are to be determined.

13. $\sum_{n=2}^{\infty} n(n - 1)x^{n-2}$

14. $\sum_{n=3}^{\infty} \frac{n}{n + 1} x^{n-1}$

15. $\sum_{n=0}^{\infty} (n^2 + 2)x^{n+1}$

16. $\sum_{n=1}^{\infty} (2n + 1)(2n + 3)x^{n+2}$

In Exercises 17–18, find power series that represent $f'(x)$ and $f''(x)$, and determine an interval on which these formulas are valid.

17. $f(x) = \sum_{n=0}^{\infty} \frac{(-1)^n x^n}{2^n(n + 1)}$

18. $f(x) = \sum_{n=0}^{\infty} \frac{(x + 1)^{2n}}{n!\,(n + 1)!}$

19. Prove Theorem 3.1.

3.2   TAYLOR SERIES

Let f be a function defined by a power series on its interval of convergence. Thus

$$f(x) = \sum_{n=0}^{\infty} a_n(x - x_0)^n, \qquad |x - x_0| < R. \tag{3.2}$$

Differentiating and using Theorem 3.3, we have

$$f'(x) = \sum_{n=1}^{\infty} n a_n (x - x_0)^{n-1},$$

$$f''(x) = \sum_{n=2}^{\infty} n(n-1) a_n (x - x_0)^{n-2},$$

$$\vdots$$

$$f^{(k)}(x) = \sum_{n=k}^{\infty} n(n-1) \cdots (n-k+1) a_n (x - x_0)^{n-k}$$

$$\vdots$$

for $|x - x_0| < R$. Setting $x = x_0$ in these formulas, we see that

$$f'(x_0) = a_1, \quad f''(x_0) = 2 \cdot 1 a_2, \ldots, \quad f^{(k)}(x_0) = k(k-1) \cdots 2 \cdot 1 a_k.$$

Thus if Eq. (3.2) holds we must have

$$a_k = \frac{f^{(k)}(x_0)}{k!} \tag{3.3}$$

for $k = 0, 1, 2, \ldots$. On the other hand, suppose that f is any function that possesses derivatives of all orders at a point x_0. Then we can form the series

$$\sum_{n=0}^{\infty} \frac{f^{(n)}(x_0)}{n!} (x - x_0)^n, \tag{3.4}$$

called the *Taylor series* of f at x_0. (In the special case when $x_0 = 0$, the series (3.4) is also referred to as the *Maclaurin series* for f.) If the series (3.4) converges to $f(x)$ for all x in some interval $(x_0 - r, x_0 + r), r > 0$, we say that f is *analytic* at x_0.

As an example, let $f(x) = e^x$ for all x. Then $f^{(n)}(x) = e^x$ and $f^{(n)}(0) = 1$ for every positive integer n. The Maclaurin series for f is

$$\sum_{n=0}^{\infty} \frac{x^n}{n!}.$$

It is easily shown, by application of Theorem 3.1, that this series converges for all x. It is more difficult to show that the sum of the series is e^x. This can be established by the use of Taylor's formula with remainder, which is discussed in most books on calculus.

For convenience of reference we list a number of Maclaurin series whose validity has been established.

$$e^x = \sum_{n=0}^{\infty} \frac{x}{n!} \qquad \text{for all } x, \tag{3.5}$$

$$\cos x = \sum_{n=0}^{\infty} \frac{(-1)^n}{(2n)!} x^{2n} \qquad \text{for all } x, \tag{3.6}$$

$$\sin x = \sum_{n=1}^{\infty} \frac{(-1)^{n+1}}{(2n-1)!} x^{2n-1} \qquad \text{for all } x, \tag{3.7}$$

$$\frac{1}{1-x} = \sum_{n=0}^{\infty} x^n, \qquad |x| < 1, \tag{3.8}$$

$$(1+x)^m = 1 + \sum_{n=1}^{\infty} \frac{m(m-1)\cdots(m-n+1)}{n!} x^n, \qquad |x| < 1. \tag{3.9}$$

The last series is called the *binomial series*. If m is a nonnegative integer there is only a finite number of nonzero terms in the series and it is valid for all x. The series (3.8) is called the *geometric series*.

By means of these formulas and Theorems 3.2 and 3.3, it is possible to establish the validity of many other Taylor series expansions rather easily. For example, we have

$$\ln(1+x) = \int_0^x \frac{1}{1+t} dt, \qquad x > -1.$$

Using the geometric series (3.8) (with x replaced by $-t$) we have

$$\ln(1+x) = \int_0^x \left[\sum_{n=0}^{\infty} (-1)^n t^n \right] dt, \qquad |x| < 1.$$

An application of Theorem 3.3 yields the formula

$$\ln(1+x) = \sum_{n=0}^{\infty} \frac{(-1)^n}{n+1} x^{n+1}, \qquad |x| < 1.$$

As a second example, let us find the Maclaurin series for the function f, where

$$f(x) = \frac{x}{2x+3}.$$

Writing

$$f(x) = x \frac{1}{3} \frac{1}{1 + \frac{2}{3}x}$$

and observing from formula (3.8) that

$$\frac{1}{1 + \frac{2}{3}x} = \sum_{n=0}^{\infty} (-1)^n (\tfrac{2}{3}x)^n, \qquad |x| < \tfrac{3}{2},$$

we have

$$f(x) = \tfrac{1}{2} \sum_{n=0}^{\infty} (-1)^n (\tfrac{2}{3}x)^{n+1}, \qquad |x| < \tfrac{3}{2}.$$

Exercises for Section 3.2

In Exercises 1–6, find the Taylor series for the function f about the point x_0 by calculating the derivatives of the function at x_0.

1. $f(x) = 2x^3 - 3x^2 + x - 3,$ $x_0 = 2$

2. $f(x) = -1/x,$ $x_0 = -1$

3. $f(x) = \ln x,$ $x_0 = 1$

4. $f(x) = \cos x,$ $x_0 = \pi/4$

5. $f(x) = (1 + x)^{1/2},$ $x_0 = 0$

6. $f(x) = e^{3x},$ $x_0 = 0$

In Exercises 7–10, use the geometric and binomial series to find the Taylor series for the given function f about the point x_0. Indicate an interval on which the series converges to the function.

7. $\dfrac{4}{4 + x},$ $x_0 = 0$

8. $\dfrac{1}{x},$ $x_0 = 2$

9. $\dfrac{-2}{(x - 1)(x + 2)},$ $x_0 = 0$

10. $(1 - x^2)^{-1/2},$ $x_0 = 0$

Exercises 11–14, find the Maclaurin series of the given function by differentiation or integration of another series.

11. $f(x) = \dfrac{1}{(1 - x)^2}$

12. $f(x) = \tan^{-1} x$

13. $f(x) = \tanh^{-1} x$

14. $f(x) = \sin^{-1} x$

In Exercises 15–18, express the sum of the series in terms of elementary functions.

15. $\displaystyle\sum_{n=0}^{\infty} \frac{n + 1}{n!} x^{n+1}$

16. $\displaystyle\sum_{n=1}^{\infty} n^2 x^n$

17. $\displaystyle\sum_{n=0}^{\infty} \frac{n + 2}{n + 1} x^{n+1}$

18. $\displaystyle\sum_{n=1}^{\infty} n^2 x^{2n}$

3.3   ORDINARY POINTS

The linear homogeneous differential equation

$$y^{(n)} + a_1 y^{(n-1)} + \cdots + a_{n-1} y' + a_n y = 0 \tag{3.10}$$

is said to have an *ordinary point* at x_0 if each of the functions a_i is analytic at x_0. A point that is not an ordinary point is called a *singular point* for the equation. For the equation

$$y'' + \frac{2x}{(2x - 1)(x + 2)} y' + \frac{\cos x}{x^2} y = 0$$

the singular points are $\frac{1}{2}, 0$, and -2. All other points are ordinary points.

The basic result about series solutions at an ordinary point is as follows. A proof for the second-order case is deferred until Section 3.8.

Theorem 3.4   Let the functions $a_1, a_2, \ldots, a_n$ in Eq. (3.10) be analytic at x_0, and let each of these functions be represented by its Taylor series at x_0 on the interval $\mathscr{I} = (x_0 - R, x_0 + R)$. Then every solution of Eq. (3.10) on $\mathscr{I}$ is analytic at x_0 and is represented on $\mathscr{I}$ by its Taylor series at x_0.

Our interest is mainly in second-order equations, and we consider two examples.

Example 1   The equation

$$(2x + 1)y'' + y' + 2y = 0, \tag{3.11}$$

which may be written as

$$y'' + \frac{1}{2x + 1} y' + \frac{2}{2x + 1} y = 0, \tag{3.12}$$

has an ordinary point at $x = 0$. Here

$$a_1(x) = \frac{1}{1 + 2x} = \sum_{n=0}^{\infty} (-2)^n x^n, \qquad |x| < \tfrac{1}{2},$$

$$a_2(x) = \frac{2}{1 + 2x} = \sum_{n=0}^{\infty} 2(-2)^n x^n, \qquad |x| < \tfrac{1}{2}.$$

According to Theorem 3.4, the Maclaurin series for every solution converges at least for $|x| < \frac{1}{2}$. The solution for which

$$y(0) = A_0, \qquad y'(0) = A_1$$

has a Maclaurin series of the form

$$y(x) = \sum_{n=0}^{\infty} A_n x^n, \qquad (3.13)$$

where A_2, A_3, and so on, must be determined. Now

$$y'(x) = \sum_{n=1}^{\infty} n A_n x^{n-1}, \qquad y''(x) = \sum_{n=2}^{\infty} n(n-1) A_n x^{n-2},$$

so if we substitute in Eq. (3.11) we obtain the requirement

$$2 \sum_{n=2}^{\infty} n(n-1) A_n x^{n-1} + \sum_{n=2}^{\infty} n(n-1) A_n x^{n-2} + \sum_{n=1}^{\infty} n A_n x^{n-1} + 2 \sum_{n=0}^{\infty} A_n x^n = 0.$$

(It is convenient to substitute in Eq. (3.11) instead of Eq. (3.12) because the coefficients of the former are polynomials.) The first series here starts with the first power of x while the last three start with x^0. Collecting the constant terms, we may write

$$(2A_2 + A_1 + 2A_0) + 2 \sum_{n=2}^{\infty} n(n-1) A_n x^{n-1} + \sum_{n=3}^{\infty} n(n-1) A_n x^{n-2}$$

$$+ \sum_{n=2}^{\infty} n A_n x^{n-1} + 2 \sum_{n=1}^{\infty} A_n x^n = 0. \qquad (3.14)$$

Now, all four series start with the first power of x. In order to combine the series, we shift the indices of summation in the first, third, and fourth, writing

$$2 \sum_{n=2}^{\infty} n(n-1) A_n x^{n-1} = 2 \sum_{n=3}^{\infty} (n-1)(n-2) A_{n-1} x^{n-2},$$

$$\sum_{n=2}^{\infty} n A_n x^{n-1} = \sum_{n=3}^{\infty} (n-1) A_{n-1} x^{n-2},$$

$$2 \sum_{n=1}^{\infty} A_n x^n = 2 \sum_{n=3}^{\infty} A_{n-2} x^{n-2}.$$

Equation (3.14) may now be written as

$$(2A_2 + A_1 + 2A_0) + \sum_{n=3}^{\infty} [n(n-1) A_n + 2(n-1)(n-2) A_{n-1}$$

$$+ (n-1) A_{n-1} + 2A_{n-2}] x^{n-2} = 0.$$

Since the coefficients in the Maclaurin series of the zero function are all zero, we must have[†]

$$2A_2 + A_1 + 2A_0 = 0 \qquad (3.15)$$

and

$$n(n-1) A_n + (n-1)(2n-3) A_{n-1} + 2A_{n-2} = 0 \qquad (3.16)$$

[†] The power series representation of a function is unique. If a function f can be represented in the form (3.2) then the coefficients in the series must be given by formula (3.3).

for $n \geq 3$. This last relation is called a *recurrence relation* for the coefficients A_i. From Eq. (3.15) we can find A_2 in terms of A_0 and A_1. By using the recurrence relation (3.16) with $n = 3$ we may express A_3 in terms of A_0, A_1, and A_2 and hence in terms of A_0 and A_1. In fact, each coefficient A_i can be expressed in terms of A_0 and A_1.

From Eq. (3.15) we have

$$A_2 = -A_0 - \tfrac{1}{2}A_1. \tag{3.17}$$

Equation (3.16) may be written as

$$A_n = -\frac{2n-3}{n}A_{n-1} - \frac{2}{n(n-1)}A_{n-2}, \qquad n \geq 3. \tag{3.18}$$

For $n = 3$, we have

$$A_3 = -A_2 - \tfrac{1}{3}A_1.$$

Substituting from Eq. (3.17) for A_2 we find that

$$A_3 = -(A_0 - \tfrac{1}{2}A_1) - \tfrac{1}{3}A_1$$

or

$$A_3 = A_0 + \tfrac{1}{6}A_1.$$

Next, setting $n = 4$ in the relation (3.18), we see that

$$\begin{aligned} A_4 &= -\tfrac{1}{6}A_2 - \tfrac{5}{4}A_3 \\ &= -\tfrac{1}{6}(-A_0 - \tfrac{1}{2}A_1) - \tfrac{5}{4}(A_0 + \tfrac{1}{6}A_1) \\ &= -\tfrac{13}{12}A_0 - \tfrac{1}{8}A_1. \end{aligned}$$

The first terms in the Maclaurin series expansion of the solution are

$$\begin{aligned} y(x) = A_0 &+ A_1 x + (-A_0 - \tfrac{1}{2}A_1)x^2 + (A_0 + \tfrac{1}{6}A_1)x^3 \\ &+ (-\tfrac{13}{12}A_0 - \tfrac{1}{8}A_1)x^4 + \cdots. \end{aligned} \tag{3.19}$$

Collecting terms that involve A_0 and A_1, we have

$$y(x) = A_0(1 - x^2 + x^3 - \tfrac{13}{12}x^4 + \cdots) + A_1(x - \tfrac{1}{2}x^2 + \tfrac{1}{6}x^3 - \tfrac{1}{8}x^4 + \cdots).$$

The series included in parentheses are obtained by setting $A_0 = 1$ and $A_1 = 0$, or $A_0 = 0$ and $A_1 = 1$ in formula (3.19). Thus each converges at least for $|x| < \tfrac{1}{2}$. If we set

$$y_1(x) = 1 - x^2 + x^3 - \tfrac{13}{12}x^4 + \cdots,$$
$$y_2(x) = x - \tfrac{1}{2}x^2 + \tfrac{1}{6}x^3 - \tfrac{1}{8}x^4 + \cdots,$$

then the general solution on $(-\tfrac{1}{2}, \tfrac{1}{2})$ consists of all functions of the form

$$y(x) = A_0\, y_1(x) + A_1 y_2(x),$$

where A_0 and A_1 are arbitrary constants.

Example 2

$$y'' - 2(x - 1)y' - y = 0. \qquad (3.20)$$

Suppose that we wish to find the Taylor series expansions of the solutions at $x = 1$. For convenience we make the change of variable

$$t = x - 1. \qquad (3.21)$$

Then $x = 1$ corresponds to $t = 0$ and Eq. (3.20) becomes

$$\frac{d^2 Y}{dt^2} - 2t\frac{dY}{dt} - Y = 0, \qquad (3.22)$$

where $Y(t) = y(t + 1)$. Seeking solutions of the form

$$Y(t) = \sum_{n=0}^{\infty} A_n t^n,$$

we obtain the requirement

$$\sum_{n=2}^{\infty} n(n - 1)A_n t^{n-2} - 2\sum_{n=1}^{\infty} nA_n t^n - \sum_{n=0}^{\infty} A_n t^n = 0.$$

By proceeding as in the previous example, we see that this equation can be written as

$$(2A_2 - A_0) + \sum_{n=3}^{\infty} \{n(n - 1)A_n - [2(n - 2) + 1]A_{n-2}\}t^{n-2} = 0.$$

Then

$$A_2 = \tfrac{1}{2}A_0$$

and

$$A_n = \frac{2n - 3}{(n - 1)n} A_{n-2}, \qquad n \geq 3.$$

From these relations we see that

$$A_2 = \tfrac{1}{2}A_0,$$

$$A_4 = \frac{5}{3 \cdot 4} A_2 = \frac{1 \cdot 5}{2 \cdot 3 \cdot 4} A_0,$$

$$A_6 = \frac{9}{5 \cdot 6} A_4 = \frac{1 \cdot 5 \cdot 9}{6!} A_0,$$

$$\vdots$$

$$A_{2m} = \frac{1 \cdot 5 \cdot 9 \cdots (4m - 3)}{(2m)!} A_0, \qquad m \geq 1.$$

and

$$A_3 = \frac{3}{2 \cdot 3} A_1,$$

$$A_5 = \frac{7}{4 \cdot 5} A_3 = \frac{3 \cdot 7}{2 \cdot 3 \cdot 4 \cdot 5} A_1$$

$$\vdots$$

$$A_{2m-1} = \frac{3 \cdot 7 \cdots (4m-5)}{(2m-1)!} A_1, \qquad m \geq 2.$$

The general solution of Eq. (3.20) (for all x) is

$$y(x) = A_0\left[1 + \sum_{m=1}^{\infty} \frac{1 \cdot 5 \cdot 9 \cdots (4m-3)}{(2m)!} (x-1)^{2m}\right]$$

$$+ A_1\left[(x-1) + \sum_{m=2}^{\infty} \frac{3 \cdot 7 \cdots (4m-5)}{(2m-1)!} (x-1)^{2m-1}\right].$$

In the general case of an equation

$$p(x)y'' + q(x)y' + r(x)y = 0,$$

where p, q, and r are analytic at x_0 and $p(x_0) \neq 0$, it can be shown (see Section 3.8) that substitution of the series

$$y(x) = \sum_{n=0}^{\infty} A_n(x-x_0)^n$$

into the equation always leads to a recurrence relation that completely determines the coefficients A_i, $i \geq 2$, in terms of A_0 and A_1.

Exercises for Section 3.3

1. Locate all singular points of the given differential equation.

   (a) $y'' + \dfrac{x}{(x-1)(x+2)} y' + \dfrac{1}{x(x-1)^2} y = 0$

   (b) $x(x+3)y'' + x^2 y' - y = 0$

   (c) $y'' + e^x y' + (\cos x)y = 0$

   (d) $(\sin x)y'' - y = 0$

In Exercises 2–11 verify that $x = 0$ is an ordinary point for the differential equation and express the general solution in terms of power series about this point. Discuss the interval of convergence of the series.

2. $y'' + xy' + y = 0$ ③ $2y'' - xy' - 2y = 0$

4. $(1 - x^2)y'' - 5xy' - 3y = 0$ ⑤ $(2 + x^2)y'' + 5xy' + 4y = 0$

6. $y'' - xy = 0$ 7. $y'' - x^2 y' - 2xy = 0$

8. $y'' - (x + 1)y' - y = 0$ 9. $(1 + x)y'' - y = 0$

10. $y'' + e^x y' + y = 0$ 11. $y'' - (\sin x)y = 0$

In Exercises 12–15, express the general solution of the differential equation in terms of power series about the indicated point x_0. *Suggestion*: Make the change of variable $t = x - x_0$.

12. $y'' + (x - 1)y' + y = 0$, $x_0 = 1$

13. $(x^2 + 2x)y'' + (x + 1)y' - 4y = 0$, $x_0 = -1$

14. $(3 - 4x + x^2)y'' - 6y = 0$, $x_0 = 2$

15. $y'' - (x^2 + 6x + 9)y' - 3(x + 3)y = 0$, $x_0 = -3$

3.4 REGULAR SINGULAR POINTS

The Cauchy–Euler equation

$$2x^2 y'' + 3xy' - y = 0$$

has a singular point at $x = 0$. Its general solution is

$$y(x) = c_1 |x|^{1/2} + c_2 x^{-1},$$

and from this formula we see that no nontrivial solution is analytic at $x = 0$. On the other hand, the occurrence of a singular point may not preclude the existence of analytic solutions. The general solution of the equation

$$x^2 y'' - 2xy' + 2y = 0$$

is

$$y(x) = c_1 x + c_2 x^2,$$

so *every* solution is analytic at $x = 0$.

We notice that every equation of the form

$$b_0 x^2 y'' + b_1 xy' + b_2 y = 0, \qquad b_0 \neq 0, \qquad (3.23)$$

possesses at least one solution of the form

$$y = x^s,$$

where s is a number that may be complex. Our concern in this section is with a generalization of the class of equations (3.23). An equation that can be written in the form

$$(x - x_0)^2 y'' + (x - x_0)P(x)y' + Q(x)y = 0 \qquad (3.24)$$

is said to have a *regular singular point* at x_0 if P and Q are analytic at x_0.†
Such an equation may be written as

$$y'' + p(x)y' + q(x)y = 0, \qquad (3.25)$$

where

$$p(x) = \frac{P(x)}{x - x_0}, \qquad q(x) = \frac{Q(x)}{(x - x_0)^2}.$$

Thus Eq. (3.25) has a regular singular point at x_0 if and only if the functions

$$(x - x_0)p(x), \qquad (x - x_0)^2 q(x)$$

are analytic at x_0. It turns out that Eq. (3.24) possesses at least one, and sometimes two solutions of the form

$$y(x) = (x - x_0)^s \sum_{n=0}^{\infty} A_n (x - x_0)^n, \qquad A_0 \neq 0, \qquad (3.26)$$

where s is a number‡ that need not be an integer. The procedure for finding solutions of the type (3.26) is known as the *method of Frobenius*. We illustrate the method with some examples.

Example 1   The equation

$$2x^2 y'' + 3xy' - (1 + x)y = 0 \qquad (3.27)$$

has a regular singular point at $x = 0$. It can be written as

$$y'' + p(x)y' + q(x)y = 0,$$

with

$$p(x) = \frac{3}{2x}, \qquad q(x) = -\frac{1 + x}{2x^2},$$

---

† More generally, the nth-order equation

$$(x - x_0)^n y^{(n)} + (x - x_0)^{n-1} b_1(x)y^{(n-1)} + \cdots + (x - x_0)b_{n-1}(x)y' + b_n(x)y = 0$$

is said to have a regular singular point at x_0 if $b_1, b_2, \ldots, b_n$ are analytic at x_0.
    ‡ It is possible that s may be complex, but this does not happen in the classical equations in which we are most interested.

and $xp(x)$ and $x^2q(x)$ are analytic at $x = 0$. If

$$y(x) = x^s \sum_{n=0}^{\infty} A_n x^n = \sum_{n=0}^{\infty} A_n x^{n+s},$$

then

$$y'(x) = \sum_{n=0}^{\infty} (n + s)A_n x^{n+s-1}$$

and

$$y''(x) = \sum_{n=0}^{\infty} (n + s)(n + s - 1)A_n x^{n+s-2}.$$

Substituting into the differential equation (3.27), we obtain the requirement

$$2 \sum_{n=0}^{\infty} (n + s)(n + s - 1)A_n x^{n+s} + 3 \sum_{n=0}^{\infty} (n + s)A_n x^{n+s}$$

$$- \sum_{n=0}^{\infty} A_n x^{n+s} - \sum_{n=0}^{\infty} A_n x^{n+s+1} = 0.$$

The last sum in this equation begins with a term involving x^{s+1}; the remaining series start with a term involving x^s. In order to combine terms with like powers of x, we separate out those terms with x^s and make a shift of index $(n \rightarrow n - 1)$ in the last series. The result is

$$[2s(s - 1) + 3s - 1]A_0 x^s + \sum_{n=1}^{\infty} \{[2(n + s)(n + s - 1)$$

$$+ 3(n + s) - 1]A_n - A_{n-1}\}x^{n+s} = 0.$$

Since $A_0 \neq 0$, we see that s must be a root of the quadratic equation

$$2s(s - 1) + 3s + 1 = 0$$

or

$$(2s - 1)(s + 1) = 0. \tag{3.28}$$

Thus s must have one of the values $s_1 = \frac{1}{2}$ or $s_2 = -1$. In either case the coefficients A_i must satisfy the recurrence relation

$$[2(n + s)(n + s - 1) + 3(n + s) - 1]A_n = A_{n-1}, \qquad n \geq 1. \tag{3.29}$$

When $s = \frac{1}{2}$, this becomes

$$n(2n + 3)A_n = A_{n-1}$$

or

$$A_n = \frac{1}{n(2n + 3)} A_{n-1}, \qquad n \geq 1.$$

Then

$$A_1 = \frac{1}{1 \cdot 5} A_0,$$

$$A_2 = \frac{1}{2 \cdot 7} A_1 = \frac{1}{(1 \cdot 2)(5 \cdot 7)} A_0,$$

$$\vdots$$

$$A_n = \frac{1}{n! 5 \cdot 7 \cdots (2n + 3)} A_0.$$

Taking $A_0 = 1$, we arrive at the specific "series solution"

$$y_1(x) = x^{1/2} \left[1 + \sum_{n=1}^{\infty} \frac{x^n}{n! 5 \cdot 7 \cdots (2n + 3)} \right]. \tag{3.30}$$

When $s = -1$, the recurrence relation (3.29) becomes

$$n(2n - 3)A_n = A_{n-1}$$

or

$$A_n = \frac{1}{n(2n - 3)} A_{n-1}, \qquad n \geq 1.$$

From this relation we find that

$$A_1 = \frac{1}{1 \cdot (-1)} A_0,$$

$$A_2 = \frac{1}{2 \cdot (1)} A_1 = \frac{1}{1 \cdot 2(-1)(1)} A_0,$$

$$A_3 = \frac{1}{3 \cdot 3} A_2 = \frac{1}{1 \cdot 2 \cdot 3(-1) \cdot 1 \cdot 3} A_0,$$

$$\vdots$$

$$A_n = \frac{1}{n!(-1)1 \cdot 3 \cdots (2n - 3)} A_0.$$

Thus a second series solution of Eq. (3.27) is

$$y_2(x) = x^{-1} \left[1 - x - \sum_{n=2}^{\infty} \frac{x^n}{n! 1 \cdot 3 \cdots (2n - 3)} \right]. \tag{3.31}$$

We have seen that a function of the form

$$f(x) = x^s \sum_{n=0}^{\infty} A_n x^n, \tag{3.32}$$

where the power series converges in some interval $(-R, R)$, is a solution of the differential equation (3.27) if and only if the exponent s and the coefficients A_i satisfy the relations (3.28) and (3.29). Now the power series in formulas (3.30) and (3.31) converge everywhere, as can be verified by the use of Theorem 3.1. Consequently, the functions y_1 and y_2 are both solutions on the interval $(0, \infty)$. These solutions are linearly independent. For if

$$c_1 y_1(x) + c_2 y_2(x) = 0$$

for $x > 0$, then, letting $x \to 0$, we see that c_2 must be zero. This is because $y_2(x) \to \infty$ as $x \to 0$. We now have

$$c_1 y_1(x) = 0$$

for $x > 0$. But y_1 is not the zero function so $c_1 = 0$ also. Hence y_1 and y_2 are linearly independent.

We now consider the general second-order equation with a regular singular point at zero. Such an equation has the form

$$Ly \equiv x^2 y'' + xP(x)y' + Q(x)y = 0, \tag{3.33}$$

where

$$P(x) = \sum_{n=0}^{\infty} P_n x^n, \qquad Q(x) = \sum_{n=0}^{\infty} Q_n x^n,$$

for $|x| < R$. If y is a function of the form

$$y(x) = y^s \sum_{n=0}^{\infty} A_n x^n = \sum_{n=0}^{\infty} A_n x^{n+s}, \tag{3.34}$$

then

$$y'(x) = \sum_{n=0}^{\infty} (n+s)A_n x^{n+s-1},$$

$$y''(x) = \sum_{n=0}^{\infty} (n+s)(n+s-1)A_n x^{n+s-2}.$$

Also

$$xP(x)y'(x) = x^s \left(\sum_{n=0}^{\infty} (n+s)A_n x^n \right) \left(\sum_{n=0}^{\infty} P_n x^n \right)$$

$$= \sum_{n=0}^{\infty} \left(\sum_{k=0}^{n} (k+s)A_k P_{n-k} \right) x^{n+s}$$

and

$$Q(x)y(x) = x^s \left(\sum_{n=0}^{\infty} A_n x^n \right) \left(\sum_{n=0}^{\infty} Q_n x^n \right)$$

$$= \sum_{n=0}^{\infty} \left(\sum_{k=0}^{n} A_k Q_{n-k} \right) x^{n+s}.$$

Here we have used Theorem 3.2 to multiply the power series. Upon substituting the various quantities into the differential equation (3.33) and combining like powers of x, we obtain the equation

$$\sum_{n=0}^{\infty} \left\{ (n+s)(n+s-1)A_n + \sum_{k=0}^{n} [(k+s)P_{n-k} + Q_{n-k}]A_k \right\} x^{n+s} = 0.$$

The coefficient of the lowest power of x (which corresponds to the value $n = 0$ for the summation index) is $f(s)A_0$, where

$$f(s) = s(s-1) + sP_0 + Q_0$$
$$= s^2 + (P_0 - 1)s + Q_0.$$

Since $A_0 \neq 0$, the possible values of s are the roots of the *indicial equation*

$$f(s) = 0.$$

The two roots, which we denote by s_1 and s_2, are called the *exponents* of the differential equation at the regular singular point.

The coefficients A_i in the series for y must satisfy the recurrence relation

$$(n+s)(n+s-1)A_n + \sum_{k=0}^{n} [(k+s)P_{n-k} + Q_{n-k}]A_k = 0$$

for $n \geq 1$. By collecting the terms that involve A_n, we can write this relation as

$$[(n+s)(n+s-1) + (n+s)P_0 + Q_0]A_n = - \sum_{k=0}^{n-1} [(k+s)P_{n-k} + Q_{n-k}]A_k,$$

where $n \geq 1$. More briefly, we may write

$$f(s+n)A_n = \sum_{k=0}^{n-1} g_n(k,s)A_k, \qquad n \geq 1, \tag{3.35}$$

where

$$f(s) = (s-s_1)(s-s_2),$$
$$f(s+n) = (s+n-s_1)(s+n-s_2),$$

and the quantities $g_n(k,s)$ depend on the coefficients P_i and Q_i but not on the coefficients A_i. If, for a given value of s, say s_1 or s_2, the quantities $f(s+n)$, $n \geq 1$, do not vanish, then each of the coefficients $A_1, A_2, A_3, \ldots$, is uniquely determined, in terms of A_0, by the recurrence relation (3.35).

Let us first take up the case where the exponents s_1 and s_2 are real and distinct. We denote the larger of the two exponents by s_1. Since

$$f(s_1 + n) = (s_1 + n - s_1)(s_1 + n - s_2)$$
$$= n[n + (s_1 - s_2)],$$

we see that $f(s_1 + n) \neq 0$ for $n \geq 1$. Thus the differential equation always possesses a formal series solution y_1 of the form

$$y_1(x) = x^{s_1} \sum_{n=0}^{\infty} A_n x^n, \qquad (3.36)$$

corresponding to the larger exponent s_1. It can be shown that the power series in this formula actually converges, at least for $|x| < R$, and that the function y_1 is a solution of the differential equation, at least on the interval $(0, R)$. We refer the reader to Exercise 3, Section 3.8, or to Coddington [1].

Considering now the smaller exponent s_2, we see that

$$f(s_2 + n) = (s_2 + n - s_1)(s_2 + n - s_2)$$
$$= n[n - (s_1 - s_2)].$$

If the difference $s_2 - s_1$ is not a positive integer, then $f(s_2 + n) \neq 0$ for $n \geq 1$, and we obtain a second series solution y_2 of the form

$$y_2(x) = x^{s_2} \sum_{n=0}^{\infty} A_n x^n \qquad (3.37)$$

corresponding to the exponent s_2. The power series in this formula also converges for $|x| < R$ and y_2 is a solution, at least on the interval $(0, R)$.

However, if $s_1 - s_2 = N$, where N is a positive integer, then $f(s_2 + n)$ is zero when and only when $n = s_1 - s_2 = N$. In this case the recurrence relation (3.35) becomes, for $n = N$,

$$0 \cdot A_N = \sum_{k=0}^{N-1} g_N(k, s_2) A_k.$$

Unless it happens that the right-hand side of this equation is zero, it is impossible to find a number A_N that satisfies the equation, and no solution of the form (3.37) exists. If it does happen that the right-hand side of the equation is zero, then we have

$$0 \cdot A_N = 0$$

and *any* value for A_N will do. (In particular we can choose $A_N = 0$.) In this case we again obtain a series solution of the form (3.37). The case where $s_1 - s_2$ is a positive integer will be treated in a later section. If the exponents are equal, there is evidently only one solution of the type (3.34). We shall consider this case in the next section.

Exercises for Section 3.4

1. Locate all regular singular points of the given differential equations.

(a) $y'' + \dfrac{1-x}{x(x+1)(x+2)} y' + \dfrac{x+3}{x^2(x+2)^3} y = 0$

(b) $(x-1)^2(x-2)y'' + xy' + y = 0$

(c) $(2x+1)(x-2)^2 y'' + (x+2)y' = 0$

(d) $y'' + \dfrac{\sin x}{x^2} y' + \dfrac{e^x}{x+1} y = 0$

In Exercises 2–10, verify that $x = 0$ is a regular singular point of the differential equation. If possible, express the general solution in terms of series of the form (3.34).

2. $2x^2 y'' - 3xy' + (3-x)y = 0$ 3. $2x^2 y'' + xy' - (x+1)y = 0$

4. $2x^2 y'' + (x-x^2)y' - y = 0$ 5. $3xy'' + 2y' + y = 0$

6. $2xy'' + 3y' - xy = 0$

7. $3x^2 y'' + (5x + 3x^3)y' + (3x^2 - 1)y = 0$

8. $2x^2 y'' + 5xy' + (1-x^3)y = 0$

9. $(2x^2 - x^3)y'' + (7x - 6x^2)y' + (3 - 6x)y = 0$

10. $(2x - 2x^2)y'' + (1+x)y' + 2y = 0$

In Exercises 11 and 12, verify that x_0 is a regular singular point for the differential equation. If possible, express the general solution in terms of series of the form (3.26). *Suggestion:* Make the change of variable $t = x - x_0$.

11. $9(x-1)^2 y'' + [9(x-1) - 3(x-1)^2]y' + (4x-5)y = 0$, $x_0 = 1$

12. $2(x+1)y'' - (1+2x)y' + 7y = 0$, $x_0 = -1$

13. Show that the solutions (3.36) and (3.37) are linearly independent.

14. Let the function P, Q, and F be analytic at $x = 0$. Show that the equation

$$x^2 y'' + xP(x)y' + Q(x)y = x^\alpha F(x)$$

possesses at least a formal solution of the form

$$y(x) = x^\alpha \sum_{n=0}^{\infty} A_n x^n$$

whenever the constant α is such that neither $\alpha - s_1$ nor $\alpha - s_2$ is a positive integer. Show, by means of an example, that the equation may still possibly have a solution of the indicated form even when α does not satisfy these conditions.

3.5   THE CASE OF EQUAL EXPONENTS

When the exponents s_1 and s_2 of the differential equation (3.33) are equal, we can find only one solution of the form (3.34). In order to get some idea as to how a second solution can be found, suppose we examine a Cauchy–Euler equation whose exponents are equal. Let the equation be

$$Ly \equiv x^2 y'' + b_1 xy' + b_2 y = 0,$$

where b_1 and b_2 are real constants. Seeking a solution of the form

$$y(x, s) = x^s,$$

we have

$$Ly(x, s) = [s(s - 1) + b_1 s + b_2]x^s.$$

The exponents are the roots of the indicial equation

$$(s - s_1)(s - s_2) = s(s - 1) + b_1 s + b_2 = 0.$$

If $s_1 = s_2$ then

$$Ly(x, s) = (s - s_1)^2 x^s. \tag{3.38}$$

Evidently $Ly(x, s_1) = 0$, so one solution is

$$y_1(x) = y(x, s_1) = x^{s_1}.$$

To obtain a second solution, let us differentiate both members of Eq. (3.38) with respect to s. We have

$$\frac{\partial Ly(x, s)}{\partial s} = L \frac{\partial y(x, s)}{\partial s}$$

$$= [2(s - s_1) + (s - s_1)^2 \ln x]x^s,$$

where the first equality involves merely the interchange of the order of differentiation between s and x. Upon setting $s = s_1$, we see that

$$L \frac{\partial y(x, s)}{\partial s}\bigg|_{s = s_1} = 0$$

so that a second solution is

$$y_2(x) = \frac{\partial y(x, s)}{\partial s}\bigg|_{s = s_1} = x^{s_1} \ln x.$$

We shall use this same technique to obtain a second solution of the equation

$$Ly = x^2 y'' + xP(x)y' + Q(x)y = 0. \tag{3.39}$$

Writing

$$y(x, s) = x^s \sum_{n=0}^{\infty} A_n(s)x^n, \tag{3.40}$$

where the coefficients A_i are functions to be determined, we find as in the previous section that

$$Ly(x, s) = f(s)A_0 x^s + \sum_{n=0}^{\infty} \left[f(s+n)A_n(x) - \sum_{k=0}^{n-1} g_n(k, s)A_k \right] x^{n+s}. \tag{3.41}$$

Here, since $s_2 = s_1$, we have

$$f(s) = (s - s_1)^2,$$
$$f(s+n) = (s+n-s_1)^2.$$

Hence $f(s+n) \neq 0$ for $n \geq 1$ and $|s - s_1| < 1$. The coefficients A_n can be determined in terms of A_0 (which we take to be a fixed nonzero constant, independent of s) by means of the recurrence relation

$$A_n(s) = \frac{1}{(s+n-s_1)^2} \sum_{k=0}^{n-1} g_n(k, s)A_k, \qquad n \geq 1. \tag{3.42}$$

The functions A_n that are so defined are rational functions of s, and hence possess derivatives of all orders for $|s - s_1| < 1$.

Let us assume that the coefficients $A_n(s)$ in the series (3.40) have been chosen in the manner just described. Then from Eq. (3.41) we have

$$Ly(x, s) = A_0(s - s_1)^2 x^s. \tag{3.43}$$

Evidently $Ly(x, s_1) = 0$, so the function

$$y_1(x) = y(x, s_1) = x^{s_1} \sum_{n=0}^{\infty} A_n(s_1)x^n \tag{3.44}$$

is a solution. Upon differentiating both sides of Eq. (3.43) with respect to s and setting $s = s_1$, we see that

$$\left. \frac{\partial y(x, s)}{\partial s} \right|_{s=s_1} = L \left. \frac{\partial y(x, s)}{\partial s} \right|_{s=s_1} = 0.$$

Thus a second solution (at least formally) is

$$y_2(x) = \left.\frac{\partial y(x, s)}{\partial s}\right|_{s=s_1}$$

$$= x^{s_1} \sum_{n=0}^{\infty} A_n(s_1)x^n \ln x + x^{s_1} \sum_{n=1}^{\infty} A_n'(s_1)x^n$$

or

$$y_2(x) = y_1(x) \ln x + x^{s_1} \sum_{n=1}^{\infty} A_n'(s_1)x^n, \qquad (3.45)$$

where y_1 is the solution (3.44). It can be shown (Exercise 5, Section 3.8) that the power series in this formula converges at least for $|x| < R$ and that y_2 is a solution, at least on the interval $(0, R)$.

Example 1   Let us consider the equation

$$Ly = x^2y'' + 3xy' + (1 - x)y = 0.$$

Setting

$$y(x, s) = \sum_{n=0}^{\infty} A_n(s)x^{n+s},$$

we find that

$$Ly(x, s) = (s + 1)^2 A_0 x^s + \sum_{n=1}^{\infty} [(n + s + 1)^2 A_n - A_{n-1}]x^{n+s}.$$

The indicial equation is $(s + 1)^2 = 0$ and the exponents are $s_1 = s_2 = -1$. We choose the coefficients $A_n(s)$ to satisfy the recurrence relation

$$(n + s + 1)^2 A_n(s) = A_{n-1}(s)$$

for $n \geq 1$. Then

$$A_1(s) = \frac{A_0}{(s + 2)^2},$$

$$A_2(s) = \frac{A_1(s)}{(s + 3)^2} = \frac{A_0}{(s + 2)^2(s + 3)^2},$$

and in general,

$$A_n(s) = \frac{A_0}{(s + 2)^2(s + 3)^2 \cdots (s + n + 1)^2}, \qquad n \geq 1. \qquad (3.46)$$

Setting $s = s_1 = -1$, we have

$$A_n(-1) = \frac{A_0}{1^2 \cdot 2^2 \cdots n^2} = \frac{A_0}{(n!)^2}.$$

Taking $A_0 = 1$, we obtain the solution

$$y_1(x) = x^{-1} \sum_{n=0}^{\infty} \frac{x^n}{(n!)^2}.$$

In order to obtain a second solution, we need to compute the derivatives $A_n'(-1)$. It is convenient to do this by logarithmic differentiation. From formula (3.46) we have

$$\log A_n(s) = \log A_0 - 2[\log (s + 2) + \log (s + 3) + \cdots + \log (s + n + 1)].$$

Differentiating with respect to s, we have

$$\frac{A_n'(s)}{A_n(s)} = -2\left[\frac{1}{s + 2} + \frac{1}{s + 3} + \cdots + \frac{1}{s + n + 1}\right].$$

Then

$$\frac{A_n'(-1)}{A_n(-1)} = -2\left[1 + \frac{1}{2} + \cdots + \frac{1}{n}\right]$$

or

$$A_n'(-1) = -2\frac{\phi(n)}{(n!)^2}, \qquad n \geq 1,$$

where we use the notation

$$\phi(n) = 1 + \frac{1}{2} + \frac{1}{3} + \cdots + \frac{1}{n}. \tag{3.47}$$

From the general formula (3.45) we see that a second solution of the differential equation is

$$y_2(x) = y_1(x) \ln x - 2x^{-1} \sum_{n=1}^{\infty} \frac{\phi(n)}{(n!)^2} x^n.$$

The second solution could also have been determined by substituting an expression of the form

$$y(x) = y_1(x) \ln x + x^{-1} \sum_{n=1}^{\infty} B_n x^n$$

into the differential equation. The coefficients B_n can be determined by collecting the like powers of x and equating the coefficient of each power of x to zero. This method, however, does not so readily yield a general formula for the coefficients B_n.

Exercises for Section 3.5

In Exercises 1–10, verify that the exponents relative to $x = 0$ are equal, and find the general solution by using the method described in this section.

1. $(x^2 - x^3)y'' - 3xy' + 4y = 0$

2. $x^2y'' + 7xy' + (9 + 2x)y = 0$

3. $x^2y'' - xy' + (1 - x)y = 0$

4. $x^2y'' - (3x + x^2)y' + (4 - x)y = 0$

5. $xy'' + y' - 2xy = 0$

6. $(x^2 + x^4)y'' + (-x + 7x^3)y' + (1 + 9x^2)y = 0$

7. $x^2y'' + 5xy' + (4 - x)y = 0$

8. $x^2y'' + (3x + x^2)y' + y = 0$

9. $(x^2 + x^3)y'' - (x^2 + x)y' + y = 0$

10. $xy'' + (1 - x^2)y' + 4xy = 0$

3.6   THE CASE WHEN THE EXPONENTS DIFFER BY AN INTEGER

When $s_1 - s_2 = N$, N a positive integer, the equation

$$Ly = x^2y'' + xP(x)y' + Q(x)y = 0 \qquad (3.48)$$

may possess either one or two solutions of the form

$$y(x) = x^s \sum_{n=0}^{\infty} A_n x^n. \qquad (3.49)$$

(In the special case of a Cauchy–Euler equation, there are always two such solutions.) In any case, there is always a solution

$$y_1(s) = x^{s_1} \sum_{n=0}^{\infty} A_n x^n \qquad (3.50)$$

of this type, corresponding to s_1.

We now consider the case where there is only one solution of the form (3.49). Substituting the series

$$y(x, s) = x^s \sum_{n=0}^{\infty} A_n(s)x^n$$

into Eq. (3.48), we find that

$$Ly(x, s) = f(s)A_0 x^s + \sum_{n=1}^{\infty} \left[f(s + n)A_n - \sum_{k=0}^{n-1} g_n(k, s)A_k \right]x^{n+s}, \quad (3.51)$$

where

$$f(s) = (s - s_1)(s - s_2) = (s - s_2 - N)(s - s_2)$$

and

$$f(s + n) = (s + n - s_2 - N)(s + N - s_2)$$

when $n \geq 1$. In particular, $f(s + N)$ is zero when $s = s_2$, because

$$f(s + N) = (s - s_2)(s + N - s_2).$$

This is the only one of the quantities $f(s + n)$ that vanishes when $s = s_2$. Let us choose the coefficient functions A_n (where A_0 is a fixed nonzero constant) so that they satisfy the recurrence relation

$$f(s + n)A_n(s) = \sum_{k=0}^{n-1} g_n(k, s)A_k(s). \quad (3.52)$$

Then the functions $A_1, A_2, \ldots, A_{N-1}$ are analytic at $s = s_2$ but for $n \geq N$, the quantities $A_n(s)$ contain the factor $s - s_2$ in the denominator. They may become infinite as s approaches s_2. However, the functions B_n, where

$$B_n(s) = (s - s_2)A_n(s),$$

are analytic at $s = s_2$ and satisfy the recurrence relation (3.52) not only for s near s_2 but also for $s = s_2$. (To see this, multiply through in Eq. (3.52) by $s - s_2$.)
    Let

$$\tilde{y}(x, s) = (s - s_2)y(x, s)$$

$$= x^s \sum_{n=0}^{\infty} B_n(s)x^n.$$

Multiplying through in Eq. (3.51) by $s - s_2$, we see that

$$L\tilde{y}(x, s) = A_0(s - s_2)f(s)x^s$$

$$= A_0(s - s_1)(s - s_2)^2 x^s.$$

Because of the occurence of the factor $(s - s_2)^2$ in the last expression, it follows that each of the quantities

$$y_1(x) = \tilde{y}(x, s_2), \qquad y_2(x) = \left. \frac{\partial \tilde{y}(x, s)}{\partial s} \right|_{s = s_2}$$

formally satisfies the differential equation.

We now examine the forms of these two formal solutions. Since $B_n(s_2) = 0$ for $0 \le n \le N - 1$, the solution $\tilde{y}_1$ has the form

$$\tilde{y}_1(x) = x^{s_2} \sum_{n=N}^{\infty} B_n(s_2)x^n$$

$$= x^{s_2 + N} \sum_{n=0}^{\infty} B_{n+N}(s_2)x^n$$

$$= x^{s_1} \sum_{n=0}^{\infty} B_{n+N}(s_2)x^n .$$

Thus $\tilde{y}_1$ must simply be a multiple of the solution y_1 given in formula (3.50). In fact,

$$\tilde{y}_1 = \frac{B_N(s_2)}{A_0} y_1 .$$

The solution y_2 is obtained by setting $s = s_2$ in the formula

$$\frac{\partial \tilde{y}(x, s)}{\partial s} = \frac{\partial}{\partial s} \left[x^s \sum_{n=0}^{\infty} B_n(s)x^n \right]$$

$$= x^s \sum_{n=0}^{\infty} B_n(s)x^n \ln x + x^s \sum_{n=0}^{\infty} B_n'(s)x^n .$$

We have

$$y_2(x) = \tilde{y}_1(x) \ln x + x^{s_2} \sum_{n=0}^{\infty} B_n'(s_2)x^n$$

or

$$y_2(x) = \frac{B_N}{A_0} y_1(x) \ln x + x^{s_2} \sum_{n=0}^{\infty} B_n'(s_2)x^n . \qquad (3.53)$$

It can be shown (Exercise 6, Section 3.8) that the power series in this formula converges, at least for $|x| < R$, and that the function y_2 is a solution of the differential equation, at least on the interval $(0, R)$.

Example 1   Let us consider the equation

$$Ly = xy'' + 2y' - y = 0.$$

Writing

$$y(x, s) = x^s \sum_{n=0}^{\infty} A_n(s)x^n,$$

we find that

$$Ly(x, s) = s(s + 1)A_0 \, x^{s-1} + \sum_{n=1}^{\infty} [(n + s)(n + s + 1)A_n - A_{n-1}]x^{n+s-1}.$$

The exponents for the equation are $s_1 = 0$ and $s_2 = -1$. The recurrence relation for the coefficients A_n is

$$(n + s)(n + s + 1)A_n(s) = A_{n-1}(s), \qquad n \geq 1.$$

From this relation we find that

$$A_1(s) = \frac{A_0}{(s + 1)(s + 2)}, \qquad A_2(s) = \frac{A_0}{(s + 1)(s + 2)^2(s + 2)},$$

and in general,

$$A_n(s) = \frac{A_0}{(s + 1)(s + 2)^2(s + 3)^2 \cdots (s + n)^2(s + n + 1)}$$

for $n \geq 2$. Setting $s = s_1 = 0$ in these formulas, we find that

$$A_n(s_1) = \frac{A_0}{1 \cdot 2^2 \cdot 3^3 \cdots n^2(n + 1)} = \frac{A_0}{n!(n + 1)!}, \qquad n \geq 0.$$

Therefore a solution of the equation which corresponds to the exponent $s_1 = 0$ is

$$y_1(x) = \sum_{n=0}^{\infty} \frac{x^n}{n!(n + 1)!}.$$

The quantity $A_1(s)$ ($N = 1$ in this example) becomes infinite as s approaches $s_2 = -1$, because of the factor $(s + 1)$ in its denominator. Hence the equation does not possess a second solution of the form (3.49) corresponding to the exponent s_2. The second solution is therefore logarithmic.

The functions

$$B_0(s) = (s + 1)A_0,$$

$$B_1(s) = (s + 1)A_1(s) = \frac{A_0}{s + 2},$$

$$B_n(s) = (s + 1)A_n(s) = \frac{A_0}{(s + 2)^2(s + 3)^2 \cdots (s + n)^2(s + n + 1)}, \qquad n \geq 2,$$

are analytic at $s = s_2 = -1$. Routine calculation shows that

$$B_0'(-1) = A_0, \qquad B_1'(-1) = -A_0,$$

$$B_n'(-1) = -\frac{\phi(n-1) + \phi(n)}{(n-1)!\,n!}\,A_0, \qquad n \geq 2,$$

where $\phi(n)$ is defined by formula (3.47). Choosing $A_0 = 1$, we obtain the solution

$$y_2(x) = y_1(x) \ln x - x^{-1}\left[1 - x - \sum_{n=2}^{\infty} \frac{\phi(n-1) + \phi(n)}{(n-1)!\,n!}\,x^n\right],$$

where $y_1(x)$ is as above.

This second solution could also have been found by substituting an expression of the form

$$y(x) = y_1(x) \ln x + x^{-1} \sum_{n=0}^{\infty} C_n x^n$$

into the differential equation and determining the coefficients C_n. However, it is difficult to find a general formula for C_n using this method.

Example 2   The equation

$$xy'' + 3y' - x^2 y = 0$$

has a regular singular point at $x = 0$. Seeking solutions of the form

$$y(x, s) = x^s \sum_{n=0}^{\infty} A_n x^n, \qquad A_0 \neq 0,$$

we find, after some calculation, that the indicial equation is

$$s(s + 2) = 0,$$

and that the coefficients A_i must satisfy the conditions

$$(s + 1)(s + 3)A_1 = 0,$$

$$(s + 2)(s + 4)A_2 = 0,$$

and

$$(n + s)(n + s + 2)A_n = A_{n-3}, \qquad n \geq 3.$$

The exponents are $s_1 = 0$ and $s_2 = -2$. For the larger exponent s_1, we have

$$A_1 = 0,$$

$$A_2 = 0,$$

$$A_n = \frac{A_{n-3}}{n(n+2)}, \qquad n \geq 3.$$

All the coefficients A_i vanish except those whose subscripts are multiples of three. We have

$$A_3 = \frac{1}{3 \cdot 5} A_0,$$

$$A_6 = \frac{1}{6 \cdot 8} A_3 = \frac{1}{(3 \cdot 6)(5 \cdot 8)} A_0,$$

and in general,

$$A_{3m} = \frac{1}{(3 \cdot 6 \cdot 9 \cdots 3m)[5 \cdot 8 \cdot 11 \cdots (3m + 2)]} A_0$$

$$= \frac{1}{3^m m! \, [5 \cdot 8 \cdot 11 \cdots (3m + 2)]} A_0.$$

The solution which corresponds to the exponent s_1 is

$$y_1(x) = 1 + \sum_{m=1}^{\infty} \frac{x^{3m}}{3^m m! \, [5 \cdot 8 \cdot 11 \cdots (3m + 2)]}.$$

For the smaller exponent $s_2 = -2$, we have

$$A_1 = 0,$$

$$0 \cdot A_2 = 0,$$

$$(n - 2)n A_n = A_{n-3}, \qquad n \geq 3.$$

(Note that A_2 is the critical coefficient, since $N = 2$ in this example.) Here A_2 is arbitrary, and we may choose $A_2 = 0$. A solution that corresponds to the exponent s_2 is found to be

$$y_2(x) = x^{-2} \left[1 + \sum_{m=1}^{\infty} \frac{x^{3m}}{3^m m! \, [1 \cdot 4 \cdot 7 \cdots (3m - 2)]} \right].$$

Exercises for Section 3.6

In Exercises 1–14, express the general solution in terms of series about $x = 0$.

1. $xy'' - xy' - y = 0$

2. $xy'' + xy' + 2y = 0$

3. $(x^2 - x^4)y'' + 4xy' + (2 + 20x^2)y = 0$

4. $x^2 y'' + x^2 y' - 2y = 0$

5. $x^2 y'' - 2xy' + (2 - x)y = 0$

6. $(x^2 - x^3)y'' + (x - 5x^2)y' - (1 + 4x)y = 0$

7. $x^2y'' + (3x - x^2)y' - xy = 0$

8. $x^2y'' + (x + x^3)y' + (x^2 + 1)y = 0$

9. $xy'' - y = 0$

10. $xy'' - y' + y = 0$

11. $x^2y'' + xy' - (2x + 1)y = 0$

12. $x^2y'' + (2x - 2)y = 0$

13. $(x^2 - x^3)y'' + (3x - 5x^2)y' - 3y = 0$

14. $(x^2 + x^3)y'' + (x + x^2)y' - (4 + x)y = 0$

3.7   THE POINT AT INFINITY

In some instances it may be desired to find the behavior of solutions of a differential equation as the independent variable x becomes infinite, rather than near some finite point. If we make the change of variable

$$x = \frac{1}{t}, \tag{3.54}$$

then as t tends to zero through positive (negative) values, x becomes positively (negatively) infinite. Setting $Y(t) = y(1/t) = y(x)$, the chain rule shows that

$$\frac{dy}{dx} = \frac{dY}{dt}\frac{dt}{dx} = -\frac{1}{x^2}\frac{dY}{dt} = -t^2\frac{dY}{dt},$$

$$\frac{d^2y}{dx^2} = \frac{1}{x^4}\frac{d^2Y}{dt^2} + \frac{2}{x^3}\frac{dY}{dt} = t^4\frac{d^2Y}{dt^2} + 2t^3\frac{dY}{dt}.$$

The equation

$$\frac{d^2y}{dx^2} + P(x)\frac{dy}{dx} + Q(x)y = 0 \tag{3.55}$$

becomes

$$\frac{d^2Y}{dt^2} + p(t)\frac{dY}{dt} + q(t)Y = 0, \tag{3.56}$$

where

$$p(t) = \frac{2}{t} - \frac{1}{t^2}P\left(\frac{1}{t}\right), \qquad q(t) = \frac{1}{t^4}Q\left(\frac{1}{t}\right).$$

If Eq. (3.56) has an ordinary point at $t = 0$, then Eq. (3.55) is said to have an ordinary point at infinity. Similarly, if Eq. (3.56) has a regular singular point at $t = 0$, then Eq. (3.55) is said to have a a regular singular point at infinity.

For purposes of illustration, let us attempt to find series solutions of the equation

$$2x^3 \frac{d^2 y}{dx^2} + 3x^2 \frac{dy}{dx} + y = 0$$

that are valid for large values of $|x|$. After the transformation (3.54), our equation becomes

$$2t \frac{d^2 Y}{dt^2} + \frac{dY}{dt} - Y = 0.$$

This equation has a regular singular point at $t = 0$. Applying the method of Frobenius, we find that the exponents at $t = 0$ are $s_1 = \frac{1}{2}$ and $s_2 = 0$, and that corresponding solutions are

$$Y_1(t) = t^{1/2} \sum_{n=0}^{\infty} \frac{2^n}{(2n + 1)!} t^n,$$

$$Y_2(t) = \sum_{n=0}^{\infty} \frac{2^n}{(2n)!} t^n.$$

Replacing t by $1/x$ in these formulas, we obtain the solutions

$$y_1(x) = x^{-1/2} \sum_{n=0}^{\infty} \frac{2^n}{(2n + 1)!} x^{-n},$$

$$y_2(x) = \sum_{n=0}^{\infty} \frac{2^n}{(2n)!} x^{-n}$$

of the original equation. Since the series for Y_1 and Y_2 converge for $|t| < \infty$, the series for y_1 and y_2 converge for $|x| > 0$.

Exercises for Section 3.7

1. Find all singular points of the given differential equation and indicate which are regular singular points. Include any singularity at infinity.

    (a) $x^4 y'' + x^3(x + 2)y' + y = 0$
    (b) $(x + 1)^2 y'' + (x + 1)y' - y = 0$
    (c) $(x - 2)y'' + y' - xy = 0$
    (d) $y'' + ay' + by = 0$, a and b constants
    (e) $y'' + x^{-2} y = 0$
    (f) $y'' + e^x y = 0$

In Exercises 2–7 verify that the point at infinity is either an ordinary point or a regular singular point. Express the general solution in terms of series of powers of $1/x$.

2. $x^4y'' + (2x^3 - x)y' + y = 0$

3. $x^4y'' + (2x^3 + x)y' - y = 0$

4. $2x^3y'' + x^2y' - (x + 1)y = 0$

5. $2x^3y'' + (5x^2 - 2x)y' + (x + 3)y = 0$

6. $x^3y'' + (x^2 - x)y' + (2 - x)y = 0$

7. $x^2(x^2 - 1)y'' + (x^3 + 5x)y' - 8y = 0$

8. Let us write $f(x) = O(x^m)$ whenever f is any function such that $f(x)/x^m$ is bounded when $|x|$ is sufficiently large. In particular, $f(x) = O(x^m)$ if $f(x)/x^m$ tends to a finite limit as $|x|$ becomes infinite. If the differential equation

$$y'' + P(x)y' + Q(x)y = 0$$

has a regular singular point at infinity, show that $P(x) = O(x^{-1})$ and that $Q(x) = O(x^{-2})$. If the equation has an ordinary point at infinity, show that $P(x) - 2/x = O(x^{-2})$ and that $Q(x) = O(x^{-4})$.

9. Verify that the equation $xy'' - (x + 1)y = 0$ has a singular point at infinity, but that the singular point is not regular. Then show that the equation possesses *formal* solutions of the forms

$$y_1(x) = x^{1/2}e^x \sum_{n=0}^{\infty} A_n x^{-n},$$

$$y_2(x) = x^{-1/2}e^{-x} \sum_{n=0}^{\infty} B_n x^{-n},$$

but that both of the series involved *diverge* for all values of x.

3.8 CONVERGENCE OF THE SERIES

In seeking series solutions of a differential equation at an ordinary point, or at a regular singular point, we substituted a series into the equation. Assuming that the series converged, we were able to find a recurrence relation that determined the coefficients in the series. In some of the examples we were able to find explicit formulas for the coefficients. These formulas enabled us to prove (using the ratio test, for example) that the series were actually convergent. In the general case it is not possible to find explicit formulas for the coefficients, and we must establish the convergence of the series in a different way. We shall consider in detail the case of solutions of a second-order equation at an ordinary point. Series solutions, including those involving logarithms, at a regular singular point are left to the exercises. We always assume that the point of interest is zero. In case the ordinary or singular point is $x_0 \neq 0$, the change of variable $t = x - x_0$ puts the point at zero.

Theorem 3.5   Let the functions P and Q be analytic at zero, and let

$$P(x) = \sum_{n=0}^{\infty} P_n x^n, \qquad Q(x) = \sum_{n=0}^{\infty} Q_n x^n$$

for $|x| < R$. Then the solution of the initial value problem

$$Ly = y'' + P(x)y' + Q(x)y = 0,$$

$$y(0) = A_0, \qquad y'(0) = A_1$$

is analytic at zero and its Taylor series converges, at least for $|x| < R$. The coefficients of this series are completely determined in terms of A_0 and A_1 by substituting a series

$$y(x) = \sum_{n=0}^{\infty} A_n x^n$$

into the differential equation and requiring that $Ly(x) = 0$; that is, by requiring that the coefficients in the Taylor series for Ly all be zero.

PROOF   We shall show that a function that is analytic at zero is a solution of the initial value problem if and only if the coefficients in its power series expansion satisfy a certain recurrence relation. We shall then show that the series whose coefficients satisfy the recurrence relation actually converges. The convergent series will therefore represent an analytic function that is the solution of the initial value problem.

Let y be a function that is analytic at $x = 0$, with Taylor series

$$y(x) = \sum_{n=0}^{\infty} A_n x^n,$$

where A_0 and A_1 are the constants given in the initial conditions. Then

$$y'(x) = \sum_{n=1}^{\infty} n A_n x^{n-1} = \sum_{n=0}^{\infty} (n + 1)A_{n+1} x^n,$$

$$y''(x) = \sum_{n=2}^{\infty} n(n - 1)A_n x^{n-2} = \sum_{n=0}^{\infty} (n + 1)(n + 2)A_{n+2} x^n,$$

and

$$P(x)y'(x) = \sum_{n=0}^{\infty} \left(\sum_{k=0}^{n} (k+1)A_{k+1}P_{n-k} \right) x^n,$$

$$Q(x)y(x) = \sum_{n=0}^{\infty} \left(\sum_{k=0}^{n} A_k Q_{n-k} \right) x^n.$$

The function Ly is analytic at $x = 0$ and

$$Ly(x) = \sum_{n=0}^{\infty} \left[(n+1)(n+2)A_{n+2} + \sum_{k=0}^{n} (k+1)A_{k+1}P_{n-k} + \sum_{k=0}^{n} A_k Q_{n-k} \right] x^n.$$

We see from this equation that y is a solution of the differential equation if and only if its coefficients satisfy the recurrence relation

$$A_{n+2} = \frac{-1}{(n+1)(n+2)} \left[\sum_{k=0}^{n} (k+1)A_{k+1}P_{n-k} + \sum_{k=0}^{n} A_k Q_{n-k} \right]$$

for $n \geq 0$. By making a shift in the index of summation (we replace n by $n - 2$) we can write this relation as

$$A_n = \frac{-1}{n(n-1)} \left[\sum_{k=0}^{n-2} (k+1)A_{k+1}P_{n-k-2} + \sum_{k=0}^{n-2} A_k Q_{n-k-2} \right] \qquad (3.57)$$

for $n \geq 2$.

Let x_1 be an arbitrary, but fixed, number in the interval $(-R, R)$. Let r be a positive number such that $|x_1| < r < R$. Since the series for $P(x)$ and $Q(x)$ converge when $x = r$, there exists a positive constant M such that

$$|P_n| \leq \frac{M}{r^n}, \qquad |Q_n| \leq \frac{M}{r^n}$$

for $n \geq 0$. From the recurrence relation (3.57) we see that

$$|A_n| \leq \frac{M}{n(n-1)} \left[\sum_{k=0}^{n-2} \frac{(k+1)|A_{k+1}|}{r^{n-k-2}} + \sum_{k=0}^{n-2} \frac{|A_k|}{r^{n-k-2}} \right], \qquad n \geq 2. \qquad (3.58)$$

We now define a sequence of positive numbers B_n in the following way. Let B_0 and B_1 be positive numbers such that

$$B_0 \geq |A_0|, \qquad B_1 \geq |A_1|.$$

(We can take $B_0 = |A_0| + 1$, $B_1 = |A_1| + 1$, for example.) The remaining terms of the sequence are defined according to the formula

$$B_n = \frac{M}{n(n-1)} \left[\sum_{k=0}^{n-2} \frac{(k+1)|A_{k+1}|}{r^{n-k-2}} + \sum_{k=0}^{n-1} \frac{|A_k|}{r^{n-k-2}} \right], \qquad n \geq 2. \qquad (3.59)$$

It should be noted that for $n \geq 2$ the expression for B_n is exactly the same as the right-hand member of the inequality (3.58), except for the additional term $r|A_{n-1}|$ in the second group of terms in brackets in formula (3.59). Therefore,

$$|A_n| \leq B_n, \qquad n \geq 0.$$

For the $(n + 1)$st term in the sequence $\{B_n\}$, we have

$$B_{n+1} = \frac{M}{n(n + 1)} \left[\sum_{k=0}^{n-1} \frac{(k + 1)|A_{k+1}|}{r^{n-k-1}} + \sum_{k=0}^{n} \frac{n|A_k|}{r^{n-k-1}} \right].$$

If the terms in this expression are grouped properly, it can be shown that

$$B_{n+1} = \frac{n - 1}{n + 1} \frac{1}{r} B_n + \frac{M}{n(n + 1)} (n + r)|A_n|, \qquad n \geq 2,$$

and hence that

$$\frac{B_{n+1}}{B_n} = \frac{n - 1}{n + 1} \frac{1}{r} + M \frac{n + r}{n(n + 1)} \frac{|A_n|}{B_n}, \qquad n \geq 2.$$

Since $|A_n|/B_n \leq 1$, $n \geq 0$, we have

$$\lim_{n \to \infty} \frac{B_{n+1}}{B_n} = \frac{1}{r}.$$

The power series

$$\sum_{n=0}^{\infty} B_n x^n$$

therefore converges absolutely for $|x| < r$. In particular, it converges absolutely for $x = x_1$. Since

$$|A_n x_1^n| \leq |B_n x_1^n|$$

for $n \geq 0$, the series

$$\sum_{n=0}^{\infty} A_n x^n$$

converges for $x = x_1$. But since x_1 was an arbitrary point on the interval $(-R, R)$, the series converges at every point of this interval.

We have shown that the power series whose coefficients satisfy the recurrence relation (3.57) converges on the interval $(-R, R)$ to a function that is analytic at $x = 0$. But we have also shown that a function that is analytic at $x = 0$ is a solution of the initial value problem if and only if its power series coefficients satisfy the relation (3.57). Hence the function defined by the power series is a solution of the initial value problem on the interval $(-R, R)$.

In proving the existence of an analytic solution of the initial-value problem, we derived a recurrence relation that can be used to calculate the coefficients in the power series expansion of the solution. In a specific problem, however, it is probably easier to determine the coefficients by substituting a series directly into the differential equation rather than by using the general formula. Also, for the purpose of calculating the coefficients of a power series solution, it may be more convenient to write the differential equation in the form

$$p(x)y'' + q(x)y' + r(x)y = 0$$

rather than

$$y'' + P(x)y' + Q(x)y = 0.$$

For example, in finding power series solutions of the equation

$$y'' + \frac{2x}{x^2 - 1} y' - \frac{1}{x - 1} y = 0$$

at $x = 0$, it is convenient to multiply through by $x^2 - 1$ and deal with the equation

$$(x^2 - 1)y'' + 2xy' - (x + 1)y = 0,$$

whose coefficients are polynomials. Any power series that satisfies one equation formally also satisfies the other. Any formal power series solution will converge at least for $|x| < 1$.

Exercises for Section 3.8

1. Let the functions P, Q, and F be analytic at zero and be represented by their Maclaurin series on the interval $(-R, R)$. Modify the proof of Theorem 3.5 to show that the problem

    $$y'' + P(x)y' + Q(x)y = F(x), \qquad y(0) = A_0, \qquad y'(0) = A_1$$

    possesses a solution that is analytic at $x = 0$, and is represented by its Maclaurin series on the interval $(-R, R)$.

2. Express the general solution of the given equation in terms of power series about the point $x = 0$. By using the result of Exercise 1, what can you say about the interval of convergence of the power series solutions?

    (a) $y'' - xy' - y = e^x$ \qquad\qquad (b) $y'' - 2xy' - 2y = \dfrac{1}{1 - x}$

3. In Eq. (3.33), which has a regular singular point at zero, assume that P and Q are represented by their Maclaurin series on the interval $(-R, R)$. Let the exponents s_1 and s_2 be real with $s_1 \geq s_2$. Prove that the power series involved in the formal solution

$$y_1(x) = x^{s_1} \sum_{n=0}^{\infty} A_n x^n$$

actually converges for $|x| < R$, and hence that the formal solution is an actual solution. Prove that when $s_1 - s_2$ is not an integer, the formal solution that corresponds to the exponent s_2 is an actual solution. Use the method of proof employed for Theorem 3.5.

4. Assume that the exponents s_1 and s_2 of Eq. (3.33) are such that $s_1 - s_2 = N$, where N is a positive integer, but that a formal solution of the form

$$y_2(x) + x^{s_2} \sum_{n=0}^{\infty} A_n x^n$$

nevertheless exists. Prove that the power series involved in the formal solution actually converges, and hence that the formal solution is an actual solution. *Suggestion*: In modifying the proof of Theorem 3.5, let $B_n = |A_n|$ for $0 \leq n \leq N$, and use the recurrence relation to define B_n when $n > N$.

5. Assume that the exponents for Eq. (3.39) are equal, and that P and Q are represented by their Maclaurin series on the interval $(-R, R)$. It is known (Exercise 2) that the power series

$$\sum_{n=0}^{\infty} A_n(s_1) x^n$$

converges for $|x| < R$. A proof that the series

$$\sum_{n=0}^{\infty} A_n'(s_1) x^n,$$

which appears in the formula (3.45) for a second solution, converges can be carried out in the following manner.

(a) Deduce from the recurrence relation that

$$A_n'(s_1) = \frac{1}{n^3} \sum_{k=0}^{n-1} [(2k + 2s_1 - n)P_{n-k} + Q_{n-k}]A_k(s_1)$$

$$- \frac{1}{n^2} \sum_{k=0}^{n-1} [(k + s_1)P_{n-k} + Q_{n-k}]A_k'(s_1), \qquad n \geq 1.$$

(b) Let r be any positive number such that $0 < r < R$. Show that there exists a positive constant M such that

$$|P_m| \le \frac{M}{r^m}, \qquad |Q_m| \le \frac{M}{r^m}, \qquad |A_m(s_1)| \le \frac{M}{r^m}, \qquad m \ge 0.$$

(c) Show that $|A_n'(s_1)| \le B_n$, $n \ge 1$, where

$$B_n = \frac{M^2}{n^2 r^n}(2n + 2|s_1| + 1) + \frac{M}{n^2} \sum_{k=0}^{n-1} \frac{k + |s_1| + 1}{r^{n-k}} |A_k'(s_1)|$$

and

$$B_{n+1} = \left(\frac{n}{n+1}\right)^2 \frac{1}{r} B_n + \frac{M(n + |s_1| + 1)}{(n+1)^2 r} |A_n'(s_1)| + \frac{2M^2}{(n+1)^2 r^{n+1}}.$$

(d) Show that

$$B_n = \frac{2M^2}{nr^n} + \alpha_n, \qquad n \ge 1,$$

where $\alpha_n \ge 0$, and hence that

$$\frac{B_{n+1}}{B_n} = \frac{1}{r}\left(\frac{n}{n+1}\right)^2 + \frac{M(n + |s_1| + 1)}{(n+1)^2 r} \frac{|A_n'(s_1)|}{B_n} + \beta_n,$$

where

$$|\beta_n| \le \frac{n}{(n+1)^2} \frac{1}{r}.$$

(e) Show that

$$\lim_{n \to \infty} \frac{B_{n+1}}{B_n} = \frac{1}{r}.$$

Deduce from this fact that the series converges for $|x| < R$.

(f) Verify that y_2 is a solution of the differential equation.

6. Assume that the exponents of Eq. (3.48) differ by a positive integer and that there is a formal solution y_2 of the form (3.53). This exercise deals with the convergence of the series in Eq. (3.53).

(a) Deduce from the recurrence relation that

$$B_n'(s_2) = \frac{-1}{n(n - N)} \sum_{k=0}^{n-1} [(k + s_2)P_{n-k} + Q_{n-k}]B_k'(s_2)$$

$$+ \frac{2n + N}{n^2(n - N)^2} \sum_{k=0}^{n-1} [(k + s_2)P_{n-k} + Q_{n-k}]B_k(s_2)$$

$$- \frac{1}{n(n - N)} \sum_{k=0}^{n-1} P_{n-k} B_k(s_2), \qquad n > N.$$

(b)   Let r be any number such that $0 < r < R$. Show that there exists a positive constant M such that

$$|P_m| \le \frac{M}{r^m}, \qquad |Q_m| \le \frac{M}{r^m}, \qquad |B_k(s_2)| \le \frac{M}{r^m}, \qquad m \ge 0.$$

(c)   Let $C_n = |B'_n(s_2)|$, $0 \le n \le N$, and let

$$C_n = \frac{M}{n(n-N)} \sum_{k=0}^{n-1} \frac{k + |s_2| + 1}{r^{n-k}} |B'_k(s_2)|$$

$$+ \frac{2n^2 + (2+N)n + N(2|s_2| + 1)}{2n(n-N)r^n} M^2, \qquad n > N.$$

Show that $|B'_n(s_2)| \le C_n$, $n \ge 0$.

(d)   Show that

$$\lim_{n \to \infty} \frac{C_{n+1}}{C_n} = \frac{1}{r}.$$

Deduce from this fact that the series in question converges for $|x| < R$

(e)   Verify that y_2 is a solution of the differential equation.

REFERENCES

1.   Coddington, E. A., *An Introduction to Ordinary Differential Equations*. Prentice-Hall, Englewood Cliffs, New Jersey, 1961.
2.   Kaplan, W., *Ordinary Differential Equations*. Addison-Wesley, Reading, Massachusetts, 1958.
3.   Rainville, E. D., *Intermediate Differential Equations*, 2nd ed. Macmillan, New York, 1964.
4.   Taylor, A. E., *Advanced Calculus*. Blaisdell, New York, 1955.

IV

Bessel Functions

4.1 THE GAMMA FUNCTION

In our study of Bessel functions, the main object of our interest in this chapter, we shall need to know certain properties of the function defined by the relation

$$\Gamma(x) = \int_0^\infty t^{x-1} e^{-t} \, dt, \qquad x > 0. \tag{4.1}$$

This function is called the *gamma function*. It should be noted that the variable t in the integrand of (4.1) is a "dummy" variable of integration, and that the value of the integral depends only on the value of the variable x. The integral is improper, first of all because the interval of integration is infinite. However, the factor e^{-t} tends to zero sufficiently rapidly as t becomes infinite, so that convergence at the upper limit is ensured no matter what value x may have. At the lower limit, $t = 0$, the factor e^{-t} tends to 1, and the factor t^{x-1} becomes infinite whenever $x < 1$. In order to obtain convergence of the integral at the lower limit, it is necessary to restrict x to the interval $x > 0$.

We shall now establish two important properties of the gamma function. These properties are

$$\Gamma(1) = 1 \tag{4.2}$$

and

$$\Gamma(x + 1) = x\Gamma(x), \qquad x > 0. \tag{4.3}$$

To prove property (4.2), we simply set $x = 1$ in formula (4.1) and integrate. Thus we have

$$\Gamma(1) = \int_0^\infty e^{-t}\, dt = 1 .$$

To establish property (4.3), we replace x by $x + 1$ in formula (4.1) and integrate by parts. We have

$$\Gamma(x + 1) = \lim_{T \to \infty} \int_0^T t^x e^{-t}\, dt$$

$$= \lim_{T \to \infty} \left\{ [-t^x e^{-t}]_0^T + x \int_0^T t^{x-1}\, dt \right\}$$

$$= x\Gamma(x) .$$

Combining properties (4.2) and (4.3), we see that

$$\Gamma(2) = 1 \cdot \Gamma(1) = 1 ,$$
$$\Gamma(3) = 2 \cdot \Gamma(2) = 1 \cdot 2 ,$$
$$\Gamma(4) = 3 \cdot \Gamma(3) = 1 \cdot 2 \cdot 3 .$$

It can be verified by mathematical induction that

$$\Gamma(n + 1) = n!$$

where n is a nonnegative integer.

The derivation of another useful fact, namely, that

$$\Gamma(\tfrac{1}{2}) = \sqrt{\pi} ,$$

is left as an exercise.

Formula (4.1) defines the gamma function only when $x > 0$. We shall define the gamma function for negative values of x in the following way. First, let us write formula (4.3) in the form

$$\Gamma(x) = \frac{\Gamma(x + 1)}{x} .$$

We have proven that this formula holds when $x > 0$. However, since $\Gamma(x + 1)$ is defined when $x > -1$, we may use this formula to define $\Gamma(x)$ for x in the interval $-1 < x < 0$. Also, since

$$\Gamma(x + 1) = \frac{\Gamma(x + 2)}{x + 1}$$

when $x > -1$, we may write

$$\Gamma(x) = \frac{\Gamma(x + 2)}{x(x + 1)}$$

for $x > 0$. But since $\Gamma(x + 2)$ is defined for $x > -2$, we may use this formula to define $\Gamma(x)$ for $-2 < x < 0$, $x \neq -1$. Continuing this process, we have

$$\Gamma(x) = \frac{\Gamma(x + k)}{x(x + 1)(x + 2) \cdots (x + k - 1)}$$

for any positive integer k and for $x > 0$. We use this formula to define (Γx) for $-k < x < 0$, $x \neq -1, -2, \ldots, -k + 1$. By defining $\Gamma(x)$ in this way for negative x, we insure that formula (4.3) holds for all values of x other than $x = 0, -1, -2, \ldots$. Evidently $\Gamma(x)$ becomes infinite when x tends to zero or to a negative integral value. The graph of $\Gamma(x)$ is shown in Fig. 4.1.

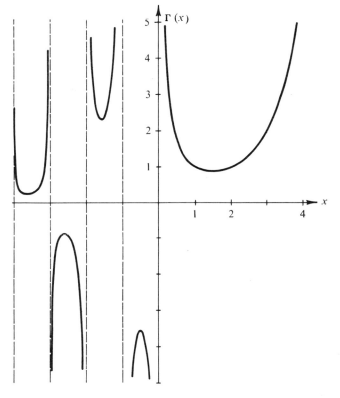

Figure 4.1

The quantity $1/\Gamma(x)$ is defined except at the points $x = -N$, $N = 0, 1, 2, \ldots$. However, as $x \to -N$,

$$\lim_{x \to -N} \frac{1}{\Gamma(x)} = 0.$$

Therefore the function

$$f(x) = \begin{cases} \dfrac{1}{\Gamma(x)}, & x \neq -N, \\ 0, & x = -N, \end{cases}$$

is defined and continuous for all x. We shall therefore adopt the convention that

$$\frac{1}{\Gamma(-N)} = 0.$$

From the definition (4.1) we find, by differentiation under the integral sign, that

$$\Gamma'(x) = \int_0^\infty t^{x-1} e^{-t} \ln t \, dt$$

for $x > 0$.

Associated with the gamma function is the function ψ, where

$$\psi(x) = \frac{\Gamma'(x+1)}{\Gamma(x+1)} = \frac{d}{dx} \ln \Gamma(x+1). \tag{4.4}$$

Since

$$\Gamma(x+1) = x\Gamma(x)$$

and

$$\Gamma'(x+1) = x\Gamma'(x) + \Gamma(x)$$

we have

$$\psi(x) = \frac{\Gamma'(x)}{\Gamma(x)} + \frac{1}{x}$$

or

$$\psi(x) = \psi(x-1) + \frac{1}{x}, \qquad x > 0. \tag{4.5}$$

If n is a positive integer, we have

$$\psi(n) = \psi(n-1) + \frac{1}{n}$$

$$= \psi(n-2) + \frac{1}{n-1} + \frac{1}{n}$$

$$= \psi(n-3) + \frac{1}{n-2} + \frac{1}{n-1} + \frac{1}{n}.$$

By repeated application of formula (4.5), we find that

$$\psi(n) = \psi(0) + 1 + \frac{1}{2} + \frac{1}{3} + \cdots + \frac{1}{n-1} + \frac{1}{n}.$$

The quantity

$$\psi(0) = \frac{\Gamma'(1)}{\Gamma(1)} = \Gamma'(1) = \int_0^\infty e^{-t} \ln t \, dt$$

is a negative constant, which we denote by $-\gamma$. The positive constant $\gamma = 0.57721 \cdots$ is known as Euler's constant. It can be shown that

$$\gamma = \lim_{n \to \infty} \left(1 + \frac{1}{2} + \frac{1}{3} + \cdots \frac{1}{n} - \ln n \right).$$

If we introduce the notation

$$\phi(n) = 1 + \frac{1}{2} + \frac{1}{3} + \cdots + \frac{1}{n}, \tag{4.6}$$

then

$$\psi(n) = \frac{\Gamma'(n+1)}{\Gamma(n+1)} = -\gamma + \phi(n).$$

Exercises for Section 4.1

1. Given that $\Gamma(\tfrac{1}{2}) = \sqrt{\pi}$, find

    (a) $\Gamma(\tfrac{3}{2})$ (b) $\Gamma(\tfrac{5}{2})$ (c) $\Gamma(-\tfrac{1}{2})$ (d) $\Gamma(-\tfrac{3}{2})$

2. If α is not zero or a negative integer, verify that

    $$\frac{\Gamma(\alpha + n)}{\Gamma(\alpha)} = \alpha(\alpha + 1)(\alpha + 2) \cdots (\alpha + n - 1),$$

    where n is a positive integer.

3. Show that the graph of the gamma function is concave up on the interval $(0, \infty)$.

4. From the definition (4.1), we have

    $$\Gamma(\tfrac{1}{2}) = \int_0^\infty t^{-1/2} e^{-t} \, dt.$$

    Show that the change of variable $t = u^2$ leads to the representation

    $$\Gamma(\tfrac{1}{2}) = 2 \int_0^\infty e^{-u^2} \, du.$$

5. Using the result of Exercise 4, we have

$$[\Gamma(\tfrac{1}{2})]^2 = 4\left(\int_0^\infty e^{-u^2}\, du\right)\left(\int_0^\infty e^{-v^2}\, dv\right) = 4\int_0^\infty \int_0^\infty e^{-(u^2+v^2)}\, du\, dv,$$

where the last expression on the right may be interpreted as a double integral. Changing to polar coordinates r and θ, where

$$u = r\cos\theta, \qquad v = r\sin\theta,$$

show that

$$[\Gamma(\tfrac{1}{2})]^2 = 4\int_0^{\pi/2}\int_0^\infty e^{-r^2} r\, dr\, d\theta = \pi$$

and hence that

$$\Gamma(\tfrac{1}{2}) = \sqrt{\pi}.$$

6. Show that

$$\Gamma(x) = 2\int_0^\infty e^{-u^2} u^{2x-1}\, du, \qquad x > 0.$$

7. Show that

$$\int_0^\infty e^{-s^3}\, ds = \tfrac{1}{3}\Gamma(\tfrac{1}{3}).$$

8. Find $\lim\limits_{x\to 0} x\Gamma(x)$.

9. Show that

$$\psi(x+n) = \psi(x) + \frac{1}{x+1} + \frac{1}{x+2} + \cdots + \frac{1}{x+n}$$

for every positive integer n.

10. The *beta function* $B(x, y)$ may be defined as

$$B(x, y) = \int_0^1 t^{x-1}(1-t)^{y-1}\, dt, \qquad x > 0, y > 0.$$

Show that

$$B(x, y) = \frac{\Gamma(x)\Gamma(y)}{\Gamma(x+y)}, \qquad x > 0, y > 0.$$

Suggestion: Start with the expression

$$\Gamma(x)\Gamma(y) = \left(2\int_0^\infty e^{-u^2} u^{2x-1}\, du\right)\left(2\int_0^\infty e^{-v^2} v^{2y-1}\, dv\right).$$

Write the product of the two integrals as a double integral, and then change to polar coordinates. Then write the resulting double integral as the product of two single integrals.

4.2 BESSEL'S EQUATION

The differential equation

$$x^2 y'' + xy' + (x^2 - \alpha^2)y = 0, \qquad (4.7)$$

where α is a constant, is known as *Bessel's equation* of order α. We shall assume that α is real. Then, without loss of generality, we can also assume that $\alpha \geq 0$, since only the quantity α^2 appears in the equation. The nontrivial solutions of this equation are called *Bessel functions* of order α.

Bessel's equation arises in the process of solving certain partial differential equations of mathematical physics. Because of the importance of these applications, we shall study the solutions of Eq. (4.7) in some detail. The applications themselves are postponed until Chapter X.

Bessel's equation has a regular singular point at zero and series solutions can be found by the methods of Chapter III. Some computation shows that a function of the form

$$y(x) = x^s \sum_{n=0}^{\infty} A_n x^n$$

is a solution if and only if

$$[s(s-1) + s - \alpha^2]A_0 x^s + [(s+1)s + s + 1 - \alpha^2]A_1 x^{s-1}$$

$$+ \sum_{n=2}^{\infty} \{[(n+s)(n+s-1) + (n+s) - \alpha^2]A_n + A_{n-2}\}x^{n+s} = 0.$$

Thus s must be a root of the equation

$$s^2 - \alpha^2 = 0 \qquad (4.8)$$

and the coefficients A_i must satisfy the relations

$$[(s+1)^2 - \alpha^2]A_1 = 0, \qquad (4.9)$$

$$[(n+s)^2 - \alpha^2]A_n = -A_{n-2}, \qquad n \geq 2. \qquad (4.10)$$

The exponents of Bessel's equation at $x = 0$, as determined from Eq. (4.8), are $s_1 = \alpha$ and $s_2 = -\alpha$.

If $s = \alpha$, the relations (4.9) and (4.10) require that $A_1 = 0$ and

$$n(n + 2\alpha)A_n = -A_{n-2}, \qquad n \geq 2.$$

Thus we have $A_1 = A_3 = A_5 = \cdots = 0$ and

$$A_2 = -\frac{1}{2(2 + 2\alpha)}\, A_0,$$

$$A_4 = -\frac{1}{4(4 + 2\alpha)}\, A_2 = \frac{1}{2 \cdot 4(2 + 2\alpha)(4 + 2\alpha)}\, A_0,$$

$$\vdots$$

$$A_{2m} = \frac{(-1)^m}{2 \cdot 4 \cdots (2m)(2 + 2\alpha)(4 + 2\alpha) \cdots (2m + 2\alpha)}\, A_0$$

$$= \frac{(-1)^m}{2^{2m} m! (1 + \alpha)(2 + \alpha) \cdots (m + \alpha)}\, A_0.$$

A solution is

$$y_1(x) = A_0\, x^\alpha \left[1 + \sum_{m=1}^{\infty} \frac{(-1)^m (x/2)^{2m}}{m!(1 + \alpha)(2 + \alpha) \cdots (m + \alpha)} \right],$$

where the power series converges for all x. Choosing

$$A_0 = \frac{1}{2^\alpha \Gamma(1 + \alpha)},$$

we obtain a specific solution, known as the *Bessel function of the first kind* of order α. We denote it by J_α. Thus

$$J_\alpha(x) = \sum_{m=0}^{\infty} \frac{(-1)^m (x/2)^{2m+\alpha}}{m!\,\Gamma(m + \alpha + 1)}. \qquad (4.11)$$

From this formula we see that $J_0(0) = 1$ and $J_\alpha(0) = 0$ for $\alpha > 0$. Graphs of J_0 and J_1 are shown in Fig. 4.2. It can be shown that every nontrivial solution of Bessel's equation has infinitely many zeros on the interval $(0, \infty)$.

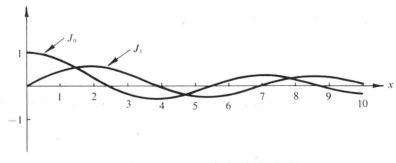

Figure 4.2

If $s = s_2 = -\alpha$, the recurrence relations (4.9) and (4.10) become

$$[(1 - \alpha)^2 - \alpha^2]A_1 = 0$$
$$[(n - \alpha)^2 - \alpha^2]A_n = -A_{n-2}, \qquad n \geq 2.$$

When $s_1 - s_2 = 2\alpha$ is not an integer, we can proceed as before to obtain a second solution. The formula for the coefficients is the same as that for the coefficients of J_α, except that α must be replaced by $-\alpha$. We therefore denote this solution by $J_{-\alpha}$. Its power series expansion is

$$J_{-\alpha}(x) = \sum_{m=0}^{\infty} \frac{(-1)^m(x/2)^{2m-\alpha}}{m!\,\Gamma(m - \alpha + 1)}. \qquad (4.12)$$

Now suppose that $s_1 - s_2 = 2\alpha$ is an integer, that is, that $2\alpha = N$ or $\alpha = N/2$. The crucial step is reached in the recurrence relation when we attempt to find A_N. We have

$$0 \cdot A_N = -A_{N-2}.$$

If N is odd, so that α is half an odd integer, we have $A_1 = A_3 = \cdots = A_{N-2} = 0$, so we may choose $A_N = 0$ also. In this case we again obtain a solution of the form (4.12). However, when N is even, so that α is an integer, any second independent solution is logarithmic. We shall nevertheless define

$$J_{-N}(x) = \sum_{m=0}^{\infty} \frac{(-1)^m(x/2)^{2m-N}}{m!\,\Gamma(m - N + 1)},$$

where N is a positive integer. But since $1/\Gamma(m - N + 1) = 0$ when $m = 0, 1, 2, \ldots, N - 1$, we have

$$J_{-N}(x) = \sum_{m=N}^{\infty} \frac{(-1)^m(x/2)^{2m-N}}{m!\,(m - N + 1)}.$$

By making the change $m = k + N$ in the index of summation, we find (Exercise 5) that

$$J_{-N}(x) = (-1)^N \sum_{k=0}^{\infty} \frac{(-1)^k(x/2)^{2k+N}}{k!\,(k + N + 1)}$$

or

$$J_{-N}(x) = (-1)^N J_N(x).$$

Thus when $\alpha = N$, J_{-N} is a solution of Bessel's equation; but J_N and J_{-N} are not linearly independent.

When $\alpha = N$, a second solution of Bessel's equation will have the form

$$y_2(x) = (A \ln x + B)J_N(x) + x^{-N} \sum_{n=0}^{\infty} c_n x^n, \qquad (4.13)$$

where A and B are constants and $A \neq 0$. We shall discuss a particular second solution in the next section.

Exercises for Section 4.2

1. Show that
    (a) $J_0(0) = 1$ and $J_\alpha(0) = 0$, when $\alpha > 0$.
    (b) $J_1'(0) = \frac{1}{2}$ and $J_\alpha'(0) = 0$, when $\alpha > 1$.

2. When n is a nonnegative integer, show that
    $$\frac{d^n}{dx^n} J_n(x)\Big|_{x=0} = 2^{-n}.$$

3. Use the power series definition of J_α to calculate the following quantities to three decimal places.
    (a) $J_0(0.2)$ (b) $J_1(0.6)$ (c) $J_{-1}(0.4)$

4. Write down the general solution of the given differential equation, for the interval $(0, \infty)$, in terms of Bessel functions.
    (a) $x^2 y'' + xy' + (x^2 - \frac{1}{9})y = 0$
    (b) $4x^2 y'' + 4xy' + (4x^2 - 9)y = 0$

5. Carry out the details of the verification that $J_{-N} = (-1)^N J_N$.

6. Show that $J_0' = -J_1$ in two ways: (a) by using the power series definitions of the functions, (b) by differentiating through in the differential equation for J_0.

7. Explain why the only solutions of Bessel's equation on the interval $(0, \infty)$ that are finite as x approaches zero are those that are constant multiples of J_α.

8. (a) Verify that
    $$J_0(x) = \frac{2}{\pi} \int_0^{\pi/2} \cos(x \sin t)\, dt.$$

    Suggestion: Show that the function represented by the integral satisfies Bessel's equation of order zero, and that it has the value 1 at $x = 0$.

    (b) Deduce from the formula of part (a) that $|J_0(x)| \leq 1$ for $x \geq 0$.

9. (a) Show that the change of variable $y = x^{-1/2} u$ in Bessel's equation leads to the equation
    $$u'' + f(x) = 0, \qquad f(x) = 1 + \frac{1 - 4\alpha^2}{4x^2}.$$

    (b) Use the result of part (a) to show that
    $$J_{1/2}(x) = \sqrt{\frac{2}{\pi x}} \sin x, \qquad J_{-1/2}(x) = \sqrt{\frac{2}{\pi x}} \cos x.$$

4.3 BESSEL FUNCTIONS OF THE SECOND AND THIRD KINDS

When α is not an integer, the functions J_α and $J_{-\alpha}$ are linearly independent solutions of Bessel's equation on the interval $(0, \infty)$. Every solution is therefore of the form

$$y(x) = c_1 J_\alpha(x) + c_2 J_{-\alpha}(x),$$

where c_1 and c_2 are constants. For nonintegral α, the function

$$Y_\alpha(x) = \frac{(\cos \pi\alpha) J_\alpha(x) - J_{-\alpha}(x)}{\sin \pi\alpha} \tag{4.14}$$

is also a solution of Bessel's equation, since it is a linear combination of J_α and $J_{-\alpha}$. The functions J_α and Y_α are linearly independent (Exercise 2), so the general solution of Bessel's equation can also be described by the formula

$$y(x) = c_1 J_\alpha(x) + c_2 Y_\alpha(x).$$

The function (4.14) is not defined when α is an integer N, since in this case it has the indeterminate form $0/0$. However, the limit as $\alpha \to N$ does exist, and we define

$$Y_N(x) = \lim_{\alpha \to N} Y_\alpha(x).$$

Applying L'Hospital's rule, we find that

$$Y_N(x) = \frac{1}{\pi} \left[\frac{\partial}{\partial \alpha} J_\alpha(x) - (-1) \frac{\partial}{\partial \alpha} J_{-\alpha}(x) \right]_{\alpha = N}. \tag{4.15}$$

This limiting process leads to a second solution of Bessel's equation of the form (4.13). We shall carry out the derivation for the case $N = 0$ only.

From the definitions (4.11) and (4.12) we find that†

$$\frac{\partial}{\partial \alpha} J_\alpha(x) = \sum_{m=0}^{\infty} \frac{(-1)^m (x/2)^{2m+\alpha}}{m! \, \Gamma(m + \alpha + 1)} \left[\ln \frac{x}{2} - \psi(m + \alpha) \right],$$

$$\frac{\partial}{\partial \alpha} J_{-\alpha}(x) = \sum_{m=0}^{\infty} \frac{(-1)^m (x/2)^{2m-\alpha}}{m! \, \Gamma(m - \alpha + 1)} \left[-\ln \frac{x}{2} + \psi(m - \alpha) \right],$$

where the function ψ is defined by formula (4.4). Setting $\alpha = 0$ and substituting into formula (4.15), we have

$$Y_0(x) = \frac{2}{\pi} \left[J_0(x) \ln \frac{x}{2} - \sum_{m=0}^{\infty} \frac{(-1)^m \psi(m)(x/2)^{2m}}{(m!)^2} \right].$$

† The termwise differentiation of the series with respect to α can be justified by theorems from advanced calculus.

Since $\psi(m) = -\gamma + \phi(m)$, we have

$$Y_0(x) = \frac{2}{\pi}\left[J_0(x)\left(\gamma + \ln \frac{x}{2}\right) - \sum_{m=0}^{\infty} \frac{(-1)^m \phi(m)(x/2)^{2m}}{(m!)^2} \right]. \qquad (4.16)$$

The derivation in the general case is more difficult. We shall content ourselves with a statement of the final result, which is

$$Y_N(x) = \frac{2}{\pi}\left[J_N(x)\left(\gamma + \ln \frac{x}{2}\right) - \frac{1}{2}\sum_{m=0}^{N-1} \frac{(N-m-1)!(x/2)^{2m-N}}{m!} \right.$$
$$\left. - \frac{1}{2}\sum_{m=0}^{\infty} \frac{(-1)^m[\phi(m) + \phi(m+N)](x/2)^{2m+N}}{m!(m+N)!} \right]. \qquad (4.17)$$

It should be noted that $Y_N(x)$ becomes infinite as $x \to 0$. When $\alpha = N$, the general solution of Bessel's equation is

$$y(x) = c_1 J_N(x) + c_2 Y_N(x).$$

The function Y_α is known as *Weber's Bessel function of the second kind*. There are, of course, infinitely many ways of defining a second solution of Bessel's equation when $\alpha = N$. Our choice amounts to choosing $A = 2/\pi$ and $B = (2/\pi)(\gamma - \ln 2)$ in formula (4.13). This choice is often convenient because of the fact that $J_\alpha(x)$ and $Y_\alpha(x)$ exhibit a certain similarity of behavior as x becomes infinite.

The *Bessel functions of the third kind* are the complex solutions of Bessel's equation that are defined by the relations

$$H_\alpha^{(1)}(x) = J_\alpha(x) + iY_\alpha(x),$$
$$H_\alpha^{(2)}(x) = J_\alpha(x) - iY_\alpha(x).$$

These functions are also known as the *Hankel functions of the first and second kinds*. They are sometimes convenient choices for solutions because of the behaviors they exhibit for large x.

Because of their importance in applications, the Bessel functions have been tabulated for various values of x and α. Tables of Bessel functions can be found in References [1] and [2]. For many practical purposes, a differential equation or other problem can be regarded as solved when its solutions can be expressed in terms of Bessel functions. The same is true, of course, when the solutions can be expressed in terms of any tabulated function, including the elementary trigonometric and exponential functions.

Exercises for Section 4.3

1. Evaluate the limits:

    (a) $\lim_{x \to 0} [x^{-\alpha} J_\alpha(x)]$ (b) $\lim_{x \to 0} [x^\alpha Y_\alpha(x)]$

2. Show that J_α and Y_α are linearly independent when α is not an integer.

3. Express the general solution of the given differential equation in terms of Bessel functions.

    (a) $x^2 y'' + xy' + (x^2 - 1)y = 0$ (b) $xy'' + y' + xy = 0$

4. Carry out the details in the derivations of the series for $\partial J_\alpha(x)/\partial \alpha$ and $\partial J_{-\alpha}(x)/\partial \alpha$.

5. Show that $Y_0' = -Y_1$ in two ways: (a) by using the series representations of the functions, and (b) by differentiating through in the differential equation for Y_0. Make use of the fact that $J_0' = -J_1$ (Exercise 6, Section 4.2).

6. (a) If y_1 and y_2 are any two solutions of Bessel's equation, show that the Wronskian of y_1 and y_2 satisfies the equation $xW'(x) + W(x) = 0$, and hence $W(x) = cx^{-1}$, where c is a constant. (See in connection with this problem, Exercise 8, Section 2.3.)

    (b) Show that $W(x; J_\alpha, J_{-\alpha}) = -\dfrac{2}{x\Gamma(\alpha)\Gamma(1 - \alpha)}.$

    (c) Show that $W(x; J_\alpha, Y_\alpha) = \dfrac{2}{\pi x}.$

7. Use the method of Section 3.5 to derive a solution of Bessel's equation of order zero of the form

$$J_0(x) \ln x + \sum_{m=1}^{\infty} B_m x^m.$$

Then show that the function Y_0, as defined by Eq. (4.16), is a linear combination of this solution and J_0.

4.4   PROPERTIES OF BESSEL FUNCTIONS

The Bessel functions of the first kind satisfy a number of recurrence relations. One of them is

$$\frac{d}{dx} [x^\alpha J_\alpha(x)] = x^\alpha J_{\alpha-1}(x). \tag{4.18}$$

Although this relation is not so easy to *discover* from the definition (4.11), it is easily verified. We have

$$\frac{d}{dx}[x^\alpha J_\alpha(x)] = \frac{d}{dx}\sum_{m=0}^\infty \frac{(-1)^m x^{2m+2\alpha}}{2^{2m+\alpha}m!\,\Gamma(m+\alpha+1)}$$

$$= \sum_{m=0}^\infty \frac{(-1)^m x^{2m+2\alpha-1}}{2^{2m+\alpha-1}m!\,\Gamma(m+\alpha)}$$

$$= x^\alpha \sum_{m=0}^\infty \frac{(-1)^m (x/2)^{2m+\alpha-1}}{m!\,\Gamma(m+\alpha)}$$

$$= x^\alpha J_{\alpha-1}(x).$$

In similar fashion it can be shown that

$$\frac{d}{dx}[x^{-\alpha} J_\alpha(x)] = -x^{-\alpha} J_{\alpha+1}(x). \tag{4.19}$$

The relations (4.18) and (4.19) are equivalent to the relations

$$J_\alpha'(x) = J_{\alpha-1}(x) - \frac{\alpha}{x} J_\alpha(x), \tag{4.20}$$

$$J_\alpha'(x) = -J_{\alpha+1}(x) + \frac{\alpha}{x} J_\alpha(x), \tag{4.21}$$

respectively. Adding, we obtain the formula

$$J_\alpha'(x) = \tfrac{1}{2}[J_{\alpha-1}(x) - J_{\alpha+1}(x)]. \tag{4.22}$$

Subtraction yields the relation

$$J_{\alpha+1}(x) = \frac{2\alpha}{x} J_\alpha(x) - J_{\alpha-1}(x). \tag{4.23}$$

Because of this last relation, it is necessary to tabulate the functions J_α only for $0 \le \alpha < 2$. In particular, every function J_n, with n an integer, can be expressed in terms of J_0 and J_1. Extensive tables of these two functions have been compiled. See, for example, References [1] and [2].

The Bessel functions of the second and third kinds satisfy the same recurrence relations as the functions of the first kind. That is, each of the formulas (4.18)–(4.23) remains valid if the symbol J is replaced by any one of the symbols Y, $H^{(1)}$, or $H^{(2)}$ throughout. We shall first establish that

$$\frac{d}{dx}[x^\alpha Y_\alpha(x)] = x^\alpha Y_{\alpha-1}(x). \tag{4.24}$$

By definition,

$$Y_\alpha(x) = \frac{(\cos \pi\alpha)J_\alpha(x) - J_{-\alpha}(x)}{\sin \pi\alpha}, \qquad \alpha \neq N.$$

From formulas (4.18) and (4.19) (with α replaced by $-\alpha$ in the latter) we have

$$\frac{d}{dx}[x^\alpha J_\alpha(x)] = x^\alpha J_{\alpha-1}(x)$$

and

$$\frac{d}{dx}[x^\alpha J_{-\alpha}(x)] = -x^\alpha J_{-\alpha+1}(x),$$

respectively. Then

$$[x^\alpha Y_\alpha(x)]' = \frac{(\cos \pi\alpha)[x^\alpha J_\alpha(x)]' - [x^\alpha J_{-\alpha}(x)]'}{\sin \pi\alpha}$$

$$= \frac{(\cos \pi\alpha)x^\alpha J_{\alpha-1}(x) + x^\alpha J_{-\alpha+1}(x)}{\sin \pi\alpha}$$

$$= x^\alpha \frac{\cos \pi(\alpha-1)J_{\alpha-1}(x) - J_{-\alpha+1}(x)}{\sin \pi(\alpha-1)}$$

$$= x^\alpha Y_{\alpha-1}(x).$$

Formula (4.24) is therefore valid for nonintegral α. It is also valid in the limit as $\alpha \to N$.

The formula

$$\frac{d}{dx}[x^{-\alpha}Y_\alpha(x)] = -x^{-\alpha}Y_{\alpha+1}(x), \qquad (4.25)$$

which corresponds to formula (4.19), can be verified in the same way. The recurrence relations for the Hankel functions follow from the fact that the real and imaginary parts of these functions satisfy the same identities.

The behaviors of Bessel functions for large values of their arguments have been investigated. The methods used are beyond the level of this book, and we content ourselves with the statement of a few basic facts. By the notation

$$f(x) \sim g(x), \qquad x \to x_0,$$

we mean that there exists a function h such that

$$f(x) = g(x)[1 + h(x)]$$

when x is sufficiently close to x_0 and such that $h(x) \to 0$ as $x \to x_0$. It can be shown that

$$H_\alpha^{(1)}(x) \sim \sqrt{\frac{2}{\pi x}} \exp\left[i\left(x - \frac{\pi}{4} - \frac{\pi\alpha}{2}\right)\right],$$

$$H_\alpha^{(2)}(x) \sim \sqrt{\frac{2}{\pi x}} \exp\left[-i\left(x - \frac{\pi}{4} - \frac{\pi\alpha}{2}\right)\right],$$

as $x \to \infty$. From these relations it can be established that

$$J_\alpha(x) = \sqrt{\frac{2}{\pi x}} \left[\cos\left(x - \frac{\pi}{4} - \frac{\pi\alpha}{2}\right) + F(x)\right],$$

$$Y_\alpha(x) = \sqrt{\frac{2}{\pi x}} \left[\sin\left(x - \frac{\pi}{4} - \frac{\pi\alpha}{2}\right) + G(x)\right],$$

where

$$\lim_{x \to \infty} F(x) = \lim_{x \to \infty} G(x) = 0.$$

One reason for adopting Y_α as a specific second solution of Bessel's equation is because of its asymptotic behavior described here.

Exercises for Section 4.4

1. Verify the identity

    $$\frac{d}{dx}[x^{-\alpha}J_\alpha(x)] = -x^{-\alpha}J_{\alpha+1}(x).$$

2. Show that

    $$\frac{d}{dx}[x^{-\alpha}Y_\alpha(x)] = -x^{-\alpha}Y_{\alpha+1}(x).$$

3. Express $Y_3(x)$ in terms of $Y_0(x)$ and $Y_1(x)$.

4. Express $J_2'(x)$ in terms of $J_0(x)$ and $J_1(x)$.

5. Show that

    $$J_\alpha'(x) = 2J_{\alpha-1}(x) - \frac{2\alpha}{x}J_\alpha(x).$$

6. If λ is a constant, show that

    $$\frac{d}{dx}J_\alpha(\lambda x) = \lambda J_{\alpha-1}(\lambda x) - \frac{\alpha}{x}J_\alpha(\lambda x)$$

    $$= -\lambda J_{\alpha+1}(\lambda x) + \frac{\alpha}{x}J_\alpha(\lambda x).$$

7. Verify the following formulas.

(a) $\int x^{\alpha+1} J_\alpha(x)\, dx = x^{\alpha+1} J_{\alpha+1}(x) + C$

(b) $\int x^{1-\alpha} J_\alpha(x)\, dx = -x^{1-\alpha} J_{\alpha-1}(x) + C$

8. Show that

$$\int x^3 J_0(x)\, dx = x^3 J_1(x) - 2x^2 J_2(x) + C.$$

Suggestion: Use the result of Exercise 7, and integration by parts.

9. Show that

$$\int x Y_2(x)\, dx = -x Y_1(x) - 2Y_0(x) + C.$$

10. Let $\tilde{y}$ be any solution of Bessel's equation on $(0, \infty)$ and let

$$\tilde{u}(x) = x^{1/2} \tilde{y}(x).$$

(a)   Show that $\tilde{u}$ is a solution of the nonhomogeneous equation

$$u'' + u = \frac{4\alpha^2 - 1}{x^2}\, \tilde{u}(x).$$

(b)   Use the method of variation of parameters to show that

$$\tilde{u}(x) = c \sin (x - k) + (4\alpha^2 - 1) \int_{x_0}^{x} \frac{\sin(x - t)}{t^2}\, \tilde{u}(t)\, dt,$$

where c and k are constants and $x_0 > 0$.

(c)   Use the inequality of Exercise 3, Section 2.13, to show that $|\tilde{u}(x)| \le M$, M a constant, for $x \ge x_0$. Thus $|\tilde{y}(x)| \le Mx^{-1/2}$ for $x \ge x_0$. In particular, $\tilde{y}(x) \to 0$ as $x \to \infty$.

4.5   MODIFIED BESSEL FUNCTIONS

The differential equation

$$x^2 y'' + xy' - (x^2 + \alpha^2)y = 0 \qquad\qquad (4.26)$$

is known as the *modified Bessel's equation* of order α. The resemblance to Bessel's equation is apparent.

Series solutions of Eq. (4.26) can be found and their properties established in much the same way as for Bessel's equation. The exponents at the regular singular point $x = 0$ are found to be $s_1 = \alpha$ and $s_2 = -\alpha$. A particular solution corresponding to s_1 is

$$I_\alpha(x) = \sum_{m=0}^{\infty} \frac{(x/2)^{2m+\alpha}}{m!\,\Gamma(m+\alpha+1)}. \tag{4.27}$$

The terms in this series are the same as those in the series for $J_\alpha(x)$ except for sign. The function I_α is called the *modified Bessel function of the first kind* of order α.

   A solution corresponding to the exponent s_2 is

$$I_{-\alpha}(x) = \sum_{m=0}^{\infty} \frac{(x/2)^{2m-\alpha}}{m!\,\Gamma(m-\alpha+1)}. \tag{4.28}$$

However, when α is an integer the functions I_α and $I_{-\alpha}$ are linearly dependent. For nonintegral α the function

$$K_\alpha(x) = \frac{\pi}{2}\frac{I_{-\alpha}(x) - I_\alpha(x)}{\sin \pi\alpha}$$

is also a solution. We obtain a second solution when α is an integer N by passing to the limit:

$$K_N(x) = \lim_{\alpha \to N} K_\alpha(x).$$

This solution must be of the form

$$K_N(x) = (A \ln x + B)I_N(x) + x^{-N}\sum_{m=0}^{\infty} c_m x^m$$

with $A \neq 0$, according to the theory of Chapter III. It becomes infinite as x approaches zero. The function K_α is known as the *modified Bessel function of the second kind* of order α. It can be shown that $I_\alpha(x)$ and $K_\alpha(x)$ exhibit the behaviors

$$I_\alpha(x) \sim \frac{e^x}{\sqrt{2\pi x}}, \qquad K_\alpha(x) \sim \sqrt{\frac{\pi}{2x}}\,e^{-x}$$

as x becomes positively infinite. When α is not an integer, the general solution of Eq. (4.26) is

$$y = c_1 I_\alpha(x) + c_2 I_{-\alpha}(x).$$

Every solution is of the form

$$y = c_1 I_\alpha(x) + c_2 K_\alpha(x)$$

regardless of whether or not α is an integer.

If we make the formal change of variable $t = ix$, where i is the imaginary unit and set $Y(t) = y(t/i)$ in Eq. (4.26), it becomes

$$t^2 \frac{d^2 Y}{dt^2} + t \frac{dY}{dt} + (t^2 - \alpha^2) Y = 0.$$

This is Bessel's equation of order α. Thus if a function F is a solution of Bessel's equation and if

$$G(x) = F(t) = F(ix),$$

then G is a solution of the modified Bessel equation. This argument is only formal, since no knowledge of functions of a complex variable is assumed. We shall nevertheless make use of the relationship between G and F in the next section.

Exercises for Section 4.5

1. Use the series definition of I_α to show that

   (a) $\dfrac{d}{dx}[x^\alpha I_\alpha(x)] = x^\alpha I_{\alpha-1}(x)$ (b) $\dfrac{d}{dx}[x^{-\alpha} I_\alpha(x)] = x^{-\alpha} I_{\alpha+1}(x)$

2. Use the results of Exercise 1 to show that

   (a) $I'_\alpha(x) = I_{\alpha-1}(x) - \dfrac{\alpha}{x} I_\alpha(x)$ (b) $I'_\alpha(x) = I_{\alpha+1}(x) + \dfrac{\alpha}{x} I_\alpha(x)$

   (c) $I_{\alpha-1}(x) - I_{\alpha+1}(x) = \dfrac{2\alpha}{x} I_\alpha(x)$ (d) $I'_\alpha(x) = \frac{1}{2}[I_{\alpha-1}(x) + I_{\alpha+1}(x)]$

3. Show that I_α is a positive increasing function whose graph is concave up on the interval $(0, \infty)$.

4. Show that I_α and K_α are linearly independent when α is not an integer.

5. Show that

   (a) $\dfrac{d}{dx}[x^\alpha K_\alpha(x)] = -x^\alpha K_{\alpha-1}(x)$ (b) $\dfrac{d}{dx}[x^{-\alpha} K_\alpha(x)] = -x^{-\alpha} K_{\alpha+1}(x)$

6. Use the results of Exercise 5 to show that

   (a) $K'_\alpha(x) = -K_{\alpha-1}(x) - \dfrac{\alpha}{x} K_\alpha(x)$

   (b) $K'_\alpha(x) = K_{\alpha+1}(x) + \dfrac{\alpha}{x} K_\alpha(x)$

   (c) $K_{\alpha+1}(x) - K_{\alpha-1}(x) = \dfrac{2\alpha}{x} K_\alpha(x)$

   (d) $K'_\alpha(x) = -\frac{1}{2}[K_{\alpha-1}(x) + K_{\alpha+1}(x)]$

7. (a) Show that (for N an integer)

$$K_N(x) = \frac{1}{2}(-1)^N \left[\frac{\partial}{\partial \alpha} I_{-\alpha}(x) - \frac{\partial}{\partial \alpha} I_\alpha(x) \right]_{\alpha = N}$$

(b) Show that

$$K_0(x) = -\left(\gamma + \ln \frac{x}{2} \right) I_0(x) + \sum_{m=1}^{\infty} \frac{\phi(m)(x/2)^{2m}}{(m!)^2}$$

8. Use the results of Exercise 1 to show that

(a) $\displaystyle \int x^{\alpha+1} I_\alpha(x)\, dx = x^{\alpha+1} I_{\alpha+1}(x) + C$

(b) $\displaystyle \int x^{1-\alpha} I_\alpha(x)\, dx = x^{1-\alpha} I_{\alpha-1}(x) + C$

4.6 OTHER FORMS FOR BESSEL'S EQUATION

Starting with Bessel's equation

$$t^2 \frac{d^2 u}{dt^2} + t \frac{du}{dt} + (t^2 - \alpha^2)u = 0, \tag{4.29}$$

let us make the variable changes

$$t = ax^r, \qquad y(x) = x^s u(t),$$

where a, r, and s are constants. Some applications of the chain rule show that

$$\frac{du}{dt} = \frac{d}{dx}(x^{-s}y) \frac{dx}{dt} = \frac{x^{-r-s}}{ar} \left(x \frac{dy}{dx} - sy \right),$$

$$\frac{d^2 u}{dt^2} = \frac{x^{-2r-s}}{a^2 r^2} \left[x^2 \frac{d^2 y}{dx^2} + (1 - r - 2s)x \frac{dy}{dx} + s(r + s)y \right],$$

and Eq. (4.29) becomes

$$x^2 \frac{d^2 y}{dx^2} + (1 - 2s)x \frac{dy}{dx} + [(s^2 - r^2 \alpha^2) + a^2 r^2 x^{2r}]y = 0. \tag{4.30}$$

The general solution of Eq. (4.30) is

$$y(x) = x^s [c_1 J_\alpha(ax^r) + c_2 Y_\alpha(ax^r)].$$

When α is not an integer, the general solution is also

$$y(x) = x^s [c_1 J_\alpha(ax^r) + c_2 J_{-\alpha}(ax^r)].$$

If a is allowed to be pure imaginary, say $a = ib$ where b is real, the quantities $J_\alpha(ibx^r)$, $J_{-\alpha}(ibx^r)$, and $Y_\alpha(ibx^r)$ may be replaced by $I_\alpha(bx^r)$, $I_{-\alpha}(bx^r)$, and $K_\alpha(bx^r)$, respectively. The general solution is

$$y(x) = x^s[c_1 I_\alpha(bx^r) + c_2 K_\alpha(bx^r)]$$

or, when α is not an integer,

$$y(x) = x^s[c_1 I_\alpha(bx^r) + c_2 I_{-\alpha}(bx^r)].$$

Example 1   Let us consider the equation

$$y'' + xy = 0.$$

In order to compare this equation with the general equation (4.30), let us multiply through by x^2, putting it in the form

$$x^2 y'' + x^3 y = 0.$$

If this equation is of the form (4.30) we must have

$$1 - 2s = 0, \qquad s^2 - r^2\alpha^2 = 0, \qquad a^2 r^2 = 1, \qquad 2r = 3.$$

These conditions are satisfied if

$$r = \tfrac{3}{2}, \qquad s = \tfrac{1}{2}, \qquad \alpha = \tfrac{1}{3}, \qquad a = \tfrac{2}{3}.$$

Therefore, the general solution of the equation of this example is

$$y(x) = x^{1/2}[c_1 J_{1/3}(\tfrac{2}{3}x^{3/2}) + c_2 J_{-1/3}(\tfrac{2}{3}x^{3/2})].$$

Example 2

$$x^2 y'' + xy' - (4 + 36x^4)y = 0.$$

Comparing with Eq. (4.30), we find that

$$r = 2, \qquad s = 0, \qquad \alpha = 1, \qquad a = 3i.$$

The general solution of the equation is

$$y(x) = c_1 I_1(3x^2) + c_2 K_1(3x^2).$$

Example 3   The general solution of the equation

$$y'' + y = 0$$

is known to be

$$y(x) = c_1 \cos x + c_2 \sin x.$$

However, the equation

$$x^2 y'' + x^2 y = 0$$

is of the form (4.30), with

$$s = \tfrac{1}{2}, \qquad r = 1, \qquad \alpha = \tfrac{1}{2}, \qquad a = 1.$$

Therefore, each of the functions

$$x^{1/2} J_{1/2}(x), \qquad x^{1/2} J_{-1/2}(x)$$

is a solution of the original equation and there must exist constants A, B, C, and D such that

$$x^{1/2} J_{1/2}(x) = A \cos x + B \sin x,$$
$$x^{1/2} J_{-1/2}(x) = C \cos x + D \sin x.$$

From the power series definition of $J_{1/2}$ we find that

$$x^{1/2} J_{1/2}(x) = \frac{1}{2^{1/2} \Gamma(\tfrac{3}{2})} x - \frac{1}{2^{5/2} \Gamma(\tfrac{5}{2})} x^3 + \cdots.$$

Since only odd powers of x are involved, we must have $A = 0$. Since

$$\sin x = x - \tfrac{1}{6} x^3 + \cdots,$$

we must take

$$B = \frac{1}{2^{1/2} \Gamma(\tfrac{3}{2})} = \frac{\sqrt{2}}{\Gamma(\tfrac{1}{2})} = \sqrt{\frac{2}{\pi}}.$$

This establishes the first of the relations

$$J_{1/2}(x) = \sqrt{\frac{2}{\pi x}} \sin x,$$

$$J_{-1/2}(x) = \sqrt{\frac{2}{\pi x}} \cos x,$$

(4.31)

and the second can be verified in similar fashion. The recurrence relation (4.23) enables us to express any function of the form $J_{N+1/2}$, where N is an integer, in terms of $J_{1/2}$ and $J_{-1/2}$. Thus all solutions of Bessel's equation can be expressed in terms of elementary functions when the order is half an odd integer.

In the case of the modified Bessel's equation, it can be shown that

$$I_{1/2}(x) = \sqrt{\frac{2}{\pi x}} \sinh x,$$

(4.32)

$$I_{-1/2}(x) = \sqrt{\frac{2}{\pi x}} \cosh x.$$

Any modified Bessel function whose order is half an odd integer can be expressed in terms of these functions.

Exercises for Section 4.6

Express the general solution of the given equation in terms of Bessel functions:

1. $y'' + x^2 y = 0$ 2. $4x^2 y'' + (1 + 4x)y = 0$

3. $x^2 y'' + 5xy' + (3 + 4x^2)y = 0$ 4. $x^2 y'' + 5xy' + (9x^6 - 12)y = 0$

5. $y'' - xy = 0$ 6. $xy'' - 3y' - 9x^5 y = 0$

7. $xy'' + 3y' - 2y = 0$ 8. $x^2 y'' - xy' - (3 + 4x^2)y = 0$

9. Express the following quantities in terms of elementary functions.

    (a) $J_{5/2}(x)$ (b) $J_{-3/2}(x^2)$ (c) $Y_{1/2}(x)$

    (d) $I_{3/2}(x)$ (e) $I_{-3/2}(x)$ (f) $K_{-1/2}(x)$

10. Derive the second of the equalities (4.31) for $J_{-1/2}$.

11. Verify the equalities (4.32) for $I_{1/2}$ and $I_{-1/2}$.

REFERENCES

1. Abramowitz, M., and Stegun, I. A., *Handbook of Mathematical Functions with Formulas, Graphs, and Mathematical Tables*. U.S. Government Printing Office, Washington, D.C., 1964.
2. Jahnke, E., and Emde, F., *Tables of Functions*, 4th ed. Dover, New York, 1945.
3. Watson, G. N., *A Treatise on the Theory of Bessel Functions*. Macmillan, New York, 1945.
4. Whittaker, E. T., and Watson, G. N., *Modern Analysis*. Cambridge Univ. Press, London and New York, 1958.

V

Orthogonal Polynomials

5.1 ORTHOGONAL FUNCTIONS

Let f and g be real-valued functions defined on an interval $[a, b]$. Let w be defined and positive on (a, b). The *inner product* of f and g with respect to the *weight function w* is defined to be the integral

$$\int_a^b w(x)f(x)g(x)\,dx.$$

We shall denote the inner product of f and g by the symbol (f, g). This symbol does not show what the weight function is or what interval is involved. This information must be given in any specific case. We shall allow w to become infinite at one or both endpoints of (a, b). We can also extend the definition of inner product to a situation in which the interval of integration is infinite in extent. In these cases it is assumed that f, g, and w are such that the integral involved converges. It is readily verified that the inner product has the properties

$$\begin{aligned}
(f, g) &= (g, f), \\
(f, g + h) &= (f, g) + (f, h), \\
(cf, g) &= c(f, g),
\end{aligned} \tag{5.1}$$

where c is a real constant.

The inner product of a function f with itself,

$$(f, f) = \int_a^b w(x)[f(x)]^2\,dx,$$

is nonnegative, since $w(x) > 0$ for $a < x < b$. We define the *norm* of f, written $\|f\|$, to be

$$\|f\| = (f,f)^{1/2}.$$

If f is continuous on $[a, b]$, its norm is zero if and only if f is the zero function. The reader is reminded that the norm of a function depends on the specified interval and weight function.

If the inner product (f, g) of f and g is zero, then f and g are said to be *orthogonal* with respect to the weight function w. In the special case where $w(x) = 1$ for $a \le x \le b$, f and g are said to be *simply orthogonal*.

A sequence of functions $\{f_n\}_{n=0}^{\infty}$ is called an *orthogonal set* of functions (or a set of orthogonal functions) if the functions are pairwise orthogonal; that is, if $(f_m, f_n) = 0$ for $m \ne n$.

A sequence of polynomials $\{\phi_n\}_{n=0}^{\infty}$, where ϕ_n is of degree n, is called a *simple set of polynomials*. In this chapter we shall be concerned with simple sets of *orthogonal* polynomials. These sets of polynomials arise in various ways, one of which is as the solutions of a class of differential equations. We shall also show that, under certain conditions, given any interval and a positive weight function on that interval, there exists a corresponding set of orthogonal polynomials.

Eigenvalue problems, the topic of Chapter VI, are another important source of sets of orthogonal functions, not necessarily polynomials. In Chapter VII we shall see that under certain conditions an arbitrary function can be expanded in an infinite series of the functions of an orthogonal set. Such series are called *Fourier series*. Finally, in Chapter X, we shall use our knowledge of Fourier series and orthogonal functions to obtain the solutions of some problems of mathematical physics.

Exercises for Section 5.1

1. For f, g, and w as given, find the inner product of f and g with respect to the weight function w on the indicated interval.

    (a) $f(x) = x$, $\quad g(x) = 1$, $\quad w(x) = \sqrt{x}$, $\quad 0 \le x \le 1$

    (b) $f(x) = \sin x$, $\quad g(x) = \cos x$, $\quad w(x) = 1$, $\quad 0 \le x \le \pi$

    (c) $f(x) = \cos x$, $\quad g(x) = \sin x$, $\quad w(x) = x$, $\quad 0 \le x \le \pi$

    (d) $f(x) = 1$, $\quad g(x) = x$, $\quad w(x) = e^{-x}$, $\quad 0 \le x < \infty$

2. Find the norm of the function f in each part of Exercise 1.

3. (a)   Let $\phi_n(x) = \sin n\pi x$ for $n = 1, 2, 3, \ldots$, and for $0 \le x \le 1$. Show that the sequence $\{\phi_n\}_{n=1}^{\infty}$ is simply orthogonal on $(0, 1)$. Find the norms of the functions ϕ_n.

(b)   Let $\psi_n(x) = \cos n\pi x$ for $n = 0, 1, 2, \ldots$, and for $0 \leq x \leq 1$. Show that the sequence $\{\psi_n\}_{n=0}^{\infty}$ is simply orthogonal on $(0, 1)$. Find the norms of the functions.

4.   If f is any function whose norm is not zero, show that the function $f/\|f\|$ has norm 1.

5.   Let f and g be orthogonal with respect to a weight function w on (a, b). Show that the functions $F = \sqrt{wf}$ and $G = \sqrt{wg}$ are simply orthogonal on (a, b).

6.   Let $f_n(x) = x^n$ for $|x| \leq 1$ and $n = 0, 1, 2, \ldots$. Show that the sequence $\{f_n\}_{n=0}^{\infty}$ is a simple set of polynomials but not a simply orthogonal set, for the interval $(-1, 1)$.

7.   Verify the properties (5.1) of an inner product.

8.   Show that
$$\|f + g\|^2 = \|f\|^2 + 2(f, g) + \|g\|^2.$$

9.   Show that
$$\|f + g\|^2 + \|f - g\|^2 = 2\|f\|^2 + 2\|g\|^2.$$

5.2   AN EXISTENCE THEOREM FOR ORTHOGONAL POLYNOMIALS

We shall eventually prove the existence of a set of orthogonal polynomials which corresponds to a given interval and given positive weight function. First, however, we must derive some properties of polynomials that will be needed in the proof. In the derivations, it will be convenient to have symbols for some basic functions. We shall use the notations
$$I(x) = x, \qquad I^n(x) = x^n$$
for all x and n a nonnegative integer. (Here I stands for "identity.") In particular
$$I^1(x) = I(x), \qquad I^0(x) = 1$$
for all x. We shall often use the symbol 1 for the function I^0 as well as for the number 1. If P is the polynomial defined by the relation
$$P(x) = c_0 + c_1 x + c_2 x^2 + \cdots + c_n x^n$$
then we may write
$$P = c_0 + c_1 I + c_2 I^2 + \cdots + c_n I^n.$$

Theorem 5.1 Let $\{\phi_n\}_{n=0}^{\infty}$ be a simple set of polynomials and let Q_m be an arbitrary polynomial of arbitrary degree m. Then Q_m is a linear combination of the polynomials $\phi_0, \phi_1, \ldots, \phi_m$.

PROOF We shall prove the theorem by induction. If Q_0 is any constant function (that is, any polynomial of degree zero) and if $C = Q_0/\phi_0$, then $Q_0 = C\phi_0$. Thus the theorem is true for $m = 0$. Suppose that the theorem is true for $m \le k$, where k is any nonnegative integer. Let Q_{k+1} be any polynomial of degree $k + 1$,

$$Q_{k+1}(x) = A_{k+1}x^{k+1} + A_k x^k + \cdots + A_0,$$

where $A_{k+1} \ne 0$. Let

$$\phi_{k+1}(x) = a_{k+1}x^{k+1} + a_k x^k + \cdots + a_0,$$

where $a_{k+1} \ne 0$. If we choose $C_{k+1} = A_{k+1}/a_{k+1}$, then $Q_{k+1} - C_{k+1}\phi_{k+1}$ is a polynomial of degree less than or equal to k. By hypothesis we have

$$Q_{k+1} - C_{k+1}\phi_{k+1} = C_0\phi_0 + C_1\phi_1 + \cdots + C_k\phi_k$$

or

$$Q_{k+1} = \sum_{j=0}^{k+1} C_j\phi_j.$$

Thus if the theorem is true for $m \le k$ it is true for $m = k + 1$. Since it is true for $m = 0$, it is true for every nonnegative integer m.

Theorem 5.2 A simple set of polynomials $\{\phi_n\}_{n=0}^{\infty}$ is an orthogonal set with respect to the weight function w on the interval (a, b) if and only if

$$(\phi_n, I^m) \equiv \int_a^b w(x)\phi_n(x)x^m \, dx = 0 \tag{5.2}$$

for $m = 0, 1, \ldots, n - 1$, for every positive integer n.

PROOF We first show that if condition (5.2) holds, then the set of polynomials is orthogonal. Let ϕ_n and ϕ_m be any two distinct polynomials of the set, and suppose that $n > m$. If

$$\phi_m = a_m I^m + a_{m-1}I^{m-1} + \cdots + a_0$$

then

$$(\phi_n, \phi_m) = a_m(\phi_n, I^m) + a_{m-1}(\phi_n, I^{m-1}) + \cdots + a_0(\phi_n, 1) = 0.$$

Hence the polynomials are orthogonal.

Next we show that if the set of polynomials is orthogonal, then the condition (5.2) is satisfied. Let n be any positive integer and let m be any integer such that $0 \le m < n$. By Theorem 5.1 there exist constants c_0, $c_1, \ldots, c_m$ such that

$$I^m = c_0 \phi_0 + c_1 \phi_1 + \cdots + c_m \phi_m.$$

Then

$$(\phi_n, I^m) = c_0(\phi_n, \phi_0) + c_1(\phi_n, \phi_1) + \cdots + c_m(\phi_n, \phi_m) = 0,$$

so the condition (5.2) is satisfied.

We are now ready to prove a basic existence theorem for orthogonal polynomials.

Theorem 5.3   Let the function w be positive and continuous† on the interval (a, b), and such that each of the integrals

$$M_n = \int_a^b w(x) x^n \, dx, \qquad n = 0, 1, 2, \ldots,$$

exists. (Either a or b or both may be infinite.) Then there exists a simple set of polynomials that is orthgonal with respect to w on the interval (a, b). Each polynomial of the set is unique except for a constant factor.

PROOF   We shall show that, for every positive integer n, there exists a polynomial ϕ_n of degree n such that

$$(\phi_n, I^m) \equiv \int_a^b w(x) \phi_n(x) x^m \, dx = 0, \qquad m = 0, 1, 2, \ldots, n - 1. \quad (5.3)$$

If ϕ_0 is then chosen to be any nonzero constant function, the set $\{\phi_n\}_{n=0}^{\infty}$ will be an orthogonal set, by Theorem 5.2.

We shall show that for every positive integer n there exist constants $c_0, c_1, \ldots, c_n$, with $c_n \neq 0$, such that the polynomial

$$\phi_n = c_0 + c_2 I + \cdots + c_{n-1} I^{n-1} + c_n I^n$$

satisfies the conditions (5.3). These n conditions can be written as

$$
\begin{aligned}
M_0 c_0 + M_1 c_1 + \cdots + M_{n-1} c_{n-1} &= -M_n c_n \\
M_1 c_0 + M_2 c_1 + \cdots + M_n c_{n-1} &= -M_{n+1} c_n \\
&\vdots \\
M_{n-1} c_0 + M_n c_1 + \cdots + M_{2n-2} c_{n-1} &= -M_{2n-1} c_n.
\end{aligned}
\qquad (5.4)
$$

† These restrictions on w can be relaxed, but they are satisfactory for our purposes.

If the determinant

$$\Delta_n = \begin{vmatrix} M_0 & M_1 & \cdots & M_{n-1} \\ M_1 & M_2 & \cdots & M_n \\ \vdots & \vdots & & \vdots \\ M_{n-1} & M_n & \cdots & M_{2n-2} \end{vmatrix}$$

is not zero, the ratios c_k/c_n, $k = 0, 1, 2, \ldots, n-1$, are uniquely determined. In this case the polynomial ϕ_n is uniquely determined except for a constant factor. For if c_n is assigned any nonzero value, the remaining coefficients $c_1, c_2, \ldots, c_{n-1}$ are uniquely determined multiples of c_n.

We now show that Δ_n cannot be zero. To do this we shall assume that $\Delta_n = 0$ and show that this assumption leads to a contradiction. If we set $c_n = 0$ in the system (5.4), the resulting *homogeneous* system has a vanishing determinant and therefore possesses a nontrivial solution. This means that there exists a polynomial Q_{n-1} of degree less than or equal to $n-1$ and not identically zero, such that

$$(Q_{n-1}, I^m) = 0, \qquad m = 0, 1, 2, \ldots, \quad n-1.$$

But this means that Q_{n-1} is orthogonal to every polynomial of degree less than n. In particular Q_{n-1} must be orthogonal to itself, so that

$$(Q_{n-1}, Q_{n-1}) \equiv \int_a^b w(x)[Q_{n-1}(x)]^2 \, dx = 0.$$

But this is impossible, since $w(x)$ is positive for $a < x < b$. Therefore our assumption that $\Delta_n = 0$ must be false, and we must have $\Delta_n \neq 0$. This concludes the proof.

Theorem 5.3 actually gives us a method for the construction of any finite number of the polynomials of an orthogonal set. For purposes of illustration, let us construct the first few orthogonal polynomials of the set which corresponds to the weight function $w(x) = \sqrt{x}$ on the interval $0 < x < 1$. If we choose $\phi_0(x) = 1$ and choose the coefficient of x^n in $\phi_n(x)$ to be unity, then the polynomials are uniquely determined. The polynomials ϕ_1 and ϕ_2 are of the forms

$$\phi_1(x) = x + a, \qquad \phi_2(x) = x^2 + bx + c.$$

The constant a is determined by the requirement that

$$(\phi_1, 1) = \int_0^1 \sqrt{x}(x + a) \, dx = \tfrac{2}{5} + \tfrac{2}{3}a = 0.$$

Hence $a = -\tfrac{3}{5}$ and

$$\phi_1(x) = x - \tfrac{3}{5}.$$

The constants b and c are determined by the requirements that

$$(\phi_2, 1) = \int_0^1 \sqrt{x}(x^2 + bx + c)\, dx = \tfrac{2}{7} + \tfrac{2}{5}b + \tfrac{2}{3}c = 0,$$

$$(\phi_2, I) = \int_0^1 x^{3/2}(x^2 + bx + c)\, dx = \tfrac{2}{9} + \tfrac{2}{7}b + \tfrac{2}{5}c = 0.$$

We find that $b = -10/9$, $c = 5/21$, and so

$$\phi_2(x) = x^2 - \frac{10}{9}x + \frac{5}{21}.$$

This method is laborious and does not provide a general formula for the polynomial ϕ_n of arbitrary degree n.

Exercises for Section 5.2

1. Find the polynomials ϕ_0, ϕ_1, and ϕ_2 of the orthogonal set $\{\phi_n\}_{n=0}^{\infty}$ that corresponds to the given weight function and interval. Assume that ϕ_n has the form $\phi_n = I^n + a_{n-1}I^{n-1} + \cdots + a_n$.
    (a) $w(x) = 1,$ $0 \le x \le 1$ (b) $w(x) = x,$ $0 \le x \le 1$
    (c) $w(x) = |x|,$ $-1 \le x \le 1$ (d) $w(x) = x^{-1/2},$ $0 < x \le 1$
    (e) $w(x) = 1,$ $-1 \le x \le 1$ (f) $w(x) = 1 - x^2,$ $-1 \le x \le 1$
    (g) $w(x) = e^{-x},$ $0 \le x < \infty$ (h) $w(x) = xe^{-x},$ $0 \le x < \infty$

2. Let $\{\phi_n\}_{n=0}^{\infty}$ be a simple set of orthogonal polynomials relative to the weight function w and the interval (a, b). If

$$\phi_n = a_n I^n + a_{n-1} I^{n-1} + \cdots + a_0,$$

show that

$$(\phi_n, I^n) = \frac{1}{a_n} \|\phi_n\|^2.$$

3. Let $\{\phi_n\}_{n=0}^{\infty}$ be a simple set of orthogonal polynomials relative to the weight function w and the interval (a, b). Show that

$$\int_a^b w(x)\phi_n(x)\, dx = 0$$

    for $n = 1, 2, 3, \ldots$.

4. Let $\{\phi_n\}_{n=0}^{\infty}$ be a set of orthogonal polynomials that is simply orthogonal on the interval $(-1, 1)$. Let

$$\psi_n(x) = \phi_n\left(\frac{2x}{b-a} - \frac{a+b}{b-a}\right),$$

where a and b are constants, with $a < b$. Show that the sequence $\{\psi\}_{n=0}^{\infty}$ is a set of orthogonal polynomials that is simply orthogonal on the interval (a, b).

5. If P is a polynomial such that $(P, I^n) = 0$ for every nonnegative integer n, show that P is the zero function.

6. An infinite sequence of functions $\{f_n\}_{n=1}^{\infty}$ is said to be linearly independent on an interval $[a, b]$ if for every positive integer k the functions f_1, $f_2, \ldots, f_k$ are linearly independent. If $\{f_n\}_{n=1}^{\infty}$ is a linearly independent sequence of continuous functions, prove that there exists an *orthogonal* sequence $\{g_n\}_{n=1}^{\infty}$, where

$$y_n = a_{n1} f_1 + a_{n2} f_2 + \cdots + a_{nn} f_n.$$

(Thus g_n is a linear combination of $f_1, f_2, \ldots, f_n$.) *Suggestion:* Let

$$g_1 = f_1, \qquad g_2 = f_2 - \frac{(g_1, f_2)}{(g_1, g_1)} g_1,$$

$$g_3 = f_3 - \frac{(g_1, f_3)}{(g_1, g_1)} g_1 - \frac{(g_2, f_3)}{(g_2, g_2)} g_2,$$

and so on. Use induction.

7. Using the definition of Exercise 6, show that the sequence $\{I^n\}_{n=0}^{\infty}$ is linearly independent on every interval of the form $[a, b]$.

8. Use the results of Exercises 6 and 7 to prove Theorem 5.3.

5.3 PROPERTIES OF ORTHOGONAL POLYNOMIALS

In this section we shall derive some basic general properties of sets of orthogonal polynomials that hold for all such sets. Properties of some specific important polynomial sets will be investigated in later sections.

The reader is reminded that the weight function w is assumed to be continuous and positive on the interval (a, b), and such that the integrals

$$M_n = \int_a^b w(x) x^n \, dx, \qquad n = 0, 1, 2, \ldots,$$

all exist. Either a or b or both may be infinite.

Theorem 5.4   Let $\{\phi_n\}_{n=0}^{\infty}$ be a set of orthogonal polynomials and let Q_m be an arbitrary polynomial of degree m. Then

$$Q_m = c_0\phi_0 + c_1\phi_1 + \cdots + c_m\phi_m\,,$$

where

$$c_k = \frac{(Q_m, \phi_k)}{\|\phi_k\|^2}\,, \qquad k = 0, 1, 2, \ldots, m\,.$$

PROOF   By Theorem 5.1 we know that there exist constants c_i such that

$$Q_m = \sum_{i=1}^{m} c_i\phi_i\,.$$

Multiplying both sides of this equation by $w\phi_k$, where k is an arbitrary integer such that $0 \le k \le m$, and integrating from a to b, we have

$$(Q_m, \phi_k) = c_0(\phi_0, \phi_k) + c_1(\phi_1, \phi_k) + \cdots + c_m(\phi_m, \phi_k)\,.$$

Since $(\phi_i, \phi_k) = 0$ when $i \ne k$, we have

$$(Q_m, \phi_k) = c_k(\phi_k, \phi_k) = c_k\|\phi_k\|^2.$$

Since $\|\phi_k\| \ne 0$, we can solve for c_k to obtain the result stated in the theorem.

Theorem 5.5   The polynomials of an orthogonal set satisfy a recurrence relation of the form

$$x\phi_n(x) = A_n\phi_{n+1}(x) + B_n\phi_n(x) + C_n\phi_{n-1}(x), \qquad n \ge 1, \qquad (5.5)$$

where A_n, B_n, and C_n are constants that may depend on n.

PROOF   Since $I\phi_n$ is a polynomial of degree $n + 1$ we have, by Theorem 5.4,

$$x\phi_n(x) = \sum_{k=1}^{n+1} a_{nk}\phi_k(x),$$

where

$$a_{nk} = \frac{(I\phi_n, \phi_k)}{\|\phi_k\|^2} = \frac{(\phi_n, I\phi_k)}{\|\phi_k\|^2}\,.$$

Since $I\phi_k$ is a polynomial of degree $k + 1$, we have $a_{nk} = 0$ for $k + 1 < n$ or $k < n - 1$. Setting $A_n = a_{n+1,n}$, $B_n = a_{nn}$, and $C_n = a_{n-1,n}$, we obtain the relation (5.5).

It can be shown (Exercise 6) that A_n and C_n are never zero in the recurrence relation (5.5).

Theorem 5.6 The nth degree polynomial ϕ_n of an orthogonal set has n real distinct zeros, all of which lie in the interval (a, b).

PROOF The polynomial ϕ_0 is a nonzero constant function, and of course has no zeros. For $n > 0$ we have

$$(\phi_n, 1) = \int_a^b w(x)\phi_n(x) \, dx = 0.$$

Since $w(x) > 0$ for $a < x < b$, the function ϕ_n changes sign at at least one point in the interval. Let $x_1, x_2, \ldots, x_m$ be the points in (a, b) where ϕ_n changes sign. Then $m \leq n$, for ϕ_n can have at most n distinct zeros. Suppose that $m < n$. The polynomial ψ_m, where

$$\psi_m(x) = (x - x_1)(x - x_2) \cdots (x - x_m)$$

also changes sign at each of the points $x_1, x_2, \ldots, x_m$, and only at these points, so the product $\phi_n \psi_m$ does not change sign at all on (a, b). But

$$(\phi_n, \psi_m) = \int_a^b w(x)\phi_n(x)\psi_m(x) \, dx = 0,$$

since ψ_m is of degree m with $m < n$. This is impossible, so we must conclude that $m = n$. Thus ϕ_n must change sign at n distinct points in (a, b), and must have n real distinct zeros in this interval.

Exercises for Section 5.3

1. Show that the polynomials $\psi_n(x) = x^{2n}$, $n = 0, 1, 2, \ldots$, are orthogonal with respect to the weight function $w(x) = x$ on the interval $(-1, 1)$. Note that ψ_n does not, in general, have n distinct zeros in the interval of orthogonality. Is this a contradiction of Theorem 5.6? Explain.

2. If the functions $f_1, f_2, \ldots, f_m$ (not necessarily polynomials) are orthogonal, that is, $(f_i, f_j) = 0$ for $i \neq j$, and if

$$F = c_1 f_1 = c_2 f_2 + \cdots + c_m f_m,$$

show that $c_k = (F, f_k)/\|f_k\|^2$.

3. Show that a simple set of orthogonal polynomials $\{\phi_n\}_{\alpha=0}^{\infty}$ satisfies a recurrence relation of the form

$$x^2 \phi_n(x) = A_n \phi_{n+2}(x) + B_n \phi_{n+1}(x) + C_n \phi_n(x) + D_n \phi_{n-1}(x).$$

Do this in two ways: (a) by using the method used to prove Theorem 5.5 and (b) by observing that

$$x^2\phi_n(x) = a_n\,x\phi_{n+1}(x) + b_n\,x\phi_n(x) + c_n\,x\phi_{n-1}(x)$$

and applying Theorem 5.5 to the terms on the right-hand side.

4. Can the polynomial set $\{I^n\}_{n=0}^{\infty}$ be orthogonal on any interval? Why?

5. Let $f_3(x) = x^3 + x$ and $f_4(x) = x^4$ for all x.

(a) Show that f_3 and f_4 are simply orthogonal on $(-1, 1)$.

(b) Can f_3 and f_4 be the third and fourth degree polynomials of a simply orthogonal set on $(-1, 1)$? Why?

6. If $\{\phi_n\}_{n=0}^{\infty}$ is a simple set of orthogonal polynomials, show that $(I\phi_n, \phi_{n+1}) \neq 0$ for $n \geq 0$ and $(I\phi_n, \phi_{n-1}) \neq 0$ for $n \geq 1$. Hence prove that $A_n \neq 0$ and $C_n \neq 0$ in the recurrence relation (5.5).

7. (a) Show that $C_n = A_{n-1}$ in the recurrence relation (5.5).

(b) Show that

$$(x - y)\phi_n(x)\phi_n(y) = A_n\,[\phi_{n+1}(x)\phi_n(y) - \phi_n(x)\phi_{n+1}(y)]$$

$$+ A_{n-1}[\phi_{n-1}(x)\phi_n(y) - \phi_n(x)\phi_{n-1}(y)].$$

(c) Show that

$$\sum_{k=0}^{n} \phi_k(x)\phi_k(y) = A_n\,\frac{\phi_{n+1}(x)\phi_n(y) - \phi_n(x)\phi_{n+1}(y)}{x - y}.$$

5.4 GENERATING FUNCTIONS

A function F of two variables is said to be a *generating function* for the set of functions $\{f_n\}_{n=0}^{\infty}$ if

$$F(x, t) = \sum_{n=0}^{\infty} f_n(x)t^n. \qquad (5.6)$$

We also say that the functions f_n are *generated* by the function F. The series in Eq. (5.6) need not converge for all x and t. We shall only require that it converge for $|t| < r$, where r is any positive constant, and for x in some interval $\mathscr{I}$.

Generating functions for many important sets of orthogonal polynomials are known. In these cases, the generating function provides a convenient method for deriving some of the important properties of the set. We shall illustrate the procedure for the set of polynomials known as the Legendre polynomials in the next few sections. In doing this, we shall have need of two theorems.

Theorem 5.7   Let the function f be analytic at zero, with power series expansion

$$f(u) = \sum_{n=0}^{\infty} a_n u^n, \qquad |u| < R. \tag{5.7}$$

Let the function g be analytic at zero, with $g(0) = 0$. Suppose that

$$g(z) = \sum_{n=1}^{\infty} b_n z^n, \qquad |z| < r. \tag{5.8}$$

and that $|g(z)| < R$ for $|z| < r$. Then the function F, where $F(z) = f[g(z)]$, is analytic at zero and is represented by its power series expansion

$$F(z) = \sum_{n=0}^{\infty} c_n z^n \tag{5.9}$$

for $|z| < r$. Furthermore, the series (5.9) for $F(z)$ can be obtained by substituting the series (5.8) into the series (5.7) for u, and collecting the terms that involve like powers of z.

A proof of this theorem or its equivalent can be found in many books on advanced calculus. See, for example, Olmsted [4], or Apostol [1].

Suppose that a function $F(x, t)$ is analytic in t at $t = 0$ for each x in an interval $\mathcal{I}$, so that

$$F(x, t) = \sum_{n=0}^{\infty} f_n(x) t^n, \qquad |t| < r, \quad x \text{ in } \mathcal{I}.$$

Then by the rule for differentiating an ordinary power series, we have

$$\frac{\partial F(x, t)}{\partial t} = \sum_{n=1}^{\infty} n f_n(x) t^{n-1}, \qquad |t| < r, \quad x \text{ in } \mathcal{I}.$$

The following question now arises: Assuming that $\partial F(x, t)/\partial x$ exists, when is it true that

$$\frac{\partial F(x, t)}{\partial x} = \sum_{n=0}^{\infty} f_n'(x) t^n \text{ ?}$$

A set of sufficient conditions for the termwise differentiation of the series for $F(x, t)$ with respect to x is given by the following theorem.

Theorem 5.8   Let $F(x, t)$ and $\partial F(x, t)/\partial x$ be analytic in t at $t = 0$ for x in an interval $\mathscr{I}$, so that

$$F(x, t) = \sum_{n=0}^{\infty} f_n(x)t^n, \qquad (5.10)$$

$$\frac{\partial F(x, t)}{\partial x} = \sum_{n=0}^{\infty} g_n(x)t^n \qquad (5.11)$$

for $|t| < r$ and for x in $\mathscr{I}$. Furthermore, let the partial derivatives of $F(x, t)$ of all orders exist and be continuous for $|t| < r$ and for x in $\mathscr{I}$. Then the derivatives f_n' exist and $g_n(x) = f_n'(x)$ for x in $\mathscr{I}$ and $n \geq 0$.

PROOF   The assumption about the continuity of the partial derivatives of $F(x, t)$ insures that the order of differentiation does not matter. Thus

$$\frac{\partial^2 F(x, t)}{\partial t \, \partial x} = \frac{\partial^2 F(x, t)}{\partial x \, \partial t}, \qquad \frac{\partial^3 F(x, t)}{\partial t^2 \, \partial x} = \frac{\partial^3 F(x, t)}{\partial x \, \partial t^2},$$

and so on. Now from Eq. (5.10), we have

$$f_n(x) = n! \left[\frac{\partial^n F(x, t)}{\partial t^n} \right]_{t=0},$$

and from Eq. (5.11), we have

$$g_n(x) = n! \left[\frac{\partial^{n+1} F(x, t)}{\partial t^n \, \partial x} \right]_{t=0}.$$

Then $f_n'(x)$ exists and

$$f_n'(x) = n! \frac{\partial}{\partial x} \left[\frac{\partial^n F(x, t)}{\partial t^n} \right]_{t=0} = n! \left[\frac{\partial^{n+1} F(x, t)}{\partial t^n \, \partial x} \right]_{t=0} = g_n(x).$$

5.5   LEGENDRE POLYNOMIALS

We shall consider the set of functions generated by the function

$$F(x, t) = (1 - 2xt + t^2)^{-1/2}.$$

In order to obtain the expansion of $F(x, t)$ in powers of t, we first write

$$F(x, t) = (1 - u)^{-1/2},$$

where

$$u(x, t) = 2xt - t^2,$$

and expand F in a power series in u. The binomial series

$$(1 + z)^{\alpha} = 1 + \sum_{m=1}^{\infty} \frac{\alpha(\alpha - 1)(\alpha - 2) \cdots (\alpha - m + 1)}{m!} z^m$$

converges for $|z| < 1$, for every real number α. (When α is a nonnegative integer, the series is finite and converges for all z.) Then

$$F(x, t) = 1 + \sum_{m=1}^{\infty} \frac{(-\frac{1}{2})(-\frac{1}{2} - 1)(-\frac{1}{2} - 2) \cdots (-\frac{1}{2} - m + 1)(-u)^m}{m!}$$

$$= 1 + \sum_{m=1}^{\infty} \frac{1 \cdot 3 \cdot 5 \cdots (2m - 1)}{2^m m!} u^m$$

$$= \sum_{m=0}^{\infty} \frac{(2m)!}{2^{2m} m!} u^m \tag{5.12}$$

whenever $|u| = |2xt - t^2|$ is less than one. In particular, the expansion is valid when $|x| \le 1$ and $|t| < \sqrt{2} - 1$, for then

$$|u| \le 2|x||t| + |t|^2 < 1.$$

Each of the quantities $u^m = (2xt - t^2)^m$ in Eq. (5.12) can be expanded in a finite power series in t,

$$u^m = \sum_{j=0}^{m} \frac{(-1)^j m! (2x)^{m-j}}{j! (m - j)!} t^{m+j},$$

valid for all x and t. Hence

$$F(x, t) = \sum_{m=0}^{\infty} \left[\sum_{j=0}^{m} \frac{(-1)^j (2m)! (2x)^{m-j}}{2^{2m} m! j! (m - j)!} t^{m+j} \right] \tag{5.13}$$

for $|x| \le 1$ and $|t| < \sqrt{2} - 1$. According to Theorem 5.7, $F(x, t)$ is analytic in t at $t = 0$, and is represented by its Maclaurin series in t for $|x| \le 1$ and $|t| < \sqrt{2} - 1$.

The Maclaurin series can be obtained by collecting the terms in formula (5.13) with like powers of t. In order to accomplish this, let us consider rectangular coordinates j and m in a plane, as in Fig. 5.1. The values assumed by the indices j and m in the series (5.13) correspond to the points with integer coordinates in the region of the jm plane that is described by means of the inequalities

$$0 \le j \le m, \qquad m \ge 0.$$

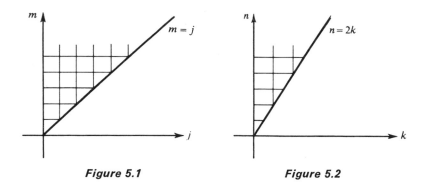

Figure 5.1   **Figure 5.2**

This region is shown in Fig. 5.1. If we introduce new indices of summation k and n by means of the equations

$$k = j, \qquad n = m + j$$
$$j = k, \qquad m = n - k,$$

the corresponding region in the kn plane is described by the inequalities

$$0 \le k \le n - k, \qquad n - k \ge 0,$$

or equivalently, by the inequalities

$$0 \le k \le \frac{n}{2}, \qquad n \ge 0.$$

This region is shown in Fig. 5.2.

For any real number α, we use the symbol $[\alpha]$ to denote the largest integer N such that $N \le \alpha$. For instance,

$$[\tfrac{5}{4}] = 1, \qquad [\pi] = 3, \qquad [-\tfrac{5}{3}] = -2.$$

Since n and k are integers when m and j are integers, we actually have

$$0 \le k \le \left[\frac{n}{2}\right]$$

for the new indices n and k.

If we introduce the new indices n and k in the series (5.13) and collect the terms with like powers of t, we find that

$$F(x, t) = \sum_{n=0}^{\infty} \left[\sum_{k=0}^{[n/2]} \frac{(-1)^k (2n - 2k)!\, x^{n-2k}}{2^n (n - k)!\, k!\, (n - 2k)!} \right] t^n$$

for $|x| \le 1$ and $|t| < \sqrt{2} - 1$.

The coefficient of t^n in the above series is a polynomial in x of degree n; we denote it by the symbol $P_n(x)$. Then

$$F(x, t) = (1 - 2xt + t^2)^{-1/2} = \sum_{n=0}^{\infty} P_n(x)t^n,$$

where

$$P_n(x) = \sum_{k=0}^{[n/2]} \frac{(-1)^k (2n - 2k)!\, x^{n-2k}}{2^n (n - k)!\, k!\, (n - 2k)!}. \qquad (5.14)$$

The polynomials P_n are called the *Legendre polynomials*.

A few properties of these polynomials are easily found. We see from formula (5.14) that $P_n(x)$ involves only even powers of x when n is even and only odd powers when n is odd. The first two Legendre polynomials are found, from formula (5.14), to be

$$P_0(x) = 1, \qquad P_1(x) = x.$$

Since

$$F(1, t) = \sum_{n=0}^{\infty} P_n(1)t^n$$

and also

$$F(1, t) = (1 - 2t + t^2)^{-1/2} = \frac{1}{1 - t} = \sum_{n=0}^{\infty} t^n,$$

we can see by comparing coefficients of like powers of t that

$$P_n(1) = 1.$$

An alternative formula for the Legendre polynomials is *Rodrigues' formula*,

$$P_n(x) = \frac{1}{2^n n!} \frac{d^n}{dx^n} (x^2 - 1)^n. \qquad (5.15)$$

In order to verify the validity of this formula, let us expand the quantity $(x^2 - 1)^n$ in a binomial series,

$$(x^2 - 1)^n = \sum_{k=0}^{n} \frac{(-1)^k n!}{k!\, (n - k)!} x^{2n - 2k}$$

and differentiate n times. Since

$$\frac{d^n}{dx^n} x^r = \begin{cases} \dfrac{r!}{(n - r)!}, & n \le r, \\[2mm] 0, & n > r, \end{cases}$$

we have

$$\frac{d^n}{dx^n} (x^2 - 1)^n = \sum_{k=0}^{[n/2]} \frac{(-1)^k n!\, (2n - 2k)!}{k!\, (n - k)!\, (n - 2k)!} x^{n - 2k}.$$

Comparing the right-hand side of this equation with the expression in formula (5.14), we see that

$$\frac{d^n}{dx^n}(x^2 - 1)^n = 2^n n!\, P_n(x).$$

In the next three sections we shall derive some of the basic properties of Legendre polynomials. The methods that we shall use are general and can be applied to other polynomial sets. Specific sets that we shall consider are those bearing the names of Hermite, Laguerre, and Tchebycheff.† Their properties are listed in a table in Section 5.10. Included in the exercises at the end of this and the following sections are requests for the derivations of these properties. In carrying these out, the reader should be able to apply the techniques used in deriving the corresponding properties of Legendre polynomials.

Exercises for Section 5.5

1. Let

$$F(t) = \sum_{m=0}^{\infty}\left(\sum_{j=0}^{m} \alpha_{j,\,m}\, t^{m+j}\right).$$

Show that the rearrangement of terms that corresponds to the change of indices

$$k = j, \qquad n = m + j$$

leads to the formula

$$F(t) = \sum_{n=0}^{\infty}\left(\sum_{k=0}^{[n/2]} \alpha_{k,\,n-k}\right)t^n.$$

2. Let

$$F(t) = \sum_{m=0}^{\infty}\left(\sum_{j=0}^{\infty} \alpha_{j,\,m}\, t^{m+j}\right).$$

Show that the rearrangement of terms that corresponds to the change of indices

$$k = j, \qquad n = m + j$$

leads to the formula

$$F(t) = \sum_{n=0}^{\infty}\left(\sum_{k=0}^{n} \alpha_{k,\,n-k}\right)t^n.$$

† Also spelled Chebychev, and other ways.

3. Let

$$F(t) = \sum_{m=0}^{\infty} \left(\sum_{j=0}^{\infty} \alpha_{j,\,m} t^{m-2j} \right).$$

Show that the change of indices

$$k = j, \qquad n = m - 2j$$

leads to the relation

$$F(t) = \sum_{n=0}^{\infty} \left(\sum_{k=0}^{[n/2]} \alpha_{k,\,n-2k} \right) t^n.$$

4. Prove that

$$P_n(-1) = (-1)^n, \qquad P_{2n+1}(0) = 0, \qquad P_{2n}(0) = \frac{(-1)^n (2n)!}{2^{2n}(n!)^2}.$$

5. Let f possess a continuous nth-order derivative on the interval $[-1, 1]$. Use Rodrigues' formula and integration by parts to show that

$$\int_{-1}^{1} f(x) P_n(x) \, dx = \frac{(-1)^n}{2^n n!} \int_{-1}^{1} (x^2 - 1)^n f^{(n)}(x) \, dx.$$

6. Use the result of Exercise 5 to show that

$$\int_{-1}^{1} x^m P_n(x) \, dx = 0$$

for $m = 0, 1, 2, \ldots, n - 1$. What does this say about the orthogonality of the Legendre polynomials?

7. Let $F(x, t) = (1 - 2xt + t^2)^{-1}$. Show that

$$F(x, t) = \sum_{n=0}^{\infty} S_n(x) t^n,$$

where

$$S_n(x) = \sum_{m=0}^{[n/2]} \frac{(n + 1)! \, (1 - x^2)^m x^{n-2m}}{(2m + 1)! \, (n - 2m)!}.$$

The polynomial S_n is the nth degree *Tchebycheff polynomial of the second kind*.

8. If

$$F(x, t) = \frac{1}{1 - t} \exp\left(\frac{-xt}{1 - t} \right),$$

show that

$$F(x, t) = \sum_{n=0}^{\infty} L_n(x)t^n,$$

where

$$L_n(x) = \sum_{k=0}^{n} \frac{(-1)^k n!\, x^k}{(k!)^2 (n-k)!}.$$

The polynomial L_n is the *Laguerre polynomial* of degree n.

9.   If $F(x, t) = \exp(2xt - t^2)$, show that

$$F(x, t) = \sum_{n=0}^{\infty} \frac{H_n(x)}{n!}\, t^n,$$

where

$$H_n(x) = \sum_{k=0}^{[n/2]} \frac{(-1)^k n!\, (2x)^{n-2k}}{k!\,(n-2k)!}.$$

The polynomial H_n is the *Hermite polynomial* of degree n.

5.6   PROPERTIES OF LEGENDRE POLYNOMIALS

The generating function

$$F(x, t) = (1 - 2xt + t^2)^{-1/2} \tag{5.16}$$

for the Legendre polynomials has as its first partial derivatives

$$\frac{\partial F(x, t)}{\partial t} = (x - t)(1 - 2xt + t^2)^{-3/2}, \tag{5.17}$$

$$\frac{\partial F(x, t)}{\partial x} = t(1 - 2xt + t^2)^{-3/2}. \tag{5.18}$$

From the formulas (5.16) and (5.17) we see that

$$(1 - 2xt + t^2)\frac{\partial F}{\partial t} = (x - t)F.$$

Substituting the series

$$F(x, t) = \sum_{n=0}^{\infty} P_n(x)t^n, \qquad \frac{\partial F(x, t)}{\partial t} = \sum_{n=1}^{\infty} n P_n(x)t^{n-1}$$

into this equation, we find that

$$\sum_{n=1}^{\infty} nP_n(x)t^{n-1} - 2x \sum_{n=1}^{\infty} nP_n(x)t^n + \sum_{n=1}^{\infty} nP_n(x)t^{n+1}$$

$$= x \sum_{n=0}^{\infty} P_n(x)t^n - \sum_{n=0}^{\infty} P_n(x)t^{n+1}.$$

By shifting indices we may write this equation as

$$\sum_{n=1}^{\infty} nP_n(x)t^{n-1} - 2x \sum_{n=2}^{\infty} (n-1)P_{n-1}(x)t^{n-1} + \sum_{n=2}^{\infty} (n-2)P_{n-2}(x)t^{n-1}$$

$$= x \sum_{n=1}^{\infty} P_{n-1}(x)t^{n-1} - \sum_{n=2}^{\infty} P_{n-2}(x)t^{n-1}$$

or

$$[P_1(x) - xP_0(x)] + \sum_{n=2}^{\infty} [nP_n(x) - x(2n-1)P_{n-1}(x) + (n-1)P_{n-2}(x)]t^{n-1} = 0.$$

Consequently the Legendre polynomials must satisfy the pure recurrence relation

$$nP_n(x) = (2n-1)xP_{n-1}(x) - (n-1)P_{n-2}(x), \qquad n \geq 2. \qquad (5.19)$$

Given that $P_0(x) = 1$ and $P_1(x) = x$, this relation can be used to calculate polynomials of higher order. The first few Legendre polynomials are found to be

$$P_0(x) = 1,$$
$$P_1(x) = x,$$
$$P_2(x) = \tfrac{1}{2}(3x^2 - 1),$$
$$P_3(x) = \tfrac{1}{2}(5x^3 - 3x),$$
$$P_4(x) = \tfrac{1}{8}(35x^4 - 30x^2 + 3),$$
$$P_5(x) = \tfrac{1}{8}(63x^5 - 70x^3 + 15x).$$

Going back to formulas (5.16) and (5.18), we see that the generating function F also satisfies the partial differential equation

$$(x - t) \frac{\partial F(x, t)}{\partial x} - t \frac{\partial F(x, t)}{\partial t} = 0.$$

Since F satisfies the hypotheses of Theorem 5.8, we have

$$\frac{\partial F(x, t)}{\partial x} = \sum_{n=0}^{\infty} P_n'(x)t^n, \qquad |x| < 1, \quad |t| < \sqrt{2} - 1.$$

Substituting the series for $F(x, t)$ and $F_x(x, t)$ into the partial differential equation, we find that

$$\sum_{n=0}^{\infty} xP'_n(x)t^n - \sum_{n=0}^{\infty} P'_n(x)t^{n+1} - \sum_{n=1}^{\infty} nP_n(x)t^n = 0,$$

or

$$\sum_{n=0}^{\infty} xP'_n(x)t^n - \sum_{n=1}^{\infty} P'_{n-1}(x)t^n - \sum_{n=1}^{\infty} nP_n(x)t^n = 0,$$

or

$$xP'_0(x) + \sum_{n=1}^{\infty} [xP'_n(x) - P'_{n-1}(x) - nP_n(x)]t^n = 0.$$

Thus the Legendre polynomials are seen to satisfy the differential recurrence relation

$$xP'_n(x) = P'_{n-1}(x) + nP_n(x), \qquad n \geq 1. \tag{5.20}$$

The recurrence relations (5.19) and (5.20) can be used to derive an equation that involves only $P_n(x)$ and its derivatives. Differentiation of the recurrence relation (5.19) yields the relation

$$nP'_n(x) = (2n-1)xP'_{n-1}(x) + (2n-1)P_{n-1}(x) - (n-1)P'_{n-2}(x). \tag{5.21}$$

From formula (5.20) we have

$$P'_{n-1}(x) = xP'_n(x) - nP_n(x), \tag{5.22}$$

and

$$P'_{n-2}(x) = xP'_{n-1}(x) - (n-1)P_{n-1}(x)$$
$$= x^2P'_n(x) - nxP_n(x) - (n-1)P_{n-1}(x).$$

Substituting these expressions for $P'_{n-1}(x)$ and $P'_{n-2}(x)$ into Eq. (5.21) and simplifying, we have

$$P'_n(x) = x^2P'_n(x) - nxP_n(x) + nP_{n-1}(x).$$

Differentiating this equation, we have

$$P''_n(x) = x^2P''_n(x) + (2-n)xP'_n(x) - nP_n(x) + nP'_{n-1}(x).$$

Using formula (5.22) to eliminate $P'_{n-1}(x)$, we find that

$$(1-x^2)P''_n(x) - 2xP'_n(x) + n(n+1)P_n(x) = 0. \tag{5.23}$$

This equation, as derived, is valid for $n \geq 2$. However, in view of the fact that $P_0(x) = 1$ and $P_1(x) = x$, it is seen to be valid for $n = 0$ and $n = 1$ also.

The differential equation

$$(1-x^2)\frac{d^2y}{dx^2} - 2x\frac{dy}{dx} + \alpha(\alpha+1)y = 0 \tag{5.24}$$

is known as *Legendre's equation of order* α. Evidently when α is a nonnegative integer n, one solution of the equation is the polynomial $P_n(x)$. The differential equation can be written in the form

$$\frac{d}{dx}\left[(1-x^2)\frac{dy}{dx}\right] + \alpha(\alpha+1)y = 0. \qquad (5.25)$$

Exercises for Section 5.6

1. The zeros of P_n lie on the interval $(-1, 1)$. Calculate the zeros of the functions P_1, P_2, and P_3.

2. Draw, on the same figure, the graphs of the functions P_i, $0 \le i \le 3$, on the interval $[-1, 1]$.

3. Verify that the generating function $F(x, t)$ satisfies the equation

    $$(1 - 2xt + t^2)F_x = tF.$$

    From this equation, deduce the recurrence relation

    $$P'_{n+2}(x) - 2xP'_{n+1}(x) - P'_n(x) = P_{n+1}(x), \qquad n \ge 0.$$

4. Deduce the recurrence relation derived in Problem 3 from the relations (5.19) and (5.20).

5. Verify that the generating function $F(x, t)$ satisfies the equation

    $$(1 - t^2)F_x - 2t^2 F_t = tF.$$

    From this equation, derive the relation

    $$P'_{n+2}(x) - P'_n(x) = 2(n + 3)P_{n+1}(x), \qquad n \ge 0.$$

6. Calculate the polynomials $P_2(x)$, $P_3(x)$ and $P_4(x)$ from the recurrence relation (5.19).

7. The Hermite polynomials H_n (Section 5.10) are generated by the function $F(x, t) = \exp(2xt - t^2)$:

    $$F(x, t) = \sum_{n=0}^{\infty} \frac{H_n(x)}{n!} t^n.$$

    (a)   Show that

    $$F_x(x, t) = 2tF(x, t), \qquad F_t(x, t) = 2(x - t)F(x, t).$$

    (b)   From the relations in part (a) derive the recurrence relations

    $$H'_n(x) = 2nH_{n-1}(x), \qquad H_n(x) = 2xH_{n-1}(x) - 2(n - 1)H_{n-2}(x).$$

(c) Using the recurrence relations in part (b) show that H_n satisfies Hermite's differential equation,

$$y'' - 2xy' + 2ny = 0.$$

8. The function F, where

$$F(x, t) = \frac{1}{1 - t} \exp\left(\frac{-xt}{1 - t}\right),$$

generates the Laguerre polynomials (Section 5.10):

$$F(x, t) = \sum_{n=0}^{\infty} L_n(x)t^n.$$

(a) Show that

$$(1 - t)F_x(x, t) + tF(x, t) = 0$$

and

$$(1 - t)^2 F_t(x, t) - (1 - t)F(x, t) + xF(x, t) = 0.$$

(b) From the results of part (a) deduce that

$$L_n'(x) - L_{n-1}'(x) + L_n(x) = 0$$

and

$$nL_n(x) + (x - 2n + 1)L_{n-1}(x) + (n - 1)L_{n-2}(x) = 0.$$

(c) Use the recurrence relations in part (b) to show that L_n satisfies Laguerre's differential equation,

$$xy'' + (1 - x)y' + ny = 0.$$

5.7 ORTHOGONALITY

That the Legendre polynomials are simply orthogonal over the interval $(-1, 1)$ can be established from the differential equation (5.25). If m and n are distinct nonnegative integers, we have

$$\frac{d}{dx}[(1 - x^2)P_n'(x)] + n(n + 1)P_n(x) = 0$$

and

$$\frac{d}{dx}[(1 - x^2)P_m'(x)] + m(m + 1)P_m(x) = 0.$$

Multiplying the first equation through by $P_m(x)$ and the second by $P_n(x)$ and subtracting, we have

$$[n(n + 1) - m(m + 1)]P_m(x)P_n(x)$$

$$= P_n(x)\frac{d}{dx}[(1 - x^2)P'_m(x)] - P_m(x)\frac{d}{dx}[(1 - x^2)P'_n(x)].$$

This equation can be written in the form

$$(n - m)(n + m + 1)P_m(x)P_n(x) = \frac{d}{dx}\{(1 - x^2)[P_n(x)P'_m(x) - P_m(x)P'_n(x)]\}.$$

Integrating both sides of this equation with respect to x from -1 to 1, we have

$$(n - m)(n + m + 1) \int_{-1}^{1} P_m(x)P_n(x)\,dx$$

$$= \{(1 - x^2)[P_n(x)P'_m(x) - P_m(x)P'_n(x)]\}_{-1}^{1} = 0.$$

Since $m \neq n$, we have

$$\int_{-1}^{1} P_m(x)P_n(x)\,dx = 0. \tag{5.26}$$

We next derive a formula for the quantities

$$C_n = \|P_n\|^2 = \int_{-1}^{1} [P_n(x)]^2\,dx.$$

From the recurrence relation (5.19), we have

$$P_n(x) = \frac{2n - 1}{n}xP_{n-1}(x) - \frac{n - 1}{n}P_{n-2}(x), \qquad n \geq 2.$$

Therefore

$$C_n = \int_{-1}^{1} P_n(x)\left[\frac{2n - 1}{n}xP_{n-1}(x) - \frac{n - 1}{n}P_{n-2}(x)\right]dx,$$

and because of the orthogonality property (5.26),

$$C_n = \frac{2n - 1}{n}\int_{-1}^{1} xP_n(x)P_{n-1}(x)\,dx, \qquad n \geq 2. \tag{5.27}$$

From the recurrence relation (5.19), we also have that

$$xP_n(x) = \frac{1}{2n - 1}[(n + 1)P_{n+1}(x) + nP_{n-1}(x)], \qquad n \geq 1.$$

Substituting this expression for $xP_n(x)$ into formula (5.27) and using the orthogonality property again, we find that

$$C_n = \frac{2n-1}{2n+1} \int_{-1}^{1} [P_{n-1}(x)]^2 \, dx$$

or

$$C_n = \frac{2n-1}{2n+1} C_{n-1}, \qquad n \geq 2. \tag{5.28}$$

Since $P_0(x) = 1$ and $P_1(x) = x$, we have

$$C_0 = \int_{-1}^{1} dx = 2, \qquad C_1 = \int_{-1}^{1} x^2 \, dx = \tfrac{2}{3}.$$

Making use of formula (5.28), we find that

$$C_2 = \tfrac{3}{5} C_1 \tfrac{2}{3} \tfrac{3}{5} = \tfrac{2}{5},$$
$$C_3 = \tfrac{5}{7} C_2 \tfrac{2}{5} \tfrac{5}{7} = \tfrac{2}{7}.$$

It is easy to show, by using mathematical induction, that

$$C_n = \frac{2}{2n+1}, \qquad n \geq 0. \tag{5.29}$$

Exercises for Section 5.7

1. Show that the second-order differential equation

    $$y'' + a_1 y' + a_2 y = 0$$

    can be written as

    $$(py')' + qy = 0,$$

    where

    $$p(x) = \exp\left(\int a_1(x) \, dx \right),$$

    $$q(x) = a_2(x) \exp\left(\int a_1(x) \, dx \right).$$

    Suggestion: Multiply through in the original equation by

    $$\exp\left(\int a_1(x) \, dx \right).$$

2. The Laguerre polynomial L_n of degree n (Section 5.10) satisfies the differential equation

    $$xy'' + (1 - x)y' + ny = 0.$$

Show that the Laguerre polynomials are orthogonal with respect to the weight function $w(x) = e^{-x}$ on the interval $(0, \infty)$. *Suggestion:* Use the result of Exercise 1 to write the equation as

$$(xe^{-x}y')' + ne^{-x}y = 0.$$

3. The Laguerre polynomials are orthogonal on the interval $(0, \infty)$ with respect to the weight function $w(x) = e^{-x}$. (See Exercise 2.) They satisfy the recurrence relation

$$nL_n(x) = (2n - 1 - x)L_{n-1}(x) - (n - 1)L_{n-2}(x),$$

where $L_0(x) = 1$ and $L_1(x) = 1 - x$. (See Exercise 8, Section 5.6.) Show that

$$\int_0^\infty e^{-x}[L_n(x)]^2 \, dx = 1.$$

4. The Hermite polynomial H_n of degree n (Section 5.10) satisfies the differential equation

$$y'' - 2xy' + 2ny = 0.$$

Show that the Hermite polynomials are orthogonal with respect to the weight function $w(x) = \exp(-x^2)$ on the interval $(-\infty, \infty)$. *Suggestion:* Use the result of Exercise 1 to write the equation as

$$(e^{-x^2}y')' + 2ne^{-x^2}y = 0.$$

5. The Hermite polynomials are orthogonal on the interval $(-\infty, \infty)$ with respect to the weight function $w(x) = \exp(-x^2)$. (See Exercise 4.) They satisfy the recurrence relation

$$H_n(x) = 2xH_{n-1}(x) - 2(n - 1)H_{n-2}(x),$$

with $H_0(x) = 1$ and $H_1(x) = 2x$. (See Exercise 7, Section 5.6.) Show that

$$\int_{-\infty}^\infty e^{-x^2}[H_n(x)]^2 \, dx = 2^n n! \sqrt{\pi}.$$

6. Let the functions $p_n^m(x)$, where m and n are nonnegative integers with $0 \le m \le n$, be defined by means of the relation

$$p_n^m(x) = \frac{d^m}{dx^m} P_n(x).$$

By differentiating Eq. (5.23) m times, show that p_n^m is a solution of the equation

$$(1 - x^2)y'' - 2(m + 1)xy' + (n - m)(n + m + 1)y = 0.$$

7. Show that the functions p_i^m and p_j^m (see Exercise 6), where $i \neq j$, are orthogonal with respect to the weight function $(1 - x^2)^m$ on the interval $(-1, 1)$.

8. The functions

$$P_n^m(x) = (1 - x^2)^{m/2} p_n^m(x) = (1 - x^2)^{m/2} \frac{d^m}{dx^m} P_n(x), \qquad 0 \le m \le n,$$

are called *associated Legendre functions*. Show that the functions P_i^m and P_j^m, $i \neq j$, are simply orthogonal on the interval $(-1, 1)$. Show that the function P_n^m is a solution of the differential equation

$$(1 - x^2)y'' - 2xy' + \left[n(n + 1) - \frac{m^2}{1 - x^2} \right] y = 0.$$

9. Prove that

$$\int_{-1}^{1} [P_n^m(x)]^2 \, dx = \frac{2}{2n + 1} \frac{(n + m)!}{(n - m)!}.$$

Suggestion: Use integration by parts, and make use of the differential equation satisfied by P_n^m.

10. Show that the function $f(\phi) = P_n^m(\cos \phi)$ is a solution of the equation

$$\frac{d}{d\phi}\left(\sin \phi \, \frac{dy}{d\phi} \right) + \left[n(n + 1) \sin \phi - \frac{m^2}{\sin \phi} \right] y = 0$$

on the interval $0 < \phi < \pi$.

5.8   LEGENDRE'S DIFFERENTIAL EQUATION

The differential equation

$$(1 - x^2)\frac{d^2 y}{dx^2} - 2x \frac{dy}{dx} + \alpha(\alpha + 1)y = 0, \qquad (5.30)$$

where α is a real constant, is known as Legendre's equation of order α. We can assume without loss of generality that $\alpha \ge -\frac{1}{2}$. For if $\alpha < -\frac{1}{2}$, we can set $\beta = -\alpha - 1$, and then $\alpha(\alpha + 1) = \beta(\beta + 1)$, where $\beta > -\frac{1}{2}$.

When α is a nonnegative integer n, we have seen that one solution of equation (5.30) is the Legendre polynomial P_n of degree n. Let us now consider the differential equation for general α.

Legendre's equation has regular singular points at $x = 1$ and $x = -1$. If we make the change of variable $t = 1 - x$, the point $x = 1$ corresponds to $t = 0$ and the differential equation becomes

$$t(2 - t)\frac{d^2Y}{dt^2} + 2(1 - t)\frac{dY}{dt} + \alpha(\alpha + 1)Y = 0,$$

where $Y(t) = y(1 - t)$. This equation has a regular singular point at $t = 0$, with both exponents equal to zero. By the methods of Chapter III, two independent solutions are found to be

$$v_1(t) = 1 + \sum_{m=1}^{\infty} \frac{[(\alpha + 1)(\alpha + 2) \cdots (\alpha + m)][(-\alpha)(1 - \alpha) \cdots (m - 1 - \alpha)]}{2^m(m!)^2} t^m$$

$$v_2(t) = v_1 \log t + \sum_{m=1}^{\infty} a_m t^m,$$

where the a_m are constants whose exact values need not concern us. In terms of the variable x, these solutions are

$$u_1(x) =$$

$$1 + \sum_{m=1}^{\infty} \frac{[(\alpha + 1)(\alpha + 2) \cdots (\alpha + m)][(-\alpha)(1 - \alpha) \cdots (m - 1 - \alpha)]}{2^m(m!)^2}(1 - x)^m$$

$$u_2(x) = u_1(x) \log(1 - x) + \sum_{m=1}^{\infty} a_m(1 - x)^m.$$

The function u_1 has the value 1 at $x = 1$ for all α. When α is not an integer, the series for $u_1(x)$ is infinite and converges for $|x - 1| < 2$. When α is a nonnegative integer n, the series is finite and u_1 is a polynomial of degree n. There is no other polynomial solution of Legendre's equation when $\alpha = n$, and so

$$P_n(x) =$$

$$1 + \sum_{m=1}^{n} \frac{[(n + 1)(n + 2) \cdots (n + m)][(-n)(1 - n) \cdots (m - 1 - n)]}{2^m(m!)^2}(1 - x)^m$$

or

$$P_n(x) = \sum_{m=0}^{n} \frac{(-1)^m(m + n)!}{2^m(m!)^2(n - m)!}(1 - x)^m. \tag{5.31}$$

The quantity $u_2(x)$ becomes infinite as $x \to 1$, for all α. It can be shown (Exercise 4) that when α is not an integer, the quantity $u_1(x)$ becomes infinite as $x \to -1$. Thus Legendre's equation has a solution that is finite at both $x = 1$ and $x = -1$ only when α is an integer n. In this case, the only solutions that are finite at $x = 1$ and $x = -1$ are those which are multiples of P_n. This fact is of interest in applications that give rise to Legendre's equation.

If we take the series solution (5.31) as our definition of the Legendre polynomial of degree n, we can use Theorem 5.5 to obtain a recurrence relation. According to this theorem, there exist constants A_n, B_n, and C_n such that

$$xP_n(x) = A_n P_{n+1}(x) + B_n P_n(x) + C_n P_{n-1}(x)$$

or

$$A_n P_{n+1}(x) + (1 - x)P_n(x) + (B_n - 1)P_n(x) + C_n P_{n-1}(x) = 0.$$

By comparing coefficients of $(1 - x)^{n+1}$, $(1 - x)^n$, and $(1 - x)^0$, we find, after some calculation, that

$$A_n = \frac{n+1}{2n+1}, \qquad B_n = 0, \qquad C_n = \frac{n}{2n+1}$$

and hence the recurrence relation is

$$(n + 1)P_{n+1}(x) = x(2n + 1)P_n(x) - nP_{n-1}(x), \qquad n \geq 1.$$

This relation may be seen to be equivalent to the relation (5.19), which was derived from the generating function.

The Legendre polynomials are also characterized, except for constant factors, as the polynomials $\{\phi_n\}_{n=0}^{\infty}$ which are orthogonal with respect to the weight function $w(x) = 1$ on the interval $(-1, 1)$. The differential equation (5.23) that is satisfied by ϕ_n can be derived from this orthogonality condition as follows: let

$$I = \int_{-1}^{1} \frac{d}{dx}\left[(1 - x^2)\frac{d}{dx}\phi_n(x)\right]Q(x)\, dx, \qquad (5.32)$$

where Q is any polynomial of degree $\leq n - 1$. Integrating by parts, we have

$$I = [(1 - x^2)\phi_n'(x)Q(x)]_{-1}^{1} - \int_{-1}^{1} (1 - x^2)\phi_n'(x)Q'(x)\, dx,$$

where the integrated part vanishes. Integrating by parts again, we have

$$I = -[(1 - x^2)\phi_n(x)Q'(x)]_{-1}^{1} + \int_{-1}^{1} \phi_n(x)\frac{d}{dx}[(1 - x^2)Q'(x)]\, dx.$$

The integrated part vanishes, and since the quantity

$$\frac{d}{dx}[(1 - x^2)Q'(x)]$$

is a polynomial of degree $\leq n - 1$, we have $I = 0$.

Since the quantity

$$\frac{d}{dx}[(1 - x^2)\phi_n'(x)]$$

in the integrand in formula (5.32) is a polynomial of degree n, and since it is orthogonal to every polynomial of degree $<n$, it must be a constant multiple of ϕ_n. Thus, there is a constant A_n such that

$$\frac{d}{dx}[(1 - x^2)\phi_n'(x)] = A_n \phi_n(x).$$

If we write

$$\phi_n(x) = a_n x^n + a_{n-1}x^{n-1} + \cdots + a_0,$$

and compare the coefficients of x^n on both sides of this equation, we find that $A_n = -n(n + 1)$, and hence

$$\frac{d}{dx}\left[(1 - x^2)\frac{d}{dx}\phi_n(x)\right] + n(n + 1)\phi_n(x) = 0.$$

This is Legendre's equation of order n.

This process for finding the differential equation from the weight function can be generalized somewhat. See Exercise 6 below, and also Exercises 7 and 8 of Section 5.10.

Exercises for Section 5.8

1. Express the polynomial $Q(x) = x^3 + 2x^2 + 2$ in terms of Legendre polynomials.

2. Derive the formula

$$\| P_n \|^2 = \int_{-1}^{1} [P_n(x)]^2 \, dx = \frac{2}{2n + 1}$$

by using Rodrigues' formula (5.15) and repeated integration by parts.

3. Let P_α be the solution of Legendre's differential equation that is finite at $x = 1$, with $P_\alpha(1) = 1$. Show that a second solution of Legendre's equation is

$$P_\alpha(x) \int \frac{dx}{(1 - x^2)[P_\alpha(x)]^2}.$$

4. In Section 5.8 it was shown that Legendre's equation possessed solutions of the form

$$u_1(x) = \sum_{m=0}^{\infty} A_m(1-x)^m, \qquad A_0 = 1,$$

$$u_2(x) = u_1(x) \log (1-x) + \sum_{m=1}^{\infty} B_m(1-x)^m,$$

where the power series converge for $|x - 1| < 2$.

(a) Show that Legendre's equation also possesses solutions of the form

$$v_1(x) = \sum_{m=0}^{\infty} A_m(1+x)^m$$

$$v_2(x) = v_1(x) \log(1+x) + \sum_{m=1}^{\infty} B_m(1+x)^m,$$

where the power series converge for $|x + 1| < 2$.

(b) Show that when α is not an integer, the solution $u_1(x)$ becomes infinite as $x \to -1$. One method is outlined by the following remarks. For $|x| < 1$, there exist constants C_1 and C_2 such that

$$u_1(x) = C_1 v_1(x) + C_2 v_2(x).$$

If $C_2 \neq 0$, then $u_1(x)$ becomes infinite as $x \to -1$. Suppose that $C_2 = 0$. Then $C_1 = 1$, since $u_1(0) = v_1(0)$. Hence $u_1(x) = v_1(x)$. But from the series for $u_1(x)$ and $v_1(x)$ it can be seen that $u_1(-x) = v_1(x)$, so that $u_1(x)$ is an even function. But then the odd derivatives of $u_1(x)$ must vanish at $x = 0$. This is not true, as an examination of the series expressions for these derivatives reveals. Hence $C_2 \neq 0$, and $u_1(x)$ becomes infinite as $x \to -1$.

5. (a) Show that the change of variable $x = \cos \phi$ transforms Legendre's equation into the equation

$$\frac{d^2Y}{d\phi^2} + \frac{dY}{d\phi} \cot \phi + \alpha(\alpha + 1)Y = 0.$$

(b) Show that this equation has nontrivial solutions that are finite at $\phi = 0, \pi$ when, and only when α is an integer n, and that these solutions are of the form $Y(\phi) = C_n P_n(\cos \phi)$, where C_n is an arbitrary constant.

6. Let $\{\phi_n\}$ be the set of orthogonal polynomials that corresponds to the positive weight function w on the finite interval (a, b). Let w be of the form

$$w(x) = (x - a)^\alpha (b - x)^\beta,$$

where $\alpha > -1$, $\beta > -1$.

(a)   Show that

$$\int_b^a \frac{d}{dx} [(x - a)(x - b)\phi_n'(x)w(x)]Q(x) \, dx = 0$$

for every polynomial Q of degree less than n.

(b)   Show that ϕ_n satisfies the second-order differential equation

$$(x - a)(x - b)\phi_n'' + [(2 + \alpha + \beta)x - a(1 + \beta) - b(1 + \alpha)]\phi_n'$$
$$= [n^2 + (\alpha + \beta + 1)n]\phi_n.$$

7. Polynomial sets that are orthogonal over the interval $(-1, 1)$ with respect to weight functions of the form $w(x) = (1 - x)^\alpha(1 + x)^\beta$, $\alpha, \beta > -1$, are known as *Jacobi polynomials*. Show that the polynomial of degree n of such a set satisfies the differential equation

$$(1 - x^2)y'' + [(\beta - \alpha) - (\alpha + \beta + 2)x]y' + n(\alpha + \beta + n + 1)y = 0.$$

(See Exercise 6.)

8. In the example that follows the proof of Theorem 5.3, we found the first few polynomials of the orthogonal set that corresponds to the weight function $w(x) = \sqrt{x}$ on the interval $(0, 1)$.

(a) Show that the nth-degree polynomial of this set satisfies the differential equation

$$2(x^2 - x)y'' + (5x - 3)y' - n(2n + 3)y = 0.$$

(b)   Show that the differential equation of (a) above possesses the polynomial solution

$$\phi_n(x) =$$

$$1 - \sum_{k=0}^n \frac{n(2n + 3)[5 - n(2n + 3)] \cdots [(k - 1)(2k + 1) - n(2n + 3)]}{k! \, 1 \cdot 3 \cdot 5 \cdots (2k + 1)} x^k.$$

(c) Show that the polynomials of part (b) are orthogonal with respect to the weight function $w(x) = \sqrt{x}$ on the interval $(0, 1)$, using part (a).

5.9   TCHEBYCHEFF POLYNOMIALS

Sets of orthogonal polynomials that are orthogonal on the interval $(-1, 1)$ with respect to weight functions of the form

$$w(x) = (1 - x)^\alpha(1 + x)^\beta, \qquad \alpha > -1, \beta > -1,$$

are known as *Jacobi polynomials*. (It is necessary to restrict the constants α and β in order that the integrals

$$\int_{-1}^{1} w(x)x^m \, dx, \qquad m = 0, 1, 2, \ldots,$$

all exist.) The Legendre polynomials are a special class of Jacobi polynomials, with $\alpha = \beta = 0$.

General treatments of Jacobi polynomials can be found in Jackson [2], Rainville[5], and Szego[7]. Here we shall be concerned with two particular classes of Jacobi polynomials. The *Tchebycheff polynomials of the first kind* have the weight function $w(x) = (1 - x^2)^{-1/2}$ and correspond to the case $\alpha = \beta = -\frac{1}{2}$. The *Tchebycheff polynomials of the second kind* have the weight function $w(x) = (1 - x^2)^{1/2}$ and correspond to the case $\alpha = \beta = \frac{1}{2}$. Generating functions for these polynomial sets are known, and their properties can be derived much in the same way as for the Legendre polynomials. However, we shall leave this approach to the exercises. Here we shall adopt a different procedure based on a special relationship between the Tchebycheff polynomials and certain trigonometric functions. We shall need the following lemma.

Lemma   Let n be any nonnegative integer. Then there exist polynomials T_n and S_n, of degree n, such that

$$\cos n\theta = T_n(\cos \theta), \tag{5.33}$$

$$\sin(n + 1)\theta = \sin \theta S_n(\cos \theta). \tag{5.34}$$

PROOF   By DeMoivre's theorem,

$$\cos n\theta + i \sin n\theta = (\cos \theta + i \sin \theta)^n$$

for every nonnegative integer n. Expanding the right-hand side of this equation by the use of the binomial theorem, we have

$$\cos n\theta + i \sin n\theta = \sum_{k=0}^{n} C(n, k)(i \sin \theta)^k (\cos \theta)^{n-k}, \tag{5.35}$$

where the quantities

$$C(n, k) = \frac{n!}{k!(n - k)!}$$

are the binomial coefficients. We now equate real and imaginary parts in Eq. (5.35). The real terms in the sum on the right in this equation correspond to the even values of k. When $k = 2m$, $m = 0, 1, 2, \ldots, [n/2]$, then

$$(i \sin \theta)^k = (i \sin \theta)^{2m} = (-1)^m (1 - \cos^2 \theta)^m.$$

Equating real parts in Eq. (5.35), we have

$$\cos n\theta = \sum_{m=0}^{[n/2]} (-1)^m C(n, 2m)(1 - \cos^2 \theta)^m (\cos \theta)^{n-2m}.$$

The right-hand side of this equation is a polynomial of degree n in $\cos \theta$, which we denote by $T_n(\cos \theta)$. Then

$$\cos n\theta = T_n(\cos \theta),$$

where

$$T_n(x) = \sum_{m=0}^{[n/2]} (-1)^m \frac{n!}{(2m)! \, (n - 2m)!} (1 - x^2)^m x^{n-2m}.$$

We note that

$$T_n(1) = \cos 0 = 1, \qquad n = 0, 1, 2, \ldots.$$

The imaginary terms in the sum on the right-hand side in Eq. (5.35) correspond to the odd values of k. When $k = 2m + 1$, $m = 0, 1, 2, \ldots$, $[(n - 1)/2]$,

$$(i \sin \theta)^k = (i \sin \theta)^{2m+1} = (-1)^m i \sin \theta (1 - \cos^2 \theta)^m.$$

Equating imaginary parts in Eq. (5.35), we have

$$\sin n\theta = \sin \theta \sum_{m=0}^{[(n-1)/2]} (-1)^m C(n, 2m + 1)(1 - \cos^2 \theta)^m (\cos \theta)^{n-2m-1}.$$

The sum on the right-hand side is a polynomial of degree $n - 1$ in $\cos \theta$. We denote it by $S_{n-1}(\cos \theta)$. Then

$$\sin n\theta = \sin \theta S_{n-1}(\cos \theta)$$

and

$$\sin (n + 1)\theta = \sin \theta S_n(\cos \theta),$$

where

$$S_n(x) = \sum_{m=0}^{[n/2]} (-1)^m \frac{(n + 1)!}{(2m + 1)! \, (n - 2m)!} (1 - x^2)^m x^{n-2m}. \qquad (5.36)$$

We note that

$$S_n(1) = \lim_{\theta \to 0} \frac{\sin(n + 1)\theta}{\sin \theta} = n + 1.$$

Theorem 5.9 The polynomial set $\{T_n\}_{n=0}^{\infty}$ is orthogonal on the interval $(-1, 1)$ with respect to the weight function $w(x) = (1 - x^2)^{-1/2}$. The polynomial set $\{S_n\}_{n=0}^{\infty}$ is orthogonal on the same interval with respect to the weight function $w(x) = (1 - x^2)^{1/2}$. Furthermore

$$\|T_0\|^2 = \pi, \qquad \|T_n\|^2 = \frac{\pi}{2}, \qquad n = 1, 2, 3, \ldots,$$

and

$$\|S_n\|^2 = \frac{\pi}{2}, \qquad n = 0, 1, 2, \ldots.$$

PROOF   First let us consider the quantities

$$(T_m, T_n) = \int_{-1}^{1} \frac{1}{\sqrt{1 - x^2}} T_m(x) T_n(x) \, dx.$$

Making the change of variable $x = \cos \theta$, where $0 \leq \theta \leq \pi$, we have

$$(T_m, T_n) = \int_0^{\pi} T_m(\cos \theta) T_n(\cos \theta) \, d\theta.$$

By virtue of property (5.33),

$$(T_m, T_n) = \int_0^{\pi} \cos m\theta \cos n\theta \, d\theta.$$

Direct integration shows that

$$(T_m, T_n) = \begin{cases} 0, & m \neq n, \\ \dfrac{\pi}{2}, & m = n \neq 0, \\ \pi, & m = n = 0. \end{cases}$$

For the polynomials S_n we have

$$(S_m, S_n) = \int_{-1}^{1} \sqrt{1 - x^2} \, S_m(x) S_n(x) \, dx,$$

$$= \int_0^{\pi} \sin^2 \theta S_m(\cos \theta) S_n(\cos \theta) \, d\theta,$$

where again we have set $x = \cos \theta$, $0 \leq \theta \leq \pi$. In view of formula (5.34), we can write

$$(S_m, S_n) = \int_0^{\pi} \sin(m + 1)\theta \sin(n + 1)\theta \, d\theta.$$

Direct integration shows that

$$(S_m, S_n) = \begin{cases} 0, & m \neq n, \\ \dfrac{\pi}{2}, & m = n. \end{cases}$$

We now define the Tchebycheff polynomials of the first and second kinds to be the polynomials $\{T_n\}$ and $\{S_n\}$, respectively. The polynomials of the first kind must satisfy a recurrence relation of the form

$$x T_n(x) = A_n T_{n+1}(x) + B_n T_n(x) + C_n T_{n-1}(x)$$

according to Theorem 5.5. Setting $x = \cos \theta$, and using property (5.33), we see that this relation can be written in the form

$$\cos n\theta \cos \theta = A_n \cos(n+1)\theta + B_n \cos n\theta + C_n \cos(n-1)\theta.$$

From the trigonometric identity

$$\cos n\theta \cos \theta = \tfrac{1}{2} \cos(n+1)\theta + \tfrac{1}{2}\cos(n-1)\theta$$

we see that $A_n = C_n = \tfrac{1}{2}$, $B_n = 0$. Hence the Tchebycheff polynomials of the first kind satisfy the recurrence relation

$$2x T_n(x) = T_{n+1}(x) + T_{n-1}(x), \qquad n \geq 1. \tag{5.37}$$

In a similar fashion, it can be shown that the Tchebycheff polynomials of the second kind satisfy the recurrence relation

$$2x S_n(x) = S_{n+1}(x) + S_{n-1}(x), \qquad n \geq 1. \tag{5.38}$$

The function $Y(\theta) = \cos n\theta$ is a solution of the differential equation

$$\frac{d^2 Y}{d\theta^2} + n^2 Y = 0.$$

Therefore the change of variable $x = \cos \theta$ leads to a differential equation that is satisfied by $T_n(x)$. Let $y(x) = Y(\theta)$. Since

$$\frac{dY}{d\theta} = \frac{dy}{dx}\frac{dx}{d\theta} = -\frac{dy}{dx}\sin \theta$$

and

$$\frac{d^2 Y}{d\theta^2} = \frac{d^2 y}{dx^2}\sin^2 \theta - \frac{dy}{dx}\cos \theta = (1 - x^2)\frac{d^2 y}{dx^2} - x\frac{dy}{dx},$$

this differential equation is

$$(1 - x^2)\frac{d^2y}{dx^2} - x\frac{dy}{dx} + n^2y = 0. \tag{5.39}$$

It is left as an exercise to show that the polynomial S_n satisfies the differential equation

$$(1 - x^2)\frac{d^2y}{dx^2} - 3x\frac{dy}{dx} + n(n + 2)y = 0. \tag{5.40}$$

Exercises for Section 5.9

1. Derive the recurrence relation (5.38) for the polynomials S_n, using the formula (5.34).

2. Derive the differential equation (5.40) that is satisfied by S_n, using the formula (5.34).

3. The generating function for the Tchebycheff polynomials of the first kind is

$$F(x, t) = \frac{1 - xt}{1 - 2xt + t^2}.$$

    From the generating function, derive:
    (a)   The formula for $T_n(x)$.
    (b)   The recurrence relation (5.37).
    (c)   The differential equation (5.39).

4. (a)   Show that when α is a nonnegative integer n, the differential equation
$$(1 - x^2)y'' - xy' + \alpha^2 y = 0$$
    possesses a polynomial solution T_n of degree n, with $y(1) = 1$. Find an explicit formula for $T_n(x)$ in terms of powers of $(x - 1)$.
    (b)   Show that the polynomials T_n of part (a) are orthogonal with respect to the weight function $w(x) = (1 - x^2)^{-1/2}$ on the interval $(-1, 1)$.
    (c)   Find the recurrence relation that is satisfied by the polynomials T_n. Use the general formula (5.5).

5. The generating function for the Tchebycheff polynomials of the second kind is

$$G(x, t) = \frac{1}{1 - 2xt + t^2}.$$

From this generating function, derive:

(a)   The formula (5.36) for $S_n(x)$.

(b)   The recurrence relation (5.38).

(c)   The differential equation (5.40).

6.   (a) Show that when α is a nonnegative integer n, the differential equation

$$(1 - x^2)y'' - 3xy' + \alpha(\alpha + 2)y = 0$$

possesses a polynomial solution S_n, of degree n, with $y(1) = n + 1$. Obtain an explicit formula for $S_n(x)$ in terms of powers of $(x - 1)$.

(b)   Show that the polynomials S_n of part (a) are orthogonal with respect to the weight function $w(x) = (1 - x^2)^{1/2}$ on the interval $(-1, 1)$.

(c)   Find the recurrence relation which is satisfied by the polynomials S_n, making use of the general formula (5.5).

7.   (a)   Show that

$$T_0(x) = 1, \quad T_1(x) = x, \quad T_2(x) = 2x^2 - 1, \quad T_3(x) = 4x^3 - 3x$$

$$T_4(x) = 8x^4 - 8x^2 + 1, \quad T_5(x) = 16x^5 - 20x^3 + 5x.$$

(b)   Show that

$$S_0(x) = 1, \quad S_1(x) = 2x, \quad S_2(x) = 4x^2 - 1, \quad S_3(x) = 8x^3 - 4x$$

$$S_4(x) = 16x^4 - 12x^2 + 1, \quad S_5(x) = 32x^5 - 32x^3 + 6x.$$

8.   Show that $|T_n(x)| \le 1$ for $|x| \le 1$. If $x_k = \cos k\pi/n$, $k = 0, 1, \ldots, n$, show that $T(x_k) = (-1)^k$.

9.   Let Q_n be a polynomial of degree n with leading coefficient 1; that is, let Q_n be of the form

$$Q_n(x) = x^n + c_1 x^{n-1} + \cdots + c_n.$$

(a)   Show that $2^{1-n}T_n$ is a polynomial of this form.

(b)   If M is the maximum value of $|Q_n|$ on $[-1, 1]$ and m is the maximum value of $2^{1-n}|T_n|$ on $[-1, 1]$, show that $M \ge m$. *Suggestion:* Suppose that $M < m$. Show that this implies $Q_n - 2^{1-n}T_n$ has at least n distinct zeros and obtain a contradiction from this fact. Make use of the results of Exercise 8.

5.10   OTHER SETS OF ORTHOGONAL POLYNOMIALS

In addition to the Jacobi polynomials, two other sets of orthogonal polynomials seem worthy of mention in an introductory treatment. These are the Laguerre and Hermite polynomials. Both sets have an infinite interval of orthogonality. The Laguerre polynomials L_n are orthogonal with respect to the weight function $w(x) = e^{-x}$ on the interval $(0, \infty)$. The Hermite polynomials H_n are orthogonal with respect to the weight function $w(x) = e^{-x^2}$ on the interval $(-\infty, \infty)$.

In the table below are listed, for convenience of reference, some of the basic properties of these and the previously discussed sets of orthogonal polynomials. The derivations of these properties are left as exercises. The reader should be warned that various authors use slightly different definitions for polynomial sets bearing the same name. However, the polynomials of two such sets usually differ only by constant factors, and by a linear change of independent variable.

TABLE OF ORTHOGONAL POLYNOMIALS

1. Legendre Polynomials

$$P_n(x) = \sum_{k=0}^{[n/2]} \frac{(-1)^k (2n - 2k)!}{2^n (n - k)! \, k! \, (n - 2k)!} x^{n - 2k}$$

(a)   Interval: $-1 < x < 1$.
(b)   Weight function: $w(x) = 1$.
(c)   Generating function:

$$(1 - 2xt + t^2)^{-1/2} = \sum_{n=0}^{\infty} P_n(x) t^n.$$

(d)   Recurrence relation:

$$nP_n(x) = (2n - 1)xP_{n-1}(x) - (n - 1)P_{n-2}(x), \qquad n > 2.$$

(e)   Differential equation:

$$(1 - x^2)P_n''(x) - 2xP_n'(x) + n(n + 1)P_n(x) = 0.$$

(f)   Rodrigues' formula:

$$P_n(x) = \frac{1}{2^n n!} \frac{d^n}{dx^n} (x^2 - 1)^n.$$

(g)   Norm:

$$\| P_n \|^2 = \int_{-1}^{1} [P_n(x)]^2 \, dx = \frac{2}{2n + 1}, \qquad n \geq 0.$$

2. Tchebycheff Polynomials of the First Kind

$$T_n(x) = \sum_{k=0}^{[n/2]} \frac{n! \, x^{n-2k} (x^2 - 1)^k}{(2k)! \, (n - 2k)!} = \cos(n \cos^{-1} x)$$

(a)   Interval: $-1 < x < 1$.
(b)   Weight function: $w(x) = (1 - x^2)^{-1/2}$.
(c)   Generating function:

$$\frac{1 - xt}{1 - 2xt + t^2} = \sum_{n=0}^{\infty} T_n(x) t^n.$$

(d)   Recurrence relation:

$$T_n(x) = 2xT_{n-1}(x) - T_{n-2}(x), \qquad n \geq 2.$$

(e)   Differential equation:

$$(1 - x^2)T_n''(x) - xT_n'(x) - n^2 T_n(x) = 0.$$

(f)   Norm:

$$\| T_n \|^2 = \int_{-1}^{1} \frac{[T_n(x)]^2}{\sqrt{1 - x^2}} \, dx = \begin{cases} \pi, & n = 0, \\ \dfrac{\pi}{2}, & n \geq 1. \end{cases}$$

3. Tchebycheff Polynomials of the Second Kind

$$S_n(x) = \sum_{k=0}^{[n/2]} \frac{(n + 1)! \, x^{n-2k} (x^2 - 1)^k}{(2k + 1)! \, (n - 2k)!} = \frac{\sin[(n + 1) \cos^{-1} x]}{\sqrt{1 - x^2}}$$

(a)   Interval: $-1 < x < 1$.
(b)   Weight function: $w(x) = (1 - x^2)^{1/2}$.
(c)   Generating function:

$$\frac{1}{1 - 2xt + t^2} = \sum_{n=0}^{\infty} S_n(x) t^n.$$

(d)   Recurrence relation:

$$S_n(x) = 2xS_{n-1}(x) - S_{n-2}(x), \qquad n \geq 2.$$

(e)   Differential equation:

$$(1 - x^2)S_n''(x) - 3xS_n'(x) + n(n+2)S_n(x) = 0.$$

(f)   Norm:

$$\| S_n \| = \int_{-1}^{1} \sqrt{1 - x^2}[S_n(x)]^2 = \frac{\pi}{2}, \qquad n \geq 0.$$

4. Laguerre Polynomials

$$L_n(x) = \sum_{k=0}^{n} \frac{(-1)^k n!\, x^k}{(k!)^2 (n-k)!}$$

(a)   Interval: $0 < x < \infty$.
(b)   Weight function: $w(x) = e^{-x}$.
(c)   Generating function:

$$\frac{1}{1-t} \exp\left(\frac{-xt}{1-t}\right) = \sum_{n=0}^{\infty} L_n(x)t^n.$$

(d)   Recurrence relation:

$$nL_n(x) = (2n - 1 - x)L_{n-1}(x) - (n-1)L_{n-2}(x), \qquad n \geq 2.$$

(e)   Differential equation:

$$xL_n''(x) + (1 - x)L_n'(x) + nL_n(x) = 0.$$

(f)   Rodrigues' formula:

$$L_n(x) = \frac{1}{n!} e^x \frac{d^n}{dx^n}(x^n e^{-x}).$$

(g)   Norm:

$$\|L_n\|^2 = \int_{0}^{\infty} e^{-x}[L_n(x)]^2\, dx = 1, \qquad n \geq 0.$$

5. Hermite Polynomials

$$H_n(x) = \sum_{k=0}^{[n/2]} \frac{(-1)^k n!\, (2x)^{n-2k}}{k!\,(n-2k)!}$$

(a)   Interval: $-\infty < x < \infty$.
(b)   Weight function: $w(x) = e^{-x^2}$.
(c)   Generating function:

$$\exp(2xt - t^2) = \sum_{n=0}^{\infty} \frac{H_n(x)}{n!} t^n.$$

(d)   Recurrence relation:

$$H_n(x) = 2xH_{n-1}(x) - 2(n-1)H_{n-2}(x), \qquad n \geq 2.$$

(e)   Differential equation:

$$H_n''(x) - 2xH_n'(x) + 2nH_n(x) = 0.$$

(f)   Rodrigues' formula:

$$H_n(x) = (-1)^n e^{x^2} \frac{d^n}{dx^n} e^{-x^2}.$$

(g)   Norm:

$$\|H_n\|^2 = \int_{-\infty}^{+\infty} e^{-x^2} [H_n(x)]^2 \, dx = 2^n n! \sqrt{\pi}, \qquad n \geq 0.$$

Exercises for Section 5.10

1.   Starting with the generating function

$$F(x, t) = \frac{1}{1-t} \exp\left[\frac{-xt}{1-t}\right]$$

for the Laguerre polynomials, derive the properties of these polynomials that are listed in the table.

2.   (a)   Show that when α is a nonnegative integer n, the differential equation

$$xy'' + (1-x)y' + \alpha y = 0$$

possesses a polynomial solution $y(x) = L_n(x)$ of degree n, with $y(0) = 1$. Obtain an explicit formula for $L_n(x)$ in terms of powers of x.

(b)   Show that the polynomials L_n of (a) above are orthogonal with respect to the weight function $w(x) = e^{-x}$ on the interval $(0, \infty)$.

(c)   Derive the recurrence relation for the polynomials L_n, using the general formula (5.5).

3. Show that

$$L_0(x) = 1, \qquad L_1(x) = 1 - x, \qquad L_2(x) = 1 - 2x + \tfrac{1}{2}x^2,$$
$$L_3(x) = 1 - 3x + \tfrac{3}{2}x^2 - \tfrac{1}{6}x^3,$$
$$L_4(x) = 1 - 4x + 3x^2 - \tfrac{2}{3}x^3 + \tfrac{1}{24}x^4$$
$$L_5(x) = 1 - 5x + 5x^2 - \tfrac{5}{3}x^3 + \tfrac{5}{24}x^4 - \tfrac{1}{120}x^5.$$

4. Starting with the generating relation

$$\exp(2xt - t^2) = \sum_{n=0}^{\infty} \frac{H_n(x)}{n!} t^n,$$

derive the properties of the Hermite polynomials H_n that are listed in the table.

5. (a) Show that when α is a nonnegative integer n, the differential equation

$$y'' - 2xy' + 2\alpha y = 0$$

possesses a polynomial solution $y(x) = H_n(x)$, of degree n.

(b) Show that the polynomials H_n are orthogonal with respect to the weight function $w(x) = \exp(-x^2)$ on the interval $(-\infty, \infty)$.

6. Show that

$$H_0(x) = 1, \quad H_1(x) = 2x, \quad H_2(x) = 4x^2 - 2, \quad H_3(x) = 8x^3 - 12x,$$
$$H_4(x) = 16x^4 - 48x^2 + 12, \quad H_5(x) = 32x^5 - 160x^3 + 120x.$$

7. Let $\{\phi_n\}_{n=0}^{\infty}$ be the polynomial set that corresponds to the positive weight function w on the infinite interval (a, ∞). Let w be of the form

$$w(x) = ce^{-\alpha x}(x - a)^\beta,$$

where $c > 0$, $\alpha > 0$, and $\beta > -1$.

(a) Show that

$$\int_a^\infty \frac{d}{dx}[(x - a)\phi_n'(x)w(x)]Q(x) \, dx = 0$$

for every polynomial Q of degrees less than n.

(b) Show that ϕ_n satisfies the differential equation

$$(x - a)\phi_n'' + (a\alpha + \beta + 1 - \alpha x)\phi_n' = [n^2 - (\alpha + 1)n]\phi_n.$$

8. Let $\{\phi_n\}_{n=0}^{\infty}$ be the polynomial set that corresponds to the positive weight function w on the interval $(-\infty, \infty)$. Let w be of the form

$$w(x) = ce^{-\alpha x + \beta x},$$

where $c < 0$, $\alpha > 0$.

(a) Show that

$$\int_{-\infty}^{\infty} \frac{d}{dx} [\phi_n'(x)w(x)]Q(x) \, dx = 0$$

for every polynomial Q of degrees less than n.

(b) Show that ϕ_n satisfies the differential equation

$$\phi_n'' + (\beta - 2\alpha x)\phi_n' = n(n - 2\alpha - 1)\phi_n.$$

REFERENCES

1. Apostol, T. M., *Mathematical Analysis.* Addison-Wesley, Reading, Massachusetts, 1957.
2. Jackson, D., *Fourier Series and Orthogonal Polynomials*, Carus Mathematical Monograph No. 6. Open Court Publishing Co., La Salle, Illinois, 1941.
3. MacRobert, T. M., *Spherical Harmonics.* Dover, New York, 1948.
4. Olmsted, S. M. H., *Real Variables.* Appleton-Century-Crofts, New York, 1956.
5. Rainville, E. D., *Special Functions.* Macmillan, New York, 1960.
6. Sansone, G., *Orthogonal Functions.* Wiley (Interscience), New York, 1959.
7. Szego, G., *Orthogonal Polynomials.* American Mathematical Society, Colloquium Publications, Vol. 23, revised ed., New York, 1959.

VI

Eigenvalue Problems

6.1 INTRODUCTION

Eigenvalue problems arise in a number of different areas of mathematics. In order to introduce the notion of an eigenvalue problem in the area of ordinary differential equations, let us consider a second-order linear homogeneous differential equation

$$a_0(x, \lambda)\frac{d^2y}{dx^2} + a_1(x, \lambda)\frac{dy}{dx} + a_2(x, \lambda)y = 0$$

on an interval $a \leq x \leq b$. At least one of the coefficients $a_i(x, \lambda)$ is assumed to depend on a parameter λ as well as on the independent variable x. In addition to satisfying the differential equation, we shall require that our unknown function y also satisfy *boundary conditions* of the form

$$\alpha_{11}y(a) + \alpha_{12}\,y'(a) + \alpha_{13}\,y(b) + \alpha_{14}\,y'(b) = 0,$$
$$\alpha_{21}y(a) + \alpha_{22}\,y'(a) + \alpha_{23}\,y(b) + \alpha_{24}\,y'(b) = 0.$$

The quantities α_{ij} are specific real constants. We note that the boundary conditions involve the values of y and its first derivative at the two endpoints a and b of the interval $[a, b]$, in general.

The differential equation and the boundary conditions constitute an *eigenvalue problem*. Evidently the trivial solution $y = 0$ of the differential equation also satisfies the boundary conditions. We may ask whether there are any values of the parameter λ for which the differential equation possesses

244

a *nontrivial* solution that satisfies the boundary conditions. Such a value of λ is called an *eigenvalue* of the problem. A corresponding nontrivial solution is called an *eigenfunction*.

The above problem can be generalized in a number of ways. For instance, the coefficients α_{ij} which appear in the boundary conditions can depend on the parameter λ, instead of being fixed constants. Also, the number of boundary conditions need not be equal to two, although this is the case in most applications. In an eigenvalue problem associated with a linear homogeneous differential equation of arbitrary order n, each linear homogeneous boundary condition may involve the values of the unknown function and its first $n - 1$ derivatives at the two points a and b. In this chapter we shall be concerned almost entirely with second-order eigenvalue problems with two boundary conditions.

Let us now consider some specific examples of eigenvalue problems.

Example 1 We consider first the eigenvalue problem that consists of the differential equation

$$\frac{d^2y}{dx^2} + \lambda y = 0 \qquad (6.1)$$

on the interval $0 \le x \le c$, and the boundary conditions

$$y(0) = 0, \qquad y(c) = 0. \qquad (6.2)$$

For real λ, it is convenient to consider the three cases $\lambda > 0$, $\lambda = 0$, and $\lambda < 0$ separately, because the solutions of the differential equation have different forms in these three cases.

For $\lambda > 0$, let $\lambda = k^2$, where $k > 0$. Then the differential equation (6.1) becomes

$$\frac{d^2y}{dx^2} + k^2 y = 0.$$

The general solution is

$$y(x) = c_1 \cos kx + c_2 \sin kx,$$

where c_1 and c_2 are arbitrary constants. The condition $y(0) = 0$ requires that $c_1 = 0$. Thus, if a nontrivial solution exists, it must be of the form

$$y(x) = c_2 \sin kx.$$

The condition $y(c) = 0$ requires that

$$c_2 \sin kc = 0.$$

This condition is satisfied if we choose $c_2 = 0$, but in this event we obtain only the trivial solution $y = 0$. However, the condition is also satisfied, regardless of the value of c_2, if we choose k to have any one of the values

$$k_n = \frac{n\pi}{c}, \qquad n = 1, 2, 3, \dots .$$

The corresponding values of λ are

$$\lambda_n = k_n^2 = \left(\frac{n\pi}{c}\right)^2, \qquad n = 1, 2, 3, \dots . \tag{6.3}$$

These numbers are eigenvalues of the problem. The functions

$$y_n(x) = \sin k_n x = \sin \frac{n\pi x}{c}, \qquad n = 1, 2, 3, \dots$$

are corresponding eigenfunctions. Here we have taken the arbitrary constant c_2 to be equal to one. Actually c_2 can have any nonzero value.

When $\lambda = 0$, Eq. (6.1) becomes

$$\frac{d^2 y}{dx^2} = 0 .$$

The general solution is

$$y(x) = c_1 + c_2 x .$$

The condition $y(0) = 0$ requires that $c_1 = 0$, so that

$$y(x) = c_2 x .$$

The condition $y(c) = 0$ satisfied if, and only if, $c_2 = 0$. Thus, when $\lambda = 0$, the only solution of the differential equation that satisfies the boundary conditions is the trivial solution $y = 0$. Hence $\lambda = 0$ is not an eigenvalue of the problem.

When $\lambda < 0$, let $\lambda = -k^2$, where $k > 0$. Then equation (6.1) becomes

$$\frac{d^2 y}{dx^2} - k^2 y = 0 .$$

The general solution is

$$y(x) = c_1 \cosh kx + c_2 \sinh kx .$$

The condition $y(0) = 0$ requires that $c_1 = 0$, so that

$$y(x) = c_2 \sinh kx .$$

The condition $y(c) = 0$ requires that

$$c_2 \sinh kc = 0.$$

But $\sinh kc > 0$ for $k > 0$, so we must have $c_2 = 0$. Hence the only solution that satisfies the boundary conditions is the trivial solution, and so the problem has no negative eigenvalues.

If we admit complex solutions, the possibility of the existence of complex eigenvalues arises. Later on, however, we shall show that for a certain class of eigenvalue problems, of which Example 1 is a special case, no complex eigenvalues exist. Hence the only eigenvalues of the problem of Example 1 are given by formula (6.3). In each of the examples which follow, it also turns out that no complex eigenvalues exist.

Example 2 We consider the same differential equation as in Example 1,

$$\frac{d^2y}{dx^2} + \lambda y = 0,$$

but this time with the boundary conditions

$$y'(0) = 0, \qquad y'(c) = 0.$$

When $\lambda > 0$, we let $\lambda = k^2$, where $k > 0$. Then

$$y(x) = c_1 \cos kx + c_2 \sin kx$$

and

$$y'(x) = -kc_1 \sin kx + kc_2 \cos kx.$$

The condition $y'(0) = 0$ requires that $c_2 = 0$, so that

$$y(x) = c_1 \cos kx, \qquad y'(x) = -kc_1 \sin kx.$$

The condition $y'(c) = 0$ requires that

$$-kc_1 \sin kc = 0.$$

This condition is satisfied if k has one of the values

$$k_n = \frac{n\pi}{c}, \qquad n = 1, 2, 3, \ldots,$$

that is, if λ has one of the values

$$\lambda_n = \left(\frac{n\pi}{c}\right)^2, \qquad n = 1, 2, 3, \ldots.$$

The corresponding eigenfunctions are

$$y_n(x) = \cos \frac{n\pi x}{c}, \qquad n = 1, 2, 3, \dots .$$

When $\lambda = 0$, the general solution of the differential equation is

$$y(x) = c_1 + c_2 x.$$

Then

$$y'(x) = c_2.$$

The condition $y'(0)$ requires that $c_2 = 0$. But then $y'(x) \equiv 0$, so the condition $y'(c) = 0$ is also satisfied. The constant c_1 is arbitrary. Thus $\lambda_0 = 0$ is an eigenvalue of the problem, and a corresponding eigenfunction is

$$y_0(x) = 1.$$

When $\lambda < 0$, let $\lambda = -k^2$, where $k > 0$. The general solution of the differential equation is

$$y(x) = c_1 \cosh kx + c_2 \sinh kx,$$

and

$$y'(x) = kc_1 \sinh kx + kc_2 \cosh kx.$$

The condition $y'(0) = 0$ requires that $c_2 = 0$, so that

$$y(x) = c_1 \cosh kx, \qquad y'(x) = kc_1 \sinh kx.$$

The condition $y'(c) = 0$ requires that

$$kc_1 \sinh kc = 0,$$

and so c_1 must zero also. But then $y = 0$, so the eigenvalue problem has no negative eigenvalues.

The eigenvalues of the problem are therefore the numbers

$$\lambda_n = \left(\frac{n\pi}{c}\right)^2, \qquad n = 0, 1, 2, \dots,$$

and the corresponding eigenfunctions are the functions

$$y_n(x) = \cos \frac{n\pi x}{c}, \qquad n = 0, 1, 2, \dots .$$

Example 3   As another example of an eigenvalue problem, we consider the fourth-order differential equation

$$\frac{d^4 y}{dx^4} + \lambda \frac{d^2 y}{dx^2} = 0, \tag{6.4}$$

with the boundary conditions

$$y(0) = 0, \qquad y''(0) = 0, \tag{6.5a}$$
$$y(1) = 0, \qquad y'(1) = 0. \tag{6.5b}$$

As in the previous examples, it is convenient to consider the cases $\lambda > 0$, $\lambda = 0$, and $\lambda < 0$ separately. When $\lambda > 0$, we let $\lambda = k^2$, where $k > 0$. The differential equation

$$\frac{d^4 y}{dx^4} + k^2 \frac{d^2 y}{dx^2} = 0$$

possesses the general solution

$$y(x) = c_1 \cos kx + c_2 \sin kx + c_3 + c_4 x.$$

The first two derivatives are

$$y'(x) = k(-c_1 \sin kx + c_2 \cos kx) + c_4,$$
$$y''(x) = -k^2(c_1 \cos kx + c_2 \sin kx).$$

The boundary conditions (6.5a) require that

$$c_1 + c_3 = 0, \qquad c_1 = 0.$$

Thus $c_1 = c_3 = 0$, and

$$y(x) = c_2 \sin kx + c_4 x,$$
$$y'(x) = kc_2 \cos kx + c_4.$$

The boundary conditions (6.5b) require that

$$\begin{aligned} c_2 \sin k + c_4 &= 0, \\ c_2 k \cos k + c_4 &= 0. \end{aligned} \tag{6.6}$$

This system of equations for c_2 and c_4 has a nontrivial solution if and only if the determinant

$$\begin{vmatrix} \sin k & 1 \\ k \cos k & 1 \end{vmatrix} = \sin k - k \cos k = \cos k \, (\tan k - k)$$

vanishes. Thus k must satisfy the equation

$$\tan k = k. \tag{6.7}$$

Although we cannot give an explicit formula for the positive roots of this equation, the fact that an infinite number of roots does exist can be seen from the graphs of the functions k and $\tan k$ in Fig. 6.1. If we denote the nth

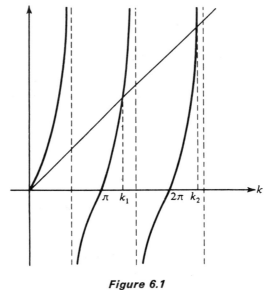

Figure 6.1

positive root of Eq. (6.7) by k_n, the corresponding eigenvalues of the problem are

$$\lambda_n = k_n^2, \qquad n = 1, 2, 3, \dots . \tag{6.8}$$

When $k = k_n$, the two equations (6.6) are equivalent, and either one can
be used to eliminate one of the constants c_2 or c_4. Taking the first equation,
we have

$$c_2 = -\frac{c_4}{\sin k_n},$$

where c_4 is arbitrary. Then as eigenfunctions, we have

$$y_n(x) = -c_4 \left[\frac{\sin k_n x}{\sin k_n} - x \right].$$

If we choose $c_4 = -\sin k_n$, then

$$y_n(x) = \sin k_n x - x \sin k_n, \qquad n = 1, 2, 3, \dots . \tag{6.9}$$

It is a routine matter to show that when $\lambda \leq 0$ the differential equation
(6.4) possesses no nontrivial solutions that satisfy the boundary conditions.
Thus all the eigenvalues and eigenfunctions of the problem are given by
formulas (6.8) and (6.9).

Exercises for Section 6.1

In Exercises 1–8 find all real eigenvalues and also find the corresponding eigenfunctions.

1. $y'' + \lambda y = 0$, $y(0) = 0$, $y'(\pi) = 0$
2. $y'' + \lambda y = 0$, $y(0) - y'(0) = 0$, $y(1) - y'(1) = 0$
3. $y'' + \lambda y = 0$, $y'(0) = 0$, $y(1) + y'(1) = 0$
4. $y'' + \lambda y = 0$, $y'(0) + 2y'(1) = 0$, $y(1) = 0$
5. $y'' + 2y' + (\lambda + 1)y = 0$, $y(0) = 0$, $y(\pi) = 0$
6. $x^2 y'' - xy' + (\lambda + 1)y = 0$, $y(1) = 0$, $y(e) = 0$
7. $y^{(4)} - \lambda y = 0$, $y'(0) = y'''(0) = y'(1) = y'''(1) = 0$
8. $y^{(4)} + \lambda y'' = 0$, $y(0) = y'(0) = y(1) = y''(1) = 0$
9. Show that every real number is an eigenvalue for the problem
$$y'' + \lambda y = 0, \qquad y(0) - y(1) = 0, \qquad y'(0) + y'(1) = 0,$$
and find the eigenfunctions.
10. Show that the problem
$$y'' + \lambda y = 0, \qquad 2y(0) - y(1) = 0, \qquad 2y'(0) + y'\ (1) = 0$$
has no real eigenvalues.

6.2 SELF-ADJOINT PROBLEMS

We first take up a preliminary matter. If the second-order differential equation
$$a_0 y'' + a_1 y' + a_2 y = 0$$
is multiplied through by
$$\frac{1}{a_0} e^P,$$
where P is any antiderivative of a_1/a_0, it takes the form
$$e^P y'' + \frac{a_1}{a_0} e^P y' + \frac{a_2}{a_0} e^P y = 0.$$

Writing

$$p = e^P, \qquad q = \frac{a_2}{a_0} e^P,$$

we have

$$py'' + p'y' + qy = 0$$

or

$$(py')' + qy = 0. \qquad\qquad (6.10)$$

A second-order equation in the form (6.10) is said to be in *self-adjoint form*.
   We now turn our attention to second-order eigenvalue problems of the
form

$$a_0 y'' + a_1 y' + (a_2 + \lambda a_3)y = 0,$$
$$\alpha_{11}y(a) + \alpha_{12} y'(a) + \alpha_{13} y(b) + \alpha_{14} y'(b) = 0,$$
$$\alpha_{21}y(a) + \alpha_{22} y'(a) + \alpha_{23} y(b) + \alpha_{24} y'(b) = 0.$$

The real functions a_0, a_1, a_2, and a_3 do not depend on λ, nor do the real
constants α_{ij}. If the differential equation is put in self-adjoint form, it becomes

$$(py')' + (q + \lambda r)y = 0,$$

where

$$p = e^P, \qquad q = \frac{a_2}{a_0} e^P, \qquad r = \frac{a_3}{a_0} e^P, \qquad P' = \frac{a_1}{a_0}.$$

Let us define *boundary operators* U_1 and U_2 by means of the formulas

$$U_1(y) = \alpha_{11}y(a) + \alpha_{12} y'(a) + \alpha_{13} y(b) + \alpha_{14} y'(b),$$
$$U_2(y) = \alpha_{21}y(a) + \alpha_{22} y'(a) + \alpha_{23} y(b) + \alpha_{24} y'(b).$$

We now consider the eigenvalue problem

$$Ly = -\lambda ry, \qquad U_1(y) = 0, \qquad U_2(y) = 0, \qquad\qquad (6.11)$$

where

$$Ly = (py')' + qy.$$

We assume that p', q, and r are continuous on $[a, b]$, with $p(x) > 0$ and
$r(x) > 0$ for $a \le x \le b$. The boundary conditions are assumed to be independent in the sense that satisfaction of one does not automatically imply
satisfaction of the other. This problem is often called a *Sturm–Liouville
problem*, after the two mathematicians who pioneered in its investigation.

The eigenfunctions of the problem (6.11) belong to the class of functions that possess continuous second derivatives on $[a, b]$ and satisfy the boundary conditions. We denote this class by B. Not every function in B is an eigenfunction, since an eigenfunction must also be a solution of the differential equation. The eigenvalue problem (6.11) is said to be *self-adjoint†* if

$$\int_a^b (vLu - uLv)\, dx = 0 \qquad\qquad (6.12)$$

for all functions u and v in B.

Although the reason for singling out problems that satisfy the condition (6.12) is not apparent, we can easily establish two important properties of such problems.

Theorem 6.1   Let λ_1 and λ_2 be distinct eigenvalues of the problem (6.11) and let y_1 and y_2 be corresponding eigenfunctions. If the problem is self-adjoint, then y_1 and y_2 are orthogonal with respect to the weight function r on $[a, b]$.

PROOF   We have

$$Ly_1 = -\lambda_1 r y_1, \qquad Ly_2 = -\lambda_2 r y_2.$$

Multiplying through in the first equation by y_2 and in the second by y_1, and subtracting, we have

$$y_2 Ly_1 - y_1 Ly_2 = (\lambda_2 - \lambda_1) r y_1 y_2.$$

Since y_1 and y_2 are eigenfunctions, they satisfy the boundary conditions and belong to the class B. Integrating from a to b in the last equation, we have

$$0 = \int_a^b (y_2 Ly_1 - y_1 Ly_2)\, dx = (\lambda_2 - \lambda_1) \int_a^b r y_1 y_2\, dx.$$

Since $\lambda_1 \neq \lambda_2$, it follows that

$$\int_a^b r y_1 y_2\, dx = 0,$$

as we wished to show.

Theorem 6.2   A self-adjoint problem has no complex eigenvalues.

---

† Associated with every Sturm–Liouville problem is an adjoint problem, which may be the same as the original problem. In this case the problem is called self-adjoint. The theory of second- and higher-order eigenvalue problems and their adjoints is developed in advanced works on differential equations and differential operators. See, however, Exercises 5 and 6, this section.

PROOF Suppose that the problem does have a complex eigenvalue, $\lambda_0 = \alpha_0 + i\beta_0$, where $\beta_0 \neq 0$. Let $y_0 = u_0 + iv_0$ be a corresponding eigenfunction. Then

$$Ly_0 = -\lambda_0 r y_0$$

or

$$(py_0)' + qy_0 = -\lambda_0 r y_0 .$$

Taking complex conjugates, and remembering that p, q, and r are real functions, we have

$$(p\bar{y}_0')' + q\bar{y}_0 = -\bar{\lambda}_0 r \bar{y}_0$$

or

$$L\bar{y}_0 = -\bar{\lambda}_0 r \bar{y}_0 .$$

The function y_0 satisfies the boundary conditions

$$U_1(y_0) = 0, \qquad U_2(y_0) = 0 .$$

Taking complex conjugates, and remembering that the boundary operators U_1 and U_2 have real coefficients, we have

$$\overline{U_1(y_0)} = U_1(\bar{y}_0) = 0, \qquad \overline{U_2(y_0)} = U_2(\bar{y}_0) = 0 .$$

Thus the function $\bar{y}_0 = u_0 - iv_0$ is also an eigenfunction of the problem, corresponding to the eigenvalue $\bar{\lambda}_0 = \alpha_0 - i\beta_0$. According to Theorem 6.1,

$$\int_a^b r y_0 \bar{y}_0 \, dx = \int_a^b r |y_0|^2 \, dx = 0 .$$

But this is impossible since y_0 is a nontrivial solution of the differential equation and $r(x) > 0$ for x in $[a, b]$. We conclude that the problem can have no complex eigenvalues.

Theorem 6.2 says that if a self-adjoint problem has any eigenvalues, they must be real. It does not guarantee that any eigenvalues exist. However, it is shown in more advanced works on differential equations that a self-adjoint problem does possess infinitely many eigenvalues, and that these eigenvalues can be arranged to form a sequence $(\lambda_1, \lambda_2, \lambda_3, \ldots)$. According to Theorem 6.1, eigenfunctions corresponding to distinct eigenvalues are orthogonal and so the self-adjoint problem gives rise to a sequence of orthogonal functions. Such sequences will be discussed further in the next chapter.

Example 1 An example of a self-adjoint problem is

$$y'' + \lambda y = 0, \qquad y(0) = 0, \qquad y(c) = 0 .$$

This is the problem in Example 1, Section 6.1. Here $Ly = y''$, so that

$$\int_0^c [v(x)Lu(x) - u(x)Lv(x)]\, dx = \int_0^c [v(x)u''(x) - u(x)v''(x)]\, dx\,.$$

It can be seen (using integration by parts is one way) that this quantity is equal to

$$[v(x)u'(x) - u(x)v'(x)]_0^c\,.$$

If u and v satisfy the boundary conditions, so that $u(0) = u(c) = v(0) = v(c) = 0$, this quantity is equal to zero. Hence the problem is self-adjoint. The eigenvalues and eigenfunctions, as derived in Section 6.1, are

$$\lambda_n = \left(\frac{n\pi}{c}\right)^2, \qquad y_n(x) = \sin\frac{n\pi x}{c}$$

for $n = 1, 2, 3, \ldots$. Theorem 6.1 asserts that

$$\int_0^c \sin\frac{m\pi x}{c} \sin\frac{n\pi x}{c}\, dx = 0 \tag{6.13}$$

if $m \neq n$ since $r(x) = 1$ for x in $[0, c]$. We leave it to the reader to verify this orthogonality property by direct integration.

Exercises for Section 6.2

1. Write the differential equation in self-adjoint form.
    (a) $x^2 y'' + xy' + (x^2 - 1)y = 0$
    (b) $y'' + ay' + by = 0,\quad a$ and b constants
    (c) $y'' + 2y' + (\lambda + 1)y = 0$
    (d) $xy'' + (1 - x)y' + y = 0$
    (e) $y'' - 2xy' + y = 0$
    (f) $y'' - (\tan x)y' + y = 0$

2. Verify the orthogonality relation (6.13). *Suggestion*: Use the identity
$$\sin A \sin B = \tfrac{1}{2}[\cos(A - B) - \cos(A + B)]\,.$$

3. If $Ly = (py')' + qy$, show that
$$\int_a^b (vLu - uLv)\, dx = [p(u'v - uv')]_a^b\,.$$

4. Show that the given eigenvalue problem is self-adjoint, making use of the result of Exercise 3 if you wish. Then verify Theorem 6.1 for the given problem by direct integration.

(a) $y'' + \lambda y = 0,$ $y'(0) = 0,$ $y'(c) = 0$ (see Example 2, Section 6.1)

(b) $y'' + \lambda y = 0,$ $y(0) = 0,$ $y'(c) = 0$

(c) $(e^{2x}y')' + e^{2x}(\lambda + 1)y = 0,$ $y(0) = 0,$ $y(\pi) = 0$

(d) $\left(\dfrac{1}{x} y'\right)' + \dfrac{\lambda + 1}{x^3} y = 0,$ $y(1) = 0,$ $y(e) = 0$

5. If $Lu = a_0 u'' + a_1 u' + a_2 u$, use integration by parts to show that

$$\int_a^b vLu \, dx = [(a_0 v)u' - (a_1 v)'u + (a_1 v)u]_a^b$$

$$+ \int_a^b u[(a_0 v)'' - (a_1 v)' + (a_2 v)] \, dx$$

or

$$\int_a^b (vLu - uL^*v) \, dx = [a_0(u'v - uv') + (a_1 - a_0')uv]_a^b,$$

where

$$L^*v = (a_0 v)'' - (a_1 v)' + (a_2 v).$$

6. The operator L^* defined in Exercise 5 is called the *adjoint* of the operator L. Show that L is self-adjoint ($L = L^*$) if and only if $a_1 = a_0'$. Show that the adjoint of the operator L^* is L.

7. The differential equation

$$\frac{d}{dx}\left[p(x)\frac{dy}{dx}\right] + [\lambda r(x) + q(x)]y = 0$$

can be put in simpler form by making appropriate changes of both independent and dependent variables. Assume that $p(x) > 0$ and $r(x) > 0$ for x in $[a, b]$.

(a) Make a change of independent variable, of the form

$$t = \int_a^b f(x) \, dx, \qquad f(x) > 0 \quad \text{for} \quad a \le x \le b,$$

where f is to be determined. Then $d/dx = f(x) \, d/dt$. Let $y(x) = Y(t)$. Show that the differential equation takes the form

$$\frac{d^2Y}{dt^2} + \frac{(pf)'}{(pf)}\frac{dY}{dt} + \left[\lambda \frac{r}{f^2 p} + \frac{q}{f^2 p}\right]Y = 0,$$

where the prime denotes differentiation with respect to t. Show that the choice

$$f(x) = \left[\frac{r(x)}{p(x)}\right]^{1/2}$$

leads to the differential equation

$$\frac{d^2Y}{dt^2} + \frac{1}{2}\frac{(rp)'}{rp}\frac{dY}{dt} + \left(\lambda + \frac{q}{r}\right)Y = 0,$$

in which the coefficient of λY is 1.

(b) Making a change of dependent variable $Y(t) = g(t)w(t)$, show that the differential equation becomes

$$gw'' + \left[2g' + \frac{1}{2}\frac{(rp)'}{rp}g\right]w' + \left[\left(\lambda + \frac{q}{r}\right)g + g'' + \frac{1}{2}\frac{(rp)'}{rp}g'\right]w = 0.$$

Show that the choice $g = (rp)^{-1/4}$ makes the coefficient of w' vanish, and that the differential equation takes on the form

$$\frac{d^2w}{dt^2} + [\lambda + Q(t)]w = 0,$$

where

$$Q = -\tfrac{7}{16}(rp)^{-2}[(rp)']^2 - \tfrac{1}{4}(rp)^{-1}(rp)''.$$

This equation is called the *Liouville normal form* for the original differential equation. Some studies of Sturm–Liouville problems start with the differential equation in this form.

6.3 SOME SPECIAL CASES

In this section we shall consider two special classes of self-adjoint eigen-value problems. These arise in a number of applications, some of which are discussed in Chapter X. In determining if the problem

$$Ly = -\lambda r y, \qquad U_1(y) = 0, \qquad U_2(y) = 0,$$
$$Ly = (py')' + qy$$

is self-adjoint, we must examine the quantity

$$\int_a^b (vLu - uLv)\, dx = \int_a^b [v(pu')' - u(pv')']\, dx,$$

which may be written as

$$\int_a^b (pu'v - puv')' \, dx = [p(u'v - uv')]_a^b.$$

If the boundary conditions are such that

$$p(b)[u'(b)v(b) - u(b)v'(b)] - p(a)[u'(a)v(a) - u(a)v'(a)] = 0 \qquad (6.14)$$

for functions u and v that satisfy them, then the problem is self-adjoint.

We consider first problems of the form

$$(py')' + qy = -\lambda r y,$$
$$\alpha y(a) + \beta y'(a) = 0, \qquad\qquad\qquad (6.15)$$
$$\gamma y(b) + \delta y'(b) = 0,$$

where $p(x) > 0$ and $r(x) > 0$ for x in $[a, b]$, and where α, β, γ, and δ are real constants. We also assume that α and β are not both zero and that γ and δ are not both zero. It should be noted that one boundary condition involves the values of y and y' at the endpoint $x = a$ only, while the other condition involves values at $x = b$ only. For this reason the problem is said to have *separated boundary conditions*. We shall now show that this problem is self-adjoint. If u and v satisfy the boundary condition at $x = a$, then

$$\alpha u(a) + \beta u'(a) = 0,$$
$$\alpha v(a) + \beta v'(a) = 0.$$

Since α and β are not both zero, we must have

$$u(a)v'(a) - v(a)u'(a) = 0.$$

In similar fashion, by considering the boundary condition at $x = b$, it can be shown that

$$u(b)v'(b) - v(b)u'(b) = 0.$$

These two equations insure that the self-adjointness condition (6.14) is satisfied.

It can be shown that the problem (6.15) possesses an infinite sequence of eigenvalues

$$\lambda_0 < \lambda_1 < \cdots < \lambda_n < \cdots,$$

such that

$$\lim_{n \to \infty} \lambda_n = \infty.$$

Thus the problem possesses at most a finite number of negative eigenvalues. If the additional requirements

$$\alpha\beta \le 0, \qquad \gamma\delta \ge 0, \qquad\qquad (6.16)$$
$$q(x) \le 0, \qquad \text{for } x \text{ in } [a, b]$$

are satisfied, it can be shown (Exercise 7) that no negative eigenvalues exist. Another important fact about problems with separated boundary conditions concerns the number of eigenfunctions associated with each eigenvalue.

Theorem 6.3   An eigenfunction of the problem (6.15) is unique except for a constant factor.

PROOF   Suppose that u and v are both eigenfunctions corresponding to an eigenvalue λ_0. We shall show that u and v are linearly dependent and hence that v is simply a constant multiple of u. Since u and v both satisfy the boundary condition at $x = a$, we have

$$\alpha u(a) + \beta u'(a) = 0,$$
$$\alpha v(a) + \beta v'(a) = 0.$$

Since α and β are not both zero, we have

$$\begin{vmatrix} u(a) & u'(a) \\ v(a) & v'(a) \end{vmatrix} = 0.$$

Thus the Wronskian of u and v at a is zero. Since u and v are both solutions of the same second-order differential equation, they must be linearly dependent. (Otherwise the Wronskian of u and v would not vanish at any point of $[a, b]$.)

The second class of problems that we consider are those of the form

$$\begin{aligned} (py')' + qy &= -\lambda ry, \\ y(a) &= y(b), \\ y'(a) &= y'(b), \end{aligned} \tag{6.17}$$

where

$$p(a) = p(b). \tag{6.18}$$

We again assume that $p(x) > 0$ and $r(x) > 0$ for $a \leq x \leq b$. Such a problem is said to have *periodic boundary conditions*. We leave it to the reader to show that the problem is self-adjoint. It can be shown that there exists an infinite sequence of eigenvalues,

$$\lambda_0 < \lambda_1 < \cdots < \lambda_n < \cdots,$$

with

$$\lim_{n \to \infty} \lambda_n = \infty.$$

However, to a given eigenvalue there may correspond either one or two linearly independent eigenfunctions.

As an example, we consider the problem

$$y'' + \lambda y = 0,$$
$$y(-c) = y(c), \qquad y'(-c) = y'(c).$$

Here $p(x) = 1$ for x in $[-c, c]$, so the condition (6.18) is satisfied. When $\lambda = 0$ the general solution of the differential equation is

$$y(x) = c_1 + c_2 x.$$

The boundary conditions require that

$$c_1 - c_2 c = c_1 + c_2 c, \qquad c_2 = c_2.$$

Then c_2 must be zero but c_1 is arbitrary. Thus $\lambda_0 = 0$ is an eigenvalue with one independent eigenfunction, $y_0(x) = 1$. When $\lambda = k^2$, $k > 0$, the general solution is

$$y(x) = c_1 \cos kx + c_2 \sin kx.$$

The boundary conditions require that

$$c_1 \cos kc - c_2 \sin kc = c_1 \cos kc + c_2 \sin kc$$
$$c_1 \sin kc + c_2 \cos kc = - c_1 \sin kc + c_2 \cos kc$$

or

$$c_1 \sin kc = 0, \qquad c_2 \sin kc = 0.$$

In order to have a nontrivial solution, k must have one of the values

$$k_n = \frac{n\pi}{c}, \qquad n = 1, 2, 3, \dots.$$

But for such a value of k, both c_1 and c_2 are arbitrary. Therefore, to each eigenvalue

$$\lambda_n = k_n^2 = \left(\frac{n\pi}{c}\right)^2$$

there correspond the eigenfunctions

$$y_n(x) = A_n \cos \frac{n\pi x}{c} + B_n \sin \frac{n\pi x}{c},$$

where A_n and B_n are not both zero but are otherwise arbitrary. Thus, to each of the eigenvalues there correspond two linearly independent eigenfunctions.

If u and v are any two functions that are linearly independent on an interval $[a, b]$, it is always possible to choose two linear combinations of u and v that are orthogonal on (a, b). For instance, let

$$f(x) = u(x), \qquad g(x) = v(x) - ku(x),$$

where

$$k = \frac{(u, v)}{\|u\|^2} = \frac{\int_a^b r(x)u(x)v(x)\, dx}{\int_a^b r(x)[u(x)]^2\, dx}.$$

Then

$$(f, g) = (u, v) - k\,\|u\|^2 = 0,$$

so f and g are orthogonal.

If two independent eigenfunctions correspond to one eigenvalue, we can find two independent eigenfunctions that are orthogonal to each other. Every eigenfunction for that eigenvalue is simply a linear combination of the two orthogonal eigenfunctions.

In this example, the eigenfunctions $\cos(n\pi x/c)$, $\sin(n\pi x/c)$, which both correspond to the eigenvalue λ_n, are orthogonal on the interval $(-c, c)$ for each $n \geq 1$. Therefore the set of eigenfunctions

$$\left\{1,\, \cos\frac{n\pi x}{c},\, \sin\frac{n\pi x}{c}\right\}, \qquad n \geq 1,$$

is an orthogonal set with weight function $r(x) = 1$ on the interval $(-c, c)$.

Exercises for Section 6.3

1. Verify that the problem (6.17), with periodic boundary conditions, is self-adjoint.

2. Show that the problem

    $$y'' + (\lambda r + q)y = 0, \qquad y(0) - y'(1) = 0, \qquad y'(0) + y(1) = 0$$

    is self-adjoint. Note that the boundary conditions are neither separated nor periodic.

3. Show that the problem
    $$y'' + (\lambda r + q)y = 0, \qquad y(0) + y'(0) + 2y'(1) = 0, \qquad y'(0) - y(1) = 0$$
    is self-adjoint.

4. Show that the boundary conditions

    $$\alpha_{11} y(a) + \alpha_{12}\, y'(a) + \alpha_{13}\, y(b) + \alpha_{14}\, y'(b) = 0,$$
    $$\alpha_{21} y(a) + \alpha_{22}\, y'(a) + \alpha_{23}\, y(b) + \alpha_{14}\, y'(b) = 0$$

    are equivalent to a set of separated boundary conditions if and only if

    $$\begin{vmatrix} \alpha_{11} & \alpha_{12} \\ \alpha_{21} & \alpha_{22} \end{vmatrix} = \begin{vmatrix} \alpha_{13} & \alpha_{14} \\ \alpha_{23} & \alpha_{24} \end{vmatrix} = 0.$$

5.   Why can the eigenvalue problem (6.17) not have more than two linearly independent eigenfunctions associated with a particular eigenvalue?

6.   Let $y_1(x, \lambda)$ and $y_2(x, \lambda)$ be the solutions of the equation $(py')' + (\lambda r + q)y = 0$ for which

$$y_1(a, \lambda) = 1, \qquad y_1'(a, \lambda) = 0, \qquad y_2(a, \lambda) = 0, \qquad y_2'(a, \lambda) = 1.$$

If λ_0 is an eigenvalue of the problem (6.17), show that there exist two independent eigenfunctions if and only if

$$y_1'(b, \lambda_0) = y_2(b, y_0) = 0, \qquad y_1(b, \lambda_0) = y_2'(b, \lambda_0) = 1.$$

7.   (a) Let y satisfy the conditions $\alpha y(a) + \beta y'(a) = 0$, $\gamma y(b) + \delta y'(b) = 0$. If $\alpha\beta \leq 0$ and $\gamma\delta \geq 0$, show that $y(a)y'(a) \geq 0$ and $y(b)y'(b) \leq 0$.

(b) Let λ_0 be an eigenfunction of the problem (6.15), and let y_0 be a corresponding eigenfunction. Show that

$$\lambda_0 \int_a^b r(y_0)^2\, dx = \int_a^b p(y_0')^2\, dx - \int_a^b q(y_0)^2\, dx$$
$$+ p(a)y_0(a)y_0'(a) - p(b)y_0(b)y_0'(b).$$

Suggestion: Multiply through in the equation for y_0 by y_0 and integrate by parts.

(c) If $\alpha\beta \leq 0$, $\gamma\delta \geq 0$, and $q(x) \leq 0$ on $[a, b]$, show that $\lambda_0 \geq 0$.

8.   It can be shown that the eigenvalue problem

$$(py')' + (\lambda r + q)y = 0, \qquad U_1(y) = 0, \qquad U_2(y) = 0$$

is self-adjoint if and only if the condition

$$\frac{\begin{vmatrix} \alpha_{11} & \alpha_{12} \\ \alpha_{21} & \alpha_{22} \end{vmatrix}}{p(a)} = \frac{\begin{vmatrix} \alpha_{13} & \alpha_{14} \\ \alpha_{23} & \alpha_{24} \end{vmatrix}}{p(b)}$$

is satisfied. Use this criterion to show that

(a) the problems (6.15) and (6.17) are self-adjoint;

(b) the problems of Exercises 2 and 3 are self-adjoint;

(c) the problems of Exercises 9 and 10, Section 6.1, are not self-adjoint.

6.4   SINGULAR PROBLEMS

In the preceding discussion, we have dealt with problems associated with a differential equation of the form

$$\frac{d}{dx}\left[p(x)\frac{dy}{dx}\right] + [\lambda r(x) + q(x)]y = 0$$

on an interval $[a, b]$. In each case, it was assumed that p', q, and r were continuous and that $p(x) \neq 0$ for $a \leq x \leq b$. Suppose now that p', q, and r are continuous and that $p(x) \neq 0$ for $a < x < b$, but that at $x = a$, or $x = b$, or both, one or more of the following events occurs:

(a) p vanishes.
(b) One or more of the functions p, q, r becomes infinite.

Eigenvalue problems associated with such a differential equation are said to be *singular*.† Many physically important eigenvalue problems are of this type.

For a *nonsingular* self-adjoint problem on an interval $[a, b]$, the relation

$$\int_a^b (vLu - uLv)\, dx = p(b)[u'(b)v(b) - u(b)v'(b)] - p(a)[u'(a)v(a) - u(a)v'(a)]$$
$$= 0$$

holds for all functions u and v with two continuous derivatives that satisfy the boundary conditions. It is this property that insures the orthogonality of the eigenfunctions.

Let us now consider a problem with a singularity at the endpoint $x = a$. If δ is a small positive number, we have

$$\int_{a+\delta}^b (vLu - uLv)\, dx = p(b)[u'(b)v(b) - u(b)v'(b)]$$
$$- p(a + \delta)[u'(a + \delta)v(a + \delta) - u(a + \delta)v'(a + \delta)]$$

for functions u and v which possess two continuous derivatives on the interval $[a, b]$. If we impose conditions on u and v that insure that

$$\lim_{x \to a+} p(x)[u'(x)v(x) - u(x)v'(x)] = 0, \tag{6.19a}$$

$$p(b)[u'(b)v(b) - u(b)v'(b)] = 0, \tag{6.19b}$$

then the property

$$\int_a^b (vLu - uLv)\, dx = 0$$

again holds. For instance, if $p(a) = 0$, the conditions

$$y(x),\ y'(x) \qquad \text{finite as} \quad x \to a+,$$
$$\gamma y(b) + \delta y'(b) = 0$$

insure that the equalities (6.19) hold.

---

† Eigenvalue problems on an *infinite* interval are also said to be singular.

The case of a singularity at the endpoint $x = b$ can be treated by working on an interval $a \le x \le b - \delta$, and then letting $\delta \to 0$. If $p(b) = 0$, the boundary conditions

$$\alpha y(a) + \beta y'(a) = 0,$$
$$y(x), \; y'(x) \quad \text{finite as} \quad x \to b -$$

insure that

$$\int_a^b (vLu - uLv)\, dx = 0$$

for functions u and v that satisfy these conditions.

If $p(a)$ and $p(b)$ are both zero, the boundary conditions

$$y(x), \; y'(x) \quad \text{finite as} \quad x \to a +,$$
$$y(x), \; y'(x) \quad \text{finite as} \quad x \to b -$$

are appropriate.

Singular eigenvalue problems with the property that

$$\int_a^b (vLu - uLv)\, dx = 0$$

for all functions u and v that satisfy the boundary conditions are said to be *self-adjoint*. For such problems, eigenfunctions that correspond to distinct eigenvalues are orthogonal with respect to r on the interval (a, b). If $r(x) \ne 0$ for $a < x < b$, then all eigenvalues of such a problem are real, just as in the nonsingular case.

In the next section we shall discuss some specific singular problems that are of importance in applications.

6.5 SOME IMPORTANT SINGULAR PROBLEMS

As a first example of a singular eigenvalue problem, let us consider the differential equation

$$[(1 - x^2)y']' + \lambda y = 0 \qquad (6.20)$$

on the interval $-1 < x < 1$ with the boundary conditions

$$y, y' \quad \text{finite as} \quad x \to -1+,$$
$$y, y' \quad \text{finite as} \quad x \to 1-.$$

In the differential equation, $p(x) = 1 - x^2$ vanishes at $x = 1$ and $x = -1$.

The boundary conditions insure the orthogonality of the eigenfunctions with respect to $r(x) = 1$ on the interval $-1 < x < 1$. Also, since $r(x) \neq 0$ on this interval, all eigenvalues are real.

The equation (6.20) is Legendre's equation. This equation possesses solutions that are finite at both $x = 1$ and $x = -1$ when, and only when,

$$\lambda = \lambda_n = n(n + 1), \qquad n = 0, 1, 2, \ldots .$$

The corresponding eigenfunctions are

$$y_n(x) = P_n(x), \qquad n = 0, 1, 2, \ldots,$$

where P_n is the Legendre polynomial of degree n. Properties of these functions were discussed in Chapter V. We state again, for purposes of reference, the property

$$\int_{-1}^{1} [P_n(x)]^2 \, dx = \frac{2}{2n + 1}, \qquad n = 0, 1, 2, \ldots .$$

As a second example of a singular eigenvalue problem, we consider the differential equation

$$x^2 y'' + xy' + (\lambda x^2 - \alpha^2)y = 0 \tag{6.21}$$

on an interval $0 < x \leq c$, with the boundary conditions

$$y, y' \qquad \text{finite as} \quad x \to 0+,$$

$$y(c) = 0.$$

Here α is assumed to be a fixed real constant. The differential equation (6.21) is not self-adjoint as it stands, but it can be put in self-adjoint form by multiplying through by $1/x$. The result is

$$(xy')' + \left(\lambda x - \frac{\alpha^2}{x}\right)y = 0.$$

Comparing this equation with the standard form, we see that

$$p(x) = x, \qquad q(x) = -\frac{\alpha^2}{x}, \qquad r(x) = x.$$

Because $p(0) = 0$, and also because $q(x)$ becomes infinite as $x \to 0$, the problem is singular. However, the boundary conditions insure the orthogonality of the eigenfunctions on the interval $(0, c)$ with respect to $r(x) = x$. All eigenvalues are real.

In order to determine the eigenvalues, let us consider the three cases $\lambda > 0$, $\lambda = 0$, and $\lambda < 0$ separately. When $\lambda > 0$, let $\lambda = k^2$, where $k > 0$. Then the general solution of the differential equation is

$$y(x) = c_1 J_\alpha(kx) + c_2 Y_\alpha(kx),$$

where J_α and Y_α are Bessel functions of the first and second kinds, respectively.

The requirement that y and y' be finite as $x \to 0+$ necessitates that $c_2 = 0$. Then

$$y = c_1 J_\alpha(kx).$$

The condition at $x = c$ requires that

$$c_1 J_\alpha(kc) = 0.$$

If μ_n is the nth positive root of the equation

$$J_\alpha(\mu) = 0,$$

then k must have one of the values

$$k_n = \frac{\mu_n}{c}, \qquad n = 1, 2, 3, \dots.$$

The values

$$\lambda_n = k_n^2 = \left(\frac{\mu_n}{c}\right)^2, \qquad n = 1, 2, 3, \dots,$$

are eigenvalues of the problem, and the corresponding eigenfunctions are

$$y_n(x) = J_\alpha(k_n x), \qquad n = 1, 2, 3, \dots. \tag{6.22}$$

When $\lambda = 0$, the differential equation (6.21) has the form

$$x^2 y'' + xy' - \alpha^2 y = 0.$$

This is an equation of the Cauchy–Euler type, with general solution

$$y(x) = c_1 x\alpha + c_2 x^{-\alpha}, \qquad \alpha > 0,$$
$$y(x) = c_1 + c_2 \log x, \qquad \alpha = 0.$$

Evidently the constant c_2 must be zero for y and y' to be finite at $x = 0$. But the condition at $x = c$ requires that $c_1 = 0$ also. Thus the only solution of the differential equation that satisfies the boundary conditions is the trivial solution, and we conclude that $\lambda = 0$ is not an eigenvalue of the problem.

When $\lambda < 0$, let $\lambda = -k^2$, where $k > 0$. The differential equation is

$$x^2 y'' + xy' - (k^2 x^2 + \alpha^2)y = 0.$$

The general solution is

$$y(x) = c_1 I_\alpha(kx) + c_2 K_\alpha(kx),$$

where I_α and K_α are modified Bessel functions. The constant c_2 must be zero if y is to be finite at $x = 0$. Then

$$y(x) = c_1 I_\alpha(kx)$$

and the boundary condition at $x = c$ requires that

$$c_1 I_\alpha(kc) = 0.$$

But

$$I_\alpha(\mu) = \sum_{n=0}^{\infty} \frac{(\mu/2)^{2n+\alpha}}{n! \Gamma(n + \alpha + 1)}$$

does not vanish for any positive values of μ since each term in the series is positive. Therefore, c_1 must be zero also, and $y \equiv 0$. The original problem, therefore, has no negative eigenvalues.

The eigenfunctions (6.22) have the property that

$$\int_0^c x J_\alpha(k_m x) J_\alpha(k_n x) \, dx = 0, \qquad m \neq n.$$

We now derive a formula for the quantities

$$\int_0^c [J_\alpha(k_n x)]^2 \, dx.$$

The eigenfunction $y_n(x) = J_\alpha(k_n x)$ satisfies the differential equation

$$x^2 y_n''(x) + x y_n'(x) + (k_n^2 x^2 - \alpha^2) y_n(x) = 0.$$

If we multiply through by the quantity $2y_n'(x)$, we find that the resulting equation can be written in the form

$$[x^2 [y_n'(x)]^2]' + (k_n^2 x^2 - \alpha^2)[[y_n(x)]^2]' = 0.$$

Integrating with respect to x from 0 to c, and using integration by parts on the second term, we find that

$$\int_0^c x[y_n(x)]^2 \, dx = \left[\frac{1}{2k_n^2} x^2 [y_n'(x)]^2 + \frac{1}{2} \left(x^2 - \frac{\alpha^2}{k_n^2} \right) [y_n(x)]^2 \right]_0^c.$$

Using the fact that

$$y_n(c) = 0,$$

we have

$$\int_0^c x[y_n(x)]^2 \, dx = \frac{c^2}{2k_n^2} [y_n'(c)]^2. \qquad (6.23)$$

The right-hand member of this equation can be further simplified by the use of the relation

$$\frac{d}{dx} J_\alpha(x) = -J_{\alpha+1}(x) + \frac{\alpha}{x} J_\alpha(x).$$

(This is Eq. (4.21).) We have

$$y_n'(x) = \frac{d}{dx} J_\alpha(k_n x) = k_n J_\alpha'(k_n x) = k_n \left[-J_{\alpha+1}(k_n x) + \frac{\alpha}{k_n x} J_\alpha(k_n x) \right]$$

and so

$$y_n'(c) = -k_n J_{\alpha+1}(k_n c).$$

From this relation and the relation (6.23) we have

$$\int_0^c x[y_n(x)]^2 \, dx = \frac{c^2}{2} [J_{\alpha+1}(k_n c)]^2, \qquad n = 1, 2, 3, \ldots . \tag{6.24}$$

We shall describe briefly two other important eigenvalue problems that are associated with the differential equation (6.21). The derivations of the various properties listed are left as exercises.

The problem

$$x^2 y'' + xy' + (\lambda x^2 - \alpha^2) y = 0, \qquad 0 < x < c,$$
$$y, y' \quad \text{finite as} \quad x \to 0_+, \tag{6.25}$$
$$y'(c) = 0,$$

possesses the eigenvalues $\lambda_n^2 = k_2$, where k_n is the nth positive root of the equation

$$J_\alpha'(kc) = 0.$$

The eigenfunctions are

$$y_n(x) = J_\alpha(k_n x), \qquad n = 1, 2, 3, \ldots ,$$

and

$$\int_0^c x[y_n(x)]^2 \, dx = \frac{k_n^2 c^2 - \alpha^2}{2k_n^2} [J_\alpha(k_n c)]^2 . \tag{6.26}$$

In the special case when $\alpha = 0$, $\lambda_0 = 0$ is also an eigenvalue, with eigenfunction

$$y_0(x) = 1 .$$

We have

$$\int_0^c x[y_0(x)]^2 \, dx = \tfrac{1}{2} c^2 .$$

The problem

$$x^2 y'' + xy' + (\lambda x^2 - \alpha^2) y = 0, \qquad 0 < x < c,$$
$$y, y' \quad \text{finite as} \quad x \to 0+, \tag{6.27}$$
$$hy(c) + y'(c) = 0, \qquad h > 0,$$

possesses the eigenvalues $\lambda_n = k_n^2$, where k_n is the nth positive root of the equation

$$hJ_\alpha(kc) + kJ'_\alpha(kc) = 0.$$

The eigenfunctions are

$$y_n(x) = J_\alpha(k_n x), \qquad n = 1, 2, 3, \ldots,$$

and

$$\int_0^c x[y_n(x)]^2 \, dx = \frac{k_n^2 c^2 - \alpha^2 + h^2 c^2}{2k_n^2} [J_\alpha(k_n c)]^2. \qquad (6.28)$$

Exercises for Section 6.5

1. Given that the function J_α has infinitely many positive zeros, use Rolle's theorem to show that the function J'_α has infinitely many positive zeros.

2. Give a detailed discussion of the problem (6.25). Include a derivation of formula (6.26).

3. Show that the function J_α actually changes sign at each point on the interval $(0, \infty)$ where it vanishes. Use this fact to show that the equation $xJ'_\alpha(x) + hJ_\alpha(x) = 0$ has infinitely many positive roots.

4. The restriction $h > 0$ in the problem (6.27) insures that the problem has no negative eigenvalues. Give a proof of this fact.

5. Give a detailed discussion of the problem (6.27). Include a derivation of formula (6.28).

6. Discuss the eigenvalues and eigenfunctions of the problem

$$xy'' + \lambda y = 0,$$
$$y, y' \quad \text{finite as} \quad x \to 0+, \qquad y(1) = 0.$$

With respect to what weight function are the eigenfunctions orthogonal on the interval $(0, 1)$?

7. Find the eigenvalues and eigenfunctions of the problem

$$4x^2 y'' + (\lambda x^2 - 3)y = 0,$$
$$y, y' \text{ finite as } x \to 0+, \quad y'(1) = 0.$$

With respect to what weight function are the eigenfunctions orthogonal on the interval $(0, 1)$?

8.   Find the eigenvalues and eigenfunctions of the problem

$$x^2 y'' - xy' + (4\lambda x^4 - 3)y = 0,$$

$$y, y' \quad \text{finite} \quad \text{as } x \to 0+, \quad y(c) = 0, \quad c > 0.$$

With respect to what weight function are the eigenfunctions orthogonal on the interval $(0, c)$?

REFERENCES

1.   Coddington, E. A., and Levinson, N., *Theory of Ordinary Differential Equations.* McGraw-Hill, New York, 1955.
2.   Cole, R. H., *Theory of Ordinary Differential Equations.* Appleton-Century-Crofts, New York, 1968.
3.   Ince, E. L., *Ordinary Differential Equations*, 4th ed. Dover, New York, 1956.
4.   Miller, K. S., *Linear Differential Equations in the Real Domain.* Norton, New York, 1963.

VII

Fourier Series

7.1 INTRODUCTION

We recall from Section 5.1 the definitions of the inner product

$$(f, g) = \int_a^b w(x)f(x)g(x)\, dx$$

of f and g and the norm

$$\|f\| = (f, f)^{1/2} = \left(\int_a^b w(x)[f(x)]^2\, dx \right)^{1/2}$$

of a function f. A sequence of functions $\{\psi_n\}_{n=1}^\infty$ is called an orthogonal set if $(\psi_m, \psi_n) = 0$ for $m \neq n$. We have encountered numerous examples of orthogonal sets. Sets of orthogonal polynomials (Chapter V) are orthogonal sets. Self-adjoint eigenvalue problems (Chapter VI) give rise to orthogonal sets of eigenfunctions.

A sequence of functions $\{\phi_n\}_{n=1}^\infty$ is called an *orthonormal set* if it is an orthogonal set and if in addition $\|\phi_n\| = 1$ for each n. If $\{\psi_n\}_{n=1}^\infty$ is an orthogonal set, then the set $\{\phi_n\}_{n=1}^\infty$, where

$$\phi_n = \frac{\psi_n}{\|\psi_n\|}, \tag{7.1}$$

is orthonormal. (We assume $\|\psi_n\| \neq 0$ for all n.) To see this, we observe that

$$(\phi_m, \phi_n) = \frac{1}{\|\psi_m\|\,\|\psi_n\|} \int_a^b w(x)\psi_m(x)\psi_n(x)\, dx = \begin{cases} 0, & m \neq n, \\ 1, & m = n. \end{cases}$$

We say that the set $\{\psi_n\}_{n=1}^{\infty}$ has been *normalized* by the procedure (7.1), which consists of dividing each function by its norm.

Example 1   The Legendre polynomials $\{P_n\}_{n=0}^{\infty}$ are simply orthogonal $(w(x) = 1)$ on the interval $[-1, 1]$ and

$$\|P_n\|^2 = \int_{-1}^{1} [P_n(x)]^2 \, dx = \frac{2}{2n + 1}.$$

If we set

$$\phi_n = \frac{P_n}{\|P_n\|} = \sqrt{\frac{2n + 1}{2}} \, P_n,$$

then the sequence $\{\phi_n\}_{n=0}^{\infty}$ is an orthonormal set with weight function $w(x) = 1$ on the interval $[-1, 1]$.

Example 2   The sequence $\{y_n\}_{n=1}^{\infty}$, where

$$y_n(x) = \sin \frac{n\pi x}{c}$$

is an orthogonal set with respect to the weight function $r(x) = 1$ on $[0, c]$ since the functions of the sequence are eigenfunctions of the problem

$$y'' + \lambda y = 0, \qquad y(0) = y(c) = 0.$$

Since

$$\|y_n\|^2 = \int_0^c \sin^2 \frac{n\pi x}{c} \, dx = \frac{c}{2}$$

for each n, the sequence $\{\phi_n\}_{n=1}^{\infty}$, where

$$\phi_n = \frac{y_n}{\|y_n\|} = \sqrt{\frac{2}{c}} \sin \frac{n\pi x}{c}$$

is orthonormal.

We shall now introduce the notion of a Fourier series. Let f be an arbitrary function defined on $[a, b]$ and let $\{\psi_n\}_{n=1}^{\infty}$ be an orthogonal set of functions on $[a, b]$ with weight function w. Let us assume that $f(x)$ can be represented by an infinite series of the form

$$f(x) = \sum_{k=1}^{\infty} C_k \psi_k(x) \tag{7.2}$$

for x in $[a, b]$, where the quantities C_k are constants. We multiply both sides of this equation by $w(x)\psi_n(x)$, where n is any positive integer, and then integrate from a to b. Assuming that termwise integration of the series is valid, we have

$$\int_a^b w(x)f(x)\psi_n(x)\,dx = \sum_{k=0}^{\infty} C_k \int_a^b w(x)\psi_k(x)\psi_n(x)\,dx\,.$$

Because of the orthogonality of the functions ψ_k, all of the terms in the series on the right vanish except for the term in which $k = n$. Then

$$(f, \psi_n) = C_n(\psi_n, \psi_n)$$

and

$$C_n = \frac{(f, \psi_n)}{\|\psi_n\|^2}\,. \tag{7.3}$$

If the set $\{\psi_n\}_{n=1}^{\infty}$ is orthonormal, so that $\|\psi_n\| = 1$, we have the simpler formula

$$C_n = (f, \psi_n)\,.$$

In deriving the formula (7.3) for the coefficients in the series (7.2), we made two large assumptions. We assumed that the function $f(x)$ could be represented by an infinite series of the form (7.2) and we also assumed that the termwise integration of an infinite series was permissible. Actually, for an arbitrary function f, we have no guarantee that the series (7.2) with coefficients (7.3) will even converge, let alone converge to $f(x)$. Nevertheless, the coefficients (7.3) are called the *Fourier coefficients* of the function f with respect to the orthogonal set $\{\psi_n\}_{n=1}^{\infty}$, and the series (7.2) with coefficients (7.3) is called the *Fourier series* for f. One of the main objects of this chapter is to describe conditions under which the Fourier series of a function will actually converge to the function.

Example 3 Let $f(x) = x$ and $\psi_n(x) = \sin n\pi x$ for $0 \le x \le 1$ and $n = 1, 2, 3, \ldots$. Making use of the results of Example 2, with $c = 1$, we see that the Fourier coefficients of f are

$$C_n = 2 \int_0^1 x \sin n\pi x\,dx$$

$$= 2\left[\frac{1}{n^2\pi^2} \sin n\pi x - \frac{1}{n\pi} x \cos n\pi x\right]_0^1$$

$$= -\frac{2}{n\pi} \cos n\pi$$

$$= \frac{2}{n\pi}(-1)^{n+1}\,.$$

The last equality follows from the useful relation $\cos n\pi = (-1)^n$. The Fourier series for f is

$$\frac{2}{\pi} \sum_{n=1}^{\infty} \frac{(-1)^{n+1}}{n} \sin n\pi x.$$

We have not proven that this series converges to $f(x)$ for every x in $[0, 1]$. In fact, when $x = 1$, the series converges to zero, which is not the same as $f(1) = 1$.

There is a certain analogy between Fourier series and vectors that should be mentioned here. Let us consider an ordinary three-dimensional Euclidean space in which $\mathbf{u}$ and $\mathbf{v}$ are vectors. Let us denote the "dot product," or inner product, of $\mathbf{u}$ and $\mathbf{v}$ by the symbol $(\mathbf{u}, \mathbf{v})$, that is,

$$(\mathbf{u}, \mathbf{v}) = \mathbf{u} \cdot \mathbf{v}.$$

If the norm, or length, of a vector $\mathbf{u}$ is denoted by $\|\mathbf{u}\|$, then

$$\|\mathbf{u}\| = (\mathbf{u}, \mathbf{u})^{1/2}.$$

In the three dimensional space, we know that if $\mathbf{u}_1$, $\mathbf{u}_2$, and $\mathbf{u}_3$ are three mutually orthogonal nonzero vectors, then every vector $\mathbf{v}$ can be written in the form

$$\mathbf{v} = C_1 \mathbf{u}_1 + C_2 \mathbf{u}_2 + C_3 \mathbf{u}_3 = \sum_{k=1}^{3} C_k \mathbf{u}_k, \tag{7.4}$$

where C_1, C_2, and C_3 are constants. In order to determine these constants for a particular vector $\mathbf{v}$, we take the inner product of both members of Eq. (7.4) with $\mathbf{u}_n$, where n is 1, 2, or 3. Then

$$(\mathbf{v}, \mathbf{u}_n) = \sum_{k=1}^{3} C_k (\mathbf{u}_k, \mathbf{u}_n).$$

Because of the orthogonality of the vectors $\mathbf{u}_k$, the only nonvanishing term in the sum on the right is the one with $k = n$. Thus

$$(\mathbf{v}, \mathbf{u}_n) = C_n (\mathbf{u}_n, \mathbf{u}_n),$$

or

$$C_n = \frac{(\mathbf{v}, \mathbf{u}_n)}{\|\mathbf{u}_n\|^2}, \qquad n = 1, 2, 3. \tag{7.5}$$

Equation (7.4) should be compared with Eq. (7.2) and formula (7.5) should be compared with formula (7.3).

In the case of Fourier series, we deal with functions defined on an interval $[a, b]$ rather than with vectors. We speak of a "function space" as opposed to a three-dimensional "vector space." This function space is *infinite dimensional*, in the sense that we need an infinite sequence of mutually orthogonal functions to represent an arbitrary function. In this infinite-dimensional space, life is somewhat more complicated than in the three-dimensional space. In the first place, it turns out that not just any sequence of mutually orthogonal functions is satisfactory. In the second place, some restrictions must be placed on the class of functions that are to be represented by a series of the orthogonal functions—that is, by a Fourier series. We shall discuss these matters further in later sections.

Exercises for Section 7.1

1. If $\psi_0(x) = 1$ and $\psi_n(x) = \cos(n\pi x/c)$ for $n = 1, 2, 3, \ldots$ and all x, show that $\{\psi_n\}_{n=0}^{\infty}$ is simply orthogonal on $[0, c]$. Find a corresponding orthonormal set.

2. Verify that the sequence $\{\psi_n\}_{n=1}^{\infty}$, where $\psi_n(x) = \sin[(2n - 1)x/2]$, is simply orthogonal on $[0, \pi]$. Find a corresponding orthonormal set.

3. Find an orthonormal set that corresponds to (a) the set of Hermite polynomials (b) the set of Tchebycheff polynomials of the first kind.

4. Let $f(x) = 1$ for $0 \le x \le 1$. Find the Fourier series of f with respect to the simply orthogonal set $\{\psi_n\}_{n=1}^{\infty}$, where $\psi_n(x) = \sin n\pi x$.

5. Let $f(x) = 1 - x$. $\psi_0(x) = 1$, and $\psi_n(x) = \cos n\pi x$ for $0 \le x \le 1$ and $n = 1, 2, 3, \ldots$. Find the Fourier series of f with respect to the simply orthogonal set $\{\psi_n\}_{n=0}^{\infty}$. (See Exercise 1.)

6. Find the Fourier series of the function $f(x) = \pi - x$, $0 \le x \le \pi$, with respect to the orthogonal sequence whose nth term is

$$\psi_n(x) = \sin [(2n - 1)x/2], \qquad n = 1, 2, 3, \ldots.$$

(See Exercise 2.)

7. Let f be a polynomial. Show that the Fourier series of f with respect to any set of orthogonal polynomials is a *finite* series and that for each x the series is equal to $f(x)$.

8. Expand the function f, where $f(x) = x^2$, in a series of (a) Legendre polynomials and (b) Laguerre polynomials.

9. Let $\{\psi_n\}_{n=1}^{\infty}$ be an orthogonal set and let $\{\phi_n\}_{n=1}^{\infty}$ be a corresponding orthonormal set. Show that corresponding terms in the Fourier series of a function f are identical.

10.   Let $\{f_n\}_{n=1}^{\infty}$ be an orthogonal set on $[a, b]$, with positive weight function w. Let $g_n = \sqrt{w}\, f_n$.

(a) Show that the functions g_n are simply orthogonal on $[a, b]$.

(b) If $\{f_n\}_{n=1}^{\infty}$ is orthonormal, show that $\{g_n\}_{n=1}^{\infty}$ is orthonormal.

(c) Find a simply orthogonal set of functions that corresponds to the Laguerre polynomials.

(d) Is the Fourier series of a function f with respect to $\{f_n\}_{n=1}^{\infty}$ the same as the Fourier series of f with respect to $\{g_n\}_{n=1}^{\infty}$?

7.2   EXAMPLES OF FOURIER SERIES

In this section we shall list formulas for the Fourier coefficients of an arbitrary function f corresponding to some specific sets of orthogonal functions. Conditions under which the series actually converge to the function will be discussed in the following sections.

(a) Series of Legendre Polynomials

The Legendre polynomials P_n are orthogonal with respect to the weight function $w(x) = 1$ on the interval $(-1, 1)$ and

$$\|P_n\|^2 = \int_{-1}^{1} [P_n(x)]^2\, dx = \frac{2}{2n+1}, \qquad n \geq 0.$$

Therefore, according to the general formula (7.3), the coefficients in the Fourier–Legendre series

$$\sum_{n=0}^{\infty} C_n P_n(x)$$

for an arbitrary function f are given by the formula

$$C_n = \frac{2n+1}{2} \int_{-1}^{1} f(x) P_n(x)\, dx, \qquad n \geq 0. \tag{7.6}$$

(b) Series of Tchebycheff Polynomials

The Tchebycheff polynomials of the first kind, T_n, are orthogonal with respect to the weight function $w(x) = (1 - x^2)^{-1/2}$ on the interval $(-1, 1)$.

Since

$$\|T_n\|^2 = \int_{-1}^{1} \frac{[T_n(x)]^2}{\sqrt{1-x^2}} \, dx = \begin{cases} \pi, & n = 0, \\ \dfrac{\pi}{2}, & n \geq 1, \end{cases}$$

we can write the Fourier–Tchebycheff series for $f(x)$ as

$$\tfrac{1}{2}C_0 T_0(x) + \sum_{n=1}^{\infty} C_n T_n(x),$$

where

$$C_n = \frac{2}{\pi} \int_{-1}^{1} \frac{f(x)T_n(x)}{\sqrt{1-x^2}} \, dx, \qquad n \geq 0. \tag{7.7}$$

(c) Series of Laguerre Polynomials

For the Laguerre polynomials L_n, $w(x) = e^{-x}$ and the interval of orthogonality is $(0, \infty)$. Since

$$\|L_n\|^2 = \int_0^{\infty} e^{-x}[L_n(x)]^2 \, dx = 1, \qquad n \geq 0,$$

the Fourier–Laguerre series

$$\sum_{n=0}^{\infty} C_n L_n(x)$$

for $f(x)$ has the coefficients

$$C_n = \int_0^{\infty} e^{-x} f(x) L_n(x) \, dx, \qquad n \geq 0. \tag{7.8}$$

(d) Series of Hermite Polynomials

For the Hermite polynomials H_n, $w(x) = \exp(-x^2)$ and the interval of orthogonality is $(-\infty, \infty)$. Since

$$\|H_n\|^2 = \int_{-\infty}^{+\infty} \exp(-x^2)[H_n(x)]^2 \, dx = 2^n n! \sqrt{\pi}, \qquad n \geq 0,$$

the coefficients in the series

$$\sum_{n=0}^{\infty} C_n H_n(x)$$

for $f(x)$ are

$$C_n = \frac{1}{2^n n! \sqrt{\pi}} \int_{-\infty}^{+\infty} \exp(-x^2) f(x) H_n(x)\, dx, \qquad n \geq 0. \qquad (7.9)$$

(e) Fourier Sine Series

The functions $\sin(n\pi x/c)$, $n \geq 1$, are simply orthogonal on the interval $(0, c)$ and

$$\int_0^c \sin^2 \frac{n\pi x}{c}\, dx = \frac{c}{2}, \qquad n \geq 1.$$

The Fourier sine series for $f(x)$ has the form

$$\sum_{n=1}^{\infty} C_n \sin \frac{n\pi x}{c},$$

where

$$C_n = \frac{2}{c} \int_0^c f(x) \sin \frac{n\pi x}{c}\, dx, \qquad n \geq 1. \qquad (7.10)$$

(f) Fourier Cosine Series

The functions $\cos(n\pi x/c)$, $n \geq 0$, are simply orthogonal on the interval $(0, c)$ and

$$\int_0^c \cos^2 \frac{n\pi x}{c}\, dx = \begin{cases} c, & n = 0, \\ \dfrac{c}{2}, & n \geq 1. \end{cases}$$

The Fourier cosine series for $f(x)$ can be written in the form

$$\frac{C_0}{2} + \sum_{n=1}^{\infty} C_n \cos \frac{n\pi x}{2}, \qquad \cdot$$

where

$$C_n = \frac{2}{c} \int_0^c f(x) \cos \frac{n\pi x}{c}\, dx, \qquad n \geq 0. \qquad (7.11)$$

(g) General Trigonometric Fourier Series

The functions $\{1, \cos(n\pi x/c), \sin(n\pi x/c)\}$, $n \geq 1$, are simply orthogonal on the interval $(-c, c)$, as can be verified by direct integration. For the norms of these functions we have

$$\int_{-c}^{c} \cos^2 \frac{n\pi x}{c}\, dx = \begin{cases} 2c, & n = 0, \\ c, & n \geq 1, \end{cases}$$

$$\int_{-c}^{c} \sin^2 \frac{n\pi x}{c}\, dx = c, \qquad n \geq 1.$$

The general trigonometric Fourier series for $f(x)$ is defined to be the series

$$\frac{1}{2} a_0 + \sum_{n=1}^{\infty} \left(a_n \cos \frac{n\pi x}{c} + b_n \sin \frac{n\pi x}{c} \right), \qquad (7.12)$$

where

$$a_n = \frac{1}{c} \int_{-c}^{c} f(x) \cos \frac{n\pi x}{c}\, dx, \qquad n \geq 0,$$
$$\tag{7.13}$$
$$b_n = \frac{1}{c} \int_{-c}^{c} f(x) \sin \frac{n\pi x}{c}\, dx, \qquad n \geq 1.$$

In some texts the term "Fourier series" refers only to this type of series, and a series of functions of an arbitrary orthogonal set is called a "generalized Fourier series."

(h) Fourier–Bessel Series

In Chapter VI we saw that the functions $\{J_\alpha(k_n x)\}$ were orthogonal with weight function $w(x) = x$ on the interval $(0, c)$ if k_n is specified as the nth positive root of one of the equations

(a) $$J_\alpha(kc) = 0,$$
(b) $$J_\alpha'(kc) = 0,$$
(c) $$hJ_\alpha(kc) + kJ_\alpha'(kc) = 0, \qquad h > 0.$$

The corresponding formulas for the quantities

$$A_n = \int_0^c x[J_\alpha(k_n c)]^2\, dx$$

are

(a')
$$A_n = \frac{c^2}{2}[J_{\alpha+1}(k_n c)]^2,$$

(b')
$$A_n = \frac{k^2 c^2 - \alpha^2}{2k_n^2}[J_\alpha(k_n c)]^2,$$

(c')
$$A_n = \frac{k_n^2 c^2 - \alpha^2 + h^2 c^2}{2k_n^2}[J_\alpha(k_n c)]^2.$$

The coefficients in the Fourier–Bessel series

$$\sum_{n=1}^{\infty} C_n J_\alpha(k_n x)$$

for $f(x)$ are given by the formula

$$C_n = \frac{1}{A_n}\int_0^c xf(x)J_\alpha(k_n x)\, dx, \qquad n \geq 1. \tag{7.14}$$

In the special case when $\alpha = 0$ and k_n is the nth positive root of Eq. (b), the series has the form

$$C_0 + \sum_{n=1}^{\infty} C_n J_0(k_n x),$$

where

$$C_0 = \frac{2}{c^2}\int_0^c xf(x)\, dx \tag{7.15}$$

and the other coefficients are still given by formula (7.14).

Let us now compute a few Fourier series for specific functions.

Example 1   We find the Fourier sine series for the function $f(x) = x$, $0 \leq x \leq c$. According to part (e) above, the coefficients in the series are

$$C_n = \frac{2}{c}\int_0^c x \sin\frac{n\pi x}{c}\, dx = \frac{2}{c}\left[\frac{c^2}{n^2\pi^2}\sin\frac{n\pi x}{c} - \frac{c}{n\pi}x\cos\frac{n\pi x}{c}\right]_0^c$$

$$= -\frac{2c}{n\pi}\cos n\pi = \frac{2c}{n\pi}(-1)^{n+1}, \qquad n \geq 1.$$

Hence the Fourier sine series is

$$\frac{2c}{\pi}\sum_{n=1}^{\infty}\frac{(-1)^{n+1}}{n}\sin\frac{n\pi x}{c}.$$

We are saying nothing yet about whether the series converges, or whether it converges to $f(x) = x$.

Example 2 Let us find the Fourier–Legendre series for the function

$$f(x) = \begin{cases} 0, & -1 \le x \le 0, \\ x, & 0 \le x \le 1. \end{cases}$$

According to part (a) above, the coefficients are given by the formula

$$C_n = \frac{2n+1}{2} \int_{-1}^{1} f(x) P_n(x)\, dx = \frac{2n+1}{2} \int_{0}^{1} x P_n(x)\, dx, \qquad n \ge 0.$$

Since

$$P_0(x) = 1, \qquad P_1(x) = x, \qquad P_2(x) = \tfrac{1}{2}(3x^2 - 1),$$

the first few coefficients are

$$C_0 = \tfrac{1}{2} \int_{0}^{1} x\, dx = \tfrac{1}{4}, \qquad C_1 = \tfrac{3}{2} \int_{0}^{1} x^2\, dx = \tfrac{1}{2},$$

$$C_2 = \tfrac{5}{2} \int_{0}^{1} (\tfrac{3}{2}x^3 - \tfrac{1}{2}x)\, dx = \tfrac{5}{16}.$$

Thus the series has the form

$$\tfrac{1}{4} P_0(x) + \tfrac{1}{2} P_1(x) + \tfrac{5}{16} P_2(x) + \cdots.$$

Example 3 As a final example, let us consider the function

$$f(x) = \begin{cases} x, & 0 < x < 1, \\ 0, & 1 < x < 2. \end{cases}$$

We shall find the Fourier–Bessel series for $f(x)$, corresponding to the functions $\{J_1(k_n x)\}$, $n \ge 1$, where k_n is the nth positive root of the equation $J_1(2k) = 0$. Using formulas (a') and (7.14) in part (h) above, with $\alpha = 1$ and $c = 2$, we obtain the following formula for the Fourier coefficients of $f(x)$:

$$C_n = \frac{1}{2[J_2(2k_n)]^2} \int_{0}^{1} x^2 J_1(k_n x)\, dx = \frac{1}{2[J_2(2k_n)]^2} \left[\frac{x^2}{k_n} J_2(k_n x) \right]_0^1$$

$$= \frac{J_2(k_n)}{2k_n[J_2(2k_n)]^2}, \qquad n \ge 1.$$

The Fourier–Bessel series is

$$\frac{1}{2} \sum_{n=1}^{\infty} \frac{J_2(k_n)}{k_n[J_2(2k_n)]^2} J_1(k_n x).$$

Exercises for Section 7.2

1. Find the Fourier sine series for the given function on the indicated interval.

    (a) $f(x) = 3 - x, \quad 0 \le x \le 3$

    (b) $g(x) = 1, \quad 0 \le x \le \pi$

    (c) $h(x) = x - x^2, \quad 0 \le x \le 1$

    (d) $k(x) = x$ for $0 \le x \le 1$ and $k(x) = 1$ for $1 < x \le 2$. The interval here is $[0, 2]$.

    (e) $p(x) = \cos x, \quad 0 \le x \le \pi$

    (f) $q(x) = \sin x, \quad 0 \le x \le \pi$

2. Find the Fourier cosine series for the functions in Exercise 1.

3. Let $f(x) = 0$ for $-1 \le x \le 0$ and $f(x) = x$ for $0 < x \le 1$. Find the first three terms in the series of Legendre polynomials for f.

4. Find the trigonometric Fourier series on $[-1, 1]$ for the function f of Exercise 3.

5. Let $f(x) = e^{-x}$ for $x \ge 0$. Find the first three terms in the series of Laguerre polynomials for f.

6. If $f(x) = \exp(x^2)$ when $0 \le x \le 1$ and $f(x) = 0$ for all other values of x, find the first three terms in the series of Hermite polynomials for f.

7. If $f(x) = x, \quad 0 < x < 2$, find the Fourier–Bessel series for $f(x)$ with respect to the given orthogonal set:

    (a) $\{J_1(k_n x)\}, \ n \ge 1$, where k_n is the nth positive root of the equation $J_1(2k) = 0$.

    (b) $\{J_1(k_n x)\}, \ n \ge 1$, where k_n is the nth positive root of the equation $J_1'(2k) = 0$.

8. Derive the formula for the coefficients in the series of Tchebycheff polynomials

$$\tfrac{1}{2}a_0 + \sum_{n=1}^{\infty} a_n T_n(x)$$

    for $f(x)$ by making the change of variable $x = \cos \theta$ and finding the Fourier cosine series for $f(\cos \theta)$.

9. (a) Let $\psi_n(x) = P_{2n}(x), \ n = 0, 1, 2, \ldots$, where the functions P_{2n} are the Legendre polynomials of even degree. Show that the functions ψ_n are

simply orthogonal on the interval $(0, 1)$ and derive the formula

$$C_n = (4n + 1) \int_0^1 f(x)\psi_n(x) \, dx$$

for the Fourier coefficients of a function f.

(b) Let $\phi_n(x) = P_{2n-1}(x)$, $n = 1, 2, 3, \ldots$, where the functions P_{2n-1} are the Legendre polynomials of odd degree. Show that the functions ϕ_n are simply orthogonal on the interval $(0, 1)$ and derive the formula

$$C_n = (4n - 1) \int_0^1 f(x)\phi_n(x) \, dx$$

of the Fourier coefficients of a function f.

10. The *Laguerre functions*, l_n, are defined by means of the equation $l_n(x) = e^{-x/2}L_n(x)$, $n = 0, 1, 2, \ldots$, where L_n is the Laguerre polynomial of degree n. If $f(x) = 1 - x$ when $0 \le x \le 1$ and $f(x) = 0$ when $x > 1$, find the first two terms in the series of Laguerre functions for $f(x)$.

11. Derive the formula

$$C_n = \frac{2}{\pi} \int_0^\pi f(x) \sin \frac{2n - 1}{2} x \, dx, \qquad n = 1, 2, 3, \ldots,$$

for the Fourier coefficients of $f(x)$ with respect to the simply orthogonal set

$$\left\{ \sin \frac{2n - 1}{2} x \right\}, \qquad 0 \le x \le \pi.$$

7.3 TYPES OF CONVERGENCE

The "distance" between two numbers p and q may be defined as $|p - q|$. When we say that a sequence of numbers $\{a_n\}_{n=1}^\infty$ converges to a number a, we mean that

$$\lim_{n \to \infty} |a_n - a| = 0;$$

that is, that the distance between the numbers a_n and a approaches zero as n becomes infinite.

Let us now consider a sequence of *functions* $\{f_n\}_{n=1}^\infty$ defined on an interval $\mathscr{I}$. In the usual definition of convergence, we say that the sequence of functions converges to the function f on $\mathscr{I}$ if the sequence $\{f_n(x)\}_{n=1}^\infty$ converges to $f(x)$ for every x in $\mathscr{I}$. This type of convergence (we shall consider others) is called *pointwise convergence*, for obvious reasons.

Let us consider the space of functions that are defined on a closed interval $[a, b]$. If we restrict ourselves to the class of *continuous* functions, we can define the distance between two functions f and g as

$$\max |f(x) - g(x)|, \qquad x \text{ in } [a, b].$$

Let $\{f_n\}_{n=1}^\infty$ be a sequence of continuous functions and let f be continuous. Let

$$\varepsilon_n = \max |f_n(x) - f(x)|, \qquad x \text{ in } [a, b].$$

Thus ε_n is the distance between the functions f_n and f. If

$$\lim_{n \to \infty} \varepsilon_n = 0,$$

then certainly the sequence $\{f_n\}_{n=1}^\infty$ converges† to f pointwise in $[a, b]$. However, it is still possible for the sequence $\{f_n(x)\}_{n=1}^\infty$ to converge to $f(x)$ for every x in $[a, b]$ even though ε_n does not approach zero. We shall presently give an alternative definition for the distance between two functions which turns out to be more natural and more satisfactory for a discussion of the convergence of Fourier series. First, however, we shall describe a certain class of functions that we shall adopt for our "function space."

A function f is said to be *piecewise continuous* on the interval $[a, b]$ if it is continuous except at a finite number of points $x_1 < x_2 < \cdots < x_N$ of $[a, b]$ and if at each point of discontinuity the left- and right-hand limits of f exist. (If $x_1 = a$, the right-hand limit must exist at x_1 and if $x_N = b$, the left-hand limit must exist at x_N.) We use the symbols

$$f(x_i -), \qquad f(x_i +)$$

to denote the left- and right-hand limits, respectively, of f at x_i. The function f which is illustrated in Fig. 7.1 is piecewise continuous on $[a, b]$. It has only one discontinuity, at $x = x_1$, and

$$f(x_1 -) = A, \qquad f(x_1 +) = B.$$

The function g, which is illustrated in Fig. 7.2, is *not* piecewise continuous on $[a, b]$. It has only one discontinuity, at x_1, but the right-hand limit of g does not exist at x_1.

Let us denote the class, or space, of functions that are piecewise continuous on the interval $[a, b]$ by the symbol $C_p[a, b]$. When it is evident what interval is under consideration, we shall use the simpler symbol C_p. If the functions f and g are both in C_p, then every function of the form

$$\alpha f + \beta g,$$

---

† In this case, the sequence not only converges at each point of $[a, b]$, but it converges *uniformly* on $[a, b]$.

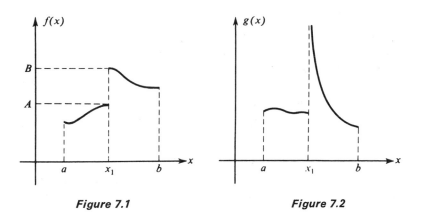

Figure 7.1   Figure 7.2

where α and β are constants, is also in C_p. The functions f^2, g^2, and fg are also in C_p (Exercise 2).

Let w be a function that is continuous and positive on (a, b), and such that the integral

$$\int_a^b w(x)\, dx$$

exists. Note that w need not be continuous at a and b. The above integral may be improper. It can be shown that if F is any function in $C_p[a, b]$, then the integral

$$\int_a^b w(x)F(x)\, dx$$

also exists.

The *inner product* (f, g) of two functions f and g in C_p, with respect to the weight function w, is defined to be

$$(f, g) = \int_a^b w(x)f(x)g(x)\, dx.$$

The *norm* $\|f\|$ of a function f in C_p is defined to be

$$\|f\| = (f, f)^{1/2} = \left(\int_a^b w(x)[f(x)]^2\, dx \right)^{1/2}.$$

The *distance* between two functions f and g in C_p is defined to be

$$\|f - g\|.$$

It should be noted that because of the properties of the space C_p and the properties of the weight function w, all of the integrals in these definitions exist. We also note that if $\|f\| = 0$, where f is in C_p, then f must be zero on (a, b) except possibly at its points of discontinuity. Thus if $\|f\| = 0$, then $f(x)$ must be zero at all but a finite number of points in $[a, b]$. If $\|f - g\| = 0$, then the functions f and g must be equal at all but a finite number of points in $[a, b]$.

If f and g both belong to C_p, then the *Schwarz inequality*

$$|(f, g)| \leq \|f\| \cdot \|g\|$$

and the *triangle inequality*

$$\|f + g\| \leq \|f\| + \|g\|$$

are both valid. The proofs of these inequalities are left as exercises.

We now define another type of convergence for sequences of functions of the space $C_p[a, b]$. Let the functions f_n, $n = 1, 2, 3, \ldots$, and f belong to the space. We say that the sequence $\{f_n\}_{n=1}^{\infty}$ *converges in the mean* to f (with respect to the weight function w on $[a, b]$) if

$$\lim_{n \to \infty} \|f_n - f\| = 0;$$

that is, if

$$\lim_{n \to \infty} \int_a^b w(x)[f_n(x) - f(x)]^2 \, dx = 0.$$

If a sequence converges in the mean on an interval $[a, b]$, it does not necessarily follow that the sequence converges pointwise at each point of the interval. Also, it is possible for a sequence to converge pointwise to a function f on an interval and yet not converge in the mean to f. Examples are presented in the exercises. Thus the two types of convergence are different, and one type does not imply the other. For theoretical purposes, convergence in the mean is more satisfactory, especially when the Lebesgue integral is used instead of the Riemann integral of elementary calculus. In applications, however, pointwise convergence is more important. We shall discuss both types of convergence for Fourier series in the sections that follow.

Exercises for Section 7.3

1. Determine whether the given function is piecewise continuous on its interval of definition.

(a) $f(x) = |x|$, $\quad -1 \leq x \leq 1$

(b) $g(x) = \begin{cases} 1, & 0 \leq x < 1 \\ 0, & 1 \leq x \leq 2 \end{cases}$

(c) $h(x) = \begin{cases} 1, & 0 \leq x \leq 2, x \neq 1 \\ 2, & x = 1 \end{cases}$

(d) $p(x) = \begin{cases} x, & -1 \leq x < 0 \\ 5, & x = 0 \\ 1 - x, & 0 < x \leq 1 \end{cases}$

(e) $q(x) = \begin{cases} 1/(1-x), & 0 \le x \le 2, \quad x \ne 1 \\ 0, & x = 1 \end{cases}$

(f) $r(x) = \begin{cases} \sin(1/x), & 0 < x \le 1/\pi \\ 0, & x = 0 \end{cases}$

2. If f and g are in $C_p[a, b]$, prove that $\alpha f + \beta g$, fg, and f^2 are in $C_p[a, b]$.

3. (a) Prove the Schwarz inequality,

$$|(f, g)| \le \|f\| \, \|g\|,$$

for functions f and g in $C_p[a, b]$. *Suggestion*: If $\|g\| \ne 0$, the function F, where $F(\lambda) = \|f + \lambda g\|^2$, is a second-degree polynomial that is never negative. Look at the discriminant of the equation $F(\lambda) = 0$.
(b) Prove the triangle inequality,

$$\|f + g\| \le \|f\| + \|g\|$$

for functions f and g in $C_p[a, b]$. *Suggestion*: Compare the squares of both members of the inequality, using the Schwarz inequality of part (a).

4. Let f be piecewise continuous on $[a, b]$. Use the Schwarz inequality to show that

$$\left| \int_a^b f(x) \, dx \right| \le \sqrt{b - a} \, \|f\| .$$

5. Let $f_n(x) = x^n$ for $0 \le x \le 1$ and n a positive integer. Show that the sequence $\{f_n\}_{n=1}^{\infty}$ converges in the mean (with $w(x) \equiv 1$) to the zero function on $[0, 1]$. Does the sequence converge pointwise to the zero function on $[0, 1]$?

6. Let the graph of each of the functions f_n, $n = 2, 3, 4, \ldots$, defined on $[0, 1]$, consist of three line segments, as shown in Fig. 7.3.

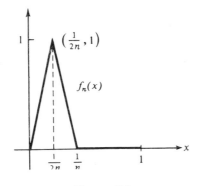

Figure 7.3

(a) Describe f_n analytically.

(b) Show that the sequence $\{f_n\}$ converges (pointwise) to zero at each point of the interval $[0, 1]$.

(c) If $\varepsilon_n = \max_{0 \le x \le 1} |f_n(x) - 0|$, show that ε_n does not approach zero as n becomes infinite.

(d) Show that the sequence $\{f_n\}$ converges in the mean (with $w(x) \equiv 1$) on the interval $[0, 1]$ to the zero function.

7.   Let the graph of the function f_n, $n = 2, 3, 4, \ldots$, consist of three line segments that join, successively, the points

$$(0, 0), \qquad \left(\frac{1}{2n}, n\right), \qquad \left(\frac{1}{n}, 0\right), \qquad \text{and} \qquad (1, 0).$$

(a) Draw a graph that shows the configuration of the functions f_n, and also describe these functions analytically.

(b) Show that the sequence $\{f_n\}$ converges (pointwise) to zero at each point of the interval $[0, 1]$.

(c) Show that the sequence $\{f_n\}$ does *not* converge in the mean to the zero function on the interval $[0, 1]$.

8.   This exercise involves the construction of a sequence of continuous functions $\{f_n\}$ that converges in the mean on the interval $[0, 1]$, but converges pointwise nowhere. To begin with, we divide the interval

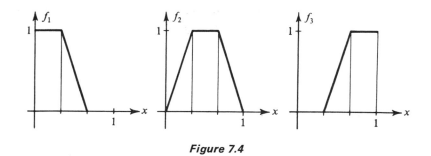

Figure 7.4

$[0, 1]$ into three equal subintervals and define functions f_1, f_2, and f_3 as shown in Fig. 7.4. Next, we subdivide the interval $[0, 1]$ into $3^2 = 9$ equal parts, and define nine functions $f_4, f_5, \ldots, f_{12}$ in such a way that each function has the value 1 on one of the subintervals and has the value 0 outside of, at most, three subintervals. A typical case is shown in Fig. 7.5. We next form $3^3 = 27$ more functions of the sequence, corresponding to 27 equal subintervals of $[0, 1]$, and so on. It is left to the reader to show that $\{f_n\}$ converges in the mean to the zero function, but converges pointwise nowhere.

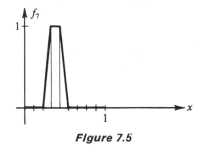

Figure 7.5

7.4 CONVERGENCE IN THE MEAN

Let $\{\phi_n\}_{n=1}^{\infty}$ be an orthonormal† set with weight function w on an interval $[a, b]$. Each ϕ_n is assumed to belong to the space $C_p[a, b]$. If f is any function in $C_p[a, b]$, its Fourier series is

$$\sum_{k=1}^{\infty} c_k \phi_k,$$

where

$$c_k = (f, \phi_k)$$

is the kth Fourier coefficient of f. Let $\{S_n\}_{n=1}^{\infty}$ be the sequence of partial sums of the series, so that

$$S_n = \sum_{k=1}^{n} c_k \phi_k.$$

The Fourier series is said to converge in the mean to f if its sequence of partial sums converges in the mean to f; that is, if

$$\lim_{n \to \infty} \|f - S_n\| = 0.$$

Before we continue with our discussion of Fourier series, let us consider the possibility of representing f by a general series of the form

$$\sum_{k=1}^{\infty} a_k \phi_k, \tag{7.16}$$

† In view of the result of Exercise 9, Section 7.1, we consider only orthogonal sets that are orthonormal.

where the coefficients a_k are not necessarily the Fourier coefficients of f. Let

$$T_n(x; a_1, a_2, \ldots, a_n) = \sum_{k=1}^{\infty} a_k \phi_k(x)$$

be the nth partial sum of this series at x, and let

$$E_n = \|f - T_n\|.$$

In order to obtain the best approximation "in the mean" to f, we must choose the coefficients a_k so as to make E_n as small as possible. We have

$$E_n^2 = \int_a^b w(x)\left[f(x) - \sum_{k=1}^{n} a_k \phi_k(x)\right]^2 dx.$$

If we square the quantity in brackets and remember that $(\phi_i, \phi_j) = 0$ when $i \neq j$, we see that

$$E_n^2 = \int_a^b w(x)\left\{[f(x)]^2 - 2\sum_{k=1}^{n} a_k f(x)\phi_k(x) + \sum_{k=1}^{n} a_k^2[\phi_k(x)]^2\right\} dx$$

or

$$E_n^2 = \|f\|^2 + \sum_{k=1}^{n} (a_k^2 - 2a_k c_k),$$

where $c_k = (f, \phi_k)$ is the kth Fourier coefficient of f. This equality may be written as

$$E_n^2 = \|f\|^2 + \sum_{k=1}^{n} (a_k - c_k)^2 - \sum_{k=1}^{n} c_k^2. \qquad (7.17)$$

Evidently, for a given positive integer n, E_n is least when $a_k = c_k$ for $k = 1$, $2, \ldots, n$. We therefore have the following result.

Theorem 7.1   For any given positive integer n, the best approximation in the mean to a function f by a sum of the form

$$\sum_{k=1}^{n} a_k \phi_k$$

is obtained when the coefficients a_k are the Fourier coefficients of f.

Additional significance is given to the Fourier coefficients by the next proposition.

Theorem 7.2   If a series of the form

$$\sum_{k=1}^{\infty} a_k \phi_k$$

converges in the mean to f, then the coefficients a_k must be the Fourier coefficients of f.

PROOF   If we set $a_k = c_k$ in formula (7.17), we have

$$\|f - S_n\|^2 = \|f\|^2 - \sum_{k=1}^{n} c_k^2 . \tag{7.18}$$

From this relation and Eq. (7.17) we see that

$$\|f - T_n\|^2 = \|f - S_n\|^2 + \sum_{k=1}^{n} (a_k - c_k)^2 , \tag{7.19}$$

and hence that

$$0 \le \|f - S_n\| \le \|f - T_n\| .$$

Thus if the series (7.16) converges in the mean to f, the Fourier series must also converge in the mean to f. But then, from Eq. (7.19), we see that

$$\lim_{n \to \infty} \sum_{k=1}^{n} (a_k - c_k)^2 = 0 .$$

But this is impossible unless $a_k = c_k$ for every positive integer k.

Let us now consider only the Fourier series, with nth partial sum S_n, for a function f in $C_p[a, b]$. From Eq. (7.18), we see that

$$\|f - S_{n+1}\| \le \|f - S_n\| .$$

The sequence of numbers whose nth term is $\|f - S_n\|$ is therefore nonincreasing, and since it is bounded below by zero, it must converge. If it converges to zero, then the Fourier series for f converges in the mean to f. Also, from Eq. (7.18), we may deduce the inequality

$$\sum_{k=1}^{n} c_k^2 \le \|f\|^2 , \qquad n \ge 1 .$$

The sequence of numbers $\{A_n\}_{n=1}^{\infty}$, whose nth term is

$$A_n = \sum_{k=1}^{n} c_k^2 ,$$

is nondecreasing and is bounded above by the number $\|f\|^2$. It therefore converges and we have

$$\sum_{k=1}^{\infty} c_k^2 \le \|f\| .$$

This inequality is known as *Bessel's inequality*. It holds regardless of whether the Fourier series for f actually converges in the mean to f. The next theorem follows from the foregoing remarks.

Theorem 7.3   Let $\{\phi_n\}_{n=1}^{\infty}$ be an orthonormal set and let $c_k = (f, \phi_k)$ be the kth Fourier coefficient of a function f in C_p. Then the series

$$\sum_{k=1}^{\infty} c_k^2$$

converges. Consequently

$$\lim_{n \to \infty} c_n = 0\,;$$

that is,

$$\lim_{n \to \infty} \int_a^b w(x)f(x)\phi_n(x)\,dx = 0\,.$$

As an application of Theorem 7.3, we shall derive two results that will be of use to us later on. If

$$\phi_n(x) = \sqrt{\frac{2}{\pi}}\,\sin\,nx\,, \qquad \psi_0(x) = \sqrt{\frac{1}{\pi}}\,, \qquad \psi_n(x) = \sqrt{\frac{2}{\pi}}\,\cos\,nx$$

for $0 \le x \le \pi$ and $n = 1, 2, 3, \ldots$, then each of the sequences $\{\phi_n\}_{n=1}^{\infty}$ and $\{\psi_n\}_{n=0}^{\infty}$ is orthonormal on $[0, \pi]$, with weight function $w(x) = 1$. If f is any function of the class $C_p[0, \pi]$, it follows from Theorem 7.3 that

$$\lim_{n \to \infty} \int_0^{\pi} f(x) \cos\,nx\,dx = 0\,,$$

$$\lim_{n \to \infty} \int_0^{\pi} f(x) \sin\,nx\,dx = 0\,. \tag{7.20}$$

Theorem 7.3 says that the series of squares of the Fourier coefficients converges regardless of whether the Fourier series converges, in the mean or otherwise. However, we see from Eq. (7.18) that the Fourier series for f actually converges in the mean to f if and only if

$$\|f\|^2 = \sum_{k=1}^{\infty} c_k^2\,. \tag{7.21}$$

This condition is known as *Parseval's equality*.

Exercises for Section 7.4

1. Let $\{\psi_n\}_{n=1}^{\infty}$ be an orthogonal, but not necessarily orthonormal, set with positive weight function w on an interval $[a, b]$. Let f be a function in $C_p[a, b]$.

   (a) If

   $$E_n(a_1, a_2, \ldots, a_n) = \int_a^b w(x)f(x) - \sum_{k=1}^{n} a_k \psi_k(x))^2 \, dx,$$

   show that E_n is a minimum when the constants a_k have the values

   $$a_k = \frac{(f, \psi_k)}{\|\psi_k\|^2}.$$

   (b) Show that

   $$\sum_{k=1}^{\infty} \frac{(f, \psi_k)^2}{\|\psi_k\|^2} \leq \int_a^b w(x)[f(x)]^2 \, dx.$$

2. Let $f(x) = x$ for x in $[0, 1]$. If f is to be approximated in the mean on the interval $[0, 1]$ (with $w(x) = 1$) by a function of the form

   $$C_1 \sin \pi x + C_2 \sin 2\pi x + C_3 \sin 3\pi x,$$

   how should the constants C_i be chosen in order to obtain the best possible approximation in the mean?

3. Let $f(x) = 0$ when $-1 \leq x \leq 0$ and $f(x) = x$ when $0 < x \leq 1$. Suppose f is to be approximated in the mean on $[-1, 1]$, with $w(x) = 1$, by a function of the form

   $$C_0 P_0 + C_1 P_1 + C_2 P_2,$$

   where P_n is the Legendre polynomial of degree n. Determine the constants C_i so that the best possible approximation in the mean is obtained.

4. Let $f(x) = e^{-x}$ for $x \geq 0$ and let L_n be the Laguerre polynomial of degree n.

   (a) If g is of the form $g = A_0 L_0 + A_1 L_1$, what should be the values of the constants A_0 and A_1 in order that

   $$\int_0^{\infty} e^{-x}[f(x) - g(x)]^2 \, dx$$

   be a minimum?

(b) Let $l_n(x) = e^{-x/2}L_n(x)$ for $x \geq 0$ and n a nonnegative integer. if h is of the form $h = B_0 l_0 + B_1 l_1$, how should the constants B_0 and B_1 be chosen in order to make the quantity

$$\int_0^\infty [f(x) - h(x)]^2 \, dx$$

as small as possible?

5. Let $f(x) = 0$ when $-1 \leq x < 0$, and $f(x) = 1$ when $0 \leq x \leq 1$. Determine the constants C_0, C_1, C_2 in such a way as to minimize the quantity

$$\int_{-1}^1 [f(x) - (C_0 + C_1 x + C_2 x^2)]^2 \, dx.$$

6. Let f belong to the class $C_p[-1, 1]$. Show that

$$\lim_{n \to \infty} \int_{-1}^1 f(x)P_n(x) \, dx = 0,$$

where P_n is the Legendre polynomial of degree n.

7. Let $f(x) = 1$ and

$$\phi_n(x) = \sqrt{\frac{2}{c}} \sin \frac{n\pi x}{c} \qquad \text{for} \quad 0 \leq x \leq c$$

and n a positive integer.

(a) What is Bessel's inequality for the function f and the orthonormal set $\{\phi_n\}_{n=1}^\infty$?

(b) What is Parseval's equality for f and $\{\phi_n\}_{n=1}^\infty$? If Parseval's equality holds, what is implied about the Fourier sine series for f?

8. Let $f(x) = x$,

$$\phi_0(x) = \sqrt{\frac{1}{c}}, \qquad \phi_n(x) = \sqrt{\frac{2}{c}} \cos \frac{n\pi x}{c} \qquad \text{for} \quad 0 \leq x \leq c$$

and n a positive integer.

(a) What is Bessel's inequality for the function f and the orthonormal set $\{\phi_n\}_{n=0}^\infty$?

(b) What is Parseval's equality for f and $\{\phi_n\}_{n=0}^\infty$? If Parseval's equality holds, what is implied about the Fourier cosine series for f?

9. Show that

$$\lim_{n \to \infty} \frac{1}{2^n n!} \int_{-\infty}^\infty \exp(-x^2)H_n(x) \, dx = 0,$$

where H_n is the Hermite polynomial of degree n.

7.5   COMPLETE ORTHOGONAL SETS

Let $\{\phi_n\}_{n=1}^{\infty}$ be an orthogonal set of functions, with each function belonging to the space $C_p[a, b]$. The orthogonal set is said to be *complete* in the space $C_p[a, b]$ if every function of the space is represented by its Fourier series, in the sense of convergence in the mean. From Eq. (7.21) of the previous section we see that an orthonormal set is complete if and only if Parseval's equality holds for every function f in the space. Another important property of complete orthogonal sets is as follows.

Theorem 7.4   If an orthogonal set $\{\psi_n\}_{n=1}^{\omega}$ is complete in the space $C_p[a, b]$ and if f is any function that is orthogonal to every member of the set, then $f(x) = 0$ for all x in $[a, b]$ except possibly for a finite number of points.

PROOF   Let $\phi_n = \psi_n / \|\psi_n\|$, so that $\{\phi_n\}_{n=1}^{\infty}$ is orthonormal. Then $c_n = (f, \phi_n)$ is zero for every n; that is, all the Fourier coefficients of f are zero. According to the Parseval relation, $\|f\| = 0$. Hence $f(x) = 0$ except when x is a point of discontinuity, and the number of such points is finite.

Theorem 7.4 implies that if we delete one element from an orthogonal set, the remaining functions cannot constitute a complete orthogonal set. For the deleted function is orthogonal to every member of the new set.

We now wish to indicate some specific complete sets. There is no single general procedure for determining whether or not an arbitrary orthogonal set is complete. However, completeness has been established for certain important classes of orthogonal sets. One of these is the class of orthogonal polynomials on a bounded interval. Another consists of the sets of eigenfunctions of self-adjoint eigenvalue problems. The results are stated in the next two theorems.

Theorem 7.5   A simple set of orthogonal polynomials for the interval $[a, b]$ and the weight function w is complete in the space $C_p[a, b]$. Here w is assumed to be continuous and positive on (a, b) and such that $\int_a^b w(x)\, dx$ exists.

The sets of Legendre and Tchebycheff polynomials are therefore complete on the interval $[-1, 1]$. Notice that Theorem 7.5 does not apply to the Laguerre and Hermite polynomials, whose intervals of orthogonality are not bounded. These functions are discussed separately at the end of this section.

Theorem 7.6 Let p', q, and r be continuous on $[a, b]$ with $p(x) > 0$ and $r(x) > 0$ for x in $[a, b]$. The set of all eigenfunctions of the self-adjoint problem

$$(py')' + (\lambda r + q)y = 0,$$
$$U_1(y) = 0, \qquad U_2(y) = 0$$

is a complete orthogonal set in the space $C_p[a, b]$. (If two linearly independent eigenfunctions correspond to the same eigenvalue, it is assumed that two mutually orthogonal eigenfunctions are chosen.)

In particular, the sets $\{f_n\}_{n=0}^{\infty}$ and $\{g_n\}_{n=1}^{\infty}$, where

$$f_0(x) = 1, \qquad f_n(x) = \cos \frac{n\pi x}{c}, \qquad g_n(x) = \sin \frac{n\pi x}{c},$$

are complete on $[0, c]$ with $w(x) = 1$. Also, the set

$$(f_0, f_1, g_1, f_2, g_2, \ldots, f_n, g_n, \ldots)$$

is complete on $[-c, c]$ with $w(x) = 1$. (See the example in Section 6.3.)

No proof of Theorem 7.6 is simple enough to present here. We shall present a proof of Theorem 7.5 that is based on two other theorems. The first of these is a famous one known as the Weierstrass approximation theorem.

Theorem 7.7 Let the function g be continuous on a bounded closed interval $[a, b]$. Then, corresponding to every positive number ε, there is a polynomial Q such that $|g(x) - Q(x)| < \varepsilon$ for all x in $[a, b]$.

This theorem says that a continuous function can be approximated *uniformly*, as closely as desired, by a polynomial on a closed interval. This theorem is proved in many advanced books on real analysis.

In proving Theorem 7.5, we shall also have need of the following result.

Theorem 7.8 Let f belong to the space $C_p[a, b]$ and let the weight function w satisfy the conditions of Theorem 7.5. Then, corresponding to every positive number ε, there is a function g, *continuous* on $[a, b]$, such that $\|f - g\| < \varepsilon$.

PROOF Let $x_1, x_2, \ldots, x_N$ be the points in (a, b), where f is discontinuous. The case $N = 2$ is illustrated in Fig. 7.6. We define g in the following way: Let $g(a) = f(a+)$, $g(b) = g(b-)$, and in (a, b) let $g(x) = f(x)$ except on the intervals $(x_i - \delta, x_i + \delta)$, $i = 1, 2, \ldots, N$, where δ is a small positive number to be specified later. On each of these intervals, let g be such that its graph is a straight-line segment, chosen so that g is continuous on $[a, b]$. (Fig. 7.7 illustrates a function g that corresponds to the function f of Fig. 7.6.) Then the function $f - g$ has zero values except possibly at a and b and on the intervals $(x_i - \delta, x_i + \delta)$. (See Fig. 7.8.) All we have to do is choose δ small enough to insure that $\|f - g\| < \varepsilon$. We proceed with the details.

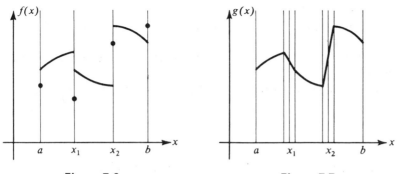

Figure 7.6   Figure 7.7

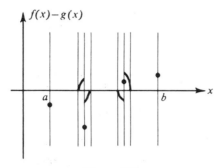

Figure 7.8

Since f is in $C_p[a, b]$, there is a positive number A such that $|f(x)| \le A$ for x in $[a, b]$. Then $|g(x)| \le A$ and $|f(x) - g(x)| \le 2A$ for x in $[a, b]$. Let c and d be numbers such that

$$a < c < x_1, \qquad x_N < d < b.$$

Then w is continuous on $[c, d]$ and there is a positive number B such that $|w(x)| \le B$ for x in $[c, d]$. We choose δ sufficiently small so that $c < x_1 - \delta$ and $x_N + \delta < d$. Then

$$\|f - g\| = \left(\int_a^b w[f - g]^2 \, dx \right)^{1/2}$$

$$= \left(\sum_{i=1}^N \int_{x_i - \delta}^{x_i + \delta} w[f - g]^2 \, dx \right)^{1/2}$$

$$\le \sqrt{8A^2 BN \, \delta}.$$

Given ε, choose

$$\delta \le \frac{\varepsilon^2}{32 A^2 BN}.$$

Then $\|f - g\| \leq \varepsilon/2 < \varepsilon$.

We now give a proof of Theorem 7.5, based on Theorems 7.7 and 7.8.

PROOF   Let $\{\phi_n\}_{n=0}^{\infty}$ be a simple set of orthogonal polynomials, with weight function w. Let $\int_a^b w(x)\,dx = K$. If f is in $C_p[a, b]$ and if ε is any positive number, we know from Theorem 7.8 that there is a continuous function g such that

$$\|f - g\| < \frac{\varepsilon}{2}.$$

Also, according to Theorem 7.7, there is a polynomial Q such that

$$|g(x) - Q(x)| < \frac{\varepsilon}{2\sqrt{K}}$$

for all x in $[a, b]$. Then

$$\|g - Q\| = \left(\int_a^b w(g - Q)^2\,dx \right)^{1/2} \leq \left(\frac{\varepsilon^2}{4K} \int_a^b w\,dx \right)^{1/2} = \frac{\varepsilon}{2}.$$

Using the triangle inequality, we see that

$$\|f - Q\| \leq \|f - g\| + \|g - Q\| < \varepsilon.$$

Let m be the degree of Q. Then there exist constants $a_0, a_1, \ldots, a_m$ such that

$$Q = \sum_{i=0}^{m} a_i \phi_i.$$

Let S_n be the nth partial sum of the Fourier series of f. By Theorem 7.1,

$$\|f - S_m\| \leq \|f - Q\| < \varepsilon,$$

and so

$$\|f - S_n\| < \varepsilon$$

whenever $n \geq m$. Hence

$$\lim_{n \to \infty} \|f - S_n\| = 0,$$

as we wished to show.

Let us now consider the Laguerre and Hermite polynomials. For both of these polynomial sets, the interval of orthogonality is unbounded. If such a set is to be complete in a space of functions, the space must at least have the property that the improper integrals used in computing the Fourier coefficients are convergent.

We define a space V as follows. A function f is said to belong to V if it is piecewise continuous on every bounded interval of the form $[0, b]$, $b > 0$, and if the integral

$$\int_0^\infty e^{-x}[f(x)]^2 \, dx$$

converges. The Laguerre polynomials L_n belong to V. It can be shown (Exercise 8) that if f and g belong to V, then the integral

$$\int_0^\infty e^{-x}f(x)g(x) \, dx$$

converges, and that $\alpha f + \beta g$ belongs to V for all constants α and β. Because of these properties, we can talk about the inner product,

$$(f, g) = \int_0^\infty e^{-x}f(x)g(x) \, dx,$$

norm,

$$\|f\| = (f,f)^{1/2},$$

and distance,

$$\|f - g\|,$$

for functions f and g in V. All the integrals involved in the definitions exist if f and g belong to V.

Likewise, we define a space W in the following manner. A function f is said to belong to W if it is piecewise continuous on every bounded closed interval, and if the integral

$$\int_{-\infty}^\infty e^{-x^2}[f(x)]^2 \, dx$$

exists. The Hermite polynomials H_n belong to W. It can be shown (Exercise 8) that if f and g belong to W, then the integral

$$\int_{-\infty}^\infty e^{-x^2} f(x)g(x) \, dx$$

exists, and that $\alpha f + \beta g$ belongs to W for all constants α and β. We may therefore define the inner product

$$(f, g) = \int_{-\infty}^\infty e^{-x^2} f(x)g(x) \, dx,$$

norm

$$\|f\| = (f,f)^{1/2},$$

and distance

$$\|f - g\|$$

for functions f and g in W.

We state without proof the following result about completeness for the Laguerre and Hermite polynomials.

Theorem 7.9   The Laguerre polynomials are complete in the space V and the Hermite polynomials are complete in the space W.

Exercises for Section 7.5

1.   Show that the simply orthogonal set $\{\phi_n\}_{n=1}^{\infty}$, where $\phi_n(x) = \cos n\pi x$, is not complete in the space $C_p[0, 1]$.

2.   (a) If f and g, of the class $C_p[a, b]$, have the same Fourier coefficients with respect to a complete orthogonal set, show that $f(x) = g(x)$ at each point x of $[a, b]$, where both functions are continuous.

   (b) If in part (a) the orthogonal set is not complete, does the same conclusion necessarily follow?

3.   Let w be positive on (a, b) and continuous on $[a, b]$. Let the orthogonal set $\{f_n\}_{n=1}^{\infty}$ be complete in the space $C_p[a, b]$, with weight function w. Let $g_n(x) = \sqrt{w(x)}\, f_n(x)$. Show that the simply orthogonal set $\{g_n\}_{n=1}^{\infty}$ is complete in $C_p[a, b]$.

4.   If an orthogonal sequence is complete in the space of continuous functions on $[a, b]$, show that it is also complete in the space $C_p[a, b]$.

5.   Let f be continuous on $[0, \pi]$. Given $\varepsilon > 0$, show that there exists an integer m and constants $c_0, c_1, \ldots, c_m$ such that

$$\left| f(\theta) - \sum_{k=0}^{m} c_k \cos k\theta \right| < \varepsilon$$

   for $0 \le \theta \le \pi$. Are the constants c_k necessarily the Fourier cosine coefficients of f? *Suggestion*: Let $x = \cos \theta$. Use the Weierstrass approximation theorem and properties of Tchebycheff polynomials.

6.   Make use of the result of Exercise 5 to prove that the Fourier cosine series of a continuous function on $[0, \pi]$ converges in the mean to the function.

7. Let f be continuous on $[0, \pi]$. Given $\varepsilon > 0$, does there always exist an integer m and constants $c_1, c_2, \ldots, c_m$ such that

$$\left| f(\theta) - \sum_{k=1}^{m} c_k \sin k\theta \right| < \varepsilon$$

for $0 \leq \theta \leq \pi$? *Suggestion*: Look at specific values of θ.

8. (a) If f and g belong to the class V, prove that the integral

$$\int_0^\infty e^{-x} f(x) g(x) \, dx$$

exists, and that $\alpha f + \beta g$ belongs to V. *Suggestion*: In the first part of the problem, integrate from 0 to b, use the Schwarz inequality, and then let b become infinite. Use Theorem 9.1.

(b) If f and g belong to the class W, prove that the integral

$$\int_{-\infty}^\infty e^{-x^2} f(x) g(x) \, dx$$

exists and that $\alpha f + \beta g$ belongs to W.

9. Which of the following functions belongs to the space V?

(a) $f(x) = 1$, $x \geq 0$ (b) $g(x) = x$, $x \geq 0$

(c) $h(x) = e^x$, $x \geq 0$ (d) $k(x) = \begin{cases} e^x, & 0 \leq x \leq 1 \\ 1, & x > 1 \end{cases}$

10. Which of the following functions belongs to the space W?

(a) $f(x) = \sin x$,   all x (b) $g(x) = x^{100}$,   all x

(c) $h(x) = e^x$,   all x (d) $k(x) = \begin{cases} 0, & x \leq 0 \\ 1, & x > 0 \end{cases}$

11. The Laguerre functions l_n and the Hermite functions h_n are defined by the relations

$$l_n(x) = e^{-x/2} L_n(x), \qquad h_n(x) = e^{-x^2/2} H_n(x),$$

with n a nonnegative integer. State and prove theorems about the completeness of the sets $\{l_n\}_{n=0}^\infty$ and $\{h_n\}_{n=0}^\infty$, using the results stated in the text about completeness for the Laguerre and Hermite polynomials.

7.6   POINTWISE CONVERGENCE OF THE TRIGONOMETRIC SERIES

In this section we shall discuss the convergence of the trigonometric Fourier series at individual points rather than on an interval as a whole. It is known that a Fourier series for an arbitrary function f need not converge at every point. In order to prove theorems about the convergence of Fourier series we must restrict ourselves to the consideration of functions of some suitable class.

One such class of functions is the class of *piecewise smooth* functions. A function f is said to be *piecewise smooth* on a closed interval $[a, b]$ if f and f' are piecewise continuous on $[a, b]$.

An important property of piecewise smooth functions is described in Theorem 7.10 below. In order to understand the statement of the theorem, however, we need the following definitions. The limit

$$\lim_{x \to x_0+} \frac{f(x) - f(x_0 +)}{x - x_0},$$

if it exists, is called the *right-hand derivative* of the function f at x_0. Similarly, the limit

$$\lim_{x \to x_0-} \frac{f(x) - f(x_0 -)}{x - x_0},$$

if it exists, is called the *left-hand derivative* of the function f at x_0. If the derivative itself of f exists at x_0, then of course the left- and right-hand derivatives both exist and are equal to $f'(x_0)$.

Theorem 7.10   Let f be piecewise smooth on the interval $[a, b]$. Then f possesses a right-hand derivative at a, a left-hand derivative at b, and both a left- and right-hand derivative at every point in (a, b).

PROOF   We consider only the right-hand derivative. The existence of the left-hand derivative can be established in a similar fashion. Let x_0 be any point in the interval $[a, b)$. Since f' has only a finite number of discontinuities, there exists an interval (x_0, x_1), where $x_1 > x_0$, on which f' is continuous. For each point x in this interval we have, by the mean value theorem,

$$\frac{f(x) - f(x_0 +)}{x - x_0} = f'(\xi),$$

where $x_0 < \xi < x$. The number ξ depends on x. Since f' is piecewise continuous, the limit

$$\lim_{x \to x_0+} f'(x) = \lim_{x \to x_0+} f'(\xi)$$

exists, so f possesses a right-hand derivative at x_0.

The first type of Fourier series that we shall consider is the general trigonometric series for a function f defined on the interval $[-\pi, \pi]$. The functions $\{1, \cos nx, \sin nx\}$, $n \geq 1$, are simply orthogonal on this interval. The corresponding Fourier series for $f(x)$ is

$$\tfrac{1}{2}a_0 + \sum_{n=1}^{\infty} (a_n \cos nx + b_n \sin nx), \tag{7.22}$$

where

$$a_n = \frac{1}{\pi} \int_{-\pi}^{\pi} f(t) \cos nt \, dt, \qquad n \geq 0,$$

$$\tag{7.23}$$

$$b_n = \frac{1}{\pi} \int_{-\pi}^{\pi} f(t) \sin nt \, dt, \qquad n \geq 1.$$

We note that every term in the series (7.22) is periodic† with period 2π. Hence, if the series converges on the interval $[-\pi, \pi]$, it will converge for all x to a function that is periodic with period 2π. Trigonometric series can be used to represent a periodic function for all x, or to represent a function that is defined only on a finite interval on the interval of definition.

In order to prove the next theorem, about the convergence of the series (7.22), we need the following result:

Lemma Let

$$D_n(\theta) = \tfrac{1}{2} + \sum_{k=1}^{n} \cos k\theta.$$

Then

$$D_n(\theta) = \begin{cases} n + \tfrac{1}{2}, & \text{when } \theta = 2N\pi, \, N = 0, \pm 1, \pm 2, \dots, \\ \dfrac{\sin(n + \tfrac{1}{2})\theta}{2 \sin \theta/2} & \text{elsewhere}, \end{cases}$$

and

$$\int_{0}^{\pi} D_n(\theta) \, d\theta = \int_{-\pi}^{0} D_n(\theta) \, d\theta = \frac{\pi}{2}.$$

† A function g, defined for all x, is said to be periodic with period T if $g(x + T) = g(x)$ for all x.

PROOF   If we multiply through in the equation that defines $D_n(\theta)$ by the quantity $2 \sin \theta/2$, we have

$$2D_n(\theta) \sin \frac{\theta}{2} = \sin \frac{\theta}{2} + \sum_{k=1}^{n} 2 \cos k\theta \sin \frac{\theta}{2}$$

for all θ. Because of the trigonometric identity

$$2 \cos k\theta \sin \frac{\theta}{2} = \sin\left(k + \frac{1}{2}\right)\theta - \sin\left(k - \frac{1}{2}\right)\theta,$$

we can write

$$2D_n(\theta) \sin \frac{\theta}{2} = \sin \frac{\theta}{2} + \sum_{k=1}^{n} \left[\sin\left(k + \frac{1}{2}\right)\theta - \sin\left(k - \frac{1}{2}\right)\theta \right].$$

The terms in the sum on the right "telescope" and we have

$$2D_n(\theta) \sin \frac{\theta}{2} = \sin\left(n + \frac{1}{2}\right)\theta.$$

Hence

$$D_n(\theta) = \frac{\sin (n + \frac{1}{2})\theta}{2 \sin \theta/2}$$

when $\sin \theta/2 \neq 0$, that is, when $\theta \neq 2N\pi$, $N = 0, \pm 1, \pm 2, \ldots$. For these particular values of θ, we have, from the definition of $D_n(\theta)$,

$$D_n(2N\pi) = \frac{1}{2} + \sum_{k=1}^{n} 1 = n + \frac{1}{2}.$$

Since the functions $\{1, \cos k\theta\}$, $k \geq 1$, are orthogonal on the interval $[0, \pi]$, we have

$$\int_0^\pi D_n(\theta) \, d\theta = \int_0^\pi 1 \cdot D_n(\theta) \, d\theta = \int_0^\pi 1 \cdot \frac{1}{2} \, d\theta = \frac{\pi}{2}.$$

Since $D_n(-\theta) = D_n(\theta)$, we have

$$\int_{-\pi}^0 D_n(\theta) \, d\theta = \int_0^\pi D_n(\theta) \, d\theta = \frac{\pi}{2}.$$

Theorem 7.11   Let f be periodic, with period 2π, and let f be piecewise smooth on the interval $[-\pi, \pi]$. Then at every point x_0, the Fourier series (7.22) for f converges to the value $\frac{1}{2}[f(x_0+) + f(x_0-)]$.

Before proving the theorem, we note that the quantity $\frac{1}{2}[f(x_0+) + f(x_0-)]$ is simply the average of the left- and right-hand limits of f at x_0.

If f is *continuous* at x_0, this quantity is simply $f(x_0)$. The situation at a point of discontinuity is illustrated in Fig. 7.9.

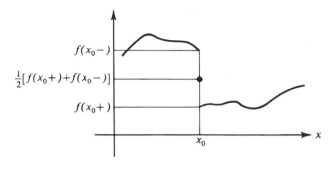

Figure 7.9

PROOF   Let

$$S_n(x_0) = \tfrac{1}{2}a_0 + \sum_{k=1}^{n} (a_k \cos kx_0 + b_k \sin kx_0)$$

be the nth partial sum of the Fourier series. In order to prove the theorem, we must show that

$$\lim_{n \to \infty} S_n(x_0) = \tfrac{1}{2}[f(x_0+) + f(x_0-)].$$

We first find a compact expression for $S_n(x_0)$. Using the formulas (7.23) for the coefficients a_k and b_k, we have

$$S_n(x_0) = \frac{1}{2\pi} \int_{-\pi}^{\pi} f(t)\, dt + \frac{1}{\pi} \sum_{k=1}^{n} \int_{-\pi}^{\pi} f(t)[\cos kt \cos kx_0 + \sin kt \sin kx_0]\, dt$$

$$= \frac{1}{\pi} \int_{-\pi}^{\pi} f(t)\left[\frac{1}{2} + \sum_{k=1}^{n} \cos k(t - x_0)\right] dt$$

$$= \frac{1}{\pi} \int_{-\pi}^{\pi} f(t) D_n(t - x_0)\, dt.$$

Making the change of variable $u = t - x_0$, we can write

$$S_n(x_0) = \frac{1}{\pi} \int_{-\pi-x_0}^{\pi-x_0} f(x_0 + u) D_n(u)\, du.$$

Since the integrand is a periodic function of u, with period 2π, we have

$$S_n(x_0) = \frac{1}{\pi} \int_{-\pi}^{\pi} f(x_0 + u)D_n(u)\, du$$

or

$$S_n(x_0) = \frac{1}{\pi} \int_{0}^{\pi} f(x_0 + u)D_n(u)\, du = \frac{1}{\pi} \int_{-\pi}^{0} f(x_0 + u)D_n(u)\, du \,.$$

In view of the lemma, we can write

$$\frac{1}{2}[f(x_0 +) + f(x_0 -)] = \frac{1}{\pi} \int_{0}^{\pi} f(x_0 +)D_n(u)\, du + \frac{1}{\pi} \int_{-\pi}^{0} f(x_0 -)D_n(u)\, du\,,$$

since the quantities $f(x_0+)$ and $f(x_0-)$ do not depend on the variable of integration u. Subtracting the last two equations, we have

$$S_n(x_0) - \frac{1}{2}[f(x_0-) + f(x_0-)] = \frac{1}{\pi}\, [A_n(x_0) + B_n(x_0)]\,,$$

where

$$A_n(x_0) = \int_{0}^{\pi} [f(x_0 + u) - f(x_0+)]D_n(u)\, du$$

and

$$B_n(x_0) = \int_{-\pi}^{0} [f(x_0 + u) - f(x_0-)]D_n(u)\, du\,.$$

If we can show that

$$\lim_{n \to \infty} A_n(x_0) = \lim_{n \to \infty} B_n(x_0) = 0\,,$$

then the theorem will be proved. The formula for $A_n(x_0)$ can be written as

$$A_n(x_0) = \int_{0}^{\pi} \frac{f(x_0 + u) - f(x_0 +)}{u}\, \frac{u/2}{\sin u/2} \sin\!\left(n + \frac{1}{2}\right)u\, du\,,$$

or

$$A_n(x_0) = \int_{0}^{\pi} \phi_1(u) \cos nu\, du + \int_{0}^{\pi} \phi_2(u) \sin nu\, du\,,$$

where

$$\phi_1(u) = \frac{f(x_0 + u) - f(x_0 +)}{u}\, \frac{u}{2}\,,$$

$$\phi_2(u) = \frac{f(x_0 + u) - f(x_0 +)}{u}\, \frac{u/2}{\sin u/2} \cos \frac{u}{2}\,.$$

Since the function f is piecewise smooth on every finite closed interval, it has a right-hand derivative at x_0. Hence ϕ_1 and ϕ_2 possess right-hand limits at 0. These functions are therefore piecewise continuous on the interval $[0, \pi]$. It now follows from the relations (7.20) of Section 7.4 that

$$\lim_{n \to \infty} A_n(x_0) = 0.$$

Similarly, the existence of a left-hand derivative of f at x_0 insures that

$$\lim_{n \to \infty} B_n(x_0) = 0.$$

We shall omit the details of the proof of this statement. This concludes the proof of the theorem.

We now consider, instead of periodic functions, functions which are defined only on the interval $[-\pi, \pi]$.

Theorem 7.12   Let f be piecewise smooth on the interval $[-\pi, \pi]$. Then the trigonometric Fourier series (7.22) for $f(x)$ converges to $\frac{1}{2}[f(x+) + f(x-)]$ for x in the interval $(-\pi, \pi)$. At $x = \pm \pi$, the series converges to the value $\frac{1}{2}[f(-\pi+) + f(\pi-)]$.

PROOF   Let F be the function such that $F(x) = f(x)$ for $-\pi \leq x < \pi$ and that is periodic with period 2π. The function F is piecewise smooth on the interval $[-\pi, \pi]$. The Fourier series for $F(x)$ is the same as that for $f(x)$, and by Theorem 7.11, this series converges to $\frac{1}{2}[F(x+) + F(x-)]$ for all x. It therefore converges to $\frac{1}{2}[f(x+) + f(x-)]$ for $-\pi < x < \pi$. Since $F(-\pi-) = f(\pi-)$ and $F(\pi+) = f(-\pi+)$, the series converges to $\frac{1}{2}[f(-\pi+) + f(\pi-)]$ at $x = \pm \pi$.

As an example, let us consider the function

$$f(x) = \begin{cases} 0, & -\pi < x < 0, \\ 1, & 0 < x < \pi. \end{cases}$$

The function f is piecewise continuous on the interval $[-\pi, \pi]$ and its derivative,

$$f'(x) = 0, \quad -\pi < x < 0, \quad 0 < x < \pi,$$

is also piecewise continuous on this interval. Hence f is piecewise smooth on the interval $[-\pi, \pi]$. The graph of f is shown in Fig. 7.10.

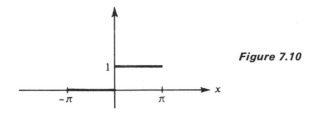

Figure 7.10

The Fourier coefficients of f are

$$a_0 = \frac{1}{\pi} \int_{-\pi}^{\pi} f(x)\, dx = \frac{1}{\pi} \int_0^{\pi} \cos nx\, dx = 1,$$

$$a_n = \frac{1}{\pi} \int_{-\pi}^{\pi} f(x) \cos nx\, dx = \frac{1}{\pi} \int_0^{\pi} \cos nx\, dx = 0, \qquad n \geq 1,$$

$$b_n = \frac{1}{\pi} \int_{-\pi}^{\pi} f(x) \sin nx\, dx = \frac{1}{\pi} \int_0^{\pi} \sin nx\, dx,$$

$$= \frac{1}{n\pi}(1 - \cos n\pi) = \frac{1}{n\pi}[1 - (-1)^n] = \begin{cases} 0, & \text{if } n \text{ is even,} \\ \dfrac{2}{n\pi}, & \text{if } n \text{ is odd.} \end{cases}$$

The Fourier series for $f(x)$ is therefore

$$\frac{1}{2} + \frac{2}{\pi} \sum_{m=1}^{\infty} \frac{\sin(2m-1)x}{2m-1}.$$

Although f is not defined outside the interval $(-\pi, \pi)$, the series converges everywhere and represents a function F that is periodic with period 2π. The graph of F is shown in Fig. 7.11.

We now consider the case of a function that is defined on an interval of the form $[-c, c]$, where c is an arbitrary positive number.

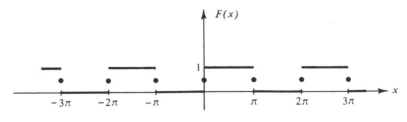

Figure 7.11

Theorem 7.13 Let f be piecewise smooth on the interval $[-c, c]$. Then the trigonometric Fourier series

$$\frac{1}{2} a_0 + \sum_{n=1}^{\infty} \left(a_n \cos \frac{n\pi x}{c} + b_n \sin \frac{n\pi x}{c} \right), \qquad (7.24)$$

where

$$a_n = \frac{1}{c} \int_{-c}^{c} f(x) \cos \frac{n\pi x}{c} \, dx, \qquad n \geq 0,$$

$$\qquad\qquad (7.25)$$

$$b_n = \frac{1}{c} \int_{-c}^{c} f(x) \sin \frac{n\pi x}{c} \, dx, \qquad n \geq 1,$$

converges to $\frac{1}{2}[f(x+) + f(x-)]$ for $-c < x < c$. At $x = \pm c$, the series converges to the value $\frac{1}{2}[f(-c+) + f(c-)]$.

PROOF If we make the change of variable $t = (\pi/c)x$, the function $F(t) = f[(c/\pi t)]$ is piecewise smooth on the interval $-\pi \leq t \leq \pi$. The proof of the theorem now follows from Theorem 7.12. The details are left as an exercise.

We note that the series (7.24) corresponds to the set of functions

$$\left\{ 1, \cos \frac{n\pi x}{c}, \sin \frac{n\pi x}{c} \right\}, \qquad n \geq 1,$$

which is orthogonal on the interval $[-c, c]$.

Exercises for Section 7.6

1. Determine whether or not the given function is piecewise smooth on the interval $[-1, 1]$.

   (a) $f(x) = |x|$

   (c) $f(x) = \sqrt{1 - x^2}$

   (b) $f(x) = \begin{cases} 1, & -1 \leq x < 0 \\ x, & 0 < x < 1 \end{cases}$

   (d) $f(x) = x^{2/3}$

2. Expand the given function in a trigonometric series of the functions $\sin nx$, $\cos nx$, $n \geq 0$. Draw a graph showing the function to which the series converges for $-3\pi \leq x \leq 3\pi$.

   (a) $f(x) = \begin{cases} 1, & -\pi < x < 0 \\ 0, & 0 < x < \pi \end{cases}$

   (c) $h(x) = \begin{cases} 1, & -\pi < x \leq 0 \\ \cos x, & 0 < x < \pi \end{cases}$

   (b) $g(x) = \begin{cases} -x, & -\pi < x < 0 \\ 0, & 0 < x < \pi \end{cases}$

   (d) $k(x) = \begin{cases} \pi + x, & -\pi < x \leq 0 \\ \pi - x, & 0 < x < \pi \end{cases}$

3. Expand the given function in a trigonometric series of the functions $\sin n\pi x/c$, $\cos n\pi x/c$, $n \geq 0$. Draw a graph showing the function to which the series converges for $-3c \leq x \leq 3c$.

(a) $f(x) = \begin{cases} 0, & -c < x < -\dfrac{c}{2} \\ 1, & -\dfrac{c}{2} < x < \dfrac{c}{2} \\ 0, & \dfrac{c}{2} < x < c \end{cases}$

(c) $h(x) = x$, $\quad -c < x < c$

(b) $g(x) = \begin{cases} c, & -c < x < 0 \\ x, & 0 < x < c \end{cases}$

(d) $k(x) = |x|$, $\quad -c \leq x \leq c$

4. Complete the proof of Theorem 7.11 by showing that

$$\lim_{n \to \infty} B_n(x_0) = 0.$$

5. Let f' be continuous and piecewise smooth on the interval $[-c, c]$. If $f(-c) = f(c)$, show that the trigonometric Fourier series for $f'(x)$ can be obtained by termwise differentiation of the series for $f(x)$. *Suggestion*: write out the series for $f'(x)$ and use integration by parts in the formulas for the coefficients.

6. Let f be piecewise continuous on the interval $[-c, c]$, and denote the Fourier coefficients of f by a_n, $n \geq 0$, and b_n, $n \geq 1$. [Note that the Fourier series of $f(x)$ need not converge to $f(x)$.] Prove that

$$\int_\alpha^\beta f(x)\, dx = \int_\alpha^\beta \frac{1}{2} a_0 \, dx + \sum_{n=1}^\infty \int_\alpha^\beta \left(a_n \cos \frac{n\pi x}{c} + b_n \sin \frac{n\pi x}{c} \right) dx$$

for every pair of numbers α, β in the interval $[-c, c]$. *Suggestions*: The function $F(x) = \int_{-c}^x [f(t) - \frac{1}{2}a_0]\, dt$ is continuous and piecewise smooth on $[-c, c]$ and $F(c) = F(-c) = 0$. Expand F in a Fourier series and use integration by parts to find its Fourier coefficients. Then find $F(\beta) - F(\alpha)$.

7. Let $f(x) = 0$ when $1 < x < 2$ and $f(x) = 1$ when $2 < x < 3$. Expand f in a trigonometric series of period 2. *Suggestion*: Find the Fourier series for the function F that is periodic with period 2 and equal to f on the interval $(1, 3)$.

8. Let f be continuous and piecewise smooth on the interval $[-\pi, \pi]$. Show that

$$f(x) = \lim_{n \to \infty} \sum_{k=-n}^{n} c_k e^{ikx}, \qquad -\pi < x < \pi,$$

where

$$c_k = \frac{1}{2\pi} \int_{-\pi}^{\pi} f(x) e^{-ikx}\, dx, \qquad k = 0, \pm 1, \pm 2, \dots.$$

9. Show that the expansion in Exercise 8 is valid when f is complex valued—that is, when $f(x) = f_1(x) + if_2(x)$. Assume that f_1 and f_2 are continuous and piecewise smooth on the interval $[-\pi, \pi]$.

10. Complete the proof of Theorem 7.13.

11. Let f be periodic with period 2π, and be piecewise *continuous* on the interval $[-\pi, \pi]$. Show, by inspection of the proof of Theorem 7.11, that the Fourier series for $f(x)$ converges to the value $\frac{1}{2}[f(x+) + f(x-)]$ at each point where the function possesses both a left and right hand derivative. (The assumption that f is piecewise *smooth* guarantees that f possesses a left- and right-hand derivative at *every* point.)

7.7   THE SINE AND COSINE SERIES

A function f that is defined on an interval of the form $(-a, a)$ or $[-a, a]$ or $(-\infty, \infty)$ is said to be *even* if $f(-x) = f(x)$ for all x in the interval; it is said to be *odd* if $f(-x) = -f(x)$ for all x in the interval. For example, if $f(x) = \cos kx$ for all x, where k is any constant, then f is even. If $g(x) = \sin kx$ for all x, then g is odd. The graph of any even function is symmetric about the vertical coordinate axis while the graph of an odd function is symmetric about the origin.

If f is even and g is odd, then fg is odd. To see this, we observe that if $F = fg$, then

$$F(-x) = f(-x)g(-x) = f(x)[-g(x)] = -f(x)g(x) = -F(x).$$

It can also be shown (Exercise 7) that if f and g are both even or both odd, then fg is even. If a function f, defined on an interval $[-a, a]$, is odd, then

$$\int_{-a}^{a} f(x)\, dx = 0,$$

and if f is even,

$$\int_{-a}^{a} f(x)\, dx = 2 \int_{0}^{a} f(x)\, dx.$$

These properties are intuitively evident from the geometrical interpretations of evenness and oddness.

We are now ready to prove the following theorem.

Theorem 7.14   Let f be piecewise smooth on the interval $[0, c]$. Then the Fourier sine series for $f(x)$,

$$\sum_{n=1}^{\infty} b_n \sin \frac{n\pi x}{c},$$

$$b_n = \frac{2}{c} \int_0^c f(x) \sin \frac{n\pi x}{c} \, dx, \qquad n \geq 1,$$

converges to $\frac{1}{2}[f(x+) + f(x-)]$ for $0 < x < c$. At $x = 0$ and $x = c$ it converges to zero. The Fourier cosine series for $f(x)$,

$$\tfrac{1}{2}a_0 + \sum_{n=1}^{\infty} a_n \cos \frac{n\pi x}{c},$$

$$a_n = \frac{2}{c} \int_0^c f(x) \cos \frac{n\pi x}{c} \, dx, \qquad n \geq 0,$$

converges to $\frac{1}{2}[f(x+) + f(x-)]$ for $0 < x < c$. At $x = 0$ it converges to $f(0+)$ and at $x = c$ it converges to $f(c-)$.

PROOF   We consider first the sine series for $f(x)$. Let F be an odd function, defined on $[-c, c]$, which is identical to f on $(0, c]$. Then F is piecewise smooth on $[-c, c]$. If we expand $F(x)$ in a full trigonometric Fourier series, the coefficients of the cosine terms

$$a_n = \frac{1}{c} \int_{-c}^c F(x) \cos \frac{n\pi x}{c} \, dx, \qquad n \geq 0,$$

all vanish because the integrand is odd and the coefficients of the sine terms become

$$b_n = \frac{1}{c} \int_{-c}^c F(x) \sin \frac{n\pi x}{c} \, dx = \frac{2}{c} \int_0^c f(x) \sin \frac{n\pi x}{c} \, dx, \qquad n \geq 1.$$

Thus the full trigonometric series for $F(x)$ is the same as the sine series for $f(x)$. The convergence of the series to the values indicated in the statement of the theorem follows from Theorem 7.13.

In order to establish the convergence of the cosine series, we form the even function G, defined on $[-c, c]$, which is identical to f on $[0, c]$. The full trigonometric series for $G(x)$ turns out to be the same as the cosine series for $f(x)$, and the convergence of the series to the indicated values follows from Theorem 7.13. This concludes the proof of the theorem.

Although f is defined only on the interval $[0, c]$, its Fourier sine series converges everywhere to a function that is odd and periodic with period $2c$. Similarly, the Fourier cosine series for $f(x)$ converges for all x to a function that is even and periodic with period $2c$.

As an example, let us consider the function $f(x) = 1 - x$, where $0 < x < 1$. Here $c = 1$. The coefficients in the sine series for f are

$$b_n = 2 \int_0^1 (1 - x) \sin n\pi x \, dx = \frac{2}{n\pi}, \qquad n \geq 1,$$

and the sine series is

$$\frac{2}{\pi} \sum_{n=1}^{\infty} \frac{\sin n\pi x}{n}.$$

This series converges for all x to represent the function shown in Fig. 7.12.

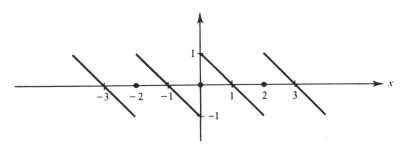

Figure 7.12

The coefficients in the cosine series for f are

$$a_0 = 2 \int_0^1 (1 - x) \, dx = 1,$$

$$a_n = 2 \int_0^1 (1 - x) \cos n\pi x \, dx = \begin{cases} 0, & \text{when } n \text{ is even}, \\ \dfrac{4}{n^2\pi^2}, & \text{when } n \text{ is odd}, \end{cases}$$

and the cosine series is

$$\frac{1}{2} + \frac{4}{\pi^2} \sum_{m=1}^{\infty} \frac{\cos (2m - 1)\pi x}{(2m - 1)^2}.$$

(We set $n = 2m - 1$ since $a_n = 0$ when n is even.) This series converges for all x to represent the function shown in Fig. 7.13. It should be noted that *both* series converge to $f(x)$ on the interval $(0, 1)$.

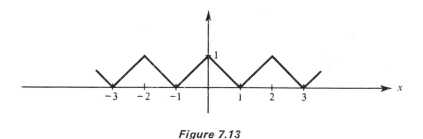

Figure 7.13

Exercises for Section 7.7

1. Expand the given function in both a Fourier cosine series and a Fourier sine series on the interval $(0, \pi)$. Draw graphs showing the functions to which the series converge for $-3\pi < x < 3\pi$.

    (a) $f(x) = x$, $\qquad 0 < x < \pi$ $\qquad\qquad$ (c) $h(x) = \sin x$, $\qquad 0 < x < \pi$

    (b) $g(x) = \begin{cases} 1, & 0 < x < \dfrac{\pi}{2} \\[2mm] 0, & \dfrac{\pi}{2} < x < \pi \end{cases}$ $\qquad\qquad$ (d) $k(x) = \cos x$, $\qquad 0 < x < \pi$

2. Deduce from the series of Exercise 1(a) that

$$\sum_{n=1}^{\infty} \frac{1}{(2n-1)^2} = \frac{\pi^2}{8}.$$

3. Expand the function $f(x) = 1$, $0 < x < \pi$, in a Fourier sine series. Deduce from the result that

$$\sum_{n=1}^{\infty} \frac{(-1)^{n+1}}{2n-1} = \frac{\pi}{4}.$$

4. Expand the function $f(x) = x^2$, $0 \le x \le \pi$, in a Fourier cosine series. Deduce from the result that

$$\sum_{n=1}^{\infty} \frac{1}{n^2} = \frac{\pi^2}{6}, \qquad \sum_{n=1}^{\infty} \frac{(-1)^{n+1}}{n^2} = \frac{\pi^2}{12}.$$

5.   Find both the Fourier sine series and the Fourier cosine series for the given function on the interval $(0, c)$. Draw graphs showing the functions to which the series converge for $-3c < x < 3c$.

(a) $f(x) = \begin{cases} 0, & 0 < x < \dfrac{c}{2} \\ 1, & \dfrac{c}{2} < x < c \end{cases}$

(c) $f(x) = \begin{cases} x, & 0 < x < \dfrac{c}{2} \\ 0, & \dfrac{c}{2} < x < c \end{cases}$

(b) $f(x) = c - x, \quad 0 < x < c$

(d) $f(x) = \begin{cases} c - 2x, & 0 < x < \dfrac{c}{2} \\ c, & \dfrac{c}{2} < x < c \end{cases}$

6.   Let f be piecewise smooth on the interval $a \leq x \leq b$. Show that

$$\frac{f(x+) + f(x-)}{2} = \frac{1}{2} a_0 + \sum_{n=1}^{\infty} a_n \cos \frac{n\pi x}{b - a}, \qquad a < x < b,$$

where

$$a_n = \frac{2}{b - a} \int_a^b f(x) \cos \frac{n\pi x}{b - a}\, dx, \qquad n \geq 0.$$

7.   If f and g are both even or both odd, show that fg is even.

8.   Show that any function f defined on an interval of the form $[-a, a]$ is the sum of an even function and an odd function. *Suggestion*: Verify that

$$f(x) = \tfrac{1}{2}[f(x) + f(-x)] + \tfrac{1}{2}[f(x) - f(-x)].$$

7.8   OTHER FOURIER SERIES

In our discussion of convergence in the mean, we were able to assert that every simple set of orthogonal polynomials was complete in the space of piecewise continuous function on the interval of orthogonality. In the case of pointwise convergence, there is no corresponding general theorem, and we must consider individual polynomial sets more or less individually. We shall consider here some of the special polynomial sets described in Chapter V.

Theorem 7.15   Let f be piecewise smooth on the interval $[-1, 1]$. Then the series of Legendre polynomials for $f(x)$ converges to the value $\frac{1}{2}[f(x+) + f(x-)]$ for $-1 < x < 1$. At $x = -1$, the series converges to $f(-1+)$ and at $x = 1$ it converges to $f(1-)$.

As in the case of the trigonometric Fourier series, it is possible to find a compact expression for the nth partial sum of the series. Proofs of the convergence of the series can be found in Churchill [1], Jackson [4], and Sansone [6].

Proofs of the convergence of series of Tchebycheff polynomials can be based on the theorem about the convergence of the Fourier sine and cosine series. We shall only state the results here. The proofs are left as exercises.

Theorem 7.16   Let f be piecewise smooth on the interval $[1-, 1]$. Then the series of Tchebycheff polynomials of the first kind for $f(x)$ converges to $\frac{1}{2}[f(x+) + f(x-)]$ for $-1 < x < 1$. At $x = -1$ it converges to $f(-1+)$ and at $x = 1$ it converges to $f(1-)$. The series of Tchebycheff polynomials of the second kind converges to $\frac{1}{2}[f(x+)] + f(x-)]$ for $-1 < x < 1$.

Conditions for the convergence of the Laguerre and Hermite series are given in the next two theorems.†

Theorem 7.17   Let f be piecewise smooth on every finite interval of the form $[0, b]$, $b > 0$, and let the integral

$$\int_{-\infty}^{\infty} \exp(-x)[f(x)]^2 \, dx$$

exist. Then the series of Laguerre polynomials for $f(x)$ converges to $\frac{1}{2}[f(x+) + f(x-)]$ for $0 < x < +\infty$.

Theorem 7.18   Let f be piecewise smooth on every finite interval and let the integral

$$\int_{-\infty}^{\infty} \exp(-x^2)[f(x)]^2 \, dx$$

exist. Then the series of Hermite polynomials for $f(x)$ converges to $\frac{1}{2}[f(x+) + f(x-)]$ for all x.

---

† From J. V. Uspensky, On the Development of Arbitrary Functions in Series of Hermite's and Laguerre's Polynomials, *Ann. Math.* (2) **28**, 593–619 (1927).

Let us now consider orthogonal sets of functions that are generated by eigenvalue problems. We consider a problem of the form†

$$[p(x)y']' + [\lambda r(x) + q(x)]y = 0,$$
$$\alpha y(a) + \beta y'(a) = 0, \qquad (7.26)$$
$$\gamma y(b) + \delta y'(b) = 0,$$

where p'', q, and r'' are continuous and $p(x) > 0$, $r(x) > 0$ for $a \le x \le b$. It should be noted that the boundary conditions are separated and that the problem is self-adjoint. A proof of the following general theorem is given by Titchmarsh [7].

Theorem 7.19   Let f be piecewise smooth on the interval $[a, b]$. Then the Fourier series for $f(x)$, in terms of the eigenfunctions of the problem (7.26), converges to the value $\frac{1}{2}[f(x+) + f(x-)]$ for $a < x < b$.

The orthogonal sets of Bessel functions that were described in Chapter VI and in Section 7.2 arise from *singular* eigenvalue problems. Nevertheless, it can be shown (see, for example, Whittaker and Watson [9] or Tolstov [8]) that if f is piecewise smooth on the interval $[0, c]$, each of the series of Bessel functions described in Section 7.2 converges to $\frac{1}{2}[f(x+) + f(x-)]$ for $0 < x < c$.

Exercises for Section 7.8

1. Find the first three nonvanishing terms when the given function is expanded in a series of Legendre polynomials on the interval $(-1, 1)$. In part (a), indicate the value of the series at $x = 0$.

    (a) $f(x) = \begin{cases} 0, & -1 < x < 0 \\ 1, & 0 < x < 1 \end{cases}$ (c) $h(x) = |x|, \qquad -1 < x < 1$

    (b) $g(x) = \begin{cases} 0, & -1 < x < 0 \\ x, & 0 < x < 1 \end{cases}$ (d) $k(x) = \begin{cases} 1, & -1 < x < 0 \\ x, & 0 < x < 1 \end{cases}$

2. Let f be continuous and piecewise smooth on the interval $[0, 1]$. Show that

---

† For similar expansion theorems for other types of self-adjoint eigenvalue problems, see the paper by A. C. Zaanen, On Some Orthogonal Systems of Functions, *Compositio Math.* 7, 253–282 (1939).

(a) $f(x) = \sum\limits_{n=0}^{\infty} A_n P_{2n}(x),\qquad 0 \le x \le 1,$

where

$$A_n = (4n + 1) \int_0^1 f(x)P_{2n}(x)\,dx, \qquad n \ge 0.$$

(b) $f(x) = \sum\limits_{n=1}^{\infty} B_n P_{2n-1}(x),\qquad 0 < x < 1,$

where

$$B_n = (4n - 1) \int_0^1 f(x)P_{2n-1}(x)\,dx, \qquad n \ge 1.$$

Suggestion: Consider the even and odd extensions of f.

3. Let f be piecewise smooth on the interval $[-c, c]$. Show that

$$\frac{f(x+) + f(x-)}{2} = \sum_{n=0}^{\infty} A_n P_n\!\left(\frac{x}{c}\right), \qquad -c < x < c,$$

where

$$A_n = \frac{2n+1}{2c} \int_{-c}^{c} f(x)P_n\!\left(\frac{x}{c}\right) dx, \qquad n \ge 0.$$

4. Let f be continuous and piecewise smooth on the interval $[0, \pi]$. Show that

$$f(\phi) = \sum_{n=0}^{\infty} A_n P_n(\cos \phi), \qquad 0 \le \phi \le \pi,$$

where

$$A_n = \frac{2n+1}{2} \int_0^{\pi} f(\phi)P_n(\cos \phi) \sin \phi \, d\phi, \qquad n \ge 0.$$

5. Find the first three terms when the given function is expanded in a series of the functions $P_n(\cos \phi)$ on the interval $(0, \pi)$. See Exercise 4.

(a) $f(\phi) = \begin{cases} 0, & 0 < \phi < \dfrac{\pi}{2} \\[2mm] 1, & \dfrac{\pi}{2} < \phi < \pi \end{cases}$
    (b) $f(\phi) = \begin{cases} \sin^2 \phi, & 0 < \phi < \dfrac{\pi}{2} \\[2mm] 0, & \dfrac{\pi}{2} < \phi < \pi \end{cases}$

6. Let f be piecewise smooth on the interval $[-1, 1]$. Show that the series of Tchebycheff polynomials T_n for f converges to $[f(x+) + f(x-)]/2$ for $-1 < x < 1$. Also show that the series of the polynomials S_n for

f converges to the same values. *Suggestion:* Let $F(\theta) = f(\cos \theta)$, $0 \le \theta \le \pi$, and examine the Fourier cosine and sine series for F.

7. Find the first three terms when the given function is expanded in a series Laguerre polynomials. To what values does the series converge at a point where the function is discontinuous?

(a) $f(x) = \begin{cases} e^x, & 0 < x < 1 \\ 0, & x > 1 \end{cases}$ (b) $g(x) = \begin{cases} 0, & 0 < x < 1 \\ 1, & x > 1 \end{cases}$

8. (a) The Laguerre functions

$$l_n(x) = e^{-x/2} L_n(x), \qquad n \ge 0,$$

are simply orthogonal on the interval $(0, \infty)$. What conditions on f will guarantee that the series expansion of $f(x)$ in terms of the functions l_n will converge to

$$\frac{f(x+) + f(x-)}{2} \qquad \text{for} \quad 0 < x < \infty ?$$

(b) Find the first three terms when the function of Exercise 7(b) is expanded in a series of the Laguerre functions l_n.

9. Find the first two nonvanishing terms when the given function is expanded in a series of Hermite polynomials.

(a) $f(x) = \begin{cases} e^{x^2}, & |x| < 1 \\ 0, & |x| > 1 \end{cases}$ (b) $g(x) = \begin{cases} 0, & x < 0 \\ 1, & x > 0 \end{cases}$

10. Let k_n be the nth positive root of the equation $J_2(kc) = 0$. Expand the given function f in a series of the functions $J_2(k_n x)$, $n \ge 1$, on the interval $(0, c)$.

(a) $f(x) = x^2, \qquad 0 < x < c$ (c) $h(x) = 1, \qquad 0 < x < c$

(b) $g(x) = \begin{cases} x^2, & 0 < x < \dfrac{c}{2} \\ 0, & \dfrac{c}{2} < x < c \end{cases}$ (d) $k(x) = \begin{cases} x^2, & 0 < x < \dfrac{c}{2} \\ \dfrac{c_2}{4}, & \dfrac{c}{2} \le x < c \end{cases}$

11. Let k_n be the nth positive root of the equation $J_2'(kc) = 0$. Expand the functions of Exercise 10 in a series of the functions $J_2(k_n x)$ on the interval $(0, c)$.

12. Let $f(x) = 1$ when $0 < x < c/2$ and $f(x) = 0$ when $c/2 < x < c$. Expand $f(x)$ in a series of the quantities $J_0(k_n x)$, where k_n is the nth positive root of the equation $J_0'(kc) = 0$.

13.   Expand the function $f(x) = 1$, $0 < x < 1$, in a series of the eigenfunctions of the problem

$$xy'' + y' + \lambda xy = 0,$$

y, y' finite as $x \to 0+$, $hy(0) + y'(0) = 0$, $h > 0$.

14.   Expand the function

$$f(x) = \begin{cases} 1, & 0 < x < \tfrac{1}{2}, \\ 0, & \tfrac{1}{2} < x < 1, \end{cases}$$

in a series of the eigenfunctions of the problem

$$y'' + \lambda y = 0, \qquad y(0) = 0, \qquad y'(1) = 0.$$

15.   Expand the function $f(x) = 1$, $0 < x < 1$, in a series of the eigenfunctions of the given problem.

(a) $y'' + 2y' + (\lambda + 1)y = 0$, $y(0) = 0$, $y(1) = 0$

(b) $y'' + \lambda y = 0$, $y(0) - y'(0) = 0$, $y(1) - y'(1) = 0$

REFERENCES

1.   Churchill, R. V., *Fourier Series and Boundary Value Problems*, 2nd ed. McGraw-Hill, New York, 1963.
2.   Courant, R., and Hilbert, D., *Methods of Mathematical Physics*, Vol. 1. Wiley (Interscience), New York, 1955.
3.   Goldberg, R. R., *Methods of Real Analysis*. Blaisdell, New York, 1964.
4.   Jackson, D., *Fourier Series and Orthogonal Polynomials*, Carus Mathematical Monograph No. 6. Open Court Publishing Co., La Salle, Illinois, 1941.
5.   Kreider, D. L., Kuller, R. G., Ostberg, D. R., and Perkins, F. W., *An Introduction to Linear Analysis*. Addison-Wesley, Reading, Massachusetts, 1966.
6.   Sansone, G., *Orthogonal Functions*. Wiley (Interscience), New York, 1959.
7.   Titchmarsh, E. C., *Eigenfunction Expansions Associated with Second-Order Differential Equations*, Part 1, 2nd ed. Oxford Univ. Press, London and New York, 1962.
8.   Tolstov, G. P., *Fourier Series*. Prentice-Hall, Englewood Cliffs, New Jersey, 1962.
9.   Whittaker, E. T., and Watson, G. N., *Modern Analysis*. Cambridge Univ. Press, London and New York, 1950.

VIII

Systems of
Differential Equations

8.1 INTRODUCTION

In this chapter we shall deal with sets of simultaneous equations that involve several unknown functions and their derivatives. Such a set of equations is called a *system of differential equations*. An example of a system is

$$\frac{d^2x_1}{dt^2} - 2\frac{dx_1}{dt} - \frac{dx_2}{dt} = -3e^{3t},$$

$$\frac{dx_2}{dt} - 6x_1 = 0. \tag{8.1}$$

A solution of this system consists of an ordered pair of functions (x_1, x_2) that satisfy both the equations. An example of a solution of the system is the pair of functions (f_1, f_2), where

$$f_1(t) = e^{3t}, \qquad f_2(t) = 2e^{3t}$$

for all t. To verify this assertion, we observe that

$$f_1''(t) - 2f_1'(t) - f_2'(t) = 9e^{3t} - 6e^{3t} - 6e^{3t} = -3e^{3t},$$
$$f_2'(t) - 6f_1(t) = 6e^{3t} - 6e^{3t} = 0.$$

We now present several examples of problems that give rise to systems of differential equations. More applications appear in Sections 8.4, 8.5, and 8.6.

Example 1   Systems of differential equations commonly arise in problems of mechanics. For example, let $x_1(t)$, $x_2(t)$, and $x_3(t)$ denote the rectangular coordinates, at time t, of the center of mass of a moving object. Then, according to Newton's laws of motion we must have

$$m\mathbf{a} = \mathbf{F}, \tag{8.2}$$

where m is the mass of the object,

$$\mathbf{a} = \ddot{x}_1\mathbf{i} + \ddot{x}_2\mathbf{j} + \ddot{x}_3\mathbf{k}$$

is the acceleration, and

$$\mathbf{F} = F_1\mathbf{i} + F_2\mathbf{j} + F_3\mathbf{k}$$

is the force. Equating corresponding components in the vector equation (8.2) we have

$$m\ddot{x}_1 = F_1, \qquad m\ddot{x}_2 = F_2, \qquad m\ddot{x}_3 = F_3.$$

In many instances the components F_1, F_2, and F_3 of the force are known functions of t, x_1, x_2, x_3, $\dot{x}_1$, $\dot{x}_2$, and $\dot{x}_3$. If this is the case, we have a system of three differential equations for x_1, x_2, and x_3.

Example 2   Suppose that two tanks each initially contain 100 gal of a solution of a chemical, with 20 lb of the chemical in the first tank and 10 lb in the second. At $t = 0$, water begins to flow into the first tank at the rate of 2 gal/min. The (stirred) mixture runs into the second tank at the rate of 2 gal/min, and the (stirred) mixture in the second tank runs out at the same rate. We wish to find formulas for the amounts of chemical in each tank at time t.

Let $x_1(t)$ and $x_2(t)$ denote the amounts in the first and second tanks, respectively. Then we must have

$$\frac{dx_1}{dt} = -\frac{2}{100}x_1,$$

$$\frac{dx_2}{dt} = \frac{2}{100}x_1 - \frac{2}{100}x_2, \tag{8.3}$$

since the rate of change of the amount of chemical in a tank must be equal to the rate at which it enters minus the rate at which it leaves. We also have

$$x_1(0) = 20, \qquad x_2(0) = 10. \tag{8.4}$$

Here the first equation of the system (8.3) involves only the one unknown x_1. Solving this equation subject to the first of the conditions (8.4), we find that

$$x_1(t) = 20e^{-t/50}. \tag{8.5}$$

Substituting for x_1 in the second equation of the system (8.3), we arrive at the equation

$$\frac{dx_2}{dt} + \frac{1}{50}x_2 = \frac{2}{5}e^{-t/50}$$

for x_2. The solution of this equation that satisfies the second of the conditions (8.4) is

$$x_2(t) = \left(\frac{2}{5}t + 10\right)e^{-t/50}. \tag{8.6}$$

Formulas (8.5) and (8.6) describe the desired solution of the system.

Example 3   Our final example is from economics. Suppose that the rate of change of the supply of a commodity is proportional to the difference between the demand and the supply. In the case of two commodities we have

$$\frac{dS_1}{dt} = h(D_1 - S_1), \qquad \frac{dS_2}{dt} = k(D_2 - S_2),$$

where h and k are positive constants. We assume that each commodity is used in the manufacture of the other. In addition, we assume that the first commodity is used in the manufacture of itself (for example, steel). Finally, we assume that there is no other significant contribution to the demand for either commodity. For our model we take

$$D_1 = aS_1 + bS_2, \qquad D_2 = cS_1,$$

where a, b, and c are positive constants. Thus we arrive at the system of differential equations

$$\frac{dS_1}{dt} = h(a - 1)S_1 + hbS_2, \qquad \frac{dS_2}{dt} = kcS_1 - kS_2.$$

A technique for solving such a system will be developed in Section 8.3.

In the examples presented in this section, the number of unknown functions was always the same as the number of differential equations of the system. This is not a coincidence, as we shall see in the next section. There we begin a more systematic discussion of systems of differential equations.

Exercises for Section 8.1

1. Verify that the ordered pair of functions (f_1, f_2), where

$$f_1(t) = t^2, \qquad f_2(t) = 2t$$

for all t, is a solution of the system

$$x_1'' - x_1'x_2 + 4x_1 = 2,$$
$$x_1 - x_2' + x_2^2 = 5t^2 - 2.$$

2. Verify that the ordered triple of functions (f_1, f_2, f_3), where

$$f_1(t) = e^t, \qquad f_2(t) = 2e^t, \qquad f_3(t) = -e^t$$

for all t, constitutes a solution of the system

$$x_1' = x_2 + x_3, \qquad x_2' - x_1 - x_3, \qquad x_3' = -x_2 - x_3.$$

Also find another solution by inspection.

3. Describe a procedure that could be used for solving a system of the form

$$F(t, x_1, x_1') = 0,$$
$$G(t, x_1, x_2, x_2') = 0,$$
$$H(t, x_1, x_2, x_3, x_3') = 0,$$

where t is the independent variable and x_1, x_2, and x_3 are the unknown functions. (Notice that the first equation involves only one unknown.)

4. Two tanks each contain 50 gal of a salt solution initially, with 10 lb of salt in the first tank and 20 lb in the second tank. A salt solution containing 2 lb of salt per gallon runs into the first tank at the rate of 1 gal/min. The mixture runs into the second tank at the rate of 1 gal/min, and the mixture in the second tank runs out at the same rate. Find the amount of salt in each tank after 30 min.

5. A radioactive substance A decays at a rate equal to k_1 times the amount of A present. Let k_2 be the proportion of A that goes into a second radioactive substance B, where B decays at a rate equal to k_3 times the amount of B present. Let $x_1(t)$ and $x_2(t)$ be the amounts of A and B present at time t, and let $x_1(0) = a$, $x_2(0) = b$.

(a)   Find a system of differential equations for x_1 and x_2.

(b)   Find formulas for x_1 and x_2. (Assume $k_1 \neq k_3$.)

6. Two bodies, of masses m_1 and m_2, are suspended from springs as shown in Fig. 8.1. The spring constants are k_1 and k_2. If x_1 and x_2 denote the directed distances downward of the bodies from their equilibrium positions, find a system of differential equations for x_1 and x_2.

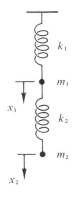

Figure 8.1

7. Two bodies, with masses m_1 and m_2, respectively, move along a straight line as shown in Fig. 8.2. Let x_1 and x_2 denote the respective directed

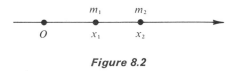

Figure 8.2

distances of the bodies from a fixed point on the line of motion. Assume that the bodies attract each other with a force equal to km_1m_2/r^2, where k is a positive constant and r is the distance between the bodies. Find a system of differential equations for x_1 and x_2.

8. In the economic model of Example 3, suppose that $D_1 = aS_2 + b$ and $D_2 = cS_1 + d$, where a, b, c, and d are positive constants. Explain the economic meaning of these assumptions and write down the system of differential equations for S_1 and S_2.

8.2   FIRST-ORDER SYSTEMS

A system of differential equations for unknown functions $x_1, x_2, \ldots, x_n$ that is of the form

$$\frac{dx_1}{dt} = f_1(t, x_1, x_2, \ldots, x_n),$$

$$\frac{dx_2}{dt} = f_2(t, x_1, x_2, \ldots, x_n),$$

$$\vdots$$

$$\frac{dx_n}{dt} = f_n(t, x_1, x_2, \ldots, x_n),$$

where the functions f_i are given, is called a *first-order system*. Notice that the number of equations is the same as the number of unknowns, and that no derivatives of order higher than 1 appear. A *solution* of the system is an ordered set of functions $(x_1, x_2, \ldots, x_n)$ that satisfies the system on some interval. The set of all solutions is called the *general solution*.

A set of auxiliary conditions of the form

$$x_1(t_0) = k_1, \qquad x_2(t_0) = k_2, \ldots, \qquad x_n(t_0) = k_n,$$

where the k_i are given numbers, is called a set of *initial conditions* for the system. The system together with the initial conditions is called an *initial value problem*. It can be shown that, with certain restrictions on the functions f_i, the initial value problem possesses a solution and that there is essentially only one solution. (See Chapter XII.) This means that if there were more equations than unknowns, we could not expect to find any solution that satisfied a set of initial conditions, while if there were fewer equations than unknowns we could expect more than one solution. We shall usually be able to find explicit formulas for the solutions of the systems that we encounter in this chapter.

We notice that although the system (8.3) is a first-order system, the system (8.1) is not. In particular, this latter system involves a derivative of order higher than 1. However, most systems that are not first-order can be rewritten as first-order systems, as we shall presently show. In developing a theory for systems of differential equations, it is more convenient to work with first-order systems. However, the theory will still be applicable to systems such as (8.1).

Let us show how the system [which is the same as (8.1)]

$$x_1'' - 2x_1' - x_2' = -3e^{3t}, \qquad x_2' - 6x_1 = 0 \tag{8.7}$$

can be replaced by a first-order system. We introduce new unknowns u_1, u_2, and u_3 by setting

$$u_1 = x_1, \qquad u_2 = x_2, \qquad u_3 = \frac{dx_1}{dt}.$$

Then

$$\frac{du_1}{dt} = u_3,$$

and from the system (8.7) we have

$$\frac{du_3}{dt} - 2u_3 - \frac{du_2}{dt} = -3e^{3t},$$

$$\frac{du_2}{dt} - 6u_1 = 0.$$

Notice that only *first* derivatives appear in these equations. Upon solving algebraically for du_2/dt and du_3/dt, we arrive at the first-order system

$$\frac{du_1}{dt} = u_3, \qquad \frac{du_2}{dt} = 6u_1,$$

$$\frac{du_3}{dt} = 6u_1 + 2u_3 - 3e^{3t} \tag{8.8}$$

for u_1, u_2, and u_3. Since initial conditions for the system (8.8) are of the form

$$u_1(t_0) = k_1, \qquad u_2(t_0) = k_2, \qquad u_3(t_0) = k_3,$$

appropriate conditions for the original system (8.7) are of the form

$$x_1(t_0) = k_1, \qquad x_2(t_0) = k_2, \qquad x_1'(t_0) = k_3.$$

More generally, suppose we have a system for two unknown functions x_1 and x_2 that is of the form

$$F[t, x_1, x_1', \ldots, x_1^{(m)}, x_2, x_2', \ldots, x_2^{(n)}] = 0,$$

$$G[t, x_1, x_1', \ldots, x_1^{(m)}, x_2, x_2', \ldots, x_2^{(n)}] = 0.$$

Here m and n are the orders of the highest order derivatives of x_1 and x_2 that appear in the two equations. Suppose that it is possible to solve algebraically for $x_1^{(m)}$ and $x_2^{(n)}$, so that we can replace the system by the equivalent† system

$$x_1^{(m)} = f[t, x_1, x_1', \ldots, x_1^{(m-1)}, x_2, x_2', \ldots, x_2^{(n-1)}],$$
$$x_2^{(n)} = g[t, x_1, x_1', \ldots, x_1^{(m-1)}, x_2, x_2', \ldots, x_2^{(n-1)}].$$

Let us set

$$u_1 = x_1, \qquad u_2 = x_1', \qquad u_3 = x_1'', \quad \ldots, \quad u_m = x_1^{(m-1)},$$
$$u_{m+1} = x_2, \qquad u_{m+2} = x_2', \qquad u_{m+3} = x_2'', \quad \ldots, \quad u_{m+n} = x_2^{(n-1)}.$$

Then we have

$$u_m' = f(t, u_1, u_2, \ldots, u_m, u_{m+1}, \ldots, u_{m+n}),$$
$$u_{m+n}' = g(t, u_1, u_2, \ldots, u_m, u_{m+1}, \ldots, u_{m+n}),$$
$$u_1' = u_2,$$
$$u_2' = u_3,$$
$$\vdots$$
$$u_{m-1}' = u_m,$$
$$u_{m+1}' = u_{m+2},$$
$$\vdots$$
$$u_{m+n-1}' = u_{m+n}.$$

This is a first-order system for the unknowns $u_1, u_2, \ldots, u_{m+n}$. Our discussion has been about a system with two equations and two unknowns, but the general case of k equations and k unknowns can be treated similarly.

An important special case is that of a single differential equation for one unknown function, of the form

$$x^{(n)} = F[t, x, x', \ldots, x^{(n-1)}]. \tag{8.9}$$

Setting

$$u_1 = x, \qquad u_2 = x', \qquad u_3 = x'', \ldots, u_n = x^{(n-1)}, \tag{8.10}$$

we have

$$u_1' = u_2,$$
$$u_2' = u_3,$$
$$\vdots \tag{8.11}$$
$$u_{n-1}' = u_n,$$
$$u_n' = F(t, u_1, u_2, \ldots, u_n).$$

The last equation of this first-order system comes from the differential equation (8.9). If x is a solution of Eq. (8.9) the relations (8.10) yield a solution

---

† Two systems are said to be *equivalent* if they have the same solutions.

$(u_1, u_2, \ldots, u_n)$ of the system (8.11). On the other hand, if a solution $(u_1, u_2, \ldots, u_n)$ of the system (8.11) is known, the function u_1 is a solution of Eq. (8.9).
As an example, we consider the equation

$$\frac{d^3x}{dt^3} = 3tx - \frac{dx}{dt} + \frac{d^2x}{dt^2}.$$

Setting

$$u_1 = x, \qquad u_2 = x', \qquad u_3 = x'',$$

we have

$$u_1' = u_2, \qquad u_2' = u_3, \qquad u_3' = 3tu_1 - u_2 + u_3.$$

Notice that the initial conditions

$$x(t_0) = k_1, \qquad x'(t_0) = k_2, \qquad x''(t_0) = k_3$$

for the original equation correspond to the initial conditions

$$u_1(t_0) = k_1, \qquad u_2(t_0) = k_2, \qquad u_3(t_0) = k_3$$

for the first-order system.

Exercises for Section 8.2

In Exercises 1–6, rewrite the given system as a first-order system. Also, indicate what quantities must be specified in an appropriate set of auxiliary conditions for the given system at a point t_0.

1. $x_1' - x_2' - x_1 = \cos t$
   $x_2' - 3x_1 = e^t$

2. $x_1' - 2x_2' - x_2 = t^2$
   $x_1' - 3x_2' = 0$

3. $x_1' - x_2' = e^t$
   $x_2'' - x_1 - x_2 - x_2' = \sin t$

4. $x_1'' = 1$
   $x_2'' = 2$

5. $x_1''' - x_1' - x_1 x_2' = \sin t$
   $x_1'' - x_2 x_1' - x_2'' = \cos t$

6. $x_1'' = x_1 \sin t + x_2 x_3$
   $x_2'' = x_1^2 x_2' + x_1'$
   $x_3' = x_1 x_2 x_3$

In Exercises 7–10, rewrite the differential equation as a first-order system.

7. $x'' - tx' + x^2 = \sin t$

8. $x'' + x = 0$

9. $x''' - x'' + x = e^t$

10. $x^{(4)} + x'''x - (x'')^2 = 0$

8.3   LINEAR SYSTEMS WITH CONSTANT COEFFICIENTS

A first-order system of the special form

$$\frac{dx_1}{dt} = a_{11}(t)x_1 + a_{12}(t)x_2 + \cdots + a_{1n}(t)x_n + b_1(t),$$

$$\frac{dx_2}{dt} = a_{21}(t)x_1 + a_{22}(t)x_2 + \cdots + a_{2n}(t)x_n + b_2(t),$$

$$\vdots$$

$$\frac{dx_n}{dt} = a_{n1}(t)x_1 + a_{n2}(t)x_2 + \cdots + a_{nn}(t)x_n + b_n(t),$$

where the functions a_{ij} and b_i are given, is called a first-order *linear* system. The functions a_{ij} are called the *coefficients* of the system. If each of the functions b_i is the zero function, the system is said to be *homogeneous*; otherwise it is said to be *nonhomogeneous*. The system can be written more briefly as

$$\frac{dx_i}{dt} = \sum_{j=1}^{n} a_{ij}(t)x_j + b_i(t), \qquad 1 \le i \le n.$$

In an initial value problem associated with the system we wish to find a solution that satisfies conditions of the form

$$x_1(t_0) = k_1, \quad x_2(t_0) = k_2, \ldots, \quad x_n(t_0) = k_n.$$

For example, when $n = 2$ (two equations and two unknowns) the initial value problem has the form

$$\frac{dx_1}{dt} = a_{11}(t)x_1 + a_{12}(t)x_2 + b_1(t),$$

$$\frac{dx_2}{dt} = a_{21}(t)x_1 + a_{22}(t)x_2 + b_2(t),$$

$$x_1(t_0) = k_1, \qquad x_2(t_0) = k_2.$$

In what follows, we restrict our attention to linear systems with *constant coefficients*. For convenience we use the operator notation

$$Df = f', \qquad Df(t) = f'(t).$$

A first-order linear system with constant coefficients has the form

$$Dx_1 = a_{11}x_1 + a_{12}x_2 + \cdots + a_{1n}x_n + b_1(t),$$
$$Dx_2 = a_{21}x_1 + a_{22}x_2 + \cdots + a_{2n}x_n + b_2(t),$$
$$\vdots$$
$$Dx_n = a_{n1}x_1 + a_{n2}x_2 + \cdots + a_{nn}x_n + b_n(t),$$

(8.12)

where the a_{ij} are constants. We shall also be concerned with more general linear systems with constant coefficients, of the form

$$P_{11}(D)x_1 + P_{12}(D)x_2 + \cdots + P_{1n}(D)x_n = b_1(t),$$
$$P_{21}(D)x_1 + P_{22}(D)x_2 + \cdots + P_{2n}(D)x_n = b_2(t),$$
$$\vdots$$
$$P_{n1}(D)x_1 + P_{n2}(D)x_2 + \cdots + P_{nn}(D)x_n = b_n(t),$$

(8.13)

where the $P_{ij}(D)$ are polynomial operators.† Every system of the form (8.12) is of the form (8.13); but not every system of the form (8.13) is a first-order system. Usually, however, a system such as (8.13) can be rewritten as a first-order system, as was shown in Section 8.2.

One procedure that can be used to solve systems of the type (8.13) is called the *method of elimination*. The theory and technique are reminiscent of the elimination method for solving systems of linear algebraic equations. Two systems of differential equations are said to be *equivalent* if they have the same solutions. In the method of elimination, we replace a given system by an equivalent, but simpler, system that is relatively easier to solve.

The reduction to a simpler system is carried out by performing a sequence of operations, each of which leads to an equivalent system. These operations are of three types. First, we can simply interchange two equations of the system. For example, the two systems

$$Dx_1 = 1, \qquad Dx_2 = 2,$$
$$Dx_2 = 2, \qquad Dx_1 = 1,$$

are equivalent. Notice, however, that the two systems

$$Dx_1 = 1, \qquad Dx_2 = 1,$$
$$Dx_2 = 2, \qquad Dx_1 = 2,$$

are *not* equivalent, because a solution consists of an *ordered* pair of functions. The second type of operation consists of simply multiplying through in one equation of the system by a nonzero constant. In the third type of operation we operate on both members of one equation of the system, say the ith with

† See Section 2.4.

a polynomial operator $Q(D)$ and add the result to another equation of the system, say the jth. In the new system, only the jth equation has changed. To illustrate, suppose that the ith and jth equations of the original system are

$$P_{i1}(D)x_1 + \cdots + P_{in}(D)x_n = b_i \,,$$
$$P_{j1}(D)x_1 + \cdots + P_{jn}(D)x_n = b_j \,. \tag{8.14}$$

Operating on both members of the ith equation with $Q(D)$ and adding the result to the jth equation, we have

$$P_{i1}(D)x_1 + \cdots + P_{in}(D)x_n = b_i \,,$$
$$[P_{j1}(D) + Q(D)P_{i1}(D)]x_1 + \cdots + [P_{jn}(D) + Q(D)P_{in}(D)]x_n \tag{8.15}$$
$$= b_j(t) + Q(D)b_i$$

Notice that the equation

$$Q(D)P_{i1}(D)x_1 + \cdots + Q(D)P_{in}(D) = Q(D)b_i$$

does not appear in either system. It is not hard to verify that if an ordered n-tuple of functions $(x_1, x_2, \ldots, x_n)$ satisfies the pair of equations (8.14) it also satisfies the pair (8.15) and vice versa.†

Example 1   In order to illustrate the method, we solve the system

$$-(D + 2)x_1 + (D^2 - 4)x_2 = 4t \,,$$
$$(D + 3)x_1 + (D + 7)x_2 = 0 \,. \tag{8.16}$$

Let us eliminate x_1. Adding the second equation to the first, we obtain

$$x_1 + (D^2 + D + 3)x_2 = 4t \,,$$
$$(D + 3)x_1 + (D + 7)x_2 = 0 \,. \tag{8.17}$$

Next we operate on both members of the first equation with $(D + 3)$, obtaining the equation

$$(D + 3)x_1 + (D + 3)(D^2 + D + 3)x_2 = 4 + 12t \,.$$

Subtracting this equation from the second equation of the system (8.17), we obtain the system

$$x_1 + (D^2 + D + 3)x_2 = 4t \,,$$
$$[-(D + 3)(D^2 + D + 3) + (D + 7)]x_2 = -4 - 12t \,. \tag{8.18}$$

The second equation, which involves only the one unknown x_2, can be written as

$$(D + 1)^2(D + 2)x_2 = 4 + 12t \,.$$

† The functions $b_i, x_1, x_2, \ldots, x_n$ must be sufficiently differentiable, so that all indicated derivatives exist. This is usually the case, in practice.

Using the methods of Chapter II to solve this equation, we have

$$x_2(t) = c_1 e^{-t} + c_2 t e^{-t} + c_3 e^{-2t} + 6t - 13. \qquad (8.19)$$

From the first equation of the system (8.18) we have

$$x_1 = -(D^2 + D + 3)x_2 + 4t$$

or

$$x_1(t) = -3c_1 e^{-t} + c_2(1 - 3t)e^{-t} - 5c_3 e^{-2t} - 14t + 33. \qquad (8.20)$$

Formulas (8.19) and (8.20) describe the general solution of the system (8.16). Notice that three arbitrary constants are involved in the description of the general solution, even though the system involves only two unknowns. This is in accordance with the fact that the system (8.16) can be replaced by a *first-order* system with three unknown functions.

In the general case where we have a system of the form (8.13), we attempt to find an equivalent system of the form†

$$Q_{11}(D)x_1 + Q_{12}(D)x_2 + \cdots + Q_{1n}(D)x_n = f_1(t),$$
$$Q_{22}(D)x_2 + \cdots + Q_{2n}(D)x_n = f_2(t),$$
$$\vdots$$
$$Q_{n-1,n-1}(D)x_{n-1} + Q_{n-1,n}(D)x_n = f_{n-1}(t),$$
$$Q_{nn}(D)x_n = f_n(t),$$

where none of the operators $Q_{ii}(D)$, $1 \le i \le n$, is the zero operator. We can solve the nth equation for x_n, then find x_{n-1} from the $(n-1)$st equation, and so on.

Example 2   As a final example, we consider the first-order homogeneous system for three unknowns,

$$Dx_1 = 3x_1 + x_2 - 2x_3,$$
$$Dx_2 = -x_1 + 2x_2 + x_3,$$
$$Dx_3 = 4x_1 + x_2 - 3x_3.$$

This system can be written as

$$(D-3)x_1 - x_2 + 2x_3 = 0,$$
$$x_1 + (D-2)x_2 - x_3 = 0,$$
$$-4x_1 - x_2 + (D+3)x_3 = 0.$$

The second equation can be used to eliminate x_1 from the first and third equations. First we multiply through in the second equation by 4 and add

† The unknowns may have to be renumbered.

the result to the third equation. Next we operate on the second equation with $(D - 3)$ and subtract the result from the first equation. In this way we arrive at the equivalent system

$$(-D^2 + 5D - 7)x_2 + (D - 1)x_3 = 0,$$
$$x_1 + (D - 2)x_2 - x_3 = 0,$$
$$(4D - 9)x_2 + (D - 1)x_3 = 0.$$

We next eliminate x_3 between the first and third equations. Subtracting the third equation from the first, we have

$$(-D^2 + D + 2)x_2 = 0,$$
$$x_1 + (D - 2)x_2 - x_3 = 0, \qquad\qquad (8.21)$$
$$(4D - 9)x_2 + (D - 1)x_3 = 0.$$

The first equation of this system, which involves only the one unknown x_2, can be written as

$$(D - 2)(D + 1)x_2 = 0.$$

Hence we have

$$x_2(t) = c_1 e^{-t} + c_2 e^{2t}. \qquad\qquad (8.22)$$

From the third equation of the system (8.21) we have

$$(D - 1)x_3 = (9 - 4D)x_2 = 13c_1 e^{-t} + c_2 e^{2t}.$$

This is a first-order equation for x_3 and we find that

$$x_3(t) = -\tfrac{13}{2}c_1 e^{-t} + c_2 e^{2t} + c_3 e^t. \qquad\qquad (8.23)$$

The unknown x_2 can now be found from the second equation of the system (8.21). We have

$$x_1 = (2 - D)x_2 + x_3$$

or

$$x_1(t) = -\tfrac{7}{2}c_1 e^{-t} + c_2 e^{2t} + c_3 e^t. \qquad\qquad (8.24)$$

The formulas (8.23) and (8.24) become slightly simpler if we set $c_1 = 2c_1'$, where c_1' is an arbitrary constant. With this change the formulas (8.22) (8.23), and (8.24) become

$$x_1(t) = -7c_1' e^{-t} + c_2 e^{2t} + c_3 e^t,$$
$$x_2(t) = 2c_1' e^{-t} + c_2 e^{2t},$$
$$x_3(t) = -13c_1' e^{-t} + c_2 e^{2t} + c_3 e^t.$$

Exercises for Section 8.3

1. Show that the linear system
$$P_{11}(D)x_1 + P_{12}(D)x_2 = b_1(t),$$
$$P_{21}(D)x_1 + P_{22}(D)x_2 = b_2(t),$$
where
$$P_{ij}(D) = a_{ij} D^2 + b_{ij} D + c_{ij}, \qquad i = 1, 2, \quad j = 1, 2,$$
can be replaced by a first-order system with four unknowns if
$$a_{11}a_{22} - a_{21}a_{12} \neq 0.$$

2. Show that the system
$$Dx_1 - x_2 = 0, \qquad -x_1 + Dx_2 = 0$$
is equivalent to the system
$$Dx_1 - x_2 = 0, \qquad (D^2 - 1)x_1 = 0,$$
but that it is not equivalent to the system
$$D^2x_1 - Dx_2 = 0, \qquad (D^2 - 1)x_1 = 0.$$

In Exercises 3–17, find the general solution of the system. If initial conditions are given, also find the solution that satisfies the conditions.

3. $Dx_1 = -4x_1 - 6x_2 + 9e^{-3t}$
   $Dx_2 = x_1 + x_2 - 5e^{-3t}, \qquad x_1(0) = -9, \qquad x_2(0) = 4$

4. $Dx_1 = -2x_1 + x_2$
   $Dx_2 = -3x_1 + 2x_2 + 2\sin t, \qquad x_1(0) = 3, \qquad x_2(0) = 4$

5. $Dx_1 = -x_1 - 3e^{-2t}$
   $Dx_2 = -2x_1 - x_2 - 6e^{-2t}$

6. $D^2x_1 + (D + 2)x_2 = 2e^{-2t}$
   $Dx_1 - (D + 2)x_2 = 0, \qquad x_1(0) = 4, \qquad x_2(0) = 1, \qquad x_1'(0) = -2$

7. $(2D + 1)x_1 + (D^2 - 4)x_2 = -7e^{-t}$
   $Dx_1 - (D + 2)x_2 = -3e^{-t}$

8. $(D + 2)x_1 + (D^2 + 2D)x_2 = 5e^{-t}$
   $(D + 1)x_1 - (D + 2)x_2 = 0$

9. $(D^2 + 1)x_1 + 2Dx_2 = 0,$
   $-3(D^2 + 1)x_1 + 2(D^2 + 2)x_2 = 0, \qquad x_1(0) = 1, \qquad x_2(0) = 1,$
   $\qquad\qquad\qquad\qquad\qquad\qquad\qquad\qquad x_1'(0) = 0, \qquad x_2'(0) = -1$

$$(D+1)6\epsilon e^{-2t}$$
$$+12e^{-2t} - 6e^{-2t}$$
$$= 6e^{-2t}$$

10. $(D^3 - 2D^2 + 3D)x_1 + (2D^2 - 8)x_2 = 4 - 6t$
$$Dx_1 - (D + 2)x_2 = -2t$$

11. $Dx_1 = x_1 - 3x_2 + 2x_3$
$Dx_2 = -x_2$
$Dx_3 = -x_2 - 2x_3 \qquad x_1(0) = -3, \qquad x_2(0) = 0, \qquad x_3(0) = 3$

12. $Dx_1 = -x_1 + x_2$ 13. $Dx_1 = x_1 - 2x_2 - t_2$
$Dx_2 = 2x_1 - 2x_2 + 2x_3$ $Dx_2 = x_1 + x_3 - 1 - t^2$
$Dx_3 = -x_2 - x_3$ $Dx_3 = -2x_1 + 2x_2 - x_3 + 2t^2 + 2t$

14. $Dx_1 = x_1 + x_2$ 15. $Dx_1 = x_1 - 3x_2 + 2x_3$
$Dx_2 = -2x_1 + x_2 - 2x_3 + e^{2t}$ $Dx_2 = -2x_2 + 2x_3$
$Dx_3 = -x_2 + x_3$ $Dx_3 = x_1 - 5x_2 + 2x_3$

16. $Dx_1 = -x_1 + x_3$ 17. $Dx_1 = -x_1 - x_3 + \cos t$
$Dx_2 = 2x_3$ $Dx_2 = -x_2 - x_3 + \sin t$
$Dx_3 = x_1 - 2x_2 - 3x_3$ $Dx_3 = -2x_3 + \cos t + 2 \sin t$

8.4   MECHANICAL SYSTEMS

In this section we consider some problems that involve the motion of one or more objects. The mathematical description of such a problem involves a system of differential equations in which the unknown functions are the co-ordinates of the centers of mass of the moving objects.

For our first example we consider the configuration of Fig. 8.3. Two bodies with masses m_1 and m_2, respectively, are suspended by springs as shown in the figure. The downward displacements of the bodies from their equilibrium positions are denoted by x_1 and x_2 respectively. At equilibrium, the forces due to gravity are balanced by forces due to a stretching of the springs. We denote by F_1 and F_2 the net forces acting on the moving bodies with masses m_1 and m_2, respectively. Suppose first that $x_1 > 0$ and that $x_2 > x_1$. Then the spring with constant k_2 is stretched by a distance $x_2 - x_1$. The net force acting on the object with mass m_1 (positive direction downward) is

$$F_1 = -k_1x_1 + k_2(x_2 - x_1) \tag{8.25}$$

while the net force acting on the second body is

$$F_2 = -k_2(x_2 - x_1). \tag{8.26}$$

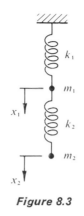

Figure 8.3

If $x_1 < 0$, the first spring is compressed and it exerts a downward force on the first object. If $x_2 - x_1 < 0$, the second spring is compressed. It then exerts an upward force on the first object and a downward force on the second. But if either or both of these situations occurs, it can be seen that the formulas (8.25) and (8.26) are still valid. Consequently our equations of motion become

$$m_1 \ddot{x}_1 = -k_1 x_1 + k_2(x_2 - x_1),$$
$$m_2 \ddot{x}_2 = -k_2(x_2 - x_1). \tag{8.27}$$

This is a linear system with constant coefficients. The nature of the solutions is discussed in Exercise 1.

   We next consider the motion of a single body in a plane, subject to a constant gravitational force. It is convenient to work in a rectangular coordinate system in the plane. We choose the origin to be at the surface of the earth, with one axis vertical, as shown in Fig. 8.4. According to Newton's law of motion,

$$m\mathbf{a} = \mathbf{F}, \tag{8.28}$$

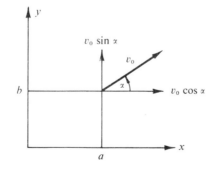

Figure 8.4

where m is the mass of the body,

$$\mathbf{a} = \ddot{x}\mathbf{i} + \ddot{y}\mathbf{j}$$

is the acceleration, and

$$\mathbf{F} = 0\mathbf{i} - mg\mathbf{j}$$

is the force acting on the body. Then Eq. (8.28) becomes

$$m(\ddot{x}\mathbf{i} + \ddot{y}\mathbf{j}) = 0\mathbf{i} - mg\mathbf{j}.$$

Equating corresponding components, we arrive at the system

$$m\ddot{x} = 0, \qquad m\ddot{y} = -mg.$$

We denote by (a, b) the position of the body at $t = 0$. We assume that the initial velocity vector $\mathbf{v}_0$ has magnitude v_0 and is inclined at an angle α with the horizontal. Thus

$$\mathbf{v}_0 = v_0(\mathbf{i}\cos\alpha + \mathbf{j}\sin\alpha).$$

The initial conditions for the system are

$$x(0) = a, \qquad y(0) = b, \qquad \dot{x}(0) = v_0\cos\alpha, \qquad \dot{y}(0) = v_0\sin\alpha.$$

Some specific cases are considered in the exercises.

In some applications that involve the motion of a body in a plane, it is more convenient to work with the polar coordinates (r, θ) of the center of mass of the body. This is the case, for example, when attempting to describe the motion of a satellite about the earth. We introduce the unit vectors $\mathbf{e}_r$ and $\mathbf{e}_\theta$, where

$$\begin{aligned}\mathbf{e}_r &= \mathbf{i}\cos\theta + \mathbf{j}\sin\theta, \\ \mathbf{e}_\theta &= -\mathbf{i}\sin\theta + \mathbf{j}\cos\theta.\end{aligned} \tag{8.29}$$

The vector $\mathbf{e}_r$ points away from the origin in the direction of increasing r. The vector $\mathbf{e}_\theta$ is perpendicular to $\mathbf{e}_r$ and points in the direction of increasing θ. The situation is illustrated in Fig. 8.5. From formulas (8.29), we deduce the relations

$$\frac{d}{d\theta}\mathbf{e}_r = \mathbf{e}_\theta, \qquad \frac{d}{d\theta}\mathbf{e}_\theta = -\mathbf{e}_r. \tag{8.30}$$

We resolve the force $\mathbf{F}$ acting on the body into radial and circumferential components, writing

$$\mathbf{F} = F_r\mathbf{e}_r + F_\theta\mathbf{e}_\theta.$$

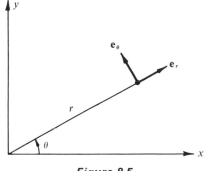

Figure 8.5

In many important cases, $F_\theta = 0$. For instance, when the origin is at the center of the earth the force exerted on a satellite of mass m by the earth is

$$\mathbf{F} = -\frac{mgR^2}{r^2}\,\mathbf{e}_r,$$ (8.31)

where R is the radius of the (spherical) earth.

Since

$$\mathbf{i}x + \mathbf{j}y = \mathbf{i}r\cos\theta + \mathbf{j}r\sin\theta = r\mathbf{e}_r,$$

the velocity of the moving body is [making use of the relations (8.30)]

$$\mathbf{v} = \dot{r}\mathbf{e}_r + r\frac{d\mathbf{e}}{d\theta}\frac{d\theta}{dt} = \dot{r}\mathbf{e}_r + r\dot{\theta}\mathbf{e}_\theta$$

and the acceleration is

$$\mathbf{a} = \ddot{r}\mathbf{e}_r + \dot{r}\dot{\theta}\mathbf{e}_\theta + (r\ddot{\theta} + \dot{r}\dot{\theta})\mathbf{e}_\theta - r\dot{\theta}^2\mathbf{e}_r$$

or

$$\mathbf{a} = (\ddot{r} - r\dot{\theta}^2)\mathbf{e}_r + (r\ddot{\theta} + 2\dot{r}\dot{\theta})\mathbf{e}_\theta.$$

Then, by equating corresponding components in the equation

$$m\mathbf{a} = \mathbf{F},$$

we arrive at the system

$$m(\ddot{r} - r\dot{\theta}^2) = F_r,$$
$$m(r\ddot{\theta} + 2\dot{r}\dot{\theta}) = F_\theta.$$ (8.32)

In the special case where $\mathbf{F}$ is given by formula (8.31), we have

$$\ddot{r} - r\dot{\theta}^2 = -gR^2r^{-2},$$
$$r\ddot{\theta} + 2\dot{r}\dot{\theta} = 0.$$ (8.33)

Exercises for Section 8.4

1. (a) Show that the system (8.27) is equivalent to the system

$$P(D)x_1 = 0, \qquad x_2 = \frac{1}{k_2}(m_1 D^2 + k_1 + k_2)x_1 ,$$

where

$$P(D) = m_1 m_2 D^4 + [m_2(k_1 + k_2) + m_1 k_2]D^2 + k_1 k_2 .$$

(b) Show that the polynomial P of part (a) has four distinct pure imaginary zeros, and hence that x_1 and x_2 are bounded functions.

2. Find the equations of motion for the mechanical system of Fig. 8.6.

3. Find the equations of motion for the mechanical system of Fig. 8.7.

4. Find the equations of motion for the mechanical system of Fig. 8.8.

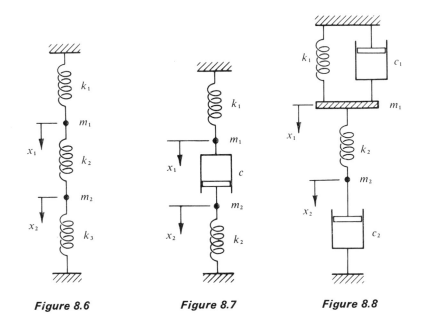

Figure 8.6   Figure 8.7   Figure 8.8

5. A ball is thrown horizontally from the top of a tower of height h, with a velocity v_0. Neglect air resistance.

(a) How far from the base of the tower will the ball land?

(b) Find the xy equation of the path of the ball and show that it is a parabola.

6. A ball is thrown horizontally from the top of a tower of height h, with a velocity v_0. Assume that the force due to air resistance is $\mathbf{F} = -c\mathbf{v}$, where c is a positive constant and $\mathbf{v}$ is the velocity vector.

   (a) Find the coordinates, $x(t)$ and $y(t)$, of the ball.

   (b) Find the xy equation of the path.

7. A projectile is fired from a gun located at the origin of the coordinate system in Fig. 8.4. The gun is inclined at an angle α with the horizontal and its muzzle velocity is v_0. Neglect air resistance.

   (a) How far from the gun will the projectile land?

   (b) Find the xy equation of the path of the projectile and show that it is a parabola.

8. In Exercise 7, suppose that the force due to air resistance is $\mathbf{F} = -c\mathbf{v}$, where c is a positive constant and $\mathbf{v}$ is the velocity vector.

   (a) Find the coordinates, $x(t)$ and $y(t)$, of the projectile.

   (b) Find the xy equation of the path.

9. An earth satellite of mass m is attracted toward the center of the earth by a force of magnitude mkr^{-2}, where k is a positive constant and r is the distance to the earth's center. Using a rectangular xy coordinate system with origin at the center of the earth, find the equations of motion of the satellite.

10. (a) Deduce from the second equation of the system (8.33) that $r^2\dot\theta = c$, where c is a constant. Then show that r satisfies the equation.
$$\ddot r = c^2 r^{-3} - gR^2 r^{-2}.$$

   (b) Setting $u = r^{-1}$, show that
$$\frac{d^2u}{d\theta^2} + u = \frac{gR^2}{c^2}.$$

   (c) From the result of part (b) deduce that the path is a conic section.

11. Two bodies of masses m_1 and m_2 move in a plane. The force of attraction between them has magnitude $km_1 m_2/r^2$, where k is a constant and r is the distance between the centers of mass.

   (a) Find a system of differential equations for the position vectors $\mathbf{R}_1$ and $\mathbf{R}_2$ of the respective centers-of-mass of the bodies.

   (b) Using the results of part (a), find a system of differential equations for the vectors $\mathbf{U} = \mathbf{R}_2 - \mathbf{R}_1$ and $\mathbf{V} = (m_1\mathbf{R}_1 + m_2\mathbf{R}_2)/(m_1 + m_2)$.

   (c) Discuss the motion of the bodies, in the light of the results of part (b) and Exercise 10.

8.5 ELECTRIC CIRCUITS

Figure 8.9 illustrates an electrical network that involves two loops. Our aim is to formulate a system of differential equations and initial conditions

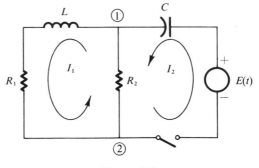

Figure 8.9

for the two unknown loop currents I_1 and I_2. We assume that the switch is closed at time $t = 0$, and that the charge on the capacitance is zero before this time.

Each loop has been oriented by assigning positive directions to the currents. The currents flowing from node 2 to node 1 must be $I_1 - I_2$. This follows from the law of Kirchhoff that says that the current leaving a node must be equal to the current entering it. Kirchhoff's other law says that the sum of the voltage drops around each loop must be equal to the applied voltage. Applying this law to each loop in turn, we arrive at the system of equations

$$L \frac{dI_1}{dt} + R_1 I_1 + R_2(I_1 - I_2) = 0, \tag{8.34}$$

$$R_2(I_2 - I_1) + \frac{1}{C} Q = E(t). \tag{8.35}$$

Differentiating through in Eq. (8.35) with respect to t and noting that $dQ/dt = I_2$, we obtain the system of differential equations

$$L \frac{dI_1}{dt} + (R_1 + R_2)I_1 - R_2 I_2 = 0,$$

$$R_2 \frac{dI_2}{dt} - R_1 \frac{dI_1}{dt} + \frac{1}{C} I_2 = E'(t)$$

for I_1 and I_2. It is not hard to see that this system is equivalent to a first-order system for I_1 and I_2. We must therefore specify $I_1(0)$ and $I_2(0)$ in our initial conditions. Because of the presence of the inductance in the loop for I_1 we must have

$$I_1(0) = 0.$$

From Eq. (8.35) (or by inspection of Fig. 8.9) we see that

$$I_2(0) = \frac{E(0)}{R_2}.$$

In the network of Fig. 8.10 there are three loops. However, it is possible to

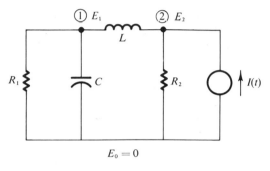

$$E_0 = 0$$

Figure 8.10

formulate a system of two differential equations for the voltage drops $E_1 - E_0$ and $E_2 - E_0$. It is convenient to set $E_0 = 0$ and work with E_1 and E_2.

We use the principle that the current leaving a node is equal to the current entering it. The net current leaving node 1 is

$$C\frac{dE_1}{dt} + \frac{1}{R_1}E_1 + \frac{1}{L}\int_0^t [E_1(s) - E_2(s)]\, ds = 0. \tag{8.36}$$

The current entering the second node is $I(t)$. We must have

$$\frac{1}{R_2}E_2 + \frac{1}{L}\int_0^t [E_2(s) - E_1(s)]\, ds = I(t). \tag{8.37}$$

Differentiating through in Eqs. (8.36) and (8.37), we arrive at the system

$$C\frac{d^2E_1}{dt^2} + \frac{1}{R_1}\frac{dE_1}{dt} + \frac{1}{L}(E_1 - E_2) = 0,$$

$$\frac{1}{R_2}\frac{dE_2}{dt} + \frac{1}{L}(E_2 - E_1) = I'(t).$$

Because of the presence of the capacitance we must have

$$E_1(0) = 0.$$

From Eq. (8.37) (or from the figure),

$$E_2(0) = R_2 I(0).$$

From Eq. (8.36),

$$E'_1(0) = 0.$$

Exercises for Section 8.5

In Exercises 1–6, formulate a system of differential equations and initial conditions for the loop currents, assuming that all initial charges are zero and that the switch is closed at $t = 0$.

1. The circuit of Fig. 8.11.

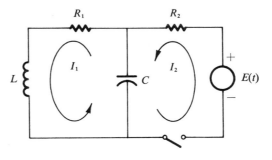

Figure 8.11

2. The circuit of Fig. 8.12.

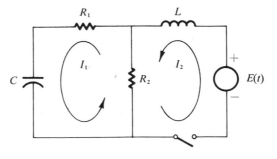

Figure 8.12

3. The circuit of Fig. 8.13. Find the loop currents if $E = 6$ volts, $R_1 = 2$ ohms, $R_2 = 1$ ohm, and $L = 4$ henrys.

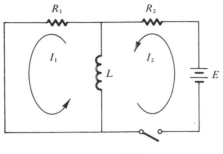

Figure 8.13

4. The circuit of Fig. 8.14. Find the *steady-state* loop currents if $R = 1.0$ ohms, $C = 0.5$ farad, $L = 0.5$ henry, and $E(t) = 2 \cos(t/2)$ volts.

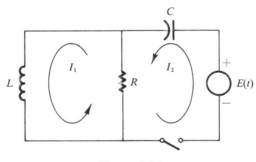

Figure 8.14

5. The circuit of Fig. 8.15.

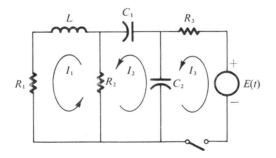

Figure 8.15

6.   The circuit of Fig. 8.16.

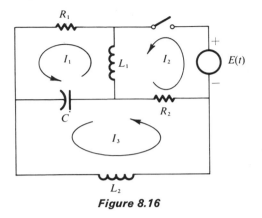

Figure 8.16

In Exercises 7 and 8, formulate a system of differential equations and initial conditions for the node voltages. Assume that all currents are zero at $t = 0$.

7.   The circuit of Fig. 8.17.

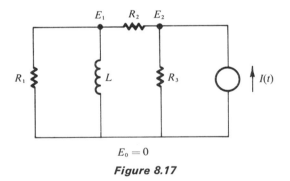

$E_0 = 0$

Figure 8.17

8.   The circuit of Fig. 8.18.

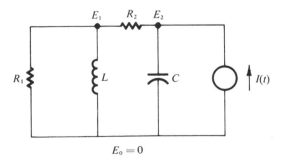

$E_0 = 0$

Figure 8.18

8.6 SOME PROBLEMS FROM BIOLOGY

In Section 1.7 we considered the growth of the population of a single species. We now consider the case where two species compete for survival. Let $x(t)$ and $y(t)$ denote the populations of the species at time t. We shall consider only models of the form

$$\frac{dx}{dt} = f(x, y), \qquad \frac{dy}{dt} = g(x, y).$$

The requirements that $f(0, y) = 0$ for all y and $g(x, 0) - 0$ for all x insure that if either species is absent at any instant its population remains at zero. If y is very small, we expect x to increase, at least if x is not too large. Even if the species whose population is y is completely absent, x should increase only until it reaches its saturation level. These remarks also apply if the roles of x and y are interchanged.

One model that incorporates the features mentioned here is given by the system of equations

$$\frac{dx}{dt} = hx(1 - ax - by), \qquad \frac{dy}{dt} = ky(1 - cx - dy), \qquad (8.38)$$

where h, k, a, b, c, and d are positive constants. These equations are known as the *Lotka–Volterra equations*. The system (8.38) is nonlinear, and in general, explicit formulas for its solutions cannot be obtained. Some special cases are considered in the exercises. See also the exercises for Section 11.4.

Our next application involves the diffusion of a dissolved substance. Consider first two bodies of fluid separated by a very thin membrane. Let x_1 and x_2 be the concentrations of the substance dissolved in the two bodies. The substance diffuses from the region of higher concentration to that of lower concentration. We make the assumption that it disperses rapidly throughout each body of fluid so that at each instant the two concentrations are uniform. According to the law of diffusion, the rate at which the dissolved substance passes from one body to the other is proportional to the difference in the concentrations. If V_1 and V_2 are the volumes, then

$$\frac{d}{dt}(V_1 x_1) = k(x_2 - x_1), \qquad \frac{d}{dt}(V_2 x_2) = k(x_1 - x_2). \qquad (8.39)$$

Of course $V_1 x_1 + V_2 x_2 = C$, where the constant C is the total amount of dissolved substance.

Consider now a cell enclosed in a membrane and surrounded by blood. We consider the diffusion of a substance in the blood into the cell. The membrane is not "very thin" and the substance diffuses first into the membrane and then into the cell. Let x_1 and x_2 be the concentrations in the membrane and cell, respectively. We assume that the concentration in the blood remains at the constant value c_0. Then, according to the law of diffusion, the relevant system of differential equations is

$$\frac{d}{dt}(V_1 x_1) = h(c_0 - x_1) + k(x_2 - x_1),$$

$$\frac{d}{dt}(V_2 x_2) = k(x_1 - x_2),$$

(8.40)

where h and k are positive constants and V_1 and V_2 are the volumes of the membrane and cell, respectively. The solution of this linear system is left to the exercises.

Exercises for Section 8.6

1. Discuss the merits (or lack of them) of the population growth model for two competing species

$$\frac{dx}{dt} = hx(1 - ay). \qquad \frac{dy}{dt} = ky(1 - bx),$$

where h, k, a, and b are positive constants. What happens if either $x(0)$ or $y(0)$ is zero?

2. Find all the constant solutions of the model in Exercise 1.

3. If $h = k$ in the model of Exercise 1, show that

$$bx(t) - ay(t) = [bx(0) - ay(0)]e^{ht}.$$

Discuss what happens as t becomes large in the cases where $bx(0) - ay(0)$ is positive, negative, and zero.

4. Find all constant solutions of the system (8.38).

5. If $ad - bc = 0$ in the system (8.38), there exists a constant p such that $c = ap$ and $d = pb$. Show that for this case

$$\frac{[x(t)]^{kp}}{[y(t)]^h} = C \exp[hk(p - 1)t].$$

Discuss what happens as t becomes infinite in the cases $p < 0$, $p > 0$, and $p = 0$.

6. Write down a system of differential equations for the populations of three competing species.

7. Consider the populations of two species, one of which is a host and the other a parasite. Assume that the larger the host population the larger the food supply for the parasite. Write down a system of differential equations for the host and parasite populations that incorporates this feature.

8. Find formulas for the concentrations x_1 and x_2 in the diffusion problem (8.39).

9. Show that the solution of the problem (8.40) is of the form

$$x_1(t) = Ae^{-\lambda_1 t} + Be^{-\lambda_2 t} + C_1,$$
$$x_2(t) = Ce^{-\lambda_1 t} + De^{-\lambda_2 t} + C_2,$$

where λ_1 and λ_2 are real and positive. Determine C_1 and C_2, the final concentrations.

REFERENCES

1. Desoer, C. A., and Kuh, E. S., *Basic Circuit Theory*. McGraw-Hill, New York, 1969.
2. Brauer, F., and Nohel, J. A., *Ordinary Differential Equations*. Benjamin, New York, 1967.
3. Kaplan, W., *Ordinary Differential Equations*. Addison-Wesley, Reading, Massachusetts, 1958.
4. Keyfitz, N., *Introduction to the Mathematics of Population*. Addison-Wesley, Reading, Massachusetts, 1968.
5. Pielou, E. C., *An Introduction to Mathematical Ecology*. Wiley (Interscience), New York, 1969.
6. Protter, M. H., and Morrey, C. B., *Modern Mathematical Analysis*. Addison-Wesley, Reading, Massachusetts, 1964.
7. Rabenstein, A. L., *Elementary Differential Equations with Linear Algebra*. Academic Press, New York, 1970.
8. Symon, K. R., *Mechanics*, 2nd ed. Addison-Wesley, Reading, Massachusetts, 1960.

IX

Laplace Transforms

9.1 THE LAPLACE TRANSFORM

Let f be a function that is defined on $[0, \infty)$. Associated with f is the improper integral

$$\int_0^\infty e^{-st}f(t) \, dt, \tag{9.1}$$

where s is a real† number. It may happen that there is no number s for which the integral converges. If not, there exists a set of real numbers, which we denote by S, such that the integral converges for s in S. In this case we define the function F by means of the relation

$$F(s) = \int_0^\infty e^{-st}f(t) \, dt, \qquad s \text{ in } S.$$

The function F is called the *Laplace transform* of the function f. We write

$$F = \mathcal{L}[f] \qquad \text{and} \qquad F(s) = \mathcal{L}[f](s)$$

to indicate the relations between the functions f and F. (In general, we shall use capital letters for transforms of functions denoted by corresponding lower case letters. Thus $\mathcal{L}[g] = G$, $\mathcal{L}[h] = H$, and so on.) Actually, we shall be interested only in functions whose transforms exist in an interval of the

† In more advanced treatments of the Laplace transform, s is permitted to be a complex number.

form (s_0, ∞) for some number s_0. Sufficient conditions that the transform of a function exist on such an interval will be discussed in the next section.

Not every function has a Laplace transform. For instance, if $f(t) = e^{t^2}$, the improper integral (9.1) diverges for all values of s. When s is positive, however, the quantity e^{-st} tends to zero fairly rapidly as t becomes infinite. Consequently many functions do possess Laplace transforms.

Let us now compute the transforms of some specific functions. Starting with the function $f(t) = e^{at}$, where a is a constant, we have

$$\int_0^\infty e^{-st} f(t) \, dt = \int_0^\infty e^{-t(s-a)} \, dt$$

$$= \lim_{T \to \infty} \left[\frac{-1}{s-a} e^{-t(s-a)} \right]_0^T$$

$$= \frac{1}{s-a}$$

if $s > a$. Thus

$$\mathcal{L}[f](s) = \frac{1}{s-a}, \qquad s > a. \tag{9.2}$$

As a second example, let $g(t) = \cos at$. Then

$$\int_0^\infty e^{-st} g(t) \, dt = \int_0^\infty e^{-st} \cos at \, dt$$

$$= \lim_{T \to \infty} \left[\frac{e^{-st}}{s^2 + a^2} (a \sin at - s \cos at) \right]_0^T$$

$$= \frac{s}{s^2 + a^2}$$

if $s > 0$. Consequently,

$$\mathcal{L}[g](s) = \frac{s}{s^2 + a^2}, \qquad s > 0. \tag{9.3}$$

If the functions f and g both possess Laplace transforms for $s > s_0$, then the function $c_1 f + c_2 g$, where c_1 and c_2 are constants, also possesses a transform for $s > s_0$. In fact, from the relation

$$\int_0^\infty e^{-st} [c_1 f(t) + c_2 g(t)] \, dt = c_1 \int_0^\infty e^{-st} f(t) \, dt + c_2 \int_0^\infty e^{-st} g(t) \, dt,$$

we see that

$$\mathcal{L}[c_1 f + c_2 g](s) = c_1 \mathcal{L}[f](s) + c_2 \mathcal{L}[g](s), \qquad s > s_0. \tag{9.4}$$

A particularly important property of Laplace transforms comes to light when we consider the transform of the *derivative* of a function f. Let us assume that f and f' are continuous on $[0, \infty)$, and that both functions possess Laplace transforms for $s > s_0$. Using integration by parts, we have

$$\int_0^T e^{-st} f'(t)\, dt = \left[f(t) e^{-st} \right]_0^T + s \int_0^T e^{-st} f(t)\, dt.$$

As $T \to \infty$, both integrals tend to finite limits for $s > s_0$. Consequently $f(T) e^{-sT}$ must also tend to a finite limit for $s > s_0$. We shall show that this limit is zero. Given any number s_1, where $s_1 > s_0$, let s_2 be a number such that $s_0 < s_2 < s_1$. Since $f(T)\exp(-s_2 T)$ tends to a finite limit,

$$f(T)\exp(-s_1 T) = f(T)\exp(-s_2 T)\exp[-(s_1 - s_2)T]$$

tends to zero. Therefore

$$\lim_{T \to \infty} \left[f(t) e^{-st} \right]_0^T = -f(0)$$

for $s > s_0$, and we have

$$\mathcal{L}[f'](s) = sF(s) - f(0), \qquad s > s_0. \tag{9.5}$$

It is because of this property and its generalization to higher derivatives that Laplace transforms are useful in solving initial value problems for certain types of differential equations. To illustrate, let us consider the simple problem

$$x'(t) + 2x(t) = e^{-t}, \qquad x(0) = 2.$$

Let us assume for the moment that the solution function x and its derivative x' both possess Laplace transforms. For the function $f(t) = e^{-t}$ we have $\mathcal{L}[f](s) = 1/(s + 1)$, according to formula (9.2). From the differential equation we see that

$$\mathcal{L}[x' + 2x](s) = \frac{1}{s + 1}$$

or

$$\mathcal{L}[x'](s) + 2\mathcal{L}[x](s) = \frac{1}{s + 1}.$$

Using the property (9.5), we have

$$sX(s) - 2 + 2X(s) = \frac{1}{s + 1}.$$

Thus the initial value problem for the function x has been transformed into an algebraic equation for the function X. Solving the last equation for $X(s)$, we have

$$X(s) = \frac{2s + 3}{(s + 1)(s + 2)},$$

or, upon using partial fractions,

$$X(s) = \frac{1}{s + 1} + \frac{1}{s + 2}.$$

Now, from formula (9.2), we recognize that the function

$$x(t) = e^{-t} + e^{-2t}$$

has X as its Laplace transform. It is easy to verify that this function is indeed the solution of the initial value problem.

In applying the method of Laplace transforms to the initial value problem, we went through three main steps. First we transformed a "hard" problem (the initial value problem) into a relatively "easy" problem (the algebraic equation for X). Then we solved the easy problem by finding X. Finally we "inverted"; that is, we found the solution x of the original problem from the solution of the transformed problem. This same procedure is followed in the solution of more complicated initial value problems.

Applications of Laplace transforms to differential equations will be considered in the final section of this chapter. Meanwhile, we shall investigate the properties of Laplace transforms in more detail.

Exercises for Section 9.1

1. Calculate the Laplace transform of the given function f. Determine the values of s for which $F(s)$ exists.

(a) $f(t) = 1$

(b) $f(t) = t$

(c) $f(t) = t^2$

(d) $f(t) = t^n$, n a positive integer

(e) $f(t) = \sin at$

(f) $f(t) = \sinh at$

(g) $f(t) = \begin{cases} 1, & 0 \le t \le 1 \\ 0, & t > 1 \end{cases}$

(h) $f(t) = \begin{cases} t, & 0 \le t \le 1 \\ 1, & t > 1 \end{cases}$

(i) $f(t) = \begin{cases} t, & 0 \le t \le 1 \\ 2 - t, & 1 < t \le 2 \\ 0, & t > 2 \end{cases}$

(j) $f(t) = \begin{cases} \sin t, & 0 \le t \le \pi \\ 0, & t > \pi \end{cases}$

2. Use formulas (9.2) and (9.3) to find $\mathscr{L}[f](s)$ if f is as given.

(a) $f(t) = e^{-5t}$ (b) $f(t) = e^{6t}$

(c) $f(t) = \cos 5t$ (d) $f(t) = \cos 2t$

(e) $f(t) = 3e^{-2t} + 4e^{t}$ (f) $f(t) = -3 \cos 2t - 5e^{-3t}$

3. Use formulas (9.2) and (9.3) to find a function whose Laplace transform F is as given.

(a) $F(s) = \dfrac{1}{s + 2}$ (b) $F(s) = \dfrac{1}{s - 3}$

(c) $F(s) = \dfrac{s}{s^2 + 4}$ (d) $F(s) = \dfrac{2s}{s^2 + 9}$

(e) $F(s) = \dfrac{3}{s - 2} - \dfrac{5}{s + 7}$ (f) $F(s) = \dfrac{3}{s + 3} - \dfrac{2s}{s^2 + 1}$

4. If $f(t) = t^{\alpha}$, $\alpha > -1$, show that

$$\mathscr{L}[f](s) = \frac{\Gamma(\alpha + 1)}{s^{\alpha+1}}, \qquad s > 0,$$

where Γ is the gamma function.

5. Use the result of Exercise 4 to find $\mathscr{L}[f]$ if

(a) $f(t) = \sqrt{t}$ (b) $f(t) = \dfrac{1}{\sqrt{t}}$

6. Let f be piecewise continuous on $[0, T]$ and periodic with period T. Show that

$$\mathscr{L}[f](s) = \frac{1}{1 - e^{-sT}} \int_0^T e^{-st}f(t)\, dt.$$

7. Use the result of Exercise 6 to find the Laplace transform of the given function.

(a) $f(t) = 1$ when $0 \le t \le T/2$, $f(t) = 0$ when $T/2 < t < T$, and $f(t + T) = f(t)$ for all t.

(b) $f(t) = |\sin t|$ for all t.

8. By using Laplace transforms, find the solution of the initial value problem. Verify that your answer is the correct one.

(a) $x'(t) - 2x(t) = 2,$ $x(0) = -3$

(b) $x'(t) + 3x(t) = e^{2t},$ $x(0) = -1$

9.2 CONDITIONS FOR THE EXISTENCE OF THE LAPLACE TRANSFORM

In the examples of the last section we were able to show that certain functions possessed Laplace transforms by actually carrying out the integration in formula (9.1). In cases where this is difficult, the following theorem from advanced calculus is often useful.

Theorem 9.1 Let f and g be piecewise continuous on every interval of the form $[c, T]$, where c is fixed and $T > c$. If $|f(t)| \le g(t)$ for $t \ge c$, and if the integral $\int_c^\infty g(t)\, dt$ converges, then the integral $\int_c^\infty f(t)\, dt$ also converges.

In a moment we shall use Theorem 9.1 to establish a set of sufficient conditions for the existence of the Laplace transform of a function. First, however, let us introduce the notation†

$$f(t) = O[g(t)],$$

which should be read "$f(t)$ is of the order of $g(t)$." This notation means that there exist positive constants M and N such that

$$|f(t)| \le Mg(t)$$

whenever $t \ge N$. In particular, if $f(t) = O[e^{at}]$, for some constant a, we say that f is of *exponential order*.

We are now ready to prove the following theorem.

Theorem 9.2 Let f be piecewise continuous on every interval of the form $[0, T]$, where $T > 0$, and let $f(t) = O[e^{at}]$, for some constant a. Then the Laplace transform $\mathscr{L}[f](s)$ exists, at least for $s > a$.

PROOF According to the hypotheses of the theorem, there exist positive constants M and t_0 such that $|f(t)| \le Me^{at}$ when $t \ge t_0$. Then $|f(t)e^{-st}| \le Me^{-(s-a)t}$ when $t \ge t_0$. Since the integral $\int_{t_0}^\infty Me^{-(s-a)t}\, dt$ converges when $s > a$, the integral $\int_{t_0}^\infty e^{-st}f(t)\, dt$ also converges when $s > a$, by Theorem 9.1. Since

$$\int_0^\infty e^{-st}f(t)\, dt = \int_0^{t_0} e^{-st}f(t)\, dt + \int_{t_0}^\infty e^{-st}f(t)\, dt, \qquad s > a,$$

the Laplace transform $\mathscr{L}[f](s)$ exists for $s > a$.

† The notation $f(t) = o[g(t)]$ also appears in the literature. It means that $f(t)/g(t) \to 0$ as $t \to \infty$.

As an important application of Theorem 9.2, we shall show that if $f(t)$ is of the form

$$t^n e^{at} \cos bt, \qquad t^n e^{at} \sin bt, \tag{9.6}$$

where n is a nonnegative integer, then $\mathscr{L}[f](s)$ exists for $s > a$. We first observe that

$$t^n = O[e^{\varepsilon t}]$$

for every positive number ε. Since $|\cos bt| \leq 1$ and $|\sin bt| \leq 1$ for all t, we have

$$f(t) = O[e^{(a+\varepsilon)t}].$$

By Theorem 9.1, $\mathscr{L}[f](s)$ exists for $s > a + \varepsilon$ for every positive number ε. Consequently $\mathscr{L}[f](s)$ exists for $s > a$.

The above result is important in the study of linear differential equations with constant coefficients. Let us consider the homogeneous equation

$$P(D)x = 0,$$

where $D = d/dt$ and $P(D)$ is a polynomial operator. Every solution of this equation is a linear combination of functions of the form (9.6). Any derivative of a solution is also a linear combination of functions of this type. We can therefore assert that every solution of the equation, and every derivative of every solution, is of exponential order and possesses a Laplace transform.

We shall give one more result about functions of exponential order.

Theorem   9.3   Let f be piecewise continuous on every interval of the form $[0, T]$, and let $f(t) = O[e^{at}]$ for some constant a. Then the function h, where

$$h(t) = \int_0^t f(u)\, du$$

is of exponential order. If $a > 0$, $h(t) = O[e^{at}]$, and if $a \leq 0$, $h(t) = O[1]$.†

PROOF   There exist positive constants t_0 and M_1 such that $|f(t)| \leq M_1 e^{at}$ for $t \geq t_0$. Also, there exists a positive constant M_2 such that $|f(t)| \leq M_2$ for $0 \leq t \leq t_0$. Since

$$h(t) = \int_0^{t_0} f(u)\, du + \int_{t_0}^t f(u)\, du$$

for $t > t_0$, we have

$$|h(t)| \leq M_2 \int_0^{t_0} du + M_1 \int_{t_0}^t e^{au}\, du$$

or

$$|h(t)| \leq M_2 t_0 + \frac{M_1}{a}(e^{at} - e^{at}{}_0).$$

† The notation $h(t) = O[1]$ means the same thing as $h(t) = O[e^{0t}]$.

If $a > 0$, then

$$|h(t)| \leq \left(M_2 t_0 + \frac{M_1}{a}\right) e^{at} \qquad \text{for } t \geq t_0$$

and $h(t) = O[e^{at}]$. If $a \leq 0$,

$$|h(t)| \leq M_2 t_0 + 2\frac{M_1}{a} \qquad \text{for } t \geq t_0,$$

and $h(t) = O[1]$.

Exercises for Section 9.2

1. Suppose that the limit

$$\lim_{t \to \infty} \frac{f(t)}{g(t)}$$

exists (and is finite). Show that $f(t) = O[|g(t)|\,]$.

2. Show that, as $t \to \infty$,

(a) $\sin t = O[1]$

(b) $\dfrac{e^{-t}}{1+t} = O[e^{-t}]$

(c) $\dfrac{e^{-t}}{1+t} = O\begin{bmatrix} 1 \\ t \end{bmatrix}$

(d) $te^t = O[e^{(1+\varepsilon)t}], \qquad \varepsilon > 0$

(e) $\sinh t = O[e^t]$

(f) $\dfrac{e^{3t}}{e^t + 1} = O[e^{2t}]$

3. Show that $\mathscr{L}[f](s)$ exists for the indicated values of s.

(a) $f(t) = \dfrac{1}{1+t}, \qquad s > 0$

(b) $f(t) = \dfrac{e^{at}}{1+t}, \qquad s > a$

(c) $f(t) = \dfrac{\sin t}{t}, \qquad s > 0$

(d) $f(t) = t \ln t, \qquad s > 0$

(e) $f(t) = e^t \sin(t^2), \qquad s > 1$

(e) $f(t) = \sqrt{e^t + 1}, \qquad s > 1/2$

4. Let f and g be of exponential order.
    (a) Show that $c_1 f + c_2 g$, where c_1 and c_2 are constants, is of exponential order.
    (b) Show that fg is of exponential order.

5. Let the function b be continuous on $[0, \infty)$ and be of exponential order. Show that every solution of the differential equation

$$x'(t) + ax(t) = b(t),$$

where a is a constant, is of exponential order.

6. If f' exists on $[0, \infty)$ and is of exponential order, show that f is of exponential order.

7. If $\lim_{t \to \infty} f(t)/g(t) = \infty$, show that $f(t) \neq O[g(t)]$.

8. If $f(t) = e^{t^2}$ for all t, show that f is not of exponential order.

9. Let $f(t) = \sin(e^{t^2})$ for all t. Show that f is of exponential order but that f' is not.

10. Let $f(t) = e^{n^2}$ for $n \leq t \leq n + e^{-n^2}$, for every positive integer n, and $f(t) = 0$ elsewhere. Show that f is not of exponential order, but that $\mathscr{L}[f](s)$ exists for $s > 0$.

9.3   PROPERTIES OF LAPLACE TRANSFORMS

In this section we shall develop some of the more useful properties of Laplace transforms. In the formulas listed below, we denote the transforms of f and g by F and G, respectively. For properties (A) through (E) we assume that f and g are piecewise continuous on every interval of the form $[0, T]$ and that $f(t) = O[e^{at}]$ and $g(t) = O[e^{bt}]$ for some constants a and b. Then $F(s)$ exists for $s > a$ and $G(s)$ exists for $s > b$.

(A) $\mathscr{L}[c_1 f + c_2 g](s) = c_1 F(s) + c_2 G(s), \qquad s > \max(a, b)$.

(B)   If $h(t) = e^{ct}f(t)$, then $H(s) = F(s - c), \qquad s > a + c$. $s = s - c$

(C)   If $k(t) = \int_0^t f(u)\, du$, then $K(s) = \dfrac{1}{s} F(s), \qquad s > \max(a, 0)$.

(D)   If $p_n(t) = t^n f(t)$, then $P_n(s) = (-1)^n \dfrac{d^n F(s)}{ds^n}, \qquad s > a$.

(E)   If $q(t) = \begin{cases} 0, & 0 < t < c, \\ f(t - c), & t > c, \end{cases}$ (3-2)   then $Q(s) = e^{-cs}F(s), \quad s > a$.

(F)   Let $f^{(n-1)}(t) = O[e^{at}]$. Let $f, f', \ldots, f^{(n-1)}$ be continuous on $[0, \infty)$ and let $f^{(n)}$ be piecewise continuous on every interval of the form $[0, T]$. Then $\mathscr{L}[f^{(n)}](s)$ exists for $s > \max(a, 0)$ and

$$\mathscr{L}[f^{(n)}](s) = s^n F(s) - [s^{n-1}f(0) + s^{n-2}f'(0) + \cdots + f^{(n-1)}(0)].$$

Property (A) follows from Theorem 9.2 and the definition of the Laplace transform.

To prove property (B), we first note that $e^{ct}f(t) = O[e^{(a+c)t}]$. Then we observe that

$$\mathscr{L}[h](s) = \int_0^\infty e^{-(s-c)t}f(t)\, dt = F(s - c).$$

To prove property (C), we use the result of Theorem 9.3, which assures us that the function k is of exponential order. Using integration by parts, and observing that $k'(t) = f(t)$, we have

$$\mathscr{L}[k](s) = \int_0^\infty e^{-st}k(t)\, dt = \left[-\frac{1}{s}e^{-st}k(t)\right]_0^\infty + \frac{1}{s}\int_0^\infty e^{-st}f(t)\, dt.$$

Since $k(0) = 0$, the integrated part vanishes and we have $\mathscr{L}[k](s) = F(s)/s$.

Now consider property (D). If we differentiate both sides of the equation

$$F(s) = \int_0^\infty e^{-st}f(t)\, dt, \qquad s > a,$$

with respect to s (the assumptions on f ensure that $F'(s)$ exists and that $F'(s)$ can be obtained by differentiation under the the integral sign), we find that

$$F'(s) = -\int_0^\infty e^{-st}tf(t)\, dt = -\mathscr{L}[p_1](s).$$

Repeated differentiation shows that

$$F^{(n)}(s) = (-1)^n \int_0^\infty e^{-st}t^n f(t)\, dt = (-1)^n \mathscr{L}[p_n](s).$$

The verification of property (E) is left as an exercise.

We shall prove property (F) by induction. When $n = 1$, f is assumed to be continuous on $[0, \infty)$. Using integration by parts, we have

$$\int_0^T e^{-st}f'(t)\, dt = [e^{-st}f(t)]_0^T + s\int_0^T e^{-st}f(t)\, dt.$$

Since $f(t) = O[e^{at}]$, it follows that $e^{-sT}f(T) \to 0$ as $T \to \infty$ for $s > a$. Letting $T \to \infty$ in the above relation, we see that the right-hand side has a limit; hence the left-hand side has a limit and

$$\mathscr{L}[f'](s) = sF(s) - f(0), \qquad s > a.$$

Now suppose that property (F) holds for $n = m$, where m is a positive integer.

Using the same arguments as in the case $n = 1$, we have

$$\mathcal{L}[f^{(m+1)}](s) = \int_0^\infty e^{-st} {}^{(m+1)}(t)\, dt$$

$$= [e^{-st} f^{(m)}(t)]_0^\infty + s \int_0^\infty e^{-st} f^{(m)}(t)\, dt$$

$$= s\mathcal{L}[f^{(m)}](s) - f^{(m)}(0).$$

The assumption that $f^{(m)}(t) = O[e^{at}]$ implies that the function $f^{(m-1)}$ is of exponential order. Consequently we can apply the property, for $n = m$, to find $\mathcal{L}[f^{(m)}](s)$. We have

$$\mathcal{L}[f^{(m+1)}](s) = s[s^m F(s) - s^{m-1}f(0) - \cdots - f^{(m-1)}(0)] - f^{(m)}(0)$$

$$= s^{m+1} F(s) - [s^m f(0) + \cdots + f^{(m)}(0)].$$

Thus if property (F) holds for $n = m$, it also holds for $n = m + 1$. Since it holds for $n = 1$, it holds for every positive integer.

These basic properties of Laplace transforms are frequently useful in finding the transforms of functions. Starting with the relations

$$f(t) = t^n, \qquad F(s) = \frac{n!}{s^{n+1}},$$

$$f(t) = e^{at}, \qquad F(s) = \frac{1}{s-a}, \qquad (9.7)$$

$$f(t) = \cos at, \qquad F(s) = \frac{s}{s^2 + a^2},$$

$$f(t) = \sin at, \qquad F(s) = \frac{a}{s^2 + a^2},$$

we can easily find the transforms of many elementary functions, with the aid of properties (A) through (F).

Example 1 Let $f(t) = \sinh at$. Since

$$f(t) = \tfrac{1}{2}e^{at} - \tfrac{1}{2}e^{-at},$$

it follows from property (A) that

$$F(s) = \frac{1}{2}\frac{1}{s-a} - \frac{1}{2}\frac{1}{s+a} = \frac{a}{s^2 - a^2}.$$

Example 2   Let $f(t) = e^{-2t} \cos 3t$. If $g(t) = \cos 3t$, then

$$\mathcal{L}[g](s) = \frac{3}{s^2 + 9},$$

and it follows from property **(B)** that

$$\mathcal{L}[f](s) = \frac{s + 2}{(s + 2)^2 + 9} = \frac{s + 2}{s^2 + 4s + 13}.$$

Example 3   As an example of the use of property **(D)**, we find the transform of the function $f(t) = t^2 \sin t$. If $g(t) = \sin t$, we have

$$\mathcal{L}[g](s) = \frac{s}{s^2 + 1}$$

and hence

$$\mathcal{L}[f](s) = \frac{d^2}{ds^2}\left(\frac{1}{s^2 + 1}\right) = 2\,\frac{3s^2 - 1}{(s^2 + 1)^3}.$$

Example 4   As a final example, we consider the function

$$f(t) = \begin{cases} 0, & 0 < t < 1, \\ (t - 1)^2, & t > 1, \end{cases}$$

whose graph is shown in Fig. 9.1.

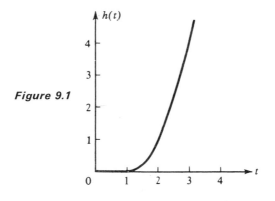

Figure 9.1

If $g(t) = t^2$, then $\mathcal{L}[g](s) = 2/s^3$ and it follows from property **(E)** that

$$\mathcal{L}[f](s) = e^{-s}\mathcal{L}[g](s) = \frac{2}{s^3}e^{-s}.$$

Exercises for Section 9.3

1. Verify property (E).

2. Find the Laplace transform of f, where $f(t)$ is:
   (a) $2e^{-t} - 3\sin 4t$ (b) $\cosh 2t$
   (c) $e^{2t}\sin 3t$ (d) $e^{-t}\cos 2t$
   (e) $e^{-3t}t^4$ (f) $t^3 e^{4t}$
   (g) $t^2 \cos t$ (h) $t \sin 2t$

3. Find the Laplace transform of f, where $f(t)$ is as given.
   (a) $e^{2t}\sqrt{t}$ (b) $\displaystyle\int_0^t \sin 2u\, du$

   (c) $\displaystyle\int_0^t x^2 e^x\, dx$ (d) $\displaystyle\int_0^t \cos^2 u\, du$

   (e) $f(t) = \begin{cases} 0, & 0 < t < 2 \\ 1, & t > 2 \end{cases}$ (f) $f(t) = \begin{cases} 0, & 0 < t < \pi \\ \sin(t - \pi), & t > \pi \end{cases}$

   (g) $f(t) = \begin{cases} 0, & 0 < t < 1 \\ t^2, & t > 1 \end{cases}$ (h) $f(t) = \begin{cases} 0, & 0 < t < 1 \\ (t - 1)e^t, & t > 1 \end{cases}$

4. If $\mathcal{L}[f] = F$, express the transform of the indicated derivative of f in terms of F.
   (a) f'', if $f(0) = 1$ and $f'(0) = 2$
   (b) f'', if $f(0) = -3$ and $f'(0) = 0$
   (c) f''', if $f(0) = 1, f'(0) = -1$, and $f''(0) = 5$
   (d) f''', if $f(0) = -2, f'(0) = 0$, and $f''(0) = 1$
   (e) $f^{(4)}$, if $f(0) = 2$ and $f'(0) = f''(0) = f'''(0) = 0$
   (f) $f^{(4)}$, if $f(0) = f'(0) = 0, f''(0) = 1$, and $f'''(0) = -1$

5. If $g(t) = f(ct)$, where c is a positive constant, show that
   $$G(s) = \frac{1}{c}F\left(\frac{s}{c}\right).$$

6. If f is continuous on $[0, \infty)$ and is the derivative of a function g $(f = g')$ of exponential order, show that f possesses a Laplace transform even though f may not be of exponential order. (See, in connection with this exercise, Exercise 9, Section 9.2.)

7. Let f and f' be piecewise continuous on every interval of the form $[0, T]$, and be of exponential order. Suppose that f has only a finite number of discontinuities on $(0, \infty)$, at the points $t_1 < t_2 < \cdots < t_k$. Show that

$$\mathscr{L}[f'](s) = sF(s) - f(0+) - \sum_{i=1}^{k} e^{-st_i}[f(t_i+) - f(t_i-)].$$

9.4 INVERSE TRANSFORMS

In this section, we shall consider the following problem. Given a function F, what functions, if any, have F as their Laplace transforms? To simplify matters, we shall consider only functions that are piecewise continuous on every interval of the form $[0, T]$ and are of exponential order. We first prove the following result.

Theorem 9.4 Let f be a function of the type described above, and let $F(s) = \mathscr{L}[f](s)$. Then

$$\lim_{s \to \infty} F(s) = 0.$$

PROOF There exist positive numbers t_0 and M_1, and a number a, such that $|f(t)| \le M_1 e^{at}$ for $t \ge t_0$. We write

$$F(s) = \int_0^{t_0} e^{-st}f(t)\,dt + \int_{t_0}^{\infty} e^{-st}f(t)\,dt.$$

Since f is piecewise continuous on the finite interval $[0, t_0]$, there exists a positive number M_2 such that $|f(t)| \le M_2$ for $0 \le t \le t_0$. Then

$$|F(s)| \le M_2 \int_0^{t_0} e^{-st}\,dt + M_1 \int_{t_0}^{\infty} e^{-t(s-a)}\,dt,$$

so

$$|F(s)| \le M_2 \frac{1}{s}(1 - e^{-st_0}) + M_1 \frac{1}{s-a} e^{-t_0(s-a)}, \qquad s > a.$$

Letting $s \to \infty$, we see that $F(s) \to 0$.

In view of this result, we can state that unless $F(s)$ tends to zero with increasing s, there exists no function of the type considered which has F as its Laplace transform. For instance, if

$$F(s) = \frac{s(s+1)}{s_2 + 2},$$

no function of the type considered has F as its transform, because $F(s) \to 1 \ne 0$ as $s \to \infty$.

We can also ask if it is possible for two different functions to have the same Laplace transform. A partial answer is given by the following theorem, which we must state without proof. A more general version of this theorem is known as *Lerch's theorem*.

Theorem 9.5 Let f and g be piecewise continuous on every interval of the form $[0, T]$, and let $\mathcal{L}[f](s) = \mathcal{L}[g](s)$ for $s > s_0$, for some number s_0. Then at each point t_0 in the interval $[0, \infty)$, where f and g are both continuous, $f(t_0) = g(t_0)$. In particular, if f and g are both continuous on $[0, \infty)$, then $f(t) = g(t)$ for $t \geq 0$.

Let us consider as an example the function

$$F(s) = \frac{1}{s-2}.$$

If $f(t) = e^{2t}$ for $t \geq 0$, we know that f has F as its transform. Because of Theorem 9.5 we can assert that f is the only *continuous* function that has F as its transform.

More generally, let F be defined on (a, ∞), for some number a, and be such that $F(s) \to 0$ as $s \to \infty$. We may ask whether there exists a function f, continuous on $[0, \infty)$ and of exponential order, which has F as its Laplace transform. We know by Theorem 9.5 that at most one such function can exist. If such a function f does exist, we call it the *inverse transform* of F and write

$$f = \mathcal{L}^{-1}[F], \qquad f(t) = \mathcal{L}^{-1}[F](t).$$

Sufficient conditions that a function F possess an inverse transform can be found in Churchill [1].

It is possible to find the inverse transforms of a number of functions by using the relations (9.7) and the properties of Laplace transforms that were derived in the last section.

Example 1 Let us consider the function

$$F(s) = \frac{3s}{s^2 + 4s + 5}.$$

By completing the square in the denominator, we can write

$$F(s) = \frac{3s}{(s+2)^2 + 1} = \frac{3(s+2)}{(s+2)^2 + 1} - \frac{6}{(s+2)^2 + 1}.$$

If $G(s) = s/(s^2 + 1)$ and $H(s) = 1/(s^2 + 1)$, we know that

$$\mathcal{L}^{-1}[G](t) = \cos t, \qquad \mathcal{L}^{-1}[H](t) = \sin t.$$

Using these facts, and properties (A) and (B) of the last section, we see that

$$\mathscr{L}^{-1}[F](t) = e^{-2t}(3 \cos t - 6 \sin t).$$

Example 2 Consider the function

$$F(s) = e^{-2s}\frac{1}{s^2}.$$

If $G(s) = 1/s^2$, then $\mathscr{L}^{-1}[G](t) = t$. By property (E) we have

$$\mathscr{L}^{-1}[F](t) = \begin{cases} 0, & 0 \le t \le 2, \\ t - 2, & t > 2. \end{cases}$$

In cases where F is a rational function, it is often convenient to expand F in a series of partial fractions.

Example 3 Let

$$F(s) = \frac{1}{(s - 2)(s^2 + 1)}.$$

Expansion of F in partial fractions yields the formula

$$F(s) = \frac{1}{5}\frac{1}{s - 2} - \frac{1}{5}\frac{s + 2}{s^2 + 1}.$$

Then we recognize that

$$\mathscr{L}^{-1}[F](t) = \tfrac{1}{5}(e^{2t} - \cos t - 2 \sin t).$$

Let us now consider the problem of finding the inverse transform of the product FG, where $F = \mathscr{L}[f]$ and $G = \mathscr{L}[g]$. We have

$$F(s)G(s) = \left(\int_0^\infty e^{-sx}f(x)\,dx\right)\left(\int_0^\infty e^{-sy}g(y)\,dy\right)$$

$$= \int_0^\infty \int_0^\infty e^{-s(x+y)}f(x)g(y)\,dx\,dy.$$

The product of the two single integrals can be interpreted as an improper double integral whose region of integration is the first quadrant of a plane in which x and y are rectangular coordinates. Let us now make the change of variables

$$\begin{aligned} x &= t - u, & u &= y, \\ y &= u, & t &= x + y, \end{aligned}$$

from (x, y) to (t, u). The first quadrant of the xy plane corresponds to the region of the tu plane that is described by means of the inequalities $u \ge 0$ and $t - u \ge 0$. This region is shown in Fig. 9.2.

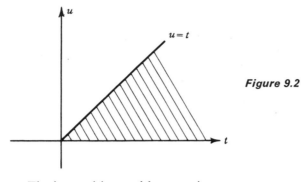

Figure 9.2

The iterated integral becomes†

$$F(s)G(s) = \int_0^\infty \int_0^t e^{-st} f(t-u)g(u) \, du \, dt$$

$$= \int_0^\infty e^{-st} \left[\int_0^t f(t-u)g(u) \, du \right] dt .$$

Therefore

$$\mathscr{L}^{-1}[FG](t) = \int_0^t f(t-u)g(u) \, du .$$

The function defined here is called the *convolution* of the functions f and g, and is denoted by $f * g$. Thus

$$f * g(t) = \int_0^t f(t-u)g(u) \, du \tag{9.8}$$

and we may write

$$\mathscr{L}[f * g] = FG .$$

It can be shown (Exercise 3) that $f * g = g * f$, so that

$$f * g(t) = g * f(t) = \int_0^t f(u)g(t-u) \, du .$$

The notion of the convolution of two functions arises in areas of mathematics other than the theory of Laplace transforms.

Example 4   As an exercise, we shall use the convolution formula (9.8) to find the inverse transform of the function

$$H(s) = \frac{1}{s^2(s^2 + 1)} .$$

---

† The Jacobian of the transformation of coordinates is unity. For an alternative treatment see Widder [4].

Since $H(s) = F(s)G(s)$, where $F(s) = 1/s^2$ and $G(s) = 1/(s^2 + 1)$, we have $h = f * g$. Now $f(t) = t$ and $g(t) = \sin t$, so

$$h(t) = f * g(t) = \int_0^t (t - u) \sin u \, du$$
$$= [-(t - u) \cos u - \sin u]_{u=0}^{u=t}$$
$$= t - \sin t.$$

This result could also have been obtained by finding the partial fractions expansion of the given function.

The techniques illustrated here can be used only when the given function F can be expressed in a fairly simple way in terms of functions whose inverse transforms are easily recognizable. For convenience, a short table of functions and their transforms is given at the end of this chapter. A more powerful and direct method for finding inverse transforms exists. This method requires a fairly deep knowledge of complex variables, however, and we cannot discuss it here. We shall be concerned mainly with the solution of initial value problems for differential equations by means of Laplace transforms. The methods at our disposal suffice for the solution of many such problems. In any case, they serve to illustrate the general approach.

Exercises for Section 9.4

1. Find the function f that is continuous on $[0, \infty)$ and has F as its transform if $F(s)$ is:

    (a) $\dfrac{1}{(s + 1)^2}$

    (b) $\dfrac{1}{(s - 2)^2 + 9}$

    (c) $\dfrac{s}{(s + 1)^2 - 4}$

    (d) $\dfrac{1}{s^2 - 3s}$

    (e) $\dfrac{1}{(s + 1)(s + 2)}$

    (f) $\dfrac{1}{s(s + 2)^2}$

2. Find the function f that is continuous on $[0, \infty)$ and has F as its transform if $F(s)$ is:

    (a) $\dfrac{6}{s^2 + s - 2}$

    (b) $\dfrac{3s - 8}{s^2 - 5s + 6}$

    (c) $\dfrac{s^2 + 20s + 9}{(s - 1)^2(s^2 + 9)}$

    (d) $\dfrac{s - 4}{s^2 + 3s + 3}$

    (e) $\dfrac{1}{s^3 - 8}$

    (f) $\dfrac{3s - 2}{s^2 - 2s + 10}$

3. Show that $g * f = f * g$.

4. Find $f * g(t)$ if f and g are as given.

(a) $f(t) = g(t) = t$ (b) $f(t) = t, \qquad g(t) = e^t$

(c) $f(t) = e^t, \qquad g(t) = e^{2t}$ (d) $f(t) = e^{-t}, \qquad g(t) = \cos t$

5. Find the inverse transform of the function whose value at s is:

(a) $e^{-s} \dfrac{1}{(s-2)^2}$ (b) $e^{-2s} \dfrac{1}{s^2 + 9\pi^2}$

(c) $\dfrac{s}{(s-2)^{3/2}(s^2+1)}$ (d) $\dfrac{1}{s^{5/2}(s^2+1)}$

(e) $\dfrac{1}{s+1} F(s)$ (f) $\dfrac{1}{s^2+1} F(s)$

6. Let f be continuous on $[0, \infty)$. Let f' be piecewise continuous on every interval of the form $[0, T]$ and be of exponential order. Show that

$$\lim_{s \to \infty} sF(s) = f(0).$$

Suggestion: Apply Theorem 9.4 to f'.

7. It can be shown that $(f * g) * h = f * (g * h)$. Verify this for the case $f(t) = t, g(t) = e^t$, and $h(t) = e^{-t}$.

8. Let f and g be piecewise continuous on every interval of the form $[0, T]$. If f and g are both of exponential order, show that $f * g$ is of exponential order.

9.5   APPLICATIONS TO DIFFERENTIAL EQUATIONS

We shall now apply the theory of Laplace transforms to the solution of initial value problems. The method that we shall describe applies to those problems where the differential equation, or system of differential equations, is linear and has constant coefficients.

As an illustration, let us consider the problem

$$x''(t) + 4x(t) = 5e^{-t}, \qquad t \geq 0,$$

$$x(0) = 2, \qquad x'(0) = 3.$$

From the theory of linear differential equations we know that this problem possesses a unique solution x on $[0, \infty)$. This solution and its first two derivatives are continuous. Let us assume, for the moment, that x and x' are of exponential order. Then x, x', and x'' possess Laplace transforms on some interval (s_0, ∞). [See property (F), Section 9.3.] If $\mathscr{L}[x] = X$, then

$$\mathscr{L}[x'](s) = sX(s) - x(0) = sX(s) - 2,$$

$$\mathscr{L}[x''](s) = s^2 X(s) - sx(0) - x'(0)$$

$$= s^2 X(s) - 2s - 3.$$

From the differential equation, we see that

$$\mathscr{L}[x'' + 4x](s) = \frac{5}{s + 1}$$

or

$$s^2 X(s) - 2s - 3 + 4X(s) = \frac{5}{s + 1}.$$

Upon solving for $X(s)$, we find that

$$X(s) = \frac{2s^2 + 5s + 8}{(s + 1)(s^2 + 4)}.$$

The use of partial fractions shows that

$$X(s) = \frac{4}{s^2 + 4} + \frac{s}{s^2 + 4} + \frac{1}{s + 1}.$$

Inverting, we arrive at the formula

$$x(t) = 2 \sin 2t + \cos 2t + e^{-t}.$$

However, we cannot immediately assert that this function is the solution of the initial value problem. For in the derivation, we made the assumption, not yet justified, that the solution and its first derivative were of exponential order.

   We shall presently show that our assumptions about the behavior of the solution and its derivatives were correct. But first let us consider the more general problem

$$P(D)x = a_0 x^{(n)} + a_1 x^{(n-1)} + \cdots + a_{n-1}x' + a_n x = b(t),$$

$$x(0) = k_0, \quad x'(0) = k_1, \ldots, \quad x^{(n-1)}(0) = k_{n-1}.$$

(9.9)

Suppose that b possesses a Laplace transform B. If we "transform" the differential equation formally, taking into account the initial conditions, we arrive at the algebraic equation

$$a_0 [s^n X(s) - k_0 s^{n-1} - \cdots - k_{n-1}] + a_1 [s^{n-1} X(s) - k_0 s^{n-2} - \cdots - k_{n-2}]$$

$$+ \cdots + a_{n-1} [sX(s) - k_0] + a_n X(s) = B(s)$$

for $X(s)$. This equation can be written as

$$P(s)X(s) = B(s) + Q(s),$$

where Q is a polynomial whose coefficients depend on the constants k_i. Then

$$X(s) = \frac{B(s) + Q(s)}{P(s)}. \tag{9.10}$$

The justification of this procedure can be based on the following theorem.

Theorem 9.6   Let the function b be continuous on $[0, \infty)$ and be of exponential order. Then the solution x of the initial value problem (9.9) is of exponential order, as are its first $n - 1$ derivatives.†

PROOF   We know from the discussion of Section 9.2 that the solutions of the associated homogeneous equation, along with their derivatives, are of exponential order. The solution of the problem (9.9) can be expressed in terms of these functions by the method of variation of parameters. The formula for the solution involves an integral. By applying Theorem 9.3, it is easy to see that x has the indicated properties. The details are left as an exercise.

When b is of exponential order, so are the functions $x, x', \ldots, x^{(n-1)}$. Then these functions, along with $x^{(n)}$, possess Laplace transforms, and the transforms of the derivatives can be expressed in terms of $\mathscr{L}[x]$ by the use of property (F). In this case, the derivation of formula (9.10) for the transform of the solution is valid. In particular, the procedure followed in the example at the beginning of this section is valid.

Let us next consider the linear system with constant coefficients,

$$x_i'(t) = \sum_{j=1}^{n} a_{ij} x_j + b_i(t), \qquad t \geq 0, \quad i = 1, 2, \ldots, n,$$
$$x_i(0) = k_i, \qquad i = 1, 2, \ldots, n. \tag{9.11}$$

Suppose that the components x_i of the solution possess transforms X_i, and that the functions b_i possess transforms B_i. If we formally transform the differential equations, we arrive at the system of algebraic equations

$$sX_i(s) - k_i = \sum_{j=1}^{n} a_{ij} X_j(s) + B_i(s), \qquad i = 1, 2, \ldots, n \tag{9.12}$$

for the quantities $X_i(s)$. Justification of this procedure can be based on the following theorem, which is the analog of Theorem 9.6.

---

† Actually the nth derivative of x is continuous and of exponential order, as we can see from the differential equation.

Theorem 9.7 Let each of the functions b_i be continuous on $[0, \infty)$ and be of exponential order. Then the components x_i of the solution of the problem (9.11) are of exponential order.

When the functions b_i are of exponential order, the functions x_i and x_i' therefore possess Laplace transforms, and

$$\mathscr{L}[x_i'] = \mathscr{L}[x_i] - x_i(0).$$

In this case, the derivation of the system (9.12) is valid.

Example 1 Let us consider the problem

$$(D + 3)x + 5y = 2,$$
$$-x + (D - 1)y = 1,$$
$$x(0) = 1, \qquad y(0) = 0.$$

We note that the hypotheses of Theorem 9.7 are satisfied. If X and Y denote the transforms of x and y, respectively. we have from the system that

$$sX(s) - 1 + 3X(s) + 5Y(s) = \frac{2}{s},$$

$$-X(s) + sY(s) - Y(s) = \frac{1}{s}.$$

Upon regrouping terms, we have

$$(s + 3)X(s) + 5Y(s) = \frac{2}{s} + 1,$$

$$-X(s) + (s - 1)Y(s) = \frac{1}{s}.$$

Solving for $X(s)$ and $Y(s)$, and using partial fractions, we obtain the formulas

$$X(s) = -\frac{7}{2}\frac{1}{s} + \frac{1}{2}\frac{9(s+1)+7}{(s+1)^2+1},$$

$$Y(s) = \frac{5}{2}\frac{1}{s} - \frac{1}{2}\frac{5(s+1)+1}{(s+1)^2+1}.$$

Taking inverse transforms, we find that

$$x(t) = -\tfrac{7}{2} + \tfrac{9}{2}e^{-t}\cos t + \tfrac{7}{2}e^{-t}\sin t,$$
$$y(t) = \tfrac{5}{2} - \tfrac{5}{2}e^{-t}\cos t - \tfrac{1}{2}e^{-t}\sin t.$$

As a check, we note that $x(0) = 1$ and $y(0) = 0$.

Example 2   As a final example, let us consider the problem

$$D^2x + y = -2,$$
$$x + D^2y = 0,$$
$$x(0) = y(0) = x'(0) = y'(0) = 0.$$
(9.13)

The system is not a first-order system, so Theorem 9.7 does not apply. However, the system can be rewritten as a first-order system for the quantities x, Dx, y, and Dy. Setting

$$x = u_1, \qquad Dx = u_2, \qquad y = u_3, \qquad Dy = u_4,$$

we obtain the first-order system

$$Du_1 = u_2, \qquad Du_2 = -u_3 - 2, \qquad Du_3 = u_4, \qquad Du_4 = -u_1. \quad (9.14)$$

The initial conditions are

$$u_1(0) = u_2(0) = u_3(0) = u_4(0) = 0.$$

The system (9.14) satisfies the hypotheses of Theorem 9.7. It possesses a unique solution which satisfies the initial conditions. The components u_i of this solution are of exponential order. Consequently, the problem (9.13) possesses a unique solution (x, y), and the quantities x, y, Dx, Dy, D^2x, D^2y possess Laplace transforms. Therefore we can apply the method of Laplace transforms directly to the problem (9.13). Transformation of the differential equations yields the relations

$$s^2 X(s) + Y(s) = -\frac{2}{s}, \qquad X(s) + s^2 Y(s) = 0.$$

From these we find that

$$X(s) = \frac{-2s}{s^4 - 1} = \frac{s}{s^2 + 1} - \frac{s}{s^2 - 1}, \qquad Y(s) = \frac{-1}{s^2 + 1} + \frac{1}{s^2 - 1}.$$

Consequently the solution of the problem is

$$x(t) = \cos t - \cosh t, \qquad y(t) = -\sin t + \sinh t.$$

Exercises for Section 9.5

1. Find the solution of the initial value problem by the use of Laplace transforms.

(a) $x'' + 3x' + 2x = 6e^t, \quad x(0) = 2, \quad x'(0) = -1$

(b) $x'' + 2x' + x = 4 \sin t, \quad x(0) = -2, \quad x'(0) = 1$

(c) $x'' + 4x = 8 \sin t,\quad x(0) = 0,\quad x'(0) = 2$

(d) $x'' + 4x' + 5x = 25t,\quad x(0) = -5,\quad x'(0) = 7$

(e) $x''' + 2x'' + x' + 2x = 2,\quad x(0) = 3,\quad x'(0) = -2,\quad x''(0) = 3$

(f) $x^{(4)} - 2x'' + x = 8e^t,\quad x(0) = 1,\quad x'(0) = 2,\quad x''(0) = 1,\quad x'''(0) = 10$

2. Consider the initial value problem

$$x'' + x = f(t),\qquad t \ge 0,\qquad x(0) = x'(0) = 0,$$

where

$$f(t) = \begin{cases} t, & 0 \le t \le 1, \\ 1, & t > 1. \end{cases}$$

(a) Find the solution by means of Laplace transforms.

(b) Find the solution by using another method.

3. Find by means of Laplace transforms the solution of the problem

$$x'' - x = f(t),\qquad t \ge 0,\qquad x(0) = 1,\qquad x'(0) = 0,$$

$$f(t) = \begin{cases} 0, & 0 \le t \le 1, \\ (t - 1), & t > 1. \end{cases}$$

4. By using Laplace transforms, express the solution of the problem

$$x'' + x = f(t),\quad x(0) = 0,\quad x'(0) = 1$$

as an integral.

5. If x satisfies the given integral equation, determine the Laplace transform of x and then determine x.

(a) $x(t) = 2 + \displaystyle\int_0^t e^{t-u} x(u)\, du$ (b) $x(t) = 1 + t + \displaystyle\int_0^t (t - u) x(u)\, du$

6. Find the solution of the initial value problem by the use of Laplace transforms.

(a) $(D + 2)x_1 - 2x_2 = 0,$
    $-x_1 + (D + 1)x_2 = 2e^t,$ $x_1(0) = 0,\quad x_2(0) = 1$

(b) $(D + 1)x_1 + x_2 = 0,$
    $-5x_1 + (D - 1)x_2 = -4,$ $x_1(0) = 1,\quad x_2(0) = 3$

(c) $(D + 2)x_1 + x_2 = e^{-t},$
    $-2x_1 + Dx_2 = -e^{-t},$ $x_1(0) = 2,\quad x_2(0) = 0$

(d) $4Dx_1 - (D^2 - D)x_2 = 0,$
    $-(D + 3)x_1 + x_2 = 0,$ $x_1(0) = 0,\quad x_2(0) = 2,\quad x_2'(0) = -1$

(e) $-4x_1 + (D^2 + D + 4)x_2 = 2,$
    $(D + 1)x_1 - x_2 = 2,$ $x_1(0) = 2,\quad x_2(0) = 4,\quad x_2'(0) = 2$

(f) $x_1' = -x_1 - 3x_2 + 3x_3, \qquad x_1(0) = -1$
$x_2' = -4x_2 + 3x_3, \qquad x_2(0) = 1$
$x_3' = -6x_2 + 5x_3, \qquad x_3(0) = 0$

7. (a) Consider the differential equation

$$x''(t) + ax'(t) + bx(t) = h(t),$$

where a and b are constants, h is continuous on $[0, \infty)$, and h is of exponential order. Show that every solution, and the first derivative of every solution, is of exponential order. *Suggestion:* Use the method of variation of parameters and Theorem 9.3.

(b) Generalize the result of part (a) to the nth-order equation $P(D)x = b$. In other words, complete the proof of Theorem 9.6.

A Table of Transforms

	$f(t)$	$F(s)$			$f(t)$	$F(s)$
1.	1	$\dfrac{1}{s}$		8.	$\cosh at$	$\dfrac{s}{s^2 - a^2}$
2.	t^n	$\dfrac{n!}{s^{n+1}}$		9.	$t \sin at$	$\dfrac{2as}{(s^2 + a^2)^2}$
3.	e^{at}	$\dfrac{1}{s - a}$		10.	$t \cos at$	$\dfrac{s^2 - a^2}{(s^2 + a^2)^2}$
4.	$t^n e^{at}$	$\dfrac{n!}{(s - a)^{n+1}}$		11.	$t \sinh at$	$\dfrac{2as}{(s^2 - a^2)^2}$
5.	$\sin at$	$\dfrac{a}{s^2 + a^2}$		12.	$t \cosh at$	$\dfrac{s^2 + a^2}{(s^2 - a^2)^2}$
6.	$\cos at$	$\dfrac{s}{s^2 + a^2}$		13.	$\sin at - at \cos at$	$\dfrac{2a^3}{(s^2 + a^2)^2}$
7.	$\sinh at$	$\dfrac{a}{s^2 - a^2}$		14.	$at \cosh at - \sinh at$	$\dfrac{2a^3}{(s^2 - a^2)^2}$

REFERENCES

1. Churchill, R. V., *Operational Mathematics*, 2nd ed. McGraw-Hill, New York, 1958.
2. Holl, D. L., Maple, C. G., and Vinograde, B., *Introduction to the Laplace Transform*. Appleton-Century-Crofts, New York, 1959.
3. Kaplan, W., *Operational Methods for Linear Systems*. Addison-Wesley, Reading, Massachusetts, 1962.
4. Widder, D. V., *Advanced Calculus*, 2nd ed. Prentice-Hall, Englewood Cliffs, New Jersey, 1960.

X

Partial Differential
Equations and Boundary Value Problems

10.1 INTRODUCTION

$t^1 e^{2t}$

Partial differential equations are classified as to order and linearity in much the same way as ordinary differential equations. The order of an equation is simply the order of the highest-order partial derivatives of the unknown function that appear in the equation. As illustrations, let us consider equations for an unknown function $u(x, y)$ of two independent variables. An equation of the form

$$Au_{xx} + Bu_{xy} + Cu_{yy} + Du_x + Eu_y + Fu = G, \qquad (10.1)$$

where $A, B, \ldots, G$, are given functions of x and y, is a second-order linear equation. (It is assumed that A, B, and C are not all identically zero.) The equation

$$\frac{\partial u}{\partial x} + xy^2 u \frac{\partial u}{\partial y} = \cos y$$

is a first-order nonlinear equation. We shall say that a function $u(x, y)$ is a *solution* of an nth-order partial differential equation if it possesses continuous partial derivatives of order† n and satisfies the equation in some region R of the xy plane.

---

† It is shown in advanced calculus that such a function is continuous and possesses continuous partial derivatives of orders 1, 2, $\ldots$, $n - 1$.

Throughout this chapter, we shall be concerned mainly with second-order linear partial differential equations of the form (10.1). Such equations are further classified according to the following scheme: An equation of the form (10.1) is said to be of *elliptic type* in a region R if, in that region, $B^2 - 4AC < 0$. It is said to be of *hyperbolic type* if $B^2 - 4AC > 0$, and of *parabolic type* if $B^2 - 4AC = 0$. Important examples of the three types of equations are the following:

(a) *Laplace's equation (elliptic):*

$$\frac{\partial^2 u}{\partial x^2} + \frac{\partial^2 u}{\partial y^2} = 0.$$

(b) *The wave equation (hyperbolic):*

$$c^2 \frac{\partial^2 u}{\partial x^2} - \frac{\partial^2 u}{\partial y^2} = 0,$$

where c is a positive constant.

(c) *The heat equation (parabolic):*

$$k \frac{\partial^2 u}{\partial x^2} - \frac{\partial u}{\partial y} = 0,$$

where k is a positive constant.

In these examples, the coefficients A, B, and C of the general form (10.1) are *constant* functions. The classification of such an equation does not depend on the region R under consideration. However, the equation

$$\frac{\partial^2 u}{\partial x^2} - x \frac{\partial^2 u}{\partial y^2} + u = 0,$$

whose coefficients are not all constant functions, is of hyperbolic type in the half-plane $x > 0$ and of elliptic type in the half-plane $x < 0$. This follows from the fact that $B^2 - 4AC = 4x$.

In the applications to be considered later in this chapter, we shall be concerned with finding a solution of a partial differential equation which also satisfies certain auxiliary conditions, called *boundary conditions*. For instance, we might require that a solution $u(x, y)$ take on prescribed values on a given curve in the xy plane. Or we might require that u and certain of its partial derivatives satisfy a given relation along a curve. A problem that consists of finding a solution of a partial differential equation which also satisfies one or more boundary conditions is called a *boundary value problem*.

In the study of boundary value problems, three basic questions are of paramount interest. First is the question of the *existence* of a solution. That is, does a given problem have a solution? The second question concerns the *uniqueness* of a solution. If a solution exists, is it the only possible solution? The third question is a little more difficult to phrase. Briefly, it is the question of whether the solution depends continuously on the prescribed values of the boundary conditions. To put it another way, we would like to know whether a small change in the prescribed values will produce only a small change in the value of the solution function at each point in the region under consideration. This question is important in applications, because the prescribed values are determined by physical measurement, and they are not exact.

A boundary value problem possessing a unique solution that depends continuously on the prescribed values in the boundary conditions is said to be a *well-posed problem*. A detailed discussion of well-posed boundary value problems is beyond the scope of this brief introduction. We do wish to point out, however, that in the case of equations of the form (10.1), the kind of boundary conditions that leads to a well-posed problem depends on the type of the equation. For instance, boundary conditions that yield a well-posed problem with a hyperbolic equation do not in general yield a well-posed problem with an equation of elliptic type. Appropriate boundary conditions for the three specific equations mentioned above will be presented in later sections.

For some partial differential equations, it is possible to find expressions that represent all solutions, that is, represent the general solution. Such expressions contain *arbitrary functions* instead of arbitrary constants, as in the case of ordinary differential equations. Let us consider as an example the equation

$$\frac{\partial^2 u}{\partial x\, \partial y} = 0 , \tag{10.2}$$

in the region consisting of the entire xy plane. If F and G are any two functions that possess continuous second derivatives, the function

$$u(x, y) = F(x) + G(y) \tag{10.3}$$

is a solution of Eq. (10.2). For we have

$$\frac{\partial u}{\partial y} = G'(y)$$

and

$$\frac{\partial^2 u}{\partial x\, \partial y} = \frac{\partial}{\partial x} G'(y) = 0 .$$

Conversely, every solution of Eq. (10.2) is of the form (10.3). For if we write the equation as

$$\frac{\partial}{\partial x}\left(\frac{\partial u}{\partial y}\right) = 0,$$

we see that

$$\frac{\partial u}{\partial y} = g(y),$$

and hence that

$$u = G(y) + F(x),$$

where $G'(y) = g(y)$.

Even when it is possible to find the general solution of a partial differential equation, it is seldom feasible to select the arbitrary functions involved so that the boundary conditions are satisfied. We shall consider in this chapter only a few specific equations which, although quite special, are very important in mathematical physics. Rather than discuss general solutions of these equations, we shall consider various boundary value problems for the equations that are motivated by physical considerations. The *method of separation of variables* will be used to obtain solutions of these problems. Although this method is very specialized, many of the problems for which it succeeds are important ones. This method yields a solution in the form of an infinite series. It is useful in establishing the *existence* of a solution. In some cases the solution, originally expressed as an infinite series, can be rewritten in a more compact and useful form. Also, in some cases, the series can be used to compute the values of the solution function.

Exercises for Section 10.1

1. Verify that the given partial differential equation has the indicated function as a solution:

   (a) $u_{xx} + u_{yy} = 0$, $u(x, y) = \cos ax \cosh ay$

   (b) $u_{xx} - u_{yy} = 0$, $u(x, y) = \cos ax \sin ay$

   (c) $u_{xx} - u_y = 0$, $u(x, y) = e^{-ay} \sin ax$

   (d) $u_{xx} - u_y = 0$, $u(x, y) = y^{-1/2} \exp(-x^2/4y)$, $y > 0$

2. Determine the type (elliptic, hyperbolic, or parabolic) of the given equation:

(a) $u_{xy} - 2u_y + 3u = 0$

(b) $u_{xx} - 2u_{xy} + 2u_{yy} - 3u_x + u = 0$

(c) $u_{xx} - 2u_{xy} + u_{yy} - x^2 u_y + y^2 u_x = 0$

(d) $(y^2 + 1)u_{xx} + (x^2 + 1)u_{yy} - (x^2 + y^2)u = 0$

3. Show that the equation

$$u_{xx} - 2xu_{xy} + yu_{yy} - u = 0$$

is elliptic on one side of the parabola $y = x^2$ and hyperbolic on the other side.

4. Show that every solution of the equation $u_{xx} = 0$, in the entire xy plane, is of the form $u(x, y) = xF(y) + G(y)$. Conversely, show that any function of this form, where F and G possess continuous second derivatives, is a solution of the equation.

5. Let u_1 and u_2 be solutions of the linear equation

$$Au_{xx} + Bu_{xy} + Cu_{yy} + Du_x + Eu_y + Fu = 0,$$

where $A, B, \ldots, F$ are given functions, in a region R of the xy plane. Show that $c_1 u_1 + c_2 u_2$, where c_1 and c_2 are constants, is also a solution.

6. Consider the equation

$$Au_{xx} + Bu_{xy} + Cu_{yy} = 0,$$

where A, B, and C are constants, with $A \neq 0$. If the equation is of hyperbolic type, show that it possesses solutions of the form

$$u(x, y) = F(\lambda_1 x + y) + G(\lambda_2 x + y),$$

where F and G are any functions possessing continuous second derivatives, and where λ_1 and λ_2 are roots of the equation

$$A\lambda^2 + B\lambda + C = 0.$$

7. Show that the equation

$$Au_{xx} + Bu_{xy} + Cu_{yy} + Du_x + Eu_y + Fu = 0,$$

where $A, B, \ldots, F$ are constants, can be put in the form

$$A'u_{x'x'} + C'u_{y'y'} + D'u_{x'} + E'u_{y'} + F'u = 0$$

by means of a rotation of axes. *Suggestion:* If the rotation is through an angle θ, then

$$x' = x \cos \theta + y \sin \theta, \qquad y' = -x \sin \theta + y \cos \theta.$$

8. If the equation with constant coefficients,

$$Au_{xx} + Cu_{yy} + Du_x + Eu_y + Fu = 0,$$

is either elliptic or hyperbolic, show that it can be put in the form

$$Av_{xx} + Cv_{yy} + Gv = 0$$

by means of a change of dependent variable,

$$u(x, y) = v(x, y) \exp(Mx + Ny),$$

where M and N are constants. Then show that a change of independent variable yields the standard form

$$v_{\xi\xi} + v_{\eta\eta} + Hv = 0$$

for an elliptic equation, and the standard form

$$v_{\xi\xi} - v_{\eta\eta} + Kv = 0$$

for a hyperbolic equation.

9. Show that the parabolic equation

$$Au_{xx} + Du_x + Eu_y + Fu = 0,$$

with constant coefficients and $A \neq 0$, can be put in the form

$$Av_{xx} + Ev_y = 0$$

by means of a change of dependent variable

$$u(x, y) = v(x, y) \exp(Mx + Ny),$$

where M and N are constants. If $E \neq 0$, show that the equation can be put in the standard form

$$v_{\xi\xi} - v_\eta = 0$$

by means of a change of independent variable.

10. Let L be the operator defined as

$$Lu = Au_{xx} + Bu_{xy} + Cu_{yy} + Du_x + Eu_y + Fu,$$

where $A, B, \ldots, F$ are constants. Under the rotation of axes

$$x' = x \cos \theta + y \sin \theta, \qquad y' = -x \sin \theta + y \cos \theta,$$

this becomes

$$Lu = A'u_{x'x'} + B'u_{x'y'} + C'u_{y'y'} + D'u_{x'} + E'u_{y'} + F'u,$$

where $A', B', \ldots, F'$ depend on θ, in general. Show that $A' = A$, $B' = B$, $\ldots$, $F' = F$ for *all* values of θ if and only if L has the form $Lu = H \Delta u + Ku$, where $\Delta u = u_{xx} + u_{yy}$ is the Laplacian of u.

10.2   THE HEAT EQUATION

Consider a very thin slab, with thickness w, of a homogeneous isotropic solid material. Let the sides, S_1 and S_2, of the slab be kept at the temperatures T_1 and T_2, respectively. Consider a cylindrical portion of the slab, with area A (Fig. 10.1). It is found by experiment that the rate at which heat is conducted across this portion of the slab is (approximately)

$$-KA \frac{T_2 - T_1}{w}, \qquad (10.4)$$

where K is a positive constant, called the thermal conductivity. Its value depends on the material of the slab. If $T_1 > T_2$, heat is transferred in the direction from S_1 to S_2, and the quantity (10.4) is positive. If $T_1 < T_2$, heat is conducted in the opposite direction, from S_2 to S_1, and the quantity (10.4) is negative.

Let us now consider a cylindrical bar† of length a and cross-sectional area A. Let x denote the distance along the bar, as measured from one end (Fig. 10.2). We assume that the curved surface of the bar is insulated, and that the temperature is uniform over each cross section at any given time. We also assume that the temperatures in the bar are described by a function $u(x, t)$ of x and t, where t denotes time.

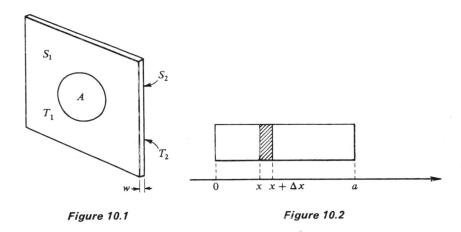

Figure 10.1   Figure 10.2

† Not necessarily with a circular cross section.

The rate at which heat is conducted across a thin section of the bar is approximately

$$-KA\,\frac{u(x + \Delta x,\, t) - u(x,\, t)}{\Delta x}\,,$$

according to formula (10.4). On passing to the limit, as $\Delta x \to 0$, we are led to the expression

$$-KAu_x(x,\, t) \tag{10.5}$$

for the rate at which heat is conducted across a cross section of the bar. Consequently, the net rate at which heat is absorbed by a section of width Δx is

$$KA[u_x(x + \Delta x,\, t) - u_x(x,\, t)]\,.$$

But the rate at which heat is absorbed by a thin section is also given by the expression

$$s\rho A u_t(x_1,\, t)\,\Delta x\,,$$

where the constant s is the specific heat of the material, ρ is the mass per unit volume, and x_1 is between x and $x + \Delta x$. Consequently we must have

$$s\rho A u_t(x_1,\, t)\,\Delta x = KA[u_x(x + \Delta x,\, t) - u_x(x,\, t)]\,.$$

Dividing through in this equation by $s\rho A\,\Delta x$ and then letting Δx approach zero, we obtain the equation

$$u_t(x,\, t) = ku_{xx}(x,\, t)\,,$$

where the constant

$$k = \frac{K}{s\rho}$$

is called the *thermal diffusivity* of the material. Thus the temperature function $u(x,\, t)$ is a solution of the partial differential equation

$$u_t = ku_{xx}\,, \tag{10.6}$$

which is called the one-dimensional *heat equation*.

In order to determine the temperature in the bar, we must solve the equation (10.6) subject to certain boundary conditions. If the temperatures at the ends of the bar are prescribed, we have boundary conditions of the form

$$u(0,\, t) = \phi(t)\,, \qquad u(a,\, t) = \psi(t)\,, \qquad t \geq 0\,,$$

where ϕ and ψ are given functions. If, instead, the ends of the bar are insulated, then the rate at which heat is conducted across the ends is zero, and we have, by formula (10.5),

$$u_x(0,\, t) = 0\,, \qquad u_x(c,\, t) = 0\,, \qquad t \geq 0\,.$$

A third possibility is that Newton's law of cooling applies at the ends of the bar. This law says that the rate per unit area at which heat is transferred across the boundary is proportional to the difference between the temperature of the boundary and that of the surrounding medium. Thus we have

$$- KAu_x(0, t) = c[T_0 - u(0, t)], \qquad - KAu_x(a, t) = c[u(a, t) - T_0], \qquad t \geq 0,$$

where c is a positive constant and T_0 is the temperature of the surrounding medium. In the special case where $T_0 = 0$, we may write

$$u_x(0, t) - hu(0, t) = 0, \qquad u_x(a, t) + hu(a, t) = 0, \qquad t \geq 0,$$

where $h = c/(KA)$. Actually an adjustment can always be made to reduce the problem to one with $T_0 = 0$. (See Exercise 4.) Finally, various combinations of the three types of conditions are possible. For example, one end of the bar might be insulated and the other kept at a prescribed temperature.

In any case, we must also know the initial temperature distribution along the bar. This knowledge corresponds to a boundary condition of the form

$$u(x, 0) = f(x), \qquad 0 \leq x \leq a,$$

where f is a given function.

In problems where the temperature depends on two rectangular space coordinates x and y, as well as on the time t, the temperature $u(x, y, t)$ is governed by the two-dimensional heat equation

$$u_t = k(u_{xx} + u_{yy}).$$

In three dimensions, the heat equation has the form

$$u_t = k(u_{xx} + u_{yy} + u_{zz}).$$

In two and three dimensions, the condition that a bounding surface S be insulated corresponds to the requirement that

$$\frac{\partial u}{\partial n} = 0$$

on S, where $\partial u/\partial n$ is the normal derivative of u, that is, the directional derivative of u in the direction normal to S. If Newton's law of cooling applies, the condition is

$$-\frac{\partial u}{\partial n} = h(u - T_0),$$

where T_0 is the temperature of the surrounding medium and $\partial u/\partial n$ is the rate of change of u in the direction of the outward normal to the surface of the solid.

Exercises for Section 10.2

1. One end of a bar 2 ft long, whose sides are insulated, is kept at the temperature $0°C$, while the other end is kept at $10°C$. If the initial temperature distribution is linear along the bar, write down the boundary value problem that governs the temperature in the bar.

2. The ends of a bar correspond to the points $x = 0$ and $x = 5$. The end at $x = 0$ is insulated and the end at $x = 5$ is kept at temperature $100°$. At time $t = 0$ the temperature at a general point x is $100 \cos(\pi x/10)$. Write down the boundary value problem for the temperature $u(x, t)$ in the bar.

3. If the temperature in a bar does not depend on time, then the temperature $u(x)$ at a point x satisfies the equation $u''(x) = 0$ for $0 < x < a$. Find $u(x)$ if:

    (a) the end at $x = 0$ is kept at constant temperature A and the end at $x = a$ is kept at constant temperature B.

    (b) The end at $x = 0$ is insulated and the temperature at $x = a$ is kept at constant temperature T.

    (c) Newton's law of cooling applies at both ends, and the temperature of the surrounding medium is T, a constant.

4. Let u be the solution of the heat equation $u_{xx} = ku_t$ for which $u(x, 0) = f(x)$ for $0 \le x \le a$ and

    $$u_x(0, t) + h[T_0 - u(0, t)] = 0, \qquad u_x(a, t) + h[u(a, t) - T_0] = 0$$

    for $t \ge 0$. Thus Newton's law of cooling is assumed to hold at the ends of the bar. If $v(x, t) = u(x, t) - T_0$, show that $v_{xx} = kv_t$, $v(x, 0) = f(x) - T_0$ for $0 \le x \le a$, and

    $$v_x(0, t) - hv(0, t) = 0, \qquad v_x(a, t) + hv(a, t) = 0$$

    for $t \ge 0$. Conversely, show that if v satisfies these conditions then $u = v + T_0$ is a solution of the original problem.

5. (a) Let each of the functions $u_1(x, t)$, $u_2(x, t)$, $\ldots$ be a solution of the equation $u_t = ku_{xx}$ in the region $0 < x < a$, $t > 0$, and let each of these functions satisfy the homogeneous boundary conditions

    $$\alpha u(0, t) + \beta u_x(0, t) = 0, \qquad \gamma u(a, t) + \delta u_x(a, t) = 0,$$

    where α, β, γ, δ are constants. If $C_1, C_2, \ldots$, are constants and N is a fixed positive integer, show that the function

    $$u(x, t) = \sum_{n=1}^{N} C_n u_n(x, t)$$

    also satisfies the differential equation and boundary conditions.

(b) Let the constants C_n be such that the infinite series

$$\sum_{n=1}^{\infty} C_n u_n(x, t)$$

converges, and can be differentiated term by term once with respect to t and twice with respect to x. Show that the function $u(x, t)$, to which the series converges, satisfies the heat equation and boundary conditions of part (a).

6. (a) Let us introduce new variables s and τ, where $s = x/a$ and $\tau = (k/a^2)t$. If $v(s, \tau) = u(as, a^2\tau/k)$, show that $v_\tau = v_{ss}$ if and only if $u_t = ku_{xx}$. (The quantities s and τ are *dimensionless*; that is, their values do not depend on the units of measurement used for length and time.)

(b) Find the boundary conditions for the function v of part (a) that correspond to the various conditions for u that were described in the text.

(c) Suppose that a bar, with initial uniform temperature zero, is immersed in a medium of constant uniform temperature T_0. If the center of a bar of length l attains the temperature $T_0/2$ in time t_0, how long does it take the center of a bar of length $2l$ (of the same material) to reach the temperature $T_0/2$? *Suggestion:* Look at the differential equation and boundary conditions for the function v of part (a) in the case $a = l$ and the case $a = 2l$.

7. Suppose that heat is being absorbed by a bar in such a way that the slice corresponding to the interval $[x, x + \Delta x]$ absorbs it at the rate $f(x', t) \Delta x$, where x' is between x and $x + \Delta x$. This heat is in addition to that which is being conducted across the faces of the slice. Show that the temperature function u satisfies the equation

$$u_t(x, t) = ku_{xx}(x, t) + hf(x, t),$$

where $h = (s\rho A)^{-1}$.

10.3   THE METHOD OF SEPARATION OF VARIABLES

Let us consider, as a special case of the problems described in the previous section, a bar of length a whose ends are kept at temperature zero, and whose initial temperature distribution is prescribed. This physical problem then corresponds to the boundary value problem

$$u_t(x, t) = ku_{xx}(x, t), \qquad 0 < x < a, \quad t > 0,$$
$$u(0, t) = 0, \qquad u(a, t) = 0, \qquad t \geq 0,$$
$$u(x, 0) = f(x), \qquad a \leq x \leq b,$$

where f is a given function. [This problem is quite special in that both ends of the bar are kept at temperature zero. However, the more general case where the conditions at the ends are

$$u(0, t) = A, \qquad u(a, t) = B, \qquad t \geq 0,$$

with A and B any constants, is easily reduced to the special case under consideration, as we shall see later on.] We must find a function u that is a solution of the heat equation in the region $\{(x, t): 0 < x < a, t > 0\}$ (Fig. 10.3) and that satisfies the boundary conditions.

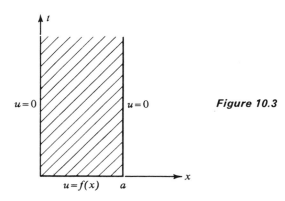

Figure 10.3

We begin our attack on the problem by attempting to find solutions of the heat equation that are of the special form

$$u(x, t) = X(x)T(t). \qquad (10.7)$$

We impose the requirements

$$X(0) = 0, \qquad X(a) = 0$$

in order that these "product solutions" will also satisfy the boundary conditions

$$u(0, t) = u(a, t) = 0, \qquad t \geq 0. \qquad (10.8)$$

If the heat equation has a solution of the form (10.7), then we must have

$$X(x)T'(t) = kX''(x)T(t),$$

or, upon dividing through by $kX(x)T(t)$,

$$\frac{X''(x)}{X(x)} = -\frac{T'(t)}{kT(t)}.$$

The left-hand side of this equation is independent of t while the right is independent of x. Therefore, both members must be equal to a constant, which we denote by $-\lambda$. Thus

$$\frac{X''(x)}{X(x)} = -\frac{T'(t)}{kT(t)} = -\lambda,$$

and so the functions X and T must be solutions of the ordinary differential equations

$$X'' + \lambda X = 0, \qquad T' + \lambda kT = 0,$$

respectively. Conversely, if X and T are solutions of the corresponding equations for the same value of λ, then the product $u(x, t) = X(x)T(t)$ is a solution of the heat equation because

$$\begin{aligned} u_t(x, t) - ku_{xx}(x, t) &= X(x)T'(t) - kX''(x)T(t) \\ &= X(x)[-\lambda kT(t)] - k[-\lambda X(x)]T(t) \\ &= 0. \end{aligned}$$

The requirements for X, namely

$$X'' + \lambda X = 0, \qquad \cdot X(0) = 0, \qquad X(a) = 0,$$

constitute an eigenvalue problem. Such problems were discussed in Chapter VI and this particular problem was presented as Example 1 of Section 6.1. The eigenvalues (the values of λ for which the problem has a nontrivial solution) are

$$\lambda_n = \left(\frac{n\pi}{a}\right)^2, \qquad n = 1, 2, 3, \ldots .$$

The corresponding eigenfunctions (nontrivial solutions) are

$$X_n(x) = \sin\frac{n\pi x}{a}, \qquad n = 1, 2, 3, \ldots .$$

For $\lambda = \lambda_n$ we have $T' + \lambda_n kT = 0$. A solution is

$$T_n(t) = \exp(-\lambda_n kt) = \exp\frac{-n^2\pi^2 kt}{a}.$$

Each of the product functions

$$u_n(x, t) = \exp\frac{-n^2\pi^2 kt}{a} \sin\frac{n\pi x}{a}, \qquad n = 1, 2, 3, \ldots,$$

is a solution of the heat equation and satisfies the boundary conditions (10.8).

If the constants C_n are such that the series

$$u(x, t) = \sum_{n=1}^{\infty} C_n u_n(x, t)$$

$$= \sum_{n=1}^{\infty} C_n \exp \frac{-n^2\pi^2 kt}{a} \sin \frac{n\pi x}{a} \qquad (10.9)$$

converges and can be differentiated termwise a sufficient number of times with respect to x and t, then this series also represents a solution of the differential equation that satisfies the homogeneous boundary conditions (10.8).

However, the constants C_n must be chosen, if possible, in such a way that the series (10.9) satisfies the nonhomogeneous boundary condition

$$u(x, 0) = f(x), \qquad 0 \le x \le a.$$

Thus we require that

$$u(x, 0) = \sum_{n=1}^{\infty} C_n \sin \frac{n\pi x}{a} = f(x), \qquad 0 \le x \le a.$$

But then C_n must be the nth coefficient in the Fourier sine series for f, that is,

$$C_n = \frac{2}{a} \int_0^a f(x) \sin \frac{n\pi x}{a} \, dx. \qquad (10.10)$$

Now let us suppose that f is continuous and piecewise smooth on $[0, a]$ and that $f(0) = f(a) = 0$. Then the series (10.9), with coefficients (10.10), converges to $f(x)$ when $t = 0$, according to the theory of Chapter VII. It can be shown that the series (10.9) converges and represents a continuous function for $0 \le x \le a$ and $t \ge 0$. It can also be shown that the series can be differentiated termwise any number of times with respect to x and t for $0 < x < a$ and $t > 0$. Consequently, the series (10.9) gives a solution of our boundary value problem. The proof that it is the only possible solution is outlined in Exercise 10. This exercise also shows that the boundary value problem we have been discussing is well posed.

Let us now consider the somewhat more general problem in which the ends of the bar are kept at constant temperatures A and B, not necessarily zero. The appropriate boundary value problem is

$$u_t(x, t) = ku_{xx}(x, t), \qquad 0 < x < a, \quad t > 0,$$
$$u(0, t) = A, \qquad u(a, t) = B, \qquad t \ge 0, \qquad (10.11)$$
$$u(x, 0) = f(x), \qquad 0 \le x \le a.$$

We shall show that by means of a change of dependent variable, this problem can be reduced to the previous one. To do this, we first determine a first-degree polynomial g,

$$g(x) = c_1 x + c_2,$$

such that $g(0) = A$ and $g(a) = B$. These conditions require that

$$g(0) = c_2 = A, \qquad g(a) = c_1 a + c_2 = B,$$

or $c_2 = A$ and $c_1 = (B - A)/a$. Consequently, the desired function is

$$g(x) = Ax + \frac{B - A}{a}.$$

Of course, $g''(x) = 0$ for all x.

Now suppose that u is a solution of the boundary value problem (10.11) and let v be defined by the equation

$$v(x, t) = u(x, t) - g(x). \qquad (10.12)$$

Then it is easy to verify that v is a solution of the boundary value problem

$$v_t(x, t) = k v_{xx}(x, t), \qquad 0 < x < a, \quad t > 0,$$
$$v(0, t) = 0, \qquad v(a, t) = 0, \quad t \geq 0, \qquad (10.13)$$
$$v(x, 0) = f(x) - g(x), \qquad 0 \leq x \leq a,$$

which is of the type discussed earlier. Conversely, if v is a solution of the problem (10.13), then the function u, where

$$u(x, t) = v(x, t) + g(x), \qquad (10.14)$$

is a solution of the original problem (10.11).

Exercises for Section 10.3

1. The ends of a cylindrical bar, at $x = 0$ and $x = a$, are kept at the temperature zero. Find an expression for the temperature $u(x, t)$ if the initial temperature distribution is

    (a) $u(x, 0) = 3 \sin \dfrac{\pi x}{a} - 5 \sin \dfrac{4\pi x}{a}$

    (b) $u(x, 0) = x^2 - ax$

    (c) $u(x, 0) = \begin{cases} x, & 0 \leq x \leq a/2 \\ a - x, & a/2 < x \leq a \end{cases}$

2. (a) Show that the function v, which is defined by Eq. (10.12), is a solution of the boundary value problem (10.13).

(b) If v is a solution of the problem (10.13), show that the function u, which is defined by Eq. (10.14), is a solution of the problem (10.11).

3. Find the temperature $u(x, t)$ in a bar with ends at $x = 0$ and $x = 1$, if the ends are kept at the indicated constant temperatures and if the initial temperature distribution is as given:

   (a) $u(0, t) = 1$, $u(1, t) = 0$, $u(x, 0) = 1 - x$
   (b) $u(0, t) = 1$, $u(1, t) = 0$, $u(x, 0) = 1 - x^2$
   (c) $u(0, t) = 0$, $u(1, t) = 2$, $u(x, 0) = 2x \cos 2\pi x$

4. A bar, with ends at $x = 0$ and $x = a$, with insulated ends, has an initial temperature distribution $u(x, 0) = f(x)$.

   (a) Write down the boundary value problem that corresponds to the physical problem.

   (b) Show that a solution of the problem is given (at least formally) by

   $$u(x, t) = \tfrac{1}{2}C_0 + \sum_{n=1}^{\infty} C_n \exp\left[-\left(n\frac{\pi}{a}\right)^2 kt\right] \cos\frac{n\pi x}{a},$$

   where

   $$C_n = \frac{2}{a} \int_0^a f(x) \cos\frac{n\pi x}{a}\, dx.$$

   (c) Find the temperature $u(x, t)$ in the special case when

   $$u(x, 0) = 2 \cos\frac{3\pi x}{a}.$$

5. A bar, of length 1, has its end at $x = 0$ insulated and its end at $x = 1$ is kept at temperature zero. Find an expression for the temperature $u(x, t)$, if

   $$u(x, 0) = \begin{cases} 1, & 0 \leq x \leq \tfrac{1}{2}, \\ 2(1 - x), & \tfrac{1}{2} < x \leq 1. \end{cases}$$

6. A bar of length 1, which has a uniform temperature of 100°C, is immersed in a medium that has the constant uniform temperature of 0°C. Assuming that the sides of the bar are insulated, and that Newton's law of cooling applies at the ends of the bar, find an expression for the temperature $u(x, t)$ in the bar.

7. Consider the boundary value problem

   $$u_t(x, t) = ku_{xx}(x, t) + F(x, t), \qquad 0 < x < a, \quad t > 0,$$
   $$u(0, t) = u(a, t) = 0, \qquad t \geq 0,$$
   $$u(x, 0) = 0, \qquad 0 \leq x \leq a,$$

where the nonhomogeneous term $F(x, t)$ can be expanded in a Fourier sine series in x for each fixed t; that is,

$$F(x, t) = \sum_{n=1}^{\infty} f_n(t) \sin \frac{n\pi x}{a}, \qquad 0 < x < a, \quad t > 0.$$

Show that the problem possesses a formal solution of the form

$$u(x, t) = \sum_{n=1}^{\infty} g_n(t) \sin \frac{n\pi x}{a}$$

and give a formula for the functions $g_n(t)$.

8. By using the result of Exercise 7, explain how the solution of the following problem can be found:

$$u_t(x, t) = k u_{xx}(x, t) + F(x, t), \qquad 0 < x < a, \quad t > 0,$$
$$u(0, t) = u(a, t) = 0, \qquad t \geq 0,$$
$$u(x, 0) = f(x), \qquad 0 \leq x \leq a.$$

9. Consider the general problem:

$$u_t(x, t) = k u_{xx}(x, t) + F(x, t), \qquad 0 < x < a, \quad t > 0,$$
$$u(0, t) = \phi(t), \qquad u(a, t) = \psi(t), \qquad t \geq 0,$$
$$u(x, 0) = f(x), \qquad 0 \leq x \leq a,$$

where F, f, ϕ, ψ are prescribed. Determine a function g, of the form

$$g(x, t) = A(t) + xB(t).$$

such that the change of variable

$$u(x, t) = v(x, t) + g(x, t)$$

leads to a boundary value problem for v of the type described in Exercise 8.

10. The purpose of this exercise is to show that the boundary value problem discussed in this section is well posed.

(a) Let $u(x, t)$ be continuous on the strip $0 \leq x \leq a$, $t \geq 0$, and be a solution of the heat equation for $0 < x < a$, $t > 0$. For an arbitrary, but fixed, positive number T, let D_T be the rectangle $0 \leq x \leq a, 0 \leq t \leq T$. Let C be the part of the boundary of D_T that falls along the lines $x = 0$, $x = a$, and $t = 0$. (The part of the boundary $t = T, 0 < x < a$, is excluded from C.) The first problem is to show that u attains its maximum, and minimum, values in D_T on C. Suppose that this is not the case, and that

u attains its maximum value M at a point (x_0, t_0) not on C. If m is the maximum value of u on C, then $m < M$. Define the function h as

$$h(x, t) = u(x, t) + \frac{M - m}{2T}(t_0 - t).$$

On C,

$$h(x, t) \le m + \frac{M - m}{2} = \frac{M + m}{2} < M,$$

while

$$h(x_0, t_0) = M.$$

Hence h attains its maximum on D_T at a point (x_1, t_1) not on C. Then $h_t(x_1, t_1) \ge 0$ and $h_{xx}(x_1, t_1) \le 0$. Since

$$u_{xx} = h_{xx},$$

we have

$$u_{xx}(x_1, t_1) \le 0,$$

and since

$$u_t = h_t + \frac{M - m}{2T},$$

we have

$$u_t(x_1, t_1) > 0.$$

But this is impossible, since u satisfies the heat equation for $0 < x < a$, $t > 0$. Hence, in D_T, u attains its maximum on C. Since $-u$ also attains its maximum on C, u attains its minimum on C.

(b) Show that there exists at most one solution of the heat equation in the strip $0 < x < a$, $t > 0$, which takes on prescribed values on the boundary of the strip. *Suggestion:* If u_1 and u_2 are both solutions, then the function $w = u_1 - u_2$ satisfies the heat equation in the strip, and is equal to zero on the boundary. Use the result of part (a).

(c) Let u and v be solutions of the heat equation in the strip $0 < x < a$, $t > 0$, and be continuous for $0 \le x \le a$, $t \ge 0$. If $|u - v| < \varepsilon$ on the boundary of the strip, show that $|u - v| < \varepsilon$ inside the strip. (This result shows that the solution of the boundary value problem is continuous with respect to the prescribed boundary values.) *Suggestion:* The function $w = u - v$ is a solution of the heat equation. Consider first a region of the type D_T, and use part (a) to show that $|u - v| < \varepsilon$ in D_T. Then use the fact that T is an arbitrary positive constant.

10.4 STEADY-STATE HEAT FLOW

When the temperature u in a solid is independent of time, it satisfies the equation

$$\Delta u \equiv u_{xx} + u_{yy} + u_{zz} = 0.$$

This equation is known as *Laplace's equation* in three dimensions. In case u depends only on two rectangular coordinates x and y, it satisfies Laplace's equation in two dimensions,

$$\Delta u \equiv u_{xx} + u_{yy} = 0.$$

A function that satisfies Laplace's equation in a region R and in addition is continuous along with its first- and second-order derivatives in R is said to be *harmonic* in R.

As an example, let us attempt to find the steady-state temperatures $u(x, y)$ in the rectangular slab $0 \le x \le a, 0 \le y \le b, |z| \le h$ whose edge temperatures are prescribed as in Fig. 10.4. We assume that the faces $z = \pm h$ are insulated,

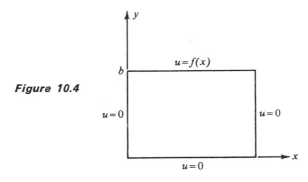

Figure 10.4

so that u depends only on x and y, and not on z. The boundary value problem that we must solve is

$$u_{xx}(x, y) + u_{yy}(x, y) = 0, \qquad 0 < x < a, \quad 0 < y < b,$$
$$u(0, y) = 0, \qquad u(a, y) = 0, \qquad 0 \le y \le b, \qquad (10.15)$$
$$u(x, 0) = 0, \qquad u(x, b) = f(x), \qquad 0 \le x \le a.$$

If the differential equation has a product solution of the form $u(x, y) = X(x)Y(y)$, then

$$X''(x)Y(y) + X(x)Y''(y) = 0$$

or

$$\frac{X''(x)}{X(x)} = -\frac{Y''(y)}{Y(y)} = -\lambda,$$

where λ is a constant. Thus X and Y must satisfy the ordinary differential equations

$$X'' + \lambda X = 0, \qquad Y'' - \lambda Y = 0.$$

In order to satisfy the homogeneous boundary conditions

$$u(0, y) = 0, \qquad u(a, y) = 0, \qquad u(x, 0) = 0,$$

we shall require that

$$X(0) = X(a) = 0, \qquad Y(0) = 0.$$

If X is not to be the zero function, λ must have one of the values

$$\lambda_n = \left(\frac{n\pi}{a}\right)^2, \qquad n = 1, 2, 3, \dots .$$

Then a corresponding nontrivial solution of the equation for X is

$$X_n(x) = \sin\frac{n\pi x}{a}.$$

The general solution of the equation for Y may be written as

$$Y_n(y) = c_1 \cosh\frac{n\pi y}{a} + c_2 \sinh\frac{n\pi y}{a}.$$

The condition $Y(0) = 0$ requires that $c_1 = 0$. Choosing $c_2 = 1$ we have

$$Y_n(y) = \sinh\frac{n\pi y}{a}.$$

Thus each of the functions

$$u_n(x, y) = \sin\frac{n\pi x}{a}\sinh\frac{n\pi y}{a}, \qquad n = 1, 2, 3, \dots$$

is a solution of the differential equation and satisfies each of the three homogeneous boundary conditions. Superimposing, we arrive at the series

$$u(x, y) = \sum_{n=1}^{\infty} C_n \sin\frac{n\pi x}{a}\sinh\frac{n\pi y}{a}, \tag{10.16}$$

where the constants C_n are to be chosen, if possible, so that the nonhomogeneous boundary condition is satisfied. We require that

$$u(x, b) = \sum_{n=1}^{\infty} C_n \sinh\frac{n\pi b}{a}\sin\frac{n\pi x}{a} = f(x).$$

Therefore the constants C_n must be chosen according to the formula

$$C_n = \frac{2}{a \sinh (n\pi b/a)} \int_0^a f(x) \sin \frac{n\pi x}{a} \, dx. \qquad (10.17)$$

If f is continuous and piecewise smooth on $[0, a]$, with $f(0) = f(a) = 0$, it can be shown that the series (10.16), with coefficients (10.17), represents a solution of the boundary value problem. It is, in fact, the only solution. A proof that the problem is well posed is outlined in Exercise 8.

The problem of finding a function that is harmonic in a region R and that takes on specified values on the boundary of R is known as the *Dirichlet problem*. It has a large literature. The example of this section is a special case in which the region R is a rectangle.

Exercises for Section 10.4

1. Calculate the solution of the problem (10.15) in the case where $f(x) = x(a - x)$.

2. Consider a rectangular slab, as in Fig. 10.4, but with the prescribed edge temperatures $u(0, y) = 0$, $u(a, y) = 0$, $u(b, x) = 0$, $u(0, x) = g(x)$. Express the solution of the boundary value problem as an infinite series.

3. (a) Consider a rectangular slab, as in Fig. 10.4, with prescribed edge temperatures $u(0, y) = 0$, $u(a, y) = 0$, $u(x, 0) = f(x)$, $u(x, b) = g(x)$. Show that the solution of the boundary value problem can be obtained by superimposing the solutions of two other problems, each of which has three homogeneous boundary conditions.

   (b) Calculate the solution of the problem in part (a) in the case where $f(x) = g(x) = x(a - x)$.

4. Find the temperatures $u(x, y)$ in a rectangular slab if the edges $x = 0$, $x = a$, and $y = 0$ are insulated, and $u(x, b) = f(x)$.

5. Find the temperatures $u(x, y)$ in a rectangular slab if the edges $x = 0$ and $x = a$ are kept at temperature zero, Newton's law of cooling applies at the edge $y = 0$, and $u(x, b) = f(x)$ for $0 \le x \le a$. Assume that the external temperature is zero.

6. Find the temperatures $u(x, y)$ in a rectangular slab if Newton's law of cooling applies at the ends $x = 0$ and $x = a$, the edge $y = 0$ is insulated, and $u(x, b) = f(x)$ for $0 \le x \le a$. Assume that the external temperature is zero.

7. Find a function u that is harmonic in the semi-infinite strip $0 < x < a$, $y > 0$, and that satisfies the conditions $u(0, y) = u(a, y) = 0$ for $y \geq 0$, $u(x, 0) = f(x)$ for $0 \leq x \leq a$, and $|u(x, y)| \leq M$ for $0 < x < a$, $y > 0$, for some constant M.

8. The purpose of this exercise is to show that the Dirichlet problem for a rectangle is well posed. In particular, the problem (10.15) is well posed.

    (a) Let u be harmonic in the rectangle $D = \{(x, y): 0 < x < a, 0 < y < b\}$ and be continuous on the rectangle $\bar{D} = \{(x, y): 0 \leq x \leq a, 0 \leq y \leq b\}$. Let C denote the boundary of $\bar{D}$. We first wish to show that u attains its maximum, and its minimum, on $\bar{D}$ at a point of C. Suppose that this is not the case. Then u attains its maximum value M at a point (x_0, y_0) in D. If m is the maximum value of u on C, then $m < M$. Define the function h as

    $$h(x, y) = u(x, y) + \frac{M - m}{2(a^2 + b^2)} [(x - x_0)^2 + (y - y_0)^2].$$

    Then $h(x_0, y_0) = M$, and on the boundary C, $h \leq m + (M - m)/2 = (M + m)/2 < M$. Hence h attains its maximum on $\bar{D}$ at a point (x_1, y_1) in D. At the point (x_1, y_1) we must have $h_{xx} \leq 0$ and $h_{yy} \leq 0$. But

    $$h_{xx} + h_{yy} = u_{xx} + u_{yy} + \frac{M - m}{a^2 + b^2} = \frac{M - m}{a^2 + b^2} > 0,$$

    which is a contradiction. Hence u attains its maximum on $\bar{D}$ at a point of C. Since $-u$ also attains its maximum value on C, u attains its minimum value on C.

    (b) Show that the Dirichlet problem has at most one solution. *Suggestion:* Suppose that u_1 and u_2 are both solutions, and let $w = u_1 - u_2$. Then w satisfies Laplace's equation in D and $w = 0$ on C. Use the result of part (a).

    (c) We wish to show that the solution of the Dirichlet problem depends continuously on the boundary values. Let u and v be solutions of Laplace's equation on D and continuous on $\bar{D}$. If $|u - v| < \varepsilon$ on C, show that $|u - v| < \varepsilon$ on D.

10.5   THE VIBRATING STRING

Consider an elastic string that is stretched between the points $x = 0$ and $x = a$ along the x axis. In its equilibrium position, the string simply lies along the x axis between the two points. (The effect of gravity will be ignored in this discussion. Its effect is considered in Exercise 1.) When set vibrating in a plane, its appearance at a particular time t is as in Fig. 10.5.

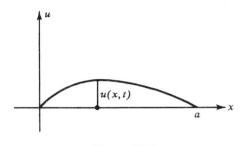

Figure 10.5

We shall assume that each point on the string moves along a line perpendicular to the x axis, and we therefore denote by $u(x, t)$ the displacement from the equilibrium position. In order to obtain the differential equation of motion of the string, we consider the forces exerted on a small portion of the string (Fig. 10.6). We assume that the string is perfectly flexible, so that the force T,

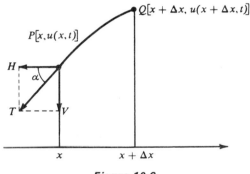

Figure 10.6

which is exerted at the point P by the part of the string to the left of P, acts in a direction tangential to the string.

The horizontal component H and the vertical component V of the tangential force T are (since $\tan \alpha = u_x$)

$$H(x, t) = T(x, t) \cos \alpha = \frac{1}{\sqrt{1 + u_x^2}} T \qquad (10.18)$$

and

$$V(x, t) = T(x, t) \sin \alpha = \frac{u_x}{\sqrt{1 + u_x^2}} \qquad (10.19)$$

Let ρ denote the uniform mass per unit length of the string when it is in its equilibrium position. Then $\rho \, \Delta x$ is still the mass of that part of the string between P and Q in Fig. 10.6. By considering the horizontal and vertical forces acting on the piece of string, we have

$$H(x + \Delta x, t) - H(x, t) = 0,$$

$$\rho \, \Delta x u_{tt}(x_1, t) = V(x + \Delta x, t) - V(x, t),$$

where x_1 is between x and $x + \Delta x$. (The second equation here corresponds to the assumption that Newton's second law of motion applies to a continuous medium.) Dividing through by Δx in both equations, and then letting Δx approach zero, we arrive at the equations

$$H_x(x, t) = 0, \qquad\qquad (10.20)$$

$$u_{tt}(x, t) = V_x(x, t). \qquad\qquad (10.21)$$

From Eqs. (10.20) and (10.18), we have

$$\frac{T}{\sqrt{1 + u_x^2}} = T_0,$$

where T_0 depends only on t, and not on x. From Eq. (10.19) we have

$$V = T_0 u_x.$$

Consequently, from Eq. (10.21), we have

$$u_{tt}(x, t) = \frac{T_0}{\rho} u_{xx}(x, t).$$

We shall now make the additional simplifying assumption that T_0 is a constant. (This approximation is justified, in particular, when T is nearly constant and uniform, and when the slope u_x is always small in magnitude, compared with unity.) We may choose for T_0 the value of the tension T when the string is at rest in its equilibrium position.

The partial differential equation

$$u_{tt} = c^2 u_{xx},$$

where

$$c^2 = \frac{T_0}{\rho},$$

is called the one-dimensional *wave equation*. In order to describe the motion of the string, we must solve this equation, subject to various boundary conditions. Since the ends of the string are fixed, we have

$$u(0, t) = 0, \qquad u(a, t) = 0, \qquad t \geq 0.$$

We must also know the initial position and velocity of the string. This information corresponds to boundary conditions of the form

$$u(x, 0) = f(x), \qquad u_t(x, 0) = g(x), \qquad 0 \le x \le a,$$

where f and g are given functions.

In passing, we mention that the equation

$$u_{tt} = c^2(u_{xx} + u_{yy}), \qquad u = u(x, y, t),$$

is known as the two-dimensional wave equation, while in three dimensions, the wave equation has the form

$$u_{tt} = c^2(u_{xx} + u_{yy} + u_{zz}), \qquad u = u(x, y, z, t).$$

Exercises for Section 10.5

1. (a) Show that when the effect of gravity on the vibrating string is taken into account, the differential equation of motion becomes $u_{tt} = c^2 u_{xx} - g$, where g is the gravitational constant.

   (b) Determine a quadratic function h such that $h(0) = h(a) = 0$ and $h''(x) = g$ for all x. Then show that the change of variable $v(x, t) = u(x, t) + h(x)$, where u is as in part (a), leads to a boundary value problem for v of the type considered in the text.

2. Suppose that the elastic string vibrates in a medium that damps the motion. Assume that the medium exerts a force on the string at each point in the vertical direction and with magnitude proportional to that of the velocity. Derive the equation of motion for the vertical displacement u.

3. (a) Show that the wave equation $u_{tt} = c^2 u_{xx}$ can, by means of the change of independent variables $r = x - ct$, $s = x + ct$, be put in the form $v_{rs} = 0$, where $v(r, s) = u(x, t)$.

   (b) By using the result of part (a), show that every solution of the wave equation is of the form

   $$u(x, t) = f(x - ct) + g(x + ct),$$

   where f and g possess continuous second derivatives.

4. (a) Verify directly, by differentiation, that a function u, of either of the forms

   $$u(x, t) = f(x - ct), \qquad u(x, t) = g(x + ct),$$

   where f and g possess continuous second derivatives, is a solution of the wave equation.

(b) Show that a solution of the form $u(x, t) = f(x - ct)$ represents a wave that travels with speed c in the positive x direction. Show that a solution of the form $u(x, t) = g(x + ct)$ represents a wave that travels with speed c in the negative x direction.

5. Consider the boundary value problem

$$u_{tt}(x, t) = c^2 u_{xx}(x, t), \qquad \text{all } x \text{ and } t > 0,$$
$$u(x, 0) = f(x), \qquad u_t(x, t) = g(x), \qquad \text{all } x,$$

where f has a continuous second derivative and g a continuous first derivative everywhere. Using the result of Exercise 3 (or 4), derive the expression

$$u(x, t) = \frac{1}{2}[f(x - ct) + f(x + ct)] + \frac{1}{2c} \int_{x-ct}^{x+ct} g(s)\, ds$$

for the solution of the problem. This is known as *d'Alembert's solution* of the wave equation.

6. Describe a physical problem for the vibrating elastic string for which the boundary conditions $u_x(0, t) = u_x(a, t) = 0$ for $t \geq 0$ apply instead of the conditions $u(0, t) = u(a, t) = 0$ for $t \geq 0$. *Suggestion:* If $u_x(x_0, t) = 0$ then $V(x_0, t) = 0$.

7. Show that the boundary value problem

$$u_{tt}(x, t) - u_{xx}(x, t) = 0, \qquad 0 < x < a, \quad 0 < t < a,$$
$$u(0, t) = u(a, t) = 0, \qquad 0 \leq t \leq a,$$
$$u(x, 0) = 0, \qquad u(x, a) = h(x), \qquad 0 \leq x \leq a,$$

has no solution unless h is identically zero. *Suggestion:* Use the result of Exercise 3.

8. Consider a perfectly flexible elastic string that vibrates in a plane, but do not assume that each "particle" of the string moves along a line perpendicular to a coordinate axis. Let $\xi = x$, $\eta = 0$ denote the coordinates of a particle when the string is at rest in its equilibrium position. At time t, the coordinates of this same particle will be $\xi = x + u(x, t)$, $\eta = v(x, t)$, where $u(x, t)$ and $v(x, t)$ are the horizontal and vertical displacements, respectively (Fig. 10.7). By considering the forces acting on a small piece of the string, show that

$$\rho u_{tt} = \frac{\partial}{\partial x}\left\{ T \frac{1 + u_x}{[(1 + u_x)^2 + v_x^2]^{1/2}} \right\}, \qquad \rho v_{tt} = \frac{\partial}{\partial x}\left\{ T \frac{v_x}{[(1 + u_x)^2 + v_x^2]^{1/2}} \right\},$$

where ρ is the density and $T(x, t)$ is the tension in the string.

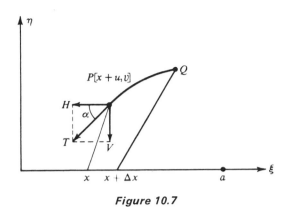

Figure 10.7

10.6   THE SOLUTION OF THE PROBLEM OF THE VIBRATING STRING

In order to determine the motion of the vibrating string, we must find a solution of the partial differential equation

$$u_{tt}(x, t) = c^2 u_{xx}(x, t), \qquad 0 < x < a, \quad t > 0, \tag{10.22}$$

that satisfies the boundary conditions

$$u(0, t) = 0, \qquad u(a, t) = 0, \qquad t \geq 0, \tag{10.23}$$

$$u(x, 0) = f(x), \qquad u_t(x, 0) = g(x), \qquad 0 \leq x \leq a. \tag{10.24}$$

Using the method of separation of variables, we seek solutions of the wave equation (10.22) that are of the form $u(x, t) = X(x)T(t)$. We find that

$$X(x)T''(t) = c^2 X''(x)T(t)$$

or

$$\frac{X''(x)}{X(x)} = \frac{T''(t)}{c^2 T(t)} = -\lambda,$$

where λ is a constant. Then X and T must satisfy the equations

$$X'' + \lambda X = 0, \qquad T'' + \lambda c^2 T = 0,$$

respectively. We shall also require that

$$X(0) = 0, \qquad X(a) = 0$$

in order that the product solutions satisfy the homogeneous boundary conditions (10.23).

By reasoning that should now be familiar to the reader, we find the values

$$\lambda_n = \left(\frac{n\pi}{a}\right)^2, \qquad n = 1, 2, 3, \ldots,$$

for τ, and the corresponding product solutions

$$u_n(x, t) = \left(A_n \cos\frac{n\pi ct}{a} + B_n \sin\frac{n\pi ct}{a}\right) \sin\frac{n\pi x}{a},$$

where A_n and B_n are constants that as yet are arbitrary. Superimposing, we obtain the formal series solution

$$u(x, t) = \sum_{n=1}^{\infty}\left(A_n \cos\frac{n\pi ct}{a} + B_n \sin\frac{n\pi ct}{a}\right) \sin\frac{n\pi x}{a}, \qquad (10.25)$$

which satisfies the homogeneous boundary conditions (10.23). We now attempt to choose the constants A_n and B_n in such a way that the nonhomogeneous boundary conditions (10.24) are satisfied. These boundary conditions yield the requirements

$$u(x, 0) = \sum_{n=1}^{\infty} A_n \sin\frac{n\pi x}{a} = f(x)$$

and

$$u_t(x, 0) = \sum_{n=1}^{\infty} \frac{n\pi c}{a} B_n \sin\frac{n\pi x}{a} = g(x).$$

We therefore choose the constants A_n and B_n according to the formulas

$$A_n = \frac{2}{a}\int_0^a f(x) \sin\frac{n\pi x}{a}\, dx, \qquad B_n = \frac{2}{a}\frac{a}{n\pi c}\int_0^a g(x) \sin\frac{n\pi x}{a}\, dx. \quad (10.26)$$

We shall now show that if f and g satisfy certain conditions, the series (10.25) with coefficients (10.26) converges to a function that is a solution of the boundary value problem. Specifically, we shall require that f'' and g' be continuous on $[0, a]$ and that

$$f(0) = f(a) = 0, \qquad f''(0) = f''(a) = 0,$$
$$g(0) = g(a) = 0.$$

By the use of the trigonometric identities

$$2 \cos\alpha \sin\beta = \sin(\beta - \alpha) + \sin(\beta + \alpha),$$
$$2 \sin\alpha \sin\beta = \cos(\beta - \alpha) - \cos(\beta + \alpha),$$

we can write the series (10.25) in the form

$$u(x, t) = \sum_{n=1}^{\infty} \left\{ \frac{1}{2} A_n \left[\sin \frac{n\pi}{a} (x - ct) + \sin \frac{n\pi}{a} (x + ct) \right] \right.$$

$$\left. + \frac{1}{2} B_n \left[\cos \frac{n\pi}{a} (x - ct) - \cos \frac{n\pi}{a} (x + ct) \right] \right\}. \quad (10.27)$$

We now define a function F in the following way. We set $F(r) = f(r)$ for $0 \le r \le a$, and require that F be odd and periodic with period $2a$. The restrictions imposed earlier on f insure that F, F', and F'' will be continuous everywhere (Exercise 3). The function F is represented by its Fourier sine series everywhere. The coefficients, b_n, in this series are

$$b_n = \frac{2}{a} \int_0^a F(r) \sin \frac{n\pi r}{a} \, dr = \frac{2}{a} \int_0^a f(r) \sin \frac{n\pi r}{a} \, dr = A_n,$$

where A_n is as in formula (10.26). Hence the first group of terms in the series (10.27) converges, for all x and t, to the quantity

$$\tfrac{1}{2}[F(x - ct) + F(x + ct)].$$

Next, we define a function G as follows. We set

$$G(s) = \int_0^s g(x) \, dx$$

for $0 \le s \le a$, and we require that G be even and periodic with period $2a$. The restrictions that we placed on g ensure that G, G', and G'' will be continuous everywhere (Exercise 4). The function G is represented by its Fourier cosine series everywhere. The coefficients a_n in this series are

$$a_n = \frac{2}{a} \int_0^a G(s) \cos \frac{n\pi s}{a} \, ds = \frac{2}{a} \left[\frac{a}{n\pi} G(s) \sin \frac{n\pi s}{a} \right]_0^a - \frac{2}{a} \frac{a}{n\pi} \int_0^a g(s) \sin \frac{n\pi s}{a} \, ds.$$

Here we have used integration by parts, and the fact that $G'(s) = g(s)$. Since the integrated part vanishes, we have

$$a_n = -cB_n.$$

Hence the second group of terms in the series (10.27) converges to

$$\frac{1}{2c} [G(x + ct) - G(x - ct)].$$

(The constant terms in the two cosine series cancel out.)
    Combining these results, we have

$$u(x, t) = \frac{1}{2} [F(x + ct) + F(x - ct)] + \frac{1}{2c} [G(x + ct) - G(x - ct)]. \quad (10.28)$$

This function possesses continuous second order partial derivatives for all x and t, since F'' and G'' are continuous everywhere. This function is also a solution of the wave equation (10.22), as can be verified directly. (See also Exercise 4, Section 10.5.) That $u(x, t)$ satisfies the boundary conditions (10.23) and (10.24) is contained in the derivation of the formula (10.28). [This can also be verified directly from formula (10.28). See Exercise 5.]

We have shown that a solution of the boundary value problem for the vibrating string exists. For a discussion of the uniqueness of this solution, and its continuous dependence on the prescribed boundary data, the reader is referred to Exercises 12 and 13.

If f and g do not satisfy the prescribed conditions at 0 and a, the functions F'' and G'' will have discontinuities at the points $m\pi/a$, where m is an integer. In this case, the second partial derivatives of the function (10.28) will be discontinuous along the lines $x + ct = m\pi/a$ and $x - ct = m\pi/a$ in the xt plane. The boundary value problem then has no solution, strictly speaking. However, the function (10.28) is called a *generalized solution* of the problem. For an interpretation of such solutions, the reader is referred to the more advanced works of Sagan [5] and Tolstov [6].

Exercises for Section 10.6

1. Show that the derivative of an odd function is even and that the derivative of an even function is odd.

2. (a) If F is an odd function that is continuous at zero, show that $F(0) = 0$.

    (b) Let F be an odd, periodic function, with period $2a$. If F is continuous everywhere, show that $F(ma) = 0$ whenever m is an integer.

3. Let f be defined and continuous on $[0, a]$. Let F be defined as $F(x) = f(x)$ for $0 < x < a$, $F(0) = F(a) = 0$, and elsewhere so as to be odd and periodic with period $2a$. We call F the odd periodic extension of f.

    (a) Show that F is continuous everywhere if $f(0) = f(a) = 0$.

    (b) If $f(0) = f(a) = 0$ and if f' exists and is continuous on $[0, a]$, show that F' exists and is continuous everywhere.

    (c) If $f(0) = f(a) = f''(0) = f''(a) = 0$ and if f'' exists and is continuous on $[0, a]$, show that F'' exists and is continuous everywhere.

4. Let h be defined and continuous on $[0, a]$. Let H be defined as $H(x) = h(x)$ for $0 \le x \le a$, $H(x) = h(-x)$ for $-a < x < 0$, and elsewhere so as to be periodic with period $2a$. We call H the even periodic extension of h.

    (a) Show that H is continuous everywhere.

(b) If h' exists and is continuous on $[0, a]$ and if $h'(0) = h'(a) = 0$, show that H' exists and is continuous everywhere.

(c) If h'' exists and is continuous on $[0, a]$, and if $h'(0) = h'(a) = 0$, show that H'' exists and is continuous everywhere.

5. Verify that the function (10.28) satisfies the boundary conditions (10.23) and (10.24).

6. If the initial displacement and velocity of the vibrating string are

$$u(x, 0) = \sin \frac{\pi x}{a}, \qquad u_t(x, 0) = 0, \qquad 0 \le x \le a,$$

find a formula for the displacement $u(x, t)$.

7. Work Exercise 6 for the case

$$u(x, 0) = \sin \frac{\pi x}{a}, \qquad u_t(x, 0) = \sin \frac{2\pi x}{a}, \qquad 0 \le x \le a.$$

8. Show that for each fixed x the displacement $u(x, t)$ of the vibrating string is periodic in time t, and find the period. Describe the effects of changes in the tension and the density on the period of vibration.

9. Consider the boundary value problem

$$u_{tt}(x, t) = c^2 u_{xx}(x, t), \qquad 0 < x < a, \quad t > 0,$$

$$u_x(0, t) = u_x(a, t) = 0, \qquad t \ge 0,$$

$$u(x, 0) = f(x), \qquad u_t(x, 0) = g(x), \qquad 0 \le x \le a,$$

where f'' and g' are continuous on $[0, a]$, with $f'(0) = f'(a) = 0$ and $g(0) = g(a) = B_0$, with $B_0 = (1/a) \int_0^a g(x)\, dx$. Use the method of separation of variables to show that

$$u(x, t) = \frac{1}{2} [F(x + ct) + F(x - ct)] + \frac{1}{2c} [G(x + ct) - G(x - ct)] + B_0 t,$$

where F is the even periodic extension of f and G is defined as

$$G(s) = \int_0^s [g(x) - B_0]\, dx$$

for $0 \le s \le a$ and elsewhere so as to be odd and periodic with period $2a$.

10.   Consider the boundary value problem

$$u_{tt} = c^2 u_{xx} + F(x, t), \qquad 0 < x < a, \quad t > 0,$$

$$u(0, t) = u(a, t) = 0, \qquad t \geq 0,$$

$$u(x, 0) = u_t(x, 0) = 0, \qquad 0 \leq x \leq a,$$

where

$$F(x, t) = \sum_{n=1}^{\infty} f_n(t) \sin \frac{n \pi x}{a}.$$

Show that this problem possesses a solution of the form

$$u(x, t) = \sum_{n=1}^{\infty} T_n(t) \sin \frac{n \pi x}{a}.$$

11.   Give a discussion of the problem

$$u_{tt} = c^2 u_{xx} + F(x, t), \qquad 0 < x < a, \quad t > 0,$$

$$u(0, t) = \phi(t), \qquad u(a, t) = \psi(t), \quad t \geq 0,$$

$$u(x, 0) = f(x), \qquad u_t(x, 0) = g(x), \quad 0 \leq x \leq a,$$

along the lines of Exercise 9, Section 10.3.

12.   This exercise deals with the uniqueness of the solution of the boundary value problem (10.22)–(10.24). Suppose that u_1 and u_2 are continuous, along with their first- and second-order partial derivatives in the region $\bar{D}: 0 \leq x \leq a, \ t \geq 0$, and satisfy the wave equation $u_{tt} = c^2 u_{xx}$ in the region $D: 0 < x < a, \ t > 0$. If $u_1 = u_2$ on the boundary of D, and if $(u_1)_t = (u_2)_t$ on the line segment $0 \leq x \leq a, \ t = 0$, we wish to show that $u_1 = u_2$ in D. Let $w = u_1 - u_2$. Then $w = 0$ on the boundary of D, $w_t = w_x = w_{xt} = w_{xx} = 0$ on the segment $0 \leq x \leq a, \ t = 0$, and $w_t = w_{tt} = w_{xt} = 0$ on the says $x = 0, \ a, \ t \geq 0$. Define the function h as

$$h(t) = \int_0^a [(w_t)^2 + c^2 (w_x)^2] \, dx, \qquad t \geq 0.$$

Show that $h(0) = 0$ and $h'(t) = 0$, and hence that $h(t) = 0$ for $t \geq 0$. Deduce from this that $w_t = w_x = 0$ in D, and hence that $w = u_1 - u_2 = 0$ in D.

13.   Deduce, from the formula (10.28), that the solution of the problem (10.22)–(10.24) depends continuously on the prescribed values $u(x, 0) = f(x), u_t(x, 0) = g(x)$ at $t = 0$.

10.7 THE LAPLACIAN IN OTHER COORDINATE SYSTEMS

Our aim in this section is to obtain expressions for the Laplacian Δu of a function u in some coordinate systems that are not rectangular. Specifically, we shall consider cylindrical and spherical coordinates.

Cylindrical coordinates r, θ, z, may be defined by means of the equations

$$x = r \cos \theta,$$
$$y = r \sin \theta, \qquad (10.29)$$
$$z = z,$$

where $r > 0$, and $-\pi < \theta \le \pi$. The coordinates r, θ, z have the simple geometrical interpretations shown in Fig. 10.8. Let us consider a fixed point

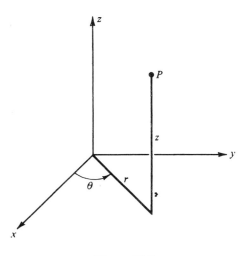

Figure 10.8

P_0, with coordinates r_0, θ_0, z_0. Then each of the equations $r = r_0$, $\theta = \theta_0$, $z = z_0$ describes a surface that passes through the point P_0. These surfaces are, respectively, a cylinder of radius r_0, a half-plane which makes an angle θ_0 with the xz plane, and a horizontal plane which lies a distance $|z_0|$ from the xy plane.

In physical problems that involve a cylindrical surface (for example, the problem of finding the temperature in a cylindrical solid) it is natural to use cylindrical coordinates. For then the equation of the boundary has the simple form $r = $ constant. The relevant partial differential equation, however, becomes more complicated in appearance, as we shall see.

In order to determine the form assumed by Δu in cylindrical coordinates, we must express the partial derivatives of u with respect to x and y in terms of partial derivatives with respect to r and θ. By using the chain rule for partial derivatives we see that

$$u_x = u_r r_x + u_\theta \theta_x, \qquad u_y = u_r r_y + u_\theta \theta_y. \qquad (10.30)$$

The partials of r and θ with respect to x and y can be found from the relations (10.29) by the use of implicit differentiation. By differentiating through in these relations, first with respect to x and then with respect to y, we find that

$$1 = r_x \cos\theta - r\theta_x \sin\theta, \qquad 0 = r_y \cos\theta - r\theta_y \sin\theta,$$
$$0 = r_x \sin\theta + r\theta_x \cos\theta, \qquad 1 = r_y \sin\theta + r\theta_y \cos\theta.$$

Upon solving the first pair of equations algebraically for r_x and θ_x, and the second pair for r_y and θ_y, we obtain the formulas

$$r_x = \cos\theta, \qquad r_y = \sin\theta,$$
$$\theta_x = -\frac{\sin\theta}{r}, \qquad \theta_y = \frac{\cos\theta}{r}.$$

Substituting these expressions into the formulas (10.30), we find that

$$u_x = u_r \cos\theta - u_\theta \frac{\sin\theta}{r}, \qquad u_y = u_r \sin\theta + u_\theta \frac{\cos\theta}{r}.$$

For the second-order derivative u_{xx}, we have, by the chain rule again,

$$u_{xx} = \frac{\partial}{\partial r}\left(u_r \cos\theta - u_\theta \frac{\sin\theta}{r}\right)r_x + \frac{\partial}{\partial\theta}\left(u_r \cos\theta - u_\theta \frac{\sin\theta}{r}\right)\theta_x$$

$$= u_{rr}\cos^2\theta - 2u_{r\theta}\frac{\sin\theta\cos\theta}{r} + u_{\theta\theta}\frac{\sin^2\theta}{r^2} + u_r\frac{\sin^2\theta}{r^2} + 2u_\theta\frac{\sin\theta\cos\theta}{r^2}.$$

In similar fashion, we find that

$$u_{yy} = u_{rr}\sin^2\theta + 2u_{r\theta}\frac{\sin\theta\cos\theta}{r} + u_{\theta\theta}\frac{\cos^2\theta}{r^2} + u_r\frac{\cos^2\theta}{r} - 2u_\theta\frac{\sin\theta\cos\theta}{r^2}.$$

From these formulas we have finally

$$\Delta u = u_{rr} + \frac{1}{r}u_r + \frac{1}{r^2}u_{\theta\theta} + u_{zz}$$

$$= \frac{1}{r}(ru_r)_r + \frac{1}{r^2}u_{\theta\theta} + u_{zz}. \qquad (10.31)$$

Spherical coordinates ρ, ϕ, θ may be defined by means of the equations

$$x = \rho \sin \phi \cos \theta,$$
$$y = \rho \sin \phi \sin \theta, \qquad (10.32)$$
$$z = \rho \cos \phi,$$

where $\rho > 0$, $0 \leq \phi \leq \pi$, and $-\pi < \theta < 2\pi$. The geometrical interpretations of the coordinates ρ, ϕ, θ are shown in Figure 10.9. Through a fixed point P_0,

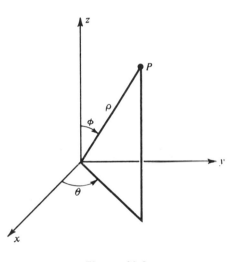

Figure 10.9

with coordinates ρ_0, ϕ_0, θ_0, there pass the three surfaces $\rho = \rho_0$, $\phi = \phi_0$, $\theta = \theta_0$. These surfaces are, respectively, a sphere of radius ρ_0, a half-cone of angle $2\phi_0$, and a half-plane. It is perhaps needless to say that spherical coordinates are convenient for problems which involve a spherical surface.

The expression for the Laplacian of a function in spherical coordinates can be derived in much the same manner as was done for cylindrical coordinates, although the algebra is a bit more complicated. We shall omit the details here, and shall state only the final result, which is

$$\Delta u = u_{\rho\rho} + \frac{2}{\rho} u_\rho + \frac{1}{\rho^2} u_{\phi\phi} + \frac{\cot \phi}{\rho^2} u_\phi + \frac{1}{\rho^2 \sin^2 \phi} u_{\theta\theta}$$

$$= \frac{1}{\rho^2} (\rho^2 u_\rho)_\rho + \frac{1}{\rho^2 \sin \phi} (u_\phi \sin \phi)_\phi + \frac{1}{\rho^2 \sin^2 \phi} u_{\theta\theta}. \qquad (10.33)$$

The formulas (10.31) and (10.33) can be derived more efficiently by vector or tensor methods. Descriptions of such methods are, however, outside the scope of this book.

Exercises for Section 10.7

1. Derive the formula for u_{yy} in terms of cylindrical coordinates.

2. Derive the relations (10.32) for spherical coordinates from the geometry of Fig. 10.9.

3. Derive an expression for u_x in spherical coordinates.

4. Derive formula (10.33).

5. Elliptical cylindrical coordinates may be defined by means of the equations

$$x = \cosh u \cos v, \qquad y = \sinh u \sin v, \qquad z = w,$$

where $u > 0$, $-\pi < v < \pi$, and $-\infty < w < \infty$.

(a) Show that the surface $u = u_0$, where u_0 is a constant, is an elliptical cylinder.

(b) Express the partial derivatives g_x and g_y of a function g in terms of the partials of g with respect to u and v.

6. Let x' and y' be rectangular coordinates that are obtained from x and y by means of a rotation of axes. Show that

$$u_{x'x'} + u_{y'y'} = u_{xx} + u_{yy}.$$

(In connection with this exercise, see Exercise 10, Section 10.1.)

7. Show that if x' and y' are the oblique coordinates defined by

$$x' = ax + by, \qquad y' = cx + dy,$$

where $ad - bc \neq 0$, then

$$u_{xx} + u_{yy} = (a^2 + b^2)u_{x'x'} + 2(ac + bd)u_{x'y'} + (c^2 + d^2)u_{y'y'}.$$

8. Consider a solid in the shape of a pipe, bounded by two cylinders of radii a and b, with $0 < a < b$. Assume that the steady-state temperature at a point in the solid depends only on the distance of that point from the axis. Let $u(r)$ denote the temperature at a distance r from the axis. Find a formula for $u(r)$ if:

(a) the inner and outer cylinders are kept at the constant temperatures A and B, respectively;

(b) the outer surface is insulated and the inner surface is kept at the constant temperature A.

9. Consider a solid in the shape of a hollow ball, bounded by two concentric spheres of radii a and b, with $0 < a < b$. Assume that the steady state temperature at a point in the solid depends only on the distance of that point from the center of the ball. Let $u(\rho)$ denote the temperature at a distance ρ from the center. Find a formula for $u(\rho)$ if:

    (a) the inner and outer spheres are kept at the constant temperatures A and B, respectively;

    (b) the inner sphere is insulated and the outer sphere is kept at the constant temperature B.

10.8 A PROBLEM IN CYLINDRICAL COORDINATES

Consider a solid circular cylinder of radius c and height h, as in Fig. 10.10. Let the top and bottom be insulated, and let the curved part of

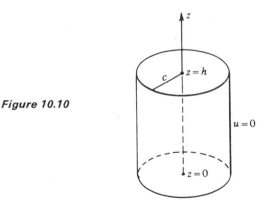

Figure 10.10

the surface of the cylinder be kept at temperature zero. Let us also assume that at time $t = 0$ the temperature at a point in the solid depends only on the distance of the point from the axis of the cylinder. In terms of cylindrical coordinates, the initial temperature distribution is a function of the radial coordinate r only, and does not depend on θ or z.

In order to describe the temperature distribution in the solid for $t > 0$, we must find a solution of the heat equation that satisfies appropriate boundary conditions. In this case, it seems reasonable to expect a solution of the heat equation that is a function of r and t only. Thus we seek a function u such that

$$u_t(r, t) = k\left[u_{rr}(r, t) + \frac{1}{r}u_r(r, t)\right], \qquad 0 < r < c, \quad t > 0. \qquad (10.34)$$

The appropriate boundary conditions are

$$u(c, t) = 0, \qquad t \geq 0, \qquad (10.35)$$

and

$$u(r, 0) = f(r), \qquad 0 \leq r \leq c, \qquad (10.36)$$

where f describes the initial temperature distribution.

Seeking solutions of the differential equation that are of the form

$$u(r, t) = R(r)T(t),$$

we find easily that

$$R(r)T'(t) = k\left[R''(r)T(t) + \frac{1}{r}R'(r)T(t)\right]$$

or

$$\frac{T'(t)}{kT(t)} = \frac{R''(r) + r^{-1}R'(r)}{R(r)} = -\lambda^2,$$

where λ is a constant. Thus R and T must satisfy the ordinary differential equations

$$rR'' + R' + \lambda^2 rR = 0,$$

$$T' + \lambda kT = 0.$$

The general solution of the equation for R is given in terms of Bessel functions by the expression

$$R(r) = c_1 J_0(\lambda r) + c_2 Y_0(\lambda r).$$

We choose $c_2 = 0$ so that $R(r)$, and hence $u(r, t)$, will be finite at $r = 0$ (along the z axis). We also require that

$$R(c) = 0,$$

so that our product solutions will satisfy the homogeneous boundary condition (10.35). Then λ must satisfy the equation

$$J_0(\lambda c) = 0.$$

Let us denote the nth positive root of this equation by λ_n. For each such value of λ, we obtain a nontrivial product solution,

$$u_n(r, t) = J_0(\lambda_n r)e^{-\lambda_n^2 kt}.$$

Superposition yields the formal series

$$u(r, t) = \sum_{n=1}^{\infty} A_n J_0(\lambda_n r)e^{-\lambda_n^2 kt}. \qquad (10.37)$$

The nonhomogeneous boundary condition (10.36) requires that

$$u(r, 0) = \sum_{n=1}^{\infty} A_n J_0(\lambda_n r) = f(r).$$

The constants A_n should therefore be the coefficients in the Fourier Bessel series (Sections 7.2 and 7.8) for f; that is,

$$A_n = \frac{2}{c^2 [J_1(\lambda_n c)]^2} \int_0^c r J_0(\lambda_n r) f(r)\, dr. \qquad (10.38)$$

Suppose that f is continuous and piecewise smooth on $[0, c]$ and that $f(c) = 0$. Then the series (10.37), with coefficients (10.38), converges to $f(r)$ when $t = 0$. It can be shown that the series (10.37) converges and represents a continuous function when $0 \le r \le c$ and $t \ge 0$. It can also be shown that the series can be differentiated term by term any number of times with respect to r and t when $0 \le r < c$ and $t > 0$, and that the series represents the (unique) solution of the boundary value problem.

Exercises for Section 10.8

1. Find an expression for the temperature $u(r, t)$ in the cylinder $0 \le r \le c$, $0 \le z \le h$, if all surfaces are insulated, and $u(r, 0) = f(r)$.

2. In the example of this section, suppose that the curved surface of the cylinder had been kept at the constant temperature A, where $A \ne 0$, and that $u(r, 0) = f(r)$, where $f(c) = A$. Find an expression for the temperature $u(r, t)$.

3. A solid cylinder $0 \le r \le c$, $0 \le z \le h$ has its ends insulated, and is immersed in a medium of constant uniform temperature zero. Assuming that Newton's law of cooling applies on the curved surface, and that $u(r, 0) = f(r)$, find $u(r, t)$.

4. The top and bottom of the cylinder $0 \le r \le c$, and $0 \le z \le h$ are kept at temperature zero, and the prescribed temperature on the surface $r = c$ is

a function of z only. Show that the steady-state temperature $u(r, z)$ in the cylinder is given by the formula

$$u(r, z) = \sum_{n=1}^{\infty} A_n I_0\left(\frac{n\pi r}{h}\right) \sin \frac{n\pi z}{h},$$

where

$$A_n = \frac{2}{h} \int_0^h f(z) \sin \frac{n\pi z}{h} \, dz,$$

I_0 is the modified Bessel function of the first kind, and $u(c, z) = f(z)$.

5. Find the steady-state temperature $u(r, z)$ in the cylinder $0 \le r \le c$, $0 \le z \le h$ if the bottom and curved surface of the cylinder are kept at temperature zero, and along the top $u(r, h) = f(r)$.

6. Consider the steady state temperature $u(r, \theta)$ in a circular plate of radius c, where the prescribed temperature on the rim is $u(c, \theta) = f(\theta)$, $-\pi < \theta \le \pi$. Show that

$$u(r, \theta) = \frac{1}{2} A_0 + \sum_{n=1}^{\infty} \left(\frac{r}{c}\right)^{n\pi/c}\left[A_n \cos \frac{n\pi\theta}{c} + B_n \sin \frac{n\pi\theta}{c}\right]$$

where A_n and B_n are the Fourier coefficients of f. Note that $u(r, \theta)$ must be periodic in θ with period 2π.

7. Show, at least formally, that the solution to Exercise 6 can be written in the form

$$u(r, \theta) = \frac{1}{2\pi} \int_{-\pi}^{\pi} f(\phi) \frac{c^2 - r^2}{c^2 - 2rc \cos(\theta - \phi) + r^2} \, d\phi.$$

This formula, for a function which satisfies Laplace's equation in the disk $r < c$ and which takes on the prescribed values $f(\theta)$ as $r \to c$, is known as the *Poisson integral formula*.

8. A semi-circular plate, described by the inequalities $0 \le r \le c$, $0 \le \theta \le \pi$, has its straight edge insulated. Find the steady-state temperature $u(r, \theta)$ if the temperature on the circular edge is given by $u(c, \theta) = f(\theta)$, $0 \le \theta \le \pi$.

9. Consider a thin elastic membrane that is stretched across a frame lying in the xy plane. Assuming that each "particle" of the membrane (or drumhead) vibrates along a line parallel to the z axis, it can be shown that the vertical displacement $u(x, y, t)$ satisfies the two-dimensional wave equation $u_{tt} = c^2 \Delta u$, at least approximately. Consider a membrane stretched across the circular frame $r = a$, $z = 0$. If initially $u = f(r)$, and if the initial velocity u_t is zero, find a formula for u in terms of r and t.

10.9   A PROBLEM IN SPHERICAL COORDINATES

Let us consider the problem of finding the steady state temperature in a sphere $0 \le \rho \le c$, if the temperature on the surface is a prescribed function of ϕ. If the temperature u depends only on ρ and ϕ, then the governing differential equation (Laplace's equation) has the form

$$u_{\rho\rho} + \frac{2}{\rho} u_\rho + \frac{1}{\rho^2} u_{\phi\phi} + \frac{\cot \phi}{\rho^2} u_\phi = 0,$$

where $u = u(\rho, \phi)$. At the boundary,

$$u(c, \phi) = f(\phi), \qquad 0 \le \phi \le \pi.$$

Seeking product solutions of the differential equation that are of the form $u(\rho, \phi) = F(\rho)G(\phi)$, we find that

$$\frac{\rho^2 F''(\rho) + 2F'(\rho)}{\rho^2} = -\frac{G''(\phi) + \cot \phi G'(\phi)}{G(\phi)} = \lambda,$$

where λ is a constant. Thus F and G must satisfy the respective equations

$$\rho^2 F'' + 2\rho F' - \lambda F = 0,$$

$$G'' + \cot \phi G + \lambda G = 0.$$

The equation for G reduces to Legendre's equation under the change of variable $s = \cos \phi$. It has a solution that is finite at $\phi = 0$ and $\phi = \pi$ if and only if λ is one of the values

$$\lambda_n = n(n + 1), \qquad n = 0, 1, 2, \ldots.$$

The corresponding solutions are

$$G_n(\phi) = P_n(\cos \phi),$$

where P_n is the Legendre polynomial of degree n. The equation for F is of the Cauchy–Euler type. Its general solution for $\lambda = \lambda_n$ is

$$F_n(\rho) = C_1 \rho^n + C_2 \rho^{-(n+1)}.$$

We must choose $c_2 = 0$ if $F_n(\rho)$ is to be finite at $\rho = 0$.

Forming the appropriate products, and superimposing, we arrive at the formal series

$$u(\rho, \phi) = \sum_{n=0}^{\infty} A_n \rho^n P_n(\cos \phi).$$

The constants A_n are to be chosen so as to satisfy the boundary condition, that is, so that

$$u(c, \phi) = \sum_{n=0}^{\infty} A_n c^n P_n(\cos \phi) = f(\phi), \qquad 0 \le \phi \le \pi.$$

Setting $s = \cos \phi$, this condition becomes

$$\sum_{n=0}^{\infty} A_n c^n P_n(s) = f(\cos^{-1} s), \qquad -1 \le s \le 1.$$

According to the theory of Fourier–Legendre series (Sections 7.2 and 7.8), we should choose the coefficients A_n to be

$$A_n = \frac{2n + 1}{2c^n} \int_{-1}^{1} f(\cos^{-1} s) P_n(s) \, ds$$

$$= \frac{2n + 1}{2c^n} \int_{0}^{\pi} f(\phi) P_n(\cos \phi) \sin \phi \, d\phi, \qquad n = 0, 1, 2, \ldots .$$

Exercises for Section 10.9

1. Find a function $u(\rho, \phi)$ that satisfies Laplace's equation in the infinite region $\rho > c$, takes on the prescribed values $u(c, \phi) = f(\phi)$ on the sphere $\rho = c$, and is finite as $\rho \to \infty$.

2. Find the steady-state temperature $u(\rho, \phi)$ in the spherical shell $a \le \rho \le b$, where $a > 0$, if $u(a, \phi) = f(\phi)$ and $u(b, \phi) = g(\phi)$, $0 \le \phi \le \pi$.

3. Find the steady-state temperature $u(\rho, \phi)$ in the hemisphere $0 \le \rho \le c$, $0 \le \phi \le \pi/2$ if the bottom of the hemisphere is kept at temperature zero and if on the curved surface, $u(c, \phi) = f(\phi)$, $0 \le \phi \le \pi/2$.

4. Suppose that at time $t = 0$, the temperature $u(\rho, t)$ in the solid sphere $0 \le \rho \le c$ is a function of ρ, that is, $u(\rho, 0) = f(\rho)$. If the surface of the sphere is kept at temperature zero, show that

$$u(\rho, t) = \frac{1}{\rho} \sum_{n=1}^{\infty} A_n \sin \frac{n\pi\rho}{c} e^{-(n\pi/c)^2 kt},$$

where

$$A_n = \frac{2}{c} \int_{0}^{c} \rho f(\rho) \sin \frac{n\pi\rho}{c} \, d\rho .$$

5. Consider a thin conical shell whose description in spherical coordinates is given by $0 \le \rho \le c$, $\phi = \alpha$, where c and α are constants. Find the

steady-state temperature $u(\rho, \theta)$ in the shell if $u(c, \theta) = f(\theta)$. Assume that the sides of the cone are insulated so that no heat is lost or gained across them.

6. Find the temperature $u(\phi, t)$ in a thin spherical shell $\rho = a$ if initially $u(\phi, 0) = f(\phi)$. Assume that the inner and outer surfaces of the shell are insulated so that no heat is lost or gained across them.

10.10   DOUBLE FOURIER SERIES

Thus far, we have considered boundary-value problems that involve two independent variables. In applying the method of separation of variables to these problems, we were led to a formal series solution consisting of super-imposed product solutions of a linear homogeneous partial differential equation. The coefficients in the series were the Fourier coefficients of a function of a single variable. In problems in which the number of independent variables is greater than two, the method of separation of variables leads, as we shall see, to the notion of a multiple Fourier series.

In order to give an illustration of such a series, let us consider a function f of two variables, such that $f(x, y)$ is defined for all (x, y) in the rectangle $0 \leq x \leq a$, $0 \leq y \leq b$. Suppose that for each fixed y in $[0, b]$ the function g_y, where $g_y(x) = f(x, y)$, can be expanded in a Fourier sine series. Then

$$f(x, y) = \sum_{m=1}^{\infty} B_m(y) \sin \frac{m\pi x}{a}, \tag{10.39}$$

where

$$B_m(y) = \frac{2}{a} \int_0^a f(x, y) \sin \frac{m\pi x}{a} \, dx, \qquad 0 \leq y \leq b.$$

If each of the functions B_m can be expanded in a sine series, then

$$B_m(y) = \sum_{n=1}^{\infty} A_{mn} \sin \frac{n\pi y}{b}, \tag{10.40}$$

where

$$A_{mn} = \frac{2}{b} \int_0^b B_m(y) \sin \frac{n\pi y}{b} \, dy$$

$$= \frac{4}{ab} \int_0^a \int_0^b f(x, y) \sin \frac{m\pi x}{a} \sin \frac{n\pi y}{b} \, dx \, dy.$$

From formulas (10.39) and (10.40), we obtain the expansion

$$f(x, y) = \sum_{m=1}^{\infty} \left(\sum_{n=1}^{\infty} A_{mn} \sin \frac{n\pi y}{b} \right) \sin \frac{m\pi x}{a}. \tag{10.41}$$

The series (10.41) is called a *doubly iterated series*. In it, the terms

$$A_{mn} \sin \frac{m\pi x}{a} \sin \frac{n\pi y}{b} \tag{10.42}$$

are first summed, for each fixed m, with respect to n. Then the results are summed with respect to m. Also associated with the doubly infinite collection of terms (10.42) is the *double series*

$$\sum_{m,n=1}^{\infty} A_{mn} \sin \frac{m\pi x}{a} \sin \frac{n\pi y}{b}. \tag{10.43}$$

To give meaning to such a series, we define the partial sums, $S_{ij}(x, y)$, according to the formula

$$S_{ij}(x, y) = \sum_{m,n=1}^{m=i, n=j} A_{mn} \sin \frac{m\pi x}{a} \sin \frac{n\pi y}{b}.$$

The series is said to converge to the sum $f(x, y)$ if to every positive number ε [and to each point (x, y) in the rectangle] there corresponds a pair of integers I and J such that

$$|S_{ij}(x, y) - f(x, y)| < \varepsilon$$

whenever $i > I$ and $j > J$. Under certain conditions, the double series (10.43) and the iterated series (10.41) have the same sum.† We shall not attempt a discussion about questions of convergence and rearrangement of terms for double series.

We shall now consider a boundary value problem that leads to a double Fourier series. Let $u(x, y, t)$ represent the time dependent temperature in a rectangular plate $0 \le x \le a$, $0 \le y \le b$, whose edges are kept at temperature zero, and whose initial temperature distribution is $u(x, y, 0) = f(x, y)$. The boundary value problem for u is

$$\begin{aligned}
u_t &= k(u_{xx} + u_{yy}), & 0 < x < a, & \quad 0 < y < b, & \quad t > 0, \\
u(0, y, t) &= u(a, y, t) = 0, & 0 \le y \le b, & \quad t \ge 0, \\
u(x, 0, t) &= u(x, b, t) = 0, & 0 \le x \le a, & \quad t \ge 0, \\
u(x, y, 0) &= f(x, y), & 0 \le x \le a, & \quad 0 \le y \le b.
\end{aligned}$$

---

† If the double series (10.43) converges absolutely, then both the series (10.43) and 10.41) converge, and they have the same sum.

We seek product solutions of the differential equation that are of the form

$$u(x, y, t) = X(x)Y(y)T(t).$$

In view of the homogeneous boundary conditions of the problem, we shall require that

$$X(0) = X(a) = 0, \qquad Y(0) = Y(b) = 0.$$

Substituting the expression for u into the the differential equation, we find that

$$XYT' = k(X''YT + XY''T),$$

or

$$\frac{X''}{X} - \frac{T'}{kT} - \frac{Y''}{Y} = -\lambda, \qquad (10.44)$$

where λ is a constant. Because of the conditions for X, λ must have one of the values

$$\lambda_n = \left(\frac{m\pi}{a}\right)^2, \qquad m = 1, 2, 3, \ldots.$$

The corresponding solutions of the equation for X are

$$X_m(x) = \sin\frac{m\pi x}{a}, \qquad m = 1, 2, 3, \ldots.$$

From Eq. (10.44), we have

$$\frac{T'}{kT} + \lambda_m = \frac{Y''}{Y} = -\mu, \qquad (10.45)$$

where μ is a constant. This constant must be one of the values

$$\mu_n = \left(\frac{n\pi}{b}\right)^2, \qquad n = 1, 2, 3, \ldots.$$

The corresponding solutions of the equation $Y'' + \mu Y = 0$ are

$$Y_n(y) = \sin\frac{n\pi y}{b}, \qquad n = 1, 2, 3, \ldots.$$

Now, from Eq. (10.45), we obtain the equation

$$T' + (\lambda_m + \mu_n)kT = 0,$$

whose solution is

$$T_{mn}(t) = \exp[-(\lambda_m + \mu_n)kt].$$

We now form the product solutions

$$\exp[-(\lambda_m + \mu_n)kt] \sin \frac{m\pi x}{a} \sin \frac{n\pi y}{b}, \qquad m, n = 1, 2, 3, \ldots,$$

each of which satisfies the homogeneous boundary conditions of the problem. Superposition gives us the formal double series

$$u(x, y, t) = \sum_{m,n=1}^{\infty} A_{mn} \exp[-(\lambda_m + \mu_n)kt] \sin \frac{m\pi x}{a} \sin \frac{n\pi y}{b}. \qquad (10.46)$$

The nonhomogeneous boundary condition of our problem requires that

$$u(x, y, 0) = \sum_{m,n=1}^{\infty} A_{mn} \sin \frac{m\pi x}{a} \sin \frac{n\pi y}{b} = f(x, y).$$

In view of our previous discussion of double Fourier series, we choose the constants A_{mn} to be

$$A_{mn} = \frac{4}{ab} \int_0^a \int_0^b f(x, y) \sin \frac{m\pi x}{a} \sin \frac{n\pi y}{b} \, dx \, dy. \qquad (10.47)$$

The series (10.46) with coefficients (10.47), is only a formal solution of our problem. In order to establish that the series represents an actual solution, it is necessary to show that it converges to $f(x, y)$ when $t = 0$. It is also necessary to show that the series converges and can be differentiated term by term the appropriate number of times with respect to x, y, and t for $0 < x < a$, $0 < y < b$, and $t > 0$.

Exercises for Section 10.10

1. Find the steady-state temperature $u(x, y, z)$ in the cube $0 \le x \le 1$, $0 \le y \le 1$, $0 \le z \le 1$, if $u(x, y, 1) = f(x, y)$ and if the other five faces are kept at temperature zero.

2. Let $u(r, \theta, t)$ represent the temperature in the semicircular plate $0 \le r \le c$, $0 \le \theta \le \pi$. If the edges of the plate are kept at temperature zero, and if $u(r, \theta, 0) = f(r, \theta)$, show that

$$u(r, \theta, t) = \sum_{m,n=1}^{\infty} A_{mn} J_m(\mu_{mn} r) \sin m\theta \exp(-k\mu_{mn}^2 t),$$

where μ_{mn} is the nth positive root of the equation $J_m(\mu c) = 0$, and

$$A_{mn} = \frac{4}{\pi c^2 [J_{m+1}(\mu_{mn} c)]^2} \int_0^c \int_0^\pi r f(r, \theta) J_m(\mu_{mn} r) \sin m\theta \, d\theta \, dr.$$

3. Find the temperature $u(r, z, t)$ in the cylinder $0 \le r \le c, 0 \le z \le h$ if the entire boundary is insulated and if $u(r, z, 0) = f(r, z)$.

4. The ends of the cylinder $0 \le r \le c, 0 \le z \le h$ are kept at temperature zero, and the temperature on the surface is a prescribed function $f(\theta, z)$ of θ and z. Show that the steady-state temperature $u(r, \theta, z)$ in the cylinder is given by

$$u(r, \theta, z) = \frac{1}{2} \sum_{m=1}^{\infty} A_{m0} \sin \frac{m\pi z}{h} I_0\left(\frac{m\pi r}{h}\right)$$

$$+ \sum_{m, n=1}^{\infty} [A_{mn} \cos n\theta + B_{mn} \sin n\theta] \sin \frac{m\pi z}{h} I_n\left(\frac{m\pi r}{h}\right),$$

where

$$A_{mn} = \frac{2}{h I_n(m\pi c/h)} \int_{-\pi}^{\pi} \int_0^h f(\theta, z) \cos n\theta \sin \frac{m\pi z}{h} \, d\theta \, dz,$$

and B_{mn} is given by a like formula, but with $\cos n\theta$ replaced by $\sin n\theta$.

5. Consider an elastic membrane which, when at rest, covers the rectangle $0 \le x \le a, 0 \le y \le b$. The edges of the membrane are fastened to a rectangular frame. When set vibrating, the displacements $u(x, y, t)$ of the membrane satisfy, approximately, the two-dimensional wave equation $u_{tt} = c^2 \Delta u$. If $u(x, y, 0) = 0$ and $u_t(x, y, 0) = g(x, y)$, express $u(x, y, t)$ as a double Fourier series.

6. Let $u(\rho, \phi, t)$ denote the temperature in the sphere $0 \le \rho \le c$, whose surface is kept at temperature zero, and whose initial temperature is $f(\rho, \phi)$. Show that

$$u(\rho, \phi, t) = \sum_{m=1, n=0}^{\infty} A_{mn} P_n(\cos \phi) \rho^{-1/2} J_{n+1/2}(\mu_{mn} \rho) e^{-\mu_{mn}^2 k t},$$

$$A_{mn} = \frac{2n+1}{c^2 [J_{n+3/2}(\mu_{mn} c)]^2}$$

$$\times \int_0^{\pi} \int_0^c \rho^{3/2} f(\rho, \phi) P_n(\cos \phi) J_{n+1/2}(\mu_{mn} \rho) \sin \phi \, d\rho \, d\phi,$$

μ_{mn} being the mth positive root of the equation $J_{n+1/2}(\mu c) = 0$.

7. Show that Laplace's equation in spherical coordinates possesses solutions of the forms

$$\rho^n \cos m\theta \, P_n^m(\cos \phi), \qquad \rho^n \sin m\theta \, P_n^m(\cos \phi),$$

where the functions $P_n^m(x)$ are the associated Legendre functions. (See the exercises of Section 5.7.)

REFERENCES

1. Churchill, R. V., *Fourier Series and Boundary Value Problems*, 2nd ed. McGraw-Hill, New York, 1963.
2. Davis, H. F., *Fourier Series and Orthogonal Functions*. Allyn and Bacon, Boston, 1963.
3. Greenspan, D., *Introduction to Partial Differential Equations*. McGraw-Hill, New York, 1961.
4. Kreider, D. L., Kuller, R. G., Ostberg, D. R., and Perkins, F. W., *An Introduction to Linear Analysis*. Addison-Wesley, Reading, Massachusetts, 1966.
5. Sagan, H., *Boundary and Eigenvalue Problems in Mathematical Physics*. Wiley, New York, 1961.
6. Tolstov, G. P., *Fourier Series*. Prentice-Hall, Englewood Cliffs, New Jersey, 1962.

XI

The Phase Plane

11.1 INTRODUCTION

In this and the next chapter we shall consider some topics in differential equations that are not directly concerned with finding solutions. For some classes of first-order equations and higher order linear equations it is possible to find a formula for the general solution. Properties of solutions can then be found from this formula. Our concern now is with the determination of certain important properties of the solutions of an equation (or system of equations) regardless of whether or not an explicit formula for the general solution can be found. In particular, we shall be concerned in this chapter with stability of solutions and the existence of periodic solutions. The meaning of these terms will be explained in the sequel.

We shall consider only second-order differential equations and first-order systems of two equations. Some, but not all, of the results that we obtain can be generalized to n-dimensional systems. In any case, the two-dimensional case is important for many applications.

Let us consider a first-order system for two unknown functions,

$$\frac{dx}{dt} = F(t, x, y), \qquad \frac{dy}{dt} = G(t, x, y). \tag{11.1}$$

For each t, the numbers $x(t)$ and $y(t)$ can be regarded as the rectangular Cartesian coordinates of a point in a plane. This plane is called the *phase plane* for the system (11.1). As t varies, the point $(x(t), y(t))$ traces out a curve in the phase plane. If (x, y) is a solution of the system (11.1), the corresponding curve is called a *trajectory* of the system. It is necessary to make a distinction between a solution of the system and a trajectory of the system. This is because different solutions may represent the same trajectory, as we shall see in later examples.

A point (x_0, y_0) such that $F(t, x_0, y_0) = G(t, x_0, y_0) = 0$ for all t is called a *critical point* of the system (11.1). If such a point exists, the constant functions $x(t) = x_0$, $y(t) = y_0$ constitute a solution of the system. The trajectory of such a solution consists of the single point (x_0, y_0).

Example 1   The system

$$\frac{dx}{dt} = x, \qquad \frac{dy}{dt} = 3x + 2y,$$

which is linear with constant coefficients, has for its general solution

$$x(t) = c_1 e^t, \qquad y(t) = c_1 e^t + c_2 e^{2t}.$$

When $c_1 = 0$ we have $x(t) = 0$ and $y(t) = c_2 e^{2t}$ for all t. In this case, the trajectory consists of the positive y axis when $c_2 > 0$ and the negative y axis when $c_2 < 0$. If $c_2 = 0$, we have $x(t) = c_1 e^t$ and $y(t) = c_1 e^t$ for all t. The trajectory consists of the ray $y = x$, $x > 0$, when $c_1 > 0$, and the ray $y = x$, $x < 0$, when $c_1 < 0$. In the general case when $c_1 c_2 \neq 0$, the trajectories lie on the parabolas $y = x + (c_2/c_1^2)x^2$. Actually, each trajectory consists of only part of a parabola, the part with $x > 0$ if $c_1 > 0$ and the part with $x < 0$ if $c_1 < 0$. Some typical trajectories are shown in Fig. 11.1. The arrows indicate the

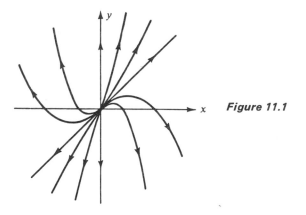

Figure 11.1

direction of increasing t.

The critical points of the system in the example are found by solving the system

$$x = 0, \qquad 3x + 2y = 0.$$

The only solution, $(0, 0)$, corresponds to the solution $x(t) = 0$, $y(t) = 0$ of the system of differential equations.

We note that the solution of the system for which $x(0) = y(0) = 1$ is given by $x(t) = e^t$, $y(t) = e^t$, while the solution for which $x(0) = y(0) = 2$ is given by $x(t) = 2e^t$, $y(t) = 2e^t$. The two solutions are different, but each represents the trajectory that consists of the ray $y = x$, $x > 0$. This illustrates the fact stated earlier, that different solutions can describe the same trajectory.

A second-order differential equation of the form

$$\frac{d^2x}{dt^2} = f\left(t, x, \frac{dx}{dt}\right) \tag{11.2}$$

is equivalent to the first-order system

$$\frac{dx}{dt} = y, \qquad \frac{dy}{dt} = f(t, x, y),$$

as was shown in Section 8.2. We can therefore speak of phase planes, trajectories, and critical points for equations such as (11.2). A critical point for such an equation is of the form $(x_0, 0)$. If x and $x' = y$ represent distance and velocity, respectively, we see that a critical point corresponds to a state of rest, or equilibrium, in which $x(t) = x_0$ and $x'(t) = 0$ for all t.

Example 2 The equation

$$\frac{d^2x}{dt^2} + x = 0$$

is equivalent to the system

$$\frac{dx}{dt} = y, \qquad \frac{dy}{dt} = -x.$$

The general solution of this system can be written as

$$x(t) = A\cos(t - \alpha), \qquad y(t) = -A\sin(t - \alpha),$$

where A and α are arbitrary constants. In the phase plane, the equations of the trajectories are $x^2 + y^2 = A^2$. The circles are traversed in the clockwise direction as t increases, because $dx/dt > 0$ when $y > 0$ and $dx/dt < 0$ when $y < 0$. Some sample trajectories are shown in Fig. 11.2. Notice that for fixed A the trajectory of the solution does not depend on α. Thus many solutions describe the same trajectory.

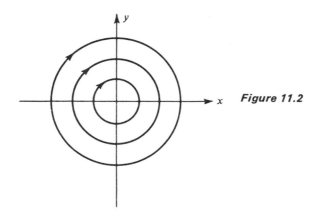

Figure 11.2

In the last example, the trajectories were closed curves. Closed trajectories of a system (11.1) arise from *periodic solutions*. A solution (x, y) is said to be periodic with period T if it exists for all t and if

$$x(t + T) + x(t), \qquad y(t + T) = y(t)$$

for all t. The trajectory which is described by a periodic solution of period T is traversed once as t traverses an interval of length T. In Example 2 the solutions are periodic with period 2π.

We shall be particularly interested in systems of the form

$$\frac{dx}{dt} = P(x, y), \qquad \frac{dy}{dt} = Q(x, y), \tag{11.3}$$

in which the independent variable t does not appear explicitly. Such a system is said to be *autonomous*. We shall consider such systems in a region D of the xy plane in which the functions P and Q, and their first partial derivatives are continuous. If P and Q satisfy these conditions, it can be shown (Chapter XII) that if (x_0, y_0) is any point of D and if t_0 is any real number, there exists a unique solution of the system (11.3) that satisfies $x(t_0) = x_0$, $y(t_0) = y_0$.

Each trajectory of an autonomous system is represented by a one-parameter family of solutions. For if (x, y) is a solution and if u and v are defined by the equations $u(t) = x(t + c)$, $v(t) = y(t + c)$, where c is any constant, it can be shown (Exercise 4) that (u, v) is a solution and represents the same trajectory as (x, y).

Suppose that $P(x, y) \neq 0$ in the region D. If (x, y) is a solution of the system, then $x'(t)$ is never zero. Hence t can be regarded as a function of x, and since

$$\frac{dy}{dt} \Big/ \frac{dx}{dt} = \frac{Q(x, y)}{P(x, y)},$$

we see that y, regarded as a function of x, satisfies the first-order equation

$$\frac{dy}{dx} = \frac{Q(x, y)}{P(x, y)}. \tag{11.4}$$

Consequently, the trajectories of the system (11.3) coincide with the integral curves of the equation (11.4). Such an interpretation is not possible, in general, for a nonautonomous system of the form (11.1).

Example 3 Let us consider the system

$$\frac{dx}{dt} = (x^2 + 1)y, \qquad \frac{dy}{dt} = 2xy^2.$$

For $y \neq 0$ we have

$$\frac{dy}{dx} = \frac{2xy}{x^2 + 1}$$

and

$$y(x) = C(x^2 + 1).$$

Some of these parabolic trajectories are shown in Fig. 11.3. The direction of

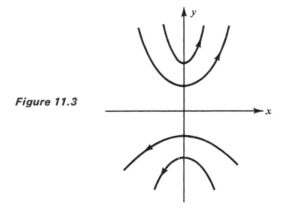

Figure 11.3

increasing t can be found from the first of the differential equations, by noting that dx/dt has the same sign as y. We also note that $x = C'$, $y = 0$ is a solution for every value of C'. These solutions are represented by points on the x axis of the phase plane.

Exercises for Section 11.1

1. Find all solutions of the given system and sketch some of its trajectories. Indicate the direction of increasing t.

    (a) $\dfrac{dx}{dt} = y$, $\dfrac{dy}{dt} = -4x$

    (c) $\dfrac{dx}{dt} = -x$, $\dfrac{dy}{dt} = x^2 y^2$

    (b) $\dfrac{dx}{dt} = -x$, $\dfrac{dy}{dt} = x - 2y$

    (d) $\dfrac{dx}{dt} = x$, $\dfrac{dy}{dt} = x + 2e^{2t}$

2. If $P(x_0, y_0) = Q(x_0, y_0) = 0$, show that the autonomous system (11.3) possesses the constant solution $x(t) = x_0$, $y(t) = y_0$.

3. Locate all critical points of the given equation or system of equations. (A dot indicates differentiation with respect to t.)

    (a) $\dot{x} = 2x - y + 1$
         $\dot{y} = 3x - y - 2$

    (b) $\dot{x} = x + y - 5e^{-t}$
         $\dot{y} = x - 2y - 2e^{-t}$

    (c) $\dot{x} = x + 2y$
         $\dot{y} = x^2 + 12y - 16$

    (d) $\dot{x} = e^t(x - y)$
         $\dot{y} = t(x^2 - 2y)$

    (e) $\ddot{x} - x^2 + 4\cos \dot{x} = 0$

    (f) $\ddot{x} + \dot{x} - x^4 + 1 = 0$

4. If (x, y) is a solution of the autonomous system (11.3) and if $u(t) = x(t + c)$, $v(t) = y(t + c)$, where c is a constant, show that (u, v) is also a solution. Show that both solutions represent the same trajectory.

5. Let (x_1, y_1) and (x_2, y_2) be solutions of the system (11.3) such that their trajectories have a common point. Show that there exists a constant c such that $x_2(t) = x_1(t + c)$ and $y_2(t) = y_1(t + c)$. Hence show, using the result of Exercise 4, that the two trajectories coincide.

6. Sketch some of the trajectories of the system

    $$\frac{dx}{dt} = -y(x^2 + y^2), \qquad \frac{dy}{dt} = x(x^2 + y^2),$$

    indicating the direction of increasing t. Suggestion: Use Eq. (11.4).

7. Sketch some of the trajectories of the system

    $$\frac{dx}{dt} = e^y, \qquad \frac{dy}{dt} = 2xe^y,$$

    indicating the direction of increasing t.

8.   Sketch some of the trajectories of the system

$$\frac{dx}{dt} = xy, \qquad \frac{dy}{dt} = y(y - 3x^2),$$

indicating the direction of increasing t.

9.   (a)   Show that a second order equation of the form

$$\frac{d^2x}{dt^2} = f\left(x, \frac{dx}{dt}\right)$$

is equivalent to an autonomous system.

(b)   Find the autonomous system which corresponds to the equation with constant coefficients,

$$\frac{d^2x}{dt^2} + a\frac{dx}{dt} + bx = 0.$$

11.2   STABILITY

In this section we shall be concerned with the behavior of solutions of an autonomous system

$$\frac{dx}{dt} = P(x, y), \qquad \frac{dy}{dt} = Q(x, y) \qquad\qquad (11.5)$$

near a critical point. The functions P and Q are assumed to be continuous, along with their first partial derivatives, in a region D. For the ensuing discussion, we shall need a number of definitions.

A critical point (x_0, y_0) of the system is said to be *isolated* if there exists a circle

$$(x - x_0)^2 + (y - y_0)^2 = h^2, \qquad h > 0,$$

inside which the system has no other critical points. For instance, the origin $(0, 0)$ is an isolated critical point of the system

$$\frac{dx}{dt} = x - y, \qquad \frac{dy}{dt} = x + y$$

because it is the only critical point. However, the origin is not an isolated critical point for the system

$$\frac{dx}{dt} = x - y, \qquad \frac{dy}{dt} = 2x - 2y$$

because every point on the line $x - y = 0$ is a critical point.

A trajectory of the system (11.5) is said to *approach* the critical point (x_0, y_0) if a solution (x, y) that represents the trajectory has the property that

$$\lim_{t \to \infty} x(t) = x_0, \qquad \lim_{t \to \infty} y(t) = y_0.$$

If (u, v) is any other solution that represents the same trajectory, then $u(t) = x(t + c)$ and $v(t) = y(t + c)$ for some constant c, as was shown in Exercise 4, Section 11.1. Hence $u(t) \to x_0$ and $v(t) \to y_0$ as $t \to \infty$.†

A critical point (x_0, y_0) is said to be *stable* if to every positive number ε there corresponds a positive number δ such that, whenever a solution (x, y) satisfies

$$\{[x(0) - x_0]^2 + [y(0) - y_0]^2\}^{1/2} < \delta,$$

the solution exists for $t \geq 0$ and satisfies

$$\{[x(t) - x_0]^2 + [y(t) - y_0]^2\}^{1/2} < \varepsilon$$

for $t \geq 0$. The critical point is said to be *asymptotically stable* if it is stable and if in addition there exists a positive number δ_0 such that

$$\lim_{t \to \infty} x(t) = x_0, \qquad \lim_{t \to \infty} y(t) = y_0$$

whenever

$$\{[x(0) - x_0]^2 + [y(0) - y_0]^2\}^{1/2} < \delta_0.$$

A critical point that is not stable is said to be *unstable*. Geometrically speaking, when a critical point is stable, solutions that start (at $t = 0$) sufficiently

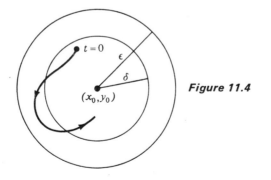

Figure 11.4

close to the point stay close to the point (Fig. 11.4).
Let us illustrate the above concepts by means of some simple examples.

† If for any solution (x, y) we have $x(t) \to x_0$ and $y(t) \to y_0$ as $t \to \infty$, and if the point (x_0, y_0) lies in D, it can be shown that (x_0, y_0) must be a critical point.

Example 1 The solution of the system

$$\frac{dx}{dt} = -x, \qquad \frac{dy}{dt} = -2y$$

for which $x(0) = x_0$, $y(0) = y_0$ is $x(t) = x_0 e^{-t}$, $y(t) = y_0 e^{-2t}$. Given ε, let $\delta = \varepsilon$. Then if $(x_0^2 + y_0^2)^{1/2} < \delta$, we have $\{[x(t)]^2 + [y(t)]^2\}^{1/2} \le (x_0^2 + y_0^2)^{1/2} < \varepsilon$ for $t \ge 0$. Hence the critical point $(0, 0)$ is stable. Since $x(t) \to 0$ and $y(t) \to 0$ as $t \to \infty$ for every solution, the critical point is asymptotically stable.

Example 2 The system

$$\frac{dx}{dt} = y, \qquad \frac{dy}{dt} = -x$$

was considered in Example 2, Section 11.1. Since the trajectories are circles with centers at the origin, a solution satisfying

$$\{[x(0)]^2 + [y(0)]^2\}^{1/2} < \varepsilon$$

satisfies

$$\{[x(t)]^2 + [y(t)]^2\}^{1/2} < \varepsilon \qquad \text{for } t \ge 0.$$

The critical point $(0, 0)$ is therefore stable. It is not asymptotically stable, because no trajectory approaches the origin.

Example 3 Consider the system

$$\frac{dx}{dt} = x, \qquad \frac{dy}{dt} = y.$$

The solution for which $x(0) = x_0$, $y(0) = 0$ is $x(t) = x_0 e^t$, $y(t) = 0$. No matter how small the value of $|x_0|$, $x(t) \to \infty$ if $x_0 \ne 0$. Hence the critical point $(0, 0)$ is unstable.

We begin our study of stability by considering critical points of *linear* autonomous systems. More specifically, we consider systems of the form

$$\frac{dx}{dt} = ax + by, \qquad \frac{dy}{dt} = cx + dy, \tag{11.6}$$

where a, b, c, and d are constants. We shall assume that $ad - bc \ne 0$. Then the system has exactly one critical point which is located at the origin of the phase plane.

Solutions of the system can be found by the methods of Chapter VIII. We consider three cases. If $b \ne 0$, we can eliminate y between the two equations. In this case, the system (11.6) is seen to be equivalent to the system

$$[(D - a)(D - d) - bc]x = 0, \qquad (D - a)x - by = 0, \tag{11.7}$$

where $D = d/dt$. Here x can be found from the first equation, and then y can be found from the second equation without integration. If $c \neq 0$, the system (11.6) is equivalent to the system

$$[(D - a)(D - d) - bc]y = 0, \qquad -cx + (D - d)y = 0. \tag{11.8}$$

If $b = c = 0$, the system (11.6) has the form

$$(D - a)x = 0, \qquad (D - d)y = 0. \tag{11.9}$$

From the equations (11.7)–(11.9), we see that the system (11.6) possesses a nontrivial solution of the form $x = Ae^{\lambda t}$, $y = Be^{\lambda t}$ if and only if λ is a root of the equation

$$(\lambda - a)(\lambda - d) - bc \equiv \lambda^2 - (a + d)\lambda + (ad - bc) = 0. \tag{11.10}$$

We note that $\lambda = 0$ cannot be a root of this equation, in view of the hypothesis that $ad - bc \neq 0$.

If λ_1 and λ_2 are distinct roots of the equation (11.10), then all solutions of the system (11.6) are of the form

$$x(t) = A_1 \exp(\lambda_1 t) + A_2 \exp(\lambda_2 t),$$
$$y(t) = B_1 \exp(\lambda_1 t) + B_2 \exp(\lambda_2 t),$$

where A_i, B_i are constants. If λ_1 and λ_2 are complex, say $\lambda_1 = \alpha + i\beta$ and $\lambda_2 = \alpha - i\beta$, the solutions may be written in real form as

$$x(t) = e^{\alpha t}(A_1 \cos \beta t + A_2 \sin \beta t),$$
$$y(t) = e^{\alpha t}(B_1 \cos \beta t + B_2 \sin \beta t).$$

If $\lambda_1 = \lambda_2$ (in which case λ_1 and λ_2 are real), the solutions are of the form

$$x(t) = (A_1 + A_2 t)\exp(\lambda_1 t), \qquad y(t) = (B_1 + B_2 t)\exp(\lambda_1 t).$$

If either, or both, of the roots λ_1 and λ_2 has a positive real part, is it clear that the critical point $(0, 0)$ cannot be stable. If both λ_1 and λ_2 have negative real parts, then the trajectory described by every nontrivial solution approaches the critical point as $t \to \infty$.

We shall now show that if λ_1 and λ_2 both have real parts which are less than, or equal to, zero, then the origin is a stable critical point. Let (x_1, y_1) and (x_2, y_2) be the solutions of the system for which $x_1(0) = 1$, $y_1(0) = 0$, $x_2(0) = 0$, $y_2(0) = 1$. Then there exists a positive constant M such that $|x_i(t)| \leq M$, $|y_i(t)| \leq M$, $i = 1, 2$, for $t \geq 0$. Let (p, q) be an arbitrary point in the xy plane. The solution (x, y) of the system for which $x(0) = p$, $y(0) = q$ is

$$x(t) = px_1(t) + qx_2(t), \qquad y(t) = py_1(t) + qy_2(t).$$

Then

$$|x(t)| \leq M(|p| + |q|), \qquad |y(t)| \leq M(|p| + |q|) \tag{11.11}$$

for $t \geq 0$. Given ε, let us choose $\delta = \varepsilon/4M$. Then if $(p^2 + q^2)^{1/2} < \delta$, certainly $|p| < \delta$, $|q| < \delta$. From the inequalities (11.11) we see that

$$|x(t)| < 2M\delta = \frac{\varepsilon}{2} \quad \text{and} \quad |y(t)| < 2M\delta = \frac{\varepsilon}{2}$$

for $t \geq 0$. Then

$$[x(t)]^2 + [y(t)]^2 < \frac{2\varepsilon^2}{4}$$

or

$$\{[x(t)]^2 + [y(t)]^2\}^{1/2} < \frac{\varepsilon}{\sqrt{2}} < \varepsilon.$$

Hence the origin is a stable critical point. We summarize these results in the following theorem.

Theorem 11.1   The critical point $(0, 0)$ of the linear system (11.6) is stable if, and only if, both roots of the auxiliary equation (11.10) have nonpositive real parts. The critical point is asymptotically stable if and only if both roots have negative real parts.

The proof of the following corollary is left as an exercise.

Corollary   The critical point $(0, 0)$ of the linear system (11.6) is asymptotically stable if, and only if, $a + d < 0$ and $ad > bc$.

Using this corollary, it is easy to show that the origin is an asymptotically stable critical point for the system of Example 1. Since $a = -1$, $b = 0$, $c = 0$, and $d = -2$, we have $a + d = -3 < 0$ and $ad - bc = 2 > 0$.

Exercises for Section 11.2

1. Locate the critical points of the given equation, or system of equations. Determine whether or not each critical point is isolated.

    (a) $\dfrac{d^2x}{dt^2} + \dfrac{dx}{dt} + (x^2 - 1) = 0$

    (b) $\dfrac{d^2x}{dt^2} + \sin x = 0$

    (c) $\dfrac{dx}{dt} = x - y, \quad \dfrac{dy}{dt} = x^2 - 3y + 2$

(d) $\dfrac{dx}{dt} = y^2 - 3x + 2, \qquad \dfrac{dy}{dt} = x^2 - y^2$

(e) $\dfrac{dx}{dt} = \cos y, \qquad \dfrac{dy}{dt} = \sin x$

2. If $ad - bc = 0$, show that the system (11.6) possesses infinitely many critical points, none of which is isolated.

3. (a) If $AD - BC \neq 0$, show that the system

$$\dfrac{dx}{dt} = Ax + By + E, \qquad \dfrac{dy}{dt} = Cx + Dy + F$$

possesses a single critical point (x_0, y_0).

(b) Show that the system of part (a) can be put in the form (11.6) by means of the change of variables $u = x - x_0$, $v = y - y_0$.

4. Show that a critical point of a system (11.5) which is not isolated cannot be asymptotically stable.

5. Prove the corollary to Theorem 11.1.

6. Determine whether the origin is a stable or unstable critical point for the given system. If it is stable, determine whether it is asymptotically stable.

(a) $\dfrac{dx}{dt} = y, \qquad \dfrac{dy}{dt} = -4x$

(b) $\dfrac{dx}{dt} = -x + y, \qquad \dfrac{dy}{dt} = x - 2y$

(c) $\dfrac{dx}{dt} = 2x + y, \qquad \dfrac{dy}{dt} = 3x - 2y$

(d) $\dfrac{dx}{dt} = -x + 2y, \qquad \dfrac{dy}{dt} = -2x - y$

7. Consider the equation

$$\dfrac{d^2 x}{dt^2} + a \dfrac{dx}{dt} + bx = 0,$$

where a and b are constants.

(a) Show that the equation has an isolated critical point at $(0, 0)$ if, and only if, $b \neq 0$.

(b) Show that the critical point $(0, 0)$ is asymptotically stable if, and only if, $a > 0$ and $b > 0$.

8. Show that the equation $d^2x/dt^2 = 2x^3$ has an isolated critical point at $(0, 0)$ which is unstable. *Suggestion*: Sketch some of the trajectories.

9. Show that the origin is a stable, but not an asymptotically stable, critical point for the system

$$\frac{dx}{dt} = ye^{x+y}, \qquad \frac{dy}{dt} = -xe^{x+y}.$$

Suggestion: Find equations of the trajectories (not the solutions).

11.3 THE METHOD OF LIAPUNOV

We begin with some geometrical considerations. Associated with the autonomous system

$$\frac{dx}{dt} = P(x, y), \qquad \frac{dy}{dt} = Q(x, y) \qquad (11.12)$$

is the vector function

$$\mathbf{V}(x, y) = P(x, y)\mathbf{i} + Q(x, y)\mathbf{j}.$$

At a point that is not a critical point of the system, $\mathbf{V}$ has a definite direction. We call the function $\mathbf{V}$ the *direction field* of the system. Consider a trajectory described by the solution (x, y). Suppose that

$$x(t_1) = x_1, \qquad y(t_1) = y_1,$$

and that the point (x_1, y_1) is not a critical point. Then the vector

$$x'(t_1)\mathbf{i} + y'(t_1)\mathbf{j} = \mathbf{V}(x_1, y_1)$$

is tangent to the trajectory at (x_1, y_1) and points in the direction of increasing t. If E is a function that is continuous along with its first partial derivatives in a region containing the trajectory, the rate of change of E along the trajectory is

$$\frac{d}{dt} E[x(t), y(t)] = \frac{\partial E}{\partial x}\frac{dx}{dt} + \frac{\partial E}{\partial y}\frac{dy}{dt} = \frac{\partial E}{\partial x}P + \frac{\partial E}{\partial y}Q.$$

In vector notation,

$$\frac{dE}{dt} = \mathbf{V} \cdot \text{grad } E,$$

where $\mathbf{V}$ is the direction field.

In what follows, it will sometimes be convenient to use polar coordinates (r, θ), as defined by the relations $x = r \cos \theta$, $y = r \sin \theta$. In talking about a solution (x, y) of the system (11.12), we shall write,

$$r(t) = \sqrt{[x(t)]^2 + [y(t)]^2} \ .$$

We shall also need the following definitions.

Let E be a function defined in a plane region of the form $0 \leq r < h$, where h is a positive constant, or throughout the entire plane. Let $E(0, 0) = 0$. Then

(1)   if $E(x, y) > 0$ for $r > 0$, E is said to be *positive definite*;
(2)   if $E(x, y) < 0$ for $r > 0$, E is said to be *negative definite*;
(3)   if $E(x, y) \geq 0$ for $r > 0$, E is said to be *positive semidefinite*;
(4)   if $E(x, y) \leq 0$ for $r > 0$, E is said to be *negative semidefinite*.

For example, if $E(x, y) = Ax^{2m} + By^{2n}$ for all (x, y), where A and B are positive constants and m and n are positive integers, then E is positive definite. Since a function E is positive definite if and only if $-E$ is negative definite, the function $V(x, y) = -(Ax^{2m} + By^{2n})$ is negative definite. The functions

$$E_1(x, y) = x^{2m}, \qquad E_2(x, y) = y^{2m}, \qquad E_3(x, y) = (x - y)^{2m},$$

where m is a positive integer, are positive semidefinite but they are not positive definite.

We now turn to the questions of stability and asymptotic stability of an isolated critical point (x_0, y_0) of the system (11.12). Without loss of generality, we can take the critical point to be $(0, 0)$. For if this is not the case, the translation of coordinates $u = x - x_0$, $v = y - y_0$ puts the critical point at the origin of the uv plane. The results of the next two theorems are due to A. M. Liapunov.

Theorem 11.2   In a region of the form $0 \leq r < h$, $h > 0$, let the function E be continuous along with its first partial derivatives and be positive definite. If the function

$$\frac{\partial E}{\partial x} P + \frac{\partial E}{\partial y} Q \qquad\qquad (11.13)$$

is negative semidefinite, the critical point $(0, 0)$ of the system (11.12) is stable; if the function (11.13) is negative definite, the critical point is asymptotically stable.

We remark that a positive definite function E with the property that $P(\partial E/\partial x) + Q(\partial E/\partial y)$ is negative semidefinite (in particular, negative definite) is called a *Liapunov function* for the system (11.12).

PROOF The proof is based on these ideas. The function E has a proper minimum at $(0, 0)$. The surface $z = E(x, y)$ resembles a paraboloid which is tangent to the xy plane at the origin. Along the trajectory of a solution (x, y), E is nonincreasing. We shall show that this implies that $r(t)$ cannot increase very much, at least if $r(0)$ is small. If dE/dt is negative definite, E is actually decreasing along the trajectory. We shall show that $E(t) \to 0$, which implies that $r(t) \to 0$ since E is positive definite.

Given ε, let α be a positive number such that $\alpha < \min(\varepsilon, h)$. Since the function E is positive definite, it has a positive minimum m on the circle $r = \alpha$. Since $E(x, y) \to 0$ as $(x, y) \to (0, 0)$, there is a positive number δ such that $E(x, y) < m$ whenever $r < \delta$. Let $x(t), y(t)$ be any solution of the system (11.12) for which $0 < r(0) < \delta$. Since $dE/dt \le 0$, $E[x(t), y(t)] < m$ for $t \ge 0$, and hence $r(t) < \alpha < \varepsilon$ for $t \ge 0$. Hence the critical point $(0, 0)$ is stable.

In case dE/dt is negative definite, $dE/dt < 0$, so E is a decreasing function of t that is bounded below by zero. Hence E must tend to a finite limit L as $t \to \infty$. The problem now is to show that $L = 0$. If this is the case, $r(t)$ must approach zero, since E is positive definite. We can then conclude that the critical point is asymptotically stable.

Clearly $L \ge 0$. Suppose that $L > 0$. Then $E[x(t), y(t)] \ge L$ for $t \ge 0$. Since $E(x, y) \to 0$ as $(x, y) \to (0, 0)$, there exists a positive number β such that $E(x, y) < L$ when $r < \beta$. In the region $\beta \le r \le \alpha$ the function $P\partial E/\partial x + Q\partial E/\partial y$ has a negative maximum which we denote by $-k$. Then $dE/dt \le -k$ for $t \ge 0$. Since

$$E[x(t), y(t)] = E[x(0), y(0)] + \int_0^t \frac{dE}{dt}\, dt,$$

we have

$$E[x(t), y(t)] \le E[x(0), y(0)] - kt$$

for $t \ge 0$. But the right member of this inequality becomes negatively infinite as $t \to \infty$, which contradicts the hypothesis that $E \ge 0$. Hence $L = 0$. This concludes the proof.

The difficulty in applying Theorem 11.2 lies in the problem of the construction of a suitable Liapunov function. In a given case, a certain amount of ingenuity may be required. We shall consider here one example. In the next section, a general class of problems will be considered.

Example 1 The system

$$\frac{dx}{dt} = -2y^3, \qquad \frac{dy}{dt} = 2x - y^3$$

has a single critical point at $(0, 0)$. We attempt to construct a Liapunov function of the form $E(x, y) = Ax^{2m} + By^{2n}$. For such a function,

$$\frac{dE}{dt} = 2mAx^{2m-1}(-2y^3) + 2nBy^{2n-1}(2x - y^3)$$

$$= 4(-mAx^{2m-1}y^3 + nBxy^{2n-1}) - 2nBy^{2n+2}.$$

If we choose $m = 1$, $n = 2$, $A = 2$, and $B = 1$, then $dE/dt = -4y^6$ (which is negative semidefinite) and $E(x, y) = 2x^2 + y^4$ (which is positive definite). Hence the critical point $(0, 0)$ of the system is stable. Notice that we have not proved that it is not asymptotically stable.

The next theorem gives a criterion for a critical point to be unstable. The reader is asked to supply a proof in Exercise 11.

Theorem 11.3   Let the function E be continuous along with its first partial derivatives in a region of the form $0 \le r < h$, $h > 0$. If every neighborhood of $(0, 0)$ contains at least one point where E is positive and if

$$\frac{\partial E}{\partial x} P + \frac{\partial E}{\partial y} Q$$

is positive definite, then the critical point $(0, 0)$ of the system (11.12) is unstable.

Example 2   Consider the system

$$\frac{dx}{dt} = -y^3, \qquad \frac{dy}{dt} = 3x^3 - y^3,$$

whose only critical point is at the origin. If $E(x, y) = x^2 - 2xy$, then

$$\frac{dE}{dt} = -y^3(2x - 2y) + (3x^3 - y^3)(-2x) = 6x^4 + 2y^4.$$

Hence dE/dt is positive definite. Since $E(x, 0) = x^2$, every neighborhood of $(0, 0)$ contains points (on the line $y = 0$) where E is positive. According to the theorem, the critical point is unstable.

In the construction of Liapunov functions, the following result is sometimes useful.

Theorem 11.4   The function

$$E(x, y) = Ax^2 + Bxy + Cy^2,$$

where A, B, and C are constants, is positive definite if and only if

$$A > 0, \qquad 4AC - B^2 > 0, \tag{11.14}$$

and it is negative definite if and only if

$$A < 0, \qquad 4AC - B^2 > 0. \tag{11.15}$$

PROOF   Setting $y = 0$ in the expression for $E(x, y)$, we have $E(x, 0) = Ax^2$. Hence $E(x, 0) > 0$ for $x \neq 0$ if and only if $A > 0$. For $y \neq 0$, we may write

$$E(x, y) = y^2 \left[A\left(\frac{x}{y}\right)^2 + B\left(\frac{x}{y}\right) + C \right].$$

But the polynomial $A\lambda^2 + B\lambda + C$, which is positive for large λ when $A > 0$, does not vanish or change sign if, and only if, its discriminant $B^2 - 4AC$ is negative. Hence the conditions (11.14) are necessary and sufficient that E be positive definite. The second part of the theorem can be proved by considering the function $-E$.

The results of this section can be generalized to higher dimensional systems. Exercise 12 serves to illustrate one case. More complete treatments of stability can be found in the references at the end of the chapter.

Exercises for Section 11.3

1. Determine whether the given function is positive definite, or negative definite, or neither.

    (a) $x^2 - xy + y^2$ (b) $2x^2 - 3xy + y^2$ (c) $-x^2 + 3xy - 3y^2$

2. Show that a function of the form $Ax^3 + Bx^2y + Cxy^2 + Dy^3$ can be neither positive definite nor negative definite.

3. What is the geometrical significance of the condition

    $$xP(x, y) + yQ(x, y) = V(x, y) \cdot (x\mathbf{i} + y\mathbf{j}) < 0, \qquad 0 < r < h?$$

    Show that if this condition is satisfied, the critical point $(0, 0)$ of the system (11.12) is asymptotically stable.

4. Show that the origin is an asymptotically stable critical point for the system

    $$\frac{dx}{dt} = -x^3 + y^3, \qquad \frac{dy}{dt} = -x^3 - y^3.$$

5. Show that the origin is an asymptotically stable critical point for the system

$$\frac{dx}{dt} = -x^3 - 2xy, \qquad \frac{dy}{dt} = x^2 - 3y^3.$$

6. Show that the critical point $(0, 0)$ of the system

$$\frac{dx}{dt} = -x^3 + y^2, \qquad \frac{dy}{dt} = -2xy$$

is stable.

7. Show that the system

$$\frac{dx}{dt} = x + y^2, \qquad \frac{dy}{dt} = -x^3y + y^3$$

has an unstable critical point at $(0, 0)$. *Suggestion*: Although this can be done by using Theorem 11.3, it can also be done by considering those solutions for which $y(t) = 0$ for all t.

8. Show that the origin is an unstable critical point for the system

$$\frac{dx}{dt} = x^2 + y^4, \qquad \frac{dy}{dt} = -x^2.$$

9. Suppose that $f(0) = 0$ and that $xf(x) > 0$ for $x \neq 0$ [that is, $f(x) > 0$ for $x > 0$ and $f(x) < 0$ for $x < 0$].
    (a) Show that the function

$$E(x, y) = \tfrac{1}{2}y^2 + \int_0^x f(s)\, ds$$

is positive definite.

    (b) Show that the critical point $x = 0$, $dx/dt = 0$ is stable for the equation

$$\frac{d^2x}{dt^2} + f(x) = 0.$$

10. Consider the equation

$$\frac{d^2x}{dt^2} + g(x)\frac{dx}{dt} + f(x) = 0,$$

where $f(0) = 0$ and $xf(x) > 0$ for $x \neq 0$. If $g(x) \geq 0$ in some interval $|x| < h$, show that the critical point $x = 0$, $dx/dt = 0$ is stable.

11. Prove Theorem 11.3.

12. Consider the n-dimensional system

$$\frac{dx_i}{dt} = F_i(x_1, x_2, \ldots, x_n), \qquad i = 1, 2, \ldots, n,$$

where $F_i(0, 0, \ldots, 0) = 0$ for $1 \le i \le n$. Definitions of critical point, stability, asymptotic stability, positive definite function, and so on, can be formulated in analogy with the case $n = 2$. State these definitions. Then state and prove the generalization of Theorem 11.2 for the n-dimensional case. *Suggestion*: Write $r = (x_1^2 + x_2^2 + \cdots + x_n^2)^{1/2}$.

11.4 PERTURBED LINEAR SYSTEMS

Suppose that the system

$$\frac{dx}{dt} = P(x, y), \qquad \frac{dy}{dt} = Q(x, y)$$

has a critical point at $(0, 0)$. If the functions P and Q can be expanded in Taylor series of two variables about the point $(0, 0)$, then we have

$$\frac{dx}{dt} = P_x(0, 0)x + P_y(0, 0)y + \cdots,$$

$$\frac{dy}{dt} = Q_x(0, 0)x + Q_y(0, 0)y + \cdots,$$

where the dots indicate terms of second degree and higher in x and y. When $|x|$ and $|y|$ are small, these higher-degree terms, and their sums, will be very small. If we simply omit these terms, the resulting system is linear. It is interesting to consider what properties of solutions of the nonlinear system are preserved in this "linearization" process.

More generally, we shall consider systems of the form

$$\frac{dx}{dt} = ax + by + p(x, y), \qquad \frac{dy}{dt} = cx + dy + q(x, y), \qquad (11.16)$$

where a, b, c, d are constants, $p(x, y)$, $q(x, y)$ are continuous along with their first partial derivatives (in a region D that contains the origin), and

$$\lim_{(x, y) \to (0, 0)} \frac{p(x, y)}{\sqrt{x^2 + y^2}} = \lim_{(x, y) \to (0, 0)} \frac{q(x, y)}{\sqrt{x^2 + y^2}} = 0. \qquad (11.17)$$

Note that these last conditions imply that $p(0, 0) = q(0, 0) = 0$, so the system has a critical point at the origin. Associated with the system (11.16) is the linear system

$$\frac{dx}{dt} = ax + by, \qquad \frac{dy}{dt} = cx + dy. \tag{11.18}$$

A system of the form (11.16), when the conditions (11.17) are satisfied, is sometimes referred to as a *perturbed linear system*. An example of such a system is

$$\frac{dx}{dt} = -y + x^2, \qquad \frac{dy}{dt} = x - y + 2xy,$$

with $p(x, y) = x^2$, and $q(x, y) = 2xy$. Using polar coordinates r and θ, we see that

$$\frac{|p(x, y)|}{\sqrt{x^2 + y^2}} = \left| \frac{r^2 \cos^2 \theta}{r} \right| \le r, \qquad \frac{|q(x, y)|}{\sqrt{x^2 + y^2}} = \left| \frac{2r^2 \cos \theta \sin \theta}{r} \right| \le 2r,$$

so $p(x, y)/r$ and $q(x, y)/r$ approach zero as $(x, y) \to (0, 0)$. Hence the conditions (11.17) are satisfied.

We now prove a theorem about the asymptotic stability of a critical point of a perturbed linear system.

Theorem 11.5   If the critical point $(0, 0)$ of the linear system (11.18) is asymptotically stable, then the critical point $(0, 0)$ of the nonlinear system (11.16) is also asymptotically stable.

PROOF   To prove the theorem, we shall exhibit a Liapunov function for the nonlinear system. We define

$$E(x, y) = \tfrac{1}{2}(Ax^2 + 2Bxy + Cy^2),$$

where

$$A = \frac{c^2 + d^2 + (ad - bc)}{\Delta}, \qquad B = -\frac{ac + bd}{\Delta},$$

$$C = \frac{a^2 + b^2 + (ad - bc)}{\Delta}, \qquad \Delta = -(a + d)(ad - bc).$$

In view of the corollary to Theorem 11.1, $a + d < 0$ and $ad - bc > 0$, so $\Delta > 0$ and $A > 0$. Also,

$$\begin{aligned}
\Delta^2(AC - B^2) &= [(a^2 + b^2 + c^2 + d^2)(ad - bc) + (a^2 + b^2)(c^2 + d^2)] \\
&\quad - (a^2c^2 + 2abcd + b^2d^2) \\
&= (a^2 + b^2 + c^2 + d^2)(ad - bc) + 2(ad - bc)^2,
\end{aligned}$$

so $AC - B^2 > 0$. According to Theorem 11.4, the function E is positive definite.

A fairly lengthy, but routine, calculation shows that†

$$(ax + by)\frac{\partial E}{\partial x} + (cx + dy)\frac{\partial E}{\partial y} = -(x^2 + y^2)$$

and this function is clearly negative definite. Hence the function E is a Liapunov function for the linear system (11.18). We shall show that it is also a Liapunov function for the nonlinear system (11.16).

Setting

$$P(x, y) = ax + by + p(x, y)$$

and

$$Q(x, y) = cx + dy + q(x, y),$$

we have

$$P\frac{\partial E}{\partial x} + Q\frac{\partial E}{\partial y} = -(x^2 + y^2) + (Ax + By)p(x, y) + (Bx + Cy)q(x, y).$$

In terms of polar coordinates, this expression can be written as

$$-r^2 + r[(A \cos \theta + B \sin \theta)p(x, y) + (B \cos \theta + C \sin \theta)q(x, y)].$$

Let $M = \max(|A|, |B|, |C|)$. In view of our hypothesis (11.17), there exists a positive constant h such that

$$|p(x, y)| < \frac{r}{6M}, \qquad |q(x, y)| < \frac{r}{6M}$$

whenever $0 \le r < h$. Then, for $0 < r < h$, we have

$$P\frac{\partial E}{\partial x} + Q\frac{\partial E}{\partial y} < -r^2 + 4Mr\frac{r}{6M} = -\frac{1}{3}r^2 < 0.$$

Hence the function E is a Liapunov function for the system (11.16). We conclude that the critical point $(0, 0)$ of this system is asymptotically stable.

The next result is an immediate consequence of the corollary following Theorem 11.1.

Theorem 11.6   If $a + d < 0$ and $ad > bc$, the origin is an asymptotically stable critical point for the nonlinear system (11.16).

† The function E was actually constructed by attempting to find constants A, B, C, such that this relation held.

Example 1   Let us again consider the system

$$\frac{dx}{dt} = -y + x^2, \qquad \frac{dy}{dt} = x - y + 2xy,$$

which we showed earlier in this section to be of the type (11.16). The associated linear system is

$$\frac{dx}{dt} = -y, \qquad \frac{dy}{dt} = x - y.$$

In this system, $a = 0$, $b = -1$, $c = 1$, and $d = -1$. Then $a + d = -1 < 0$ and $ad - bc = 1 > 0$. According to Theorem 11.6 the origin is an asymptotically stable critical point for the nonlinear system.

Example 2   As a second example, let us consider the damped motion of a simple pendulum (Exercise 9, Section 1.11). If the pendulum has mass m and length L, and if the damping force is equal to c times the velocity, we have

$$mL^2 \frac{d^2\theta}{dt^2} + cL^2 \frac{d\theta}{dt} + mgL \sin \theta = 0$$

or

$$\frac{d^2\theta}{dt^2} + \frac{c}{m}\frac{d\theta}{dt} + \frac{g}{L} \sin \theta = 0.$$

Setting $\theta = x$ and $d\theta/dt = y$, we obtain the system formulation

$$\frac{dx}{dt} = y, \qquad \frac{dy}{dt} = -\frac{c}{m}y - \frac{g}{L}\sin x.$$

Since

$$\sin x = x - \frac{x^3}{3!} + \cdots,$$

we may write

$$\frac{dx}{dt} = y, \qquad \frac{dy}{dt} = -\frac{g}{L}x - \frac{c}{m}y + \frac{g}{L}(x - \sin x),$$

where

$$\lim_{(x,\,y)\to(0,\,0)} \frac{g}{L}\frac{x - \sin x}{\sqrt{x^2 + y^2}} = 0.$$

It is easy to verify that the critical point $(0, 0)$ of the associated linear system

$$\frac{dx}{dt} = y, \qquad \frac{dy}{dt} = -\frac{g}{L}x - \frac{c}{m}y$$

is asymptotically stable. Consequently the origin is also an asymptotically stable critical point for the nonlinear system. Thus, for small initial disturbances, the oscillations of the pendulum die out with time.

The linear system (11.18) has an unstable critical point if either or both of the roots of the equation

$$\lambda^2 - (a + d)\lambda + (ad - bc) = 0 \qquad\qquad (11.19)$$

has a positive real part. This can be seen from the discussion in Section 11.2. It can be shown (Exercise 1) that there is a root with a positive real part if and only if at least one of the inequalities $a + d > 0$, $ad - bc < 0$ is satisfied. The following result, a proof of which can be found in the references, concerns the nonlinear system.

Theorem 11.7 If either, or both, of the inequalities

$$a + d > 0, \qquad ad < bc$$

is satisfied, the origin is an unstable critical point for the system (11.16).

Example 3 The origin is unstable for the system

$$\frac{dx}{dt} = x + p(x, y), \qquad \frac{dy}{dt} = y + q(x, y)$$

if p and q satisfy the conditions (11.17), since $a + d = 2 > 0$.

Exercises for Section 11.4

1. Show that Eq. (11.19) possesses a root with a positive real part if and only if at least one of the inequalities $a + d > 0$, $ad - bc < 0$ is satisfied. *Suggestion*: Show that both roots possess nonpositive real parts if and only if $a + d \leq 0$ and $ad - bc \geq 0$. Consider the cases where both roots are complex and both are real separately.

In Exercises 2–5, verify that the origin is a critical point for the given system, and investigate its stability.

2. $\dfrac{dx}{dt} = -x + y - 2xy$, $\dfrac{dy}{dt} = -y + xy - y^3$

3. $\dfrac{dx}{dt} = -3y + x \cos y$, $\dfrac{dy}{dt} = x - 2y + x^2$

4. $\dfrac{dx}{dt} = 2x + y + x(e^y - 1)$, $\dfrac{dy}{dt} = x + y + 3xy^4$

5. $\dfrac{dx}{dt} = x + (x^2 + y^2)^{3/2}$, $\dfrac{dy}{dt} = x + 2y$

In Exercises 6 and 7, find all the critical points of the system and investigate their stability.

6. $\dfrac{dx}{dt} = x + y$, $\dfrac{dy}{dt} = -3x - 2y + x^2$

7. $\dfrac{dx}{dt} = -x + y^2$, $\dfrac{dy}{dt} = x + y - 2y^2$

8. Show that the system

$$\frac{dx}{dt} = xy, \qquad \frac{dy}{dt} = y^2 - x^2$$

has an unstable critical point at the origin. (Notice that Theorem 11.7 does not apply.) *Suggestion*: Find some solutions (x, y) with $x(t) = 0$.

9. The Lotka–Volterra equations for the populations x and y of competing species are (Section 8.6)

$$\frac{dx}{dt} = hx(1 - ax - by), \qquad \frac{dy}{dt} = ky(1 - cx - dy),$$

where h, k, a, b, c, and d are positive constants.

(a)   Find all the critical points of the system and discuss their biological significance.

(b)   Assuming that the system has a critical point (x_0, y_0) in the first quadrant, determine sufficient conditions to be satisfied by the constants of the system for it to be asymptotically stable.

10. If the critical point $(0, 0)$ of the linear system (11.18) is stable, but not asymptotically stable, the origin may or may not be stable for the nonlinear system (11.16). Show this by proving that $(0, 0)$ is asymptotically stable for the system

$$\frac{dx}{dt} = y - x^3, \qquad \frac{dy}{dt} = -x - y^3,$$

but unstable for the system

$$\frac{dx}{dt} = y + x^3, \qquad \frac{dy}{dt} = -x + y^3.$$

11. (a) Show that both roots of Eq. (11.19) have positive real parts if and only if $a + d > 0$ and $ad - bc > 0$. *Suggestion*: Let $\lambda = -\mu$.

(b) Prove that the origin is an unstable critical point for the nonlinear system (11.16) if *both* roots of Eq. (11.19) have positive real parts. *Suggestion*: Find a function E of the form

$$E(x, y) = \tfrac{1}{2}(Ax^2 + 2Bxy + Cy^2)$$

such that

$$(ax + by)E_x(x, y) + (cx + dy)E_y(x, y) = x^2 + y^2.$$

11.5 PERIODIC SOLUTIONS

It will be recalled that a solution (x, y) of the system

$$\frac{dx}{dt} = P(x, y), \qquad \frac{dy}{dt} = Q(x, y) \qquad (11.20)$$

is said to be periodic with period T if the solution exists for all t and if $x(t + T) = x(t)$, $y(t + T) = y(t)$ for all t. The trajectory of a periodic solution is a closed curve in the phase plane. If P and Q possess continuous first partial derivatives (in a region D), then only one trajectory can pass through a given point. Consequently, if a solution (x, y) exists for $t_0 \le t \le t_0 + T$ for some number t_0, and if

$$x(t_0 + T) = x(t_0), \qquad y(t_0 + T) = y(t_0),$$

then the solution must exist for all t and be periodic with period T. Of course, a constant solution $x(t) = x_0$, $y(t) = y_0$, which corresponds to a critical point of the system, is periodic. Every positive number T is a period of such a solution, according to our definition. From now on, when we speak of a periodic solution, we shall mean a nonconstant periodic solution.

In the case of a linear system,

$$\frac{dx}{dt} = ax + by, \qquad \frac{dy}{dt} = cx + dy, \qquad (11.21)$$

a periodic solution occurs when and only when the roots of the auxiliary equation

$$\lambda^2 - (a + d)\lambda + (ad - bc) = 0$$

are pure imaginary. In this case, *every* nonconstant solution is periodic. The trajectories are ellipses (Exercise 1). Thus, for a linear system, either every nonconstant solution is periodic or else no solution (other than $x(t) = y(t) = 0$) is periodic.

For a nonlinear system, this is not the case, as the following example shows.

Example 1   Consider the system

$$\frac{dx}{dt} = -y + x(1 - x^2 - y^2), \qquad \frac{dy}{dt} = x + y(1 - x^2 - y^2). \quad (11.22)$$

Solutions of this system can be found by introducing polar coordinates r, θ, where

$$x = r \cos \theta, \qquad y = r \sin \theta.$$

Implicit differentiation yields the relations

$$x\frac{dx}{dt} + y\frac{dy}{dt} = r\frac{dr}{dt}, \qquad x\frac{dy}{dt} - y\frac{dx}{dt} = r^2\frac{d\theta}{dt}$$

between the derivatives with respect to t of x and y and the derivatives of r and θ. If we multiply through in the first equation of the system (11.22) by x and in the second by y, and add, we find that

$$r\frac{dr}{dt} = r^2(1 - r^2).$$

Similarly, if we multiply through in the first equation by y and in the second by x, and subtract, we find that

$$r^2\frac{d\theta}{dt} = r^2.$$

Now $r = 0$ corresponds to the solution $x = 0$, $y = 0$ of the system (11.22). For $r \neq 0$ we consider the system

$$\frac{dr}{dt} = r(1 - r^2), \qquad \frac{d\theta}{dt} = 1.$$

The equations are uncoupled and separable, and the solutions are found to be

$$r(t) = \frac{1}{\sqrt{1 + c_1 e^{-2t}}}, \qquad \theta(t) = t + c_2, \quad (11.23)$$

where c_1 and c_2 are constants. The corresponding solutions of the original system are

$$x(t) = \frac{\cos(t + c_2)}{\sqrt{1 + c_1 e^{-2t}}}, \qquad y(t) = \frac{\sin(t + c_2)}{\sqrt{1 + c_1 e^{-2t}}}.$$

Let us now study the relations (11.23). For $c_1 = 0$, we have the solution

$$r(t) = 1, \qquad \theta(t) = t + c_2,$$

which describes the circular trajectory $x^2 + y^2 = 1$. When $c_1 < 0$, we see that $r > 1$ and that $r \to 1$ as $t \to \infty$. When $c_1 > 0$, we have $r < 1$, and again $r \to 1$ as $t \to \infty$. Thus the other trajectories spiral toward the circle $x^2 + y^2 = 1$ as $t \to \infty$, either from the inside or from the outside. This situation is illustrated in Fig. 11.5. The nonlinear system (11.22) possesses only one closed trajectory.

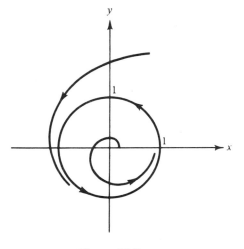

Figure 11.5

We were able to show the existence of a periodic solution of the system (11.22) by actually finding the solutions of the system. In most cases, however, we cannot expect to be able to do this. Sufficient conditions for the existence of a periodic solution are given by the Poincare–Bendixon theorem, which we now state without proof.

Theorem 11.8 Let P and Q possess continuous first partial derivatives in a region G. Let D be a *bounded* region such that D and its boundary are contained in G. Let R denote the region that consists of D and its boundary and assume that R contains no critical point of the system (11.20). If (x, y) is a solution of the system such that $(x(t), y(t))$ exists and stays in R for $t \geq t_0$, for some number t_0, then either (a) the solution is periodic, or (b) the solution spirals toward a periodic solution of the system (11.20) as $t \to \infty$. In either case, the system possesses a periodic solution.

The difficulty in applying the Poincare–Bendixon theorem is in showing that a solution stays inside a region R. One way to do this is to show that on the boundary of R, the vector $\mathbf{V} = P\mathbf{i} + Q\mathbf{j}$ points into R. Then a solution that once enters R can never leave it.

Example 2 We consider as an illustration the system

$$\frac{dx}{dt} = 2x + y - x(x^2 + y^2)^2, \qquad \frac{dy}{dt} = -x + 2y - y(x^2 + y^2)^2.$$

This system possesses the single critical point $(0, 0)$. The component of $\mathbf{V}$ in the direction away from the origin (the radial component) is

$$\mathbf{V} \cdot \frac{x\mathbf{i} + y\mathbf{j}}{r} = \frac{1}{r} [2x^2 + xy - x^2(x^2 + y^2)^2 - xy + 2y^2 - y^2(x^2 + y^2)^2]$$

$$= \frac{1}{r} (2r^2 - r^5) = 2r - r^4.$$

On the circle $r = 1$, this component is positive, while on the circle $r = 2$, it is negative. If we take for our region R the annular region $1 \leq r \leq 2$, we see that the vector $\mathbf{V}$ points into R on the boundary of R. Also, R contains no critical points of the system. According to the Poincare–Bendixon theorem, the system must possess at least one periodic solution.

Although it is quite general, the Poincare–Bendixon theorem is usually not easy to apply. Other, less general, but more practical, critéria for the existence of periodic solutions have been developed. Liénard established the existence of periodic solutions for certain classes of equations of the general form

$$\frac{d^2x}{dt^2} + f(x)\frac{dx}{dt} + g(x) = 0. \tag{11.24}$$

(An equation of this form is called a *Liénard equation*.) Levinson and Smith later gave more general results. We shall present one theorem without proof. In order to state the theorem, we define the functions F and G as

$$F(x) = \int_0^x f(s)\,ds, \qquad G(x) = \int_0^x g(s)\,ds,$$

where f and g are the same functions that appear in the equation (11.24).

Theorem 11.9 Let the functions f and g' be continuous everywhere and satisfy the following conditions:

(a) f is even and g is odd, with $g(x) > 0$ for $x > 0$.

(b) There exists a positive number a such that $F(x) < 0$ for $0 < x < a$, $F(x) > 0$ for $x > a$, and F is monotonically increasing† on (a, ∞).

(c) $\lim_{x \to \infty} F(x) = \infty$, $\lim_{x \to \infty} G(x) = \infty$.

Then the equation (11.24) possesses a periodic solution whose closed trajectory encloses the origin of the phase plane. This periodic solution is unique in the sense that the equation has no other closed trajectory. Furthermore, every other trajectory except the point $(0, 0)$ spirals toward the closed trajectory as $t \to \infty$.

Example 3   As an application for this theorem, we consider the *van der Pol* equation

$$\frac{d^2x}{dt^2} + \mu(x^2 - 1)\frac{dx}{dt} + x = 0,$$

where μ is a positive constant. This equation arises in the study of vacuum tube circuits. Here $f(x) = \mu(x^2 - 1)$ and $g(x) = x$. Clearly f is even and g is odd, and $g(x) > 0$ for $x > 0$. Since $F(x) = \mu(\frac{1}{3}x^3 - x)$ and $G(x) = \frac{1}{2}x^2$, we have $F(x) \to \infty$ and $G(x) \to \infty$ as $x \to \infty$. Also, writing $F(x) = \frac{1}{3}\mu x(x^2 - 3)$, we see that $F(x) < 0$ for $0 < x < \sqrt{3}$ and $F(x) > 0$ for $x > \sqrt{3}$. Since $F'(x) = f(x) = \mu(x^2 - 1)$ is positive for $x > 1$, certainly $F(x)$ is increasing for $x > \sqrt{3}$. Thus the hypotheses of Theorem 11.9 are satisfied and we conclude that the equation has a periodic solution.

Exercises for Section 11.5

1. Show that when the roots of its auxiliary equation are pure imaginary, the trajectories of the linear system (11.21) are ellipses.

2. Find the solutions of the system

$$\frac{dx}{dt} = y + 8x(x^2 + y^2 - 4), \qquad \frac{dy}{dt} = -x + 8y(x^2 + y^2 - 4).$$

Show on a graph the pattern of the trajectories.

---

† A function F is said to be monotonically increasing if $F(x_2) \geq F(x_1)$ whenever $x_2 > x_1$. A sufficient condition for F to be monotonically increasing on an interval is that $F'(x) \geq 0$ for all x in the interval.

3. Show that the system

$$\frac{dx}{dt} = 3x + y - x\exp(x^2 + y^2), \qquad \frac{dy}{dt} = -x + 3y - y\exp(x^2 + y^2)$$

possesses at least one periodic solution.

4. Show that the given equation possesses a periodic solution:

(a) $\dfrac{d^2x}{dt^2} + (x^4 - x^2)\dfrac{dx}{dt} + x = 0$;

(b) $\dfrac{d^2x}{dt^2} + c(x^{2m} - k^2)\dfrac{dx}{dt} + x^{2n-1} = 0$,

where c and k are positive constants, and m and n are positive integers.

5. Consider the equation $(d^2x/dt^2) + f(x) = 0$, where $f(0) = 0$ and $xf(x) > 0$ for $x \neq 0$. Show that the trajectories are closed curves that enclose the origin. *Suggestion*: Show that the trajectories are given by $\frac{1}{2}y^2 + F(x) = C$, where

$$F(x) = \int_0^x f(s)\,ds.$$

6. (a) Assume that the system (11.20) has an isolated critical point at $(0, 0)$. Also assume that there exists a positive definite Liapunov function E such that $P(\partial E/\partial x) + Q(\partial E/\partial y)$ is identically zero in a region of the form $0 \leq r \leq h$. Show that the equation possesses a periodic solution. *Suggestion*: Use the Poincare–Bendixon theorem.

(b) Show that the equation of Exercise 5 is a special case, with

$$E(x, y) = \tfrac{1}{2}y^2 + F(x).$$

(c) Show that the system

$$\frac{dx}{dt} = -x^3y + y^2, \qquad \frac{dy}{dt} = -xy + x^4$$

possesses a periodic solution.

REFERENCES

1. Cesari, L., *Asymptotic Behavior and Stability Problems in Ordinary Differential Equations*. Springer, Berlin, 1959.
2. Coddington, E. A., and Levinson, N., *Theory of Ordinary Differential Equations*. McGraw-Hill, New York, 1955.

3. Hahn, W., *Theory and Application of Liapunov's Direct Method*. Prentice-Hall, Englewood Cliffs, New Jersey, 1963.
4. Hurewicz, W., *Lectures on Ordinary Differential Equations*. MIT Press, Cambridge, Massachusetts. 1958.
5. LaSalle, J. P., and Lefschetz, S., *Stability by Liapunov's Direct Method with Applications*. Academic Press, New York, 1961.
6. Lefschetz, S., *Differential Equations: Geometric Theory*, 2nd ed. Wiley, New York, 1963.
7. Pontryagin, L. S., *Ordinary Differential Equations*. Addison-Wesley, Reading, Massachusetts, 1962.
8. Saaty, T. L., and Bram. J., *Nonlinear Mathematics*. McGraw-Hill, New York, 1964.

XII

Existence
and Uniqueness of Solutions

12.1 PRELIMINARIES

Let us consider an initial value problem for a first-order differential equation,

$$y' = f(x, y), \qquad y(x_0) = k, \tag{12.1}$$

where the function f is defined in some region D of the xy-plane that contains the point (x_0, k). We now pose the general questions of whether the problem has a solution, and if it does, whether there can be more than one solution. In other words, we want to know if a solution *exists*, and if it does, whether the solution is *unique*.

In a specific case where it is possible to find a formula that describes the set of all solutions, it may be easy to answer these questions. Our concern is with a more general situation. Consider, for example, the problem

$$y' = x^2 + y^4, \qquad y(0) = 1.$$

Here we cannot find a simple formula for the general solution of the differential equation. Nevertheless, it can be shown that a solution of the initial value problem exists and that it is unique.

It will be necessary to impose some restrictions on the function f in the problem (12.1). One is that f be continuous. We shall also require that f satisfy a condition known as a *Lipschitz condition*. A function $f(x, y)$ is said to satisfy a Lipschitz condition with respect to y in a region D of the xy-plane if there exists a positive number K such that

$$|f(x, y_1) - f(x, y_2)| \leq K|y_1 - y_2|$$

whenever the points (x, y_1) and (x, y_2) both lie in D. The number K is called a *Lipschitz constant* for f.

As an example, let us consider a function of the form

$$f(x, y) = p(x)y + q(x),$$

where p and q are defined on a closed interval $[a, b]$. If p is continuous in $[a, b]$, then f satisfies a Lipschitz condition in the region D that consists of the points (x, y) for which $a \leq x \leq b$. For $|p|$ has a maximum value K on $[a, b]$ and hence

$$|f(x, y_1) - f(x, y_2)| = |p(x)(y_1 - y_2)| \leq K|y_1 - y_2|$$

for (x, y_1) and (x, y_2) in D.

Next, suppose that $f(x, y)$ is any function that is continuous, along with its first partial derivative with respect to y, on a rectangle R of the form

$$R = \{(x, y) : a \leq x \leq b, \quad c \leq y \leq d\}.$$

Then f satisfies a Lipschitz condition in R. To see this, let (x, y_1) and (x, y_2) be in R. We may use the mean value theorem to write

$$f(x, y_1) - f(x, y_2) = f_y(x, y_3)(y_1 - y_2),$$

where y_3 is between y_1 and y_2. If K is the maximum value of $|f_y|$ on R, then

$$|f(x, y_1) - f(x, y_2)| \leq K|y_1 - y_2|.$$

In order to study the questions posed about the initial value problem, it will be convenient to reformulate that problem in a manner now to be described. If a function u is a solution of the initial value problem (12.1) on an interval $\mathscr{I}$ that contains x_0, then

$$u'(x) = f[x, u(x)] \tag{12.2}$$

for x in $\mathscr{I}$, and

$$u(x_0) = k. \tag{12.3}$$

If f is continuous in a region that contains the points $[x, u(x)]$ for x in $\mathscr{I}$, then u' is continuous on $\mathscr{I}$. Integrating both members of Eq. (12.2) from x_0 to x, we have

$$u(x) = y_0 + \int_{x_0}^{x} f[t, u(t)] \, dt \tag{12.4}$$

for x in $\mathcal{I}$. Thus a solution of the initial value problem (12.1) is also a solution of the integral equation (12.4). On the other hand, suppose that u is a continuous function that satisfies Eq. (12.4). Setting $x = x_0$ in that equation, we see that $u(x_0) = y_0$. Upon differentiating both members of the equation, we see that $u'(x) = f[x, u(x)]$. Hence the initial value problem (12.1) is equivalent to the integral equation (12.4). In the next section we shall exhibit a method for the construction of a solution of the integral equation.

Exercises for Section 12.1

1. Let $f(x, y) = xy^2$ for all (x, y).

    (a) Show that f satisfies a Lipschitz condition on any rectangle of the form $a \leq x \leq b, c \leq y \leq d$.

    (b) Show that f satisfies a Lipschitz condition on any *bounded* region. (A region is bounded if it is contained in the interior of some circle.)

    (c) Show that f does not satisfy a Lipschitz condition in the region that consists of the entire xy-plane.

2. If $f(x, y)$ satisfies a Lipschitz condition with respect to y in a region D, show that f is a continuous function of y for each fixed x.

3. If $f(x, y)$ and $f_y(x, y)$ are continuous and $f_y(x, y)$ is bounded on a convex region D, show that f satisfies a Lipschitz condition on D. (A region D is convex if for every pair of points in D the line segment joining the points is in D.) Where in your proof is the assumption of convexity needed?

4. Let $f(x, y)$ and $g(x, y)$ satisfy Lipschitz conditions with respect to y in a region D. Show that

    (a) $f + g$ satisfies a Lipschitz condition.

    (b) fg does not necessarily satisfy a Lipschitz condition.

5. If $f(x, y) = y^{2/3}$, show that f does not satisfy a Lipschitz condition in any rectangle of the form $|x| \leq a, |y| \leq b$.

6. If $f(x, y) = (\sin y)/(1 + x^2)$ for all (x, y), show that f satisfies a Lipschitz condition.

7. Find an integral equation that is equivalent to the given initial value problem.

    (a) $y' = xy + y^2$, $y(1) = 2$ (b) $y' = \sin xy$, $y(0) = 1$

8. Find a solution of the given integral equation.

(a) $y(x) = 5 + \int_0^x [e^t + y(t)]\, dt$

(b) $y(x) = -1 + \int_0^x [y(t)]^2 \sin t \, dt$

12.2 SUCCESSIVE APPROXIMATIONS

As explained at the end of Section 12.1, we can establish the existence of a solution of the initial value problem

$$y' = f(x, y), \qquad y(x_0) = k, \qquad (12.5)$$

by showing that the integral equation

$$y(x) = k + \int_{x_0}^x f[t, y(t)]\, dt \qquad (12.6)$$

has a continuous solution.

Theorem 12.1 Let the function f be continuous and satisfy a Lipschitz condition on the rectangle

$$R = \{(x, y) : |x - x_0| \le a, \quad |y - k| \le b\}.$$

If M is a positive number such that $|f(x, y)| \le M$ for (x, y) in R (the existence of such a number M is assured because f is continuous and hence bounded on the closed rectangle) and if

$$\alpha = \min\left(a, \frac{b}{M}\right),$$

then the initial value problem (12.5) has a solution on the interval $[x_0 - \alpha, x_0 + \alpha]$. The solution of the problem is unique in the following sense. If u and v are both solutions on an interval $\mathscr{I}$ that contains x_0, then $u(x) = v(x)$ for all x in $\mathscr{I}$.

PROOF The proof of the existence of a solution involves the construction of a sequence of functions which can be shown to converge to a solution of the problem. The functions of the sequence are sometimes called *successive approximations*, and hence the title of this section. The name of Picard is associated with this method. We define the functions of our sequence by means of the formulas

$$y_0(x) = k, \tag{12.7}$$

$$y_n(x) = k + \int_{x_0}^x f[t, y_{n-1}(t)] \, dt \tag{12.8}$$

for $n \geq 1$ and for $|x - x_0| \leq \alpha$. Actually, for y_n to be well defined, y_{n-1} must be defined and continuous and the points $(x, y_{n-1}(x))$, $|x - x_0| \leq \alpha$, must lie in the rectangle R. We shall use mathematical induction to show that each function y_n is defined, continuous, and satisfies $|y_n(x) - k| \leq b$ for $|x - x_0| \leq \alpha$.

Certainly the constant function y_0 is defined and continuous, and we have $|y_0(x) - k| = 0 < b$ for $|x - x_0| \leq \alpha$. Suppose that y_k is defined and continuous and that $(x, y_k(x))$ is in R for $|x - x_0| \leq \alpha$. Then $f[x, y_k(x)]$ is defined and continuous and y_{k+1}, where

$$y_{k+1}(x) = k + \int_{x_0}^x f[t, y_k(t)] \, dt,$$

is defined and continuous. Also

$$|y_{k+1}(x) - k| \leq \left| \int_{x_0}^x |f[t, y_k(t)]| \, dt \right| \leq \left| \int_{x_0}^x M \, dt \right|,$$

so that

$$|y_{k+1}(x) - k| \leq M|x - x_0| \leq M\alpha \leq b.$$

Thus $(x, y_{k+1}(x))$ is in R for $|x - x_0| \leq \alpha$. Hence each function y_n of the sequence is defined and continuous, and

$$|y_n(x) - k| \leq M\alpha \leq b \qquad \text{for} \quad n = 0, 1, 2, \ldots.$$

The next order of business is to show that the sequence converges. In order to do this, it suffices to show that the infinite series

$$y_0 + \sum_{n=1}^{\infty} (y_n - y_{n-1}) \tag{12.9}$$

converges, because the nth partial sum of this series is y_n. We shall use a comparison test. From Eq. (12.8) with $n = 1$, we have

$$|y_1(x) - k| \leq \left| \int_{x_0}^x |f(t, k)| \, dt \right| \leq M|x - x_0|.$$

Next, since

$$y_2(x) = k + \int_{x_0}^x f[t, y_1(t)] \, dt,$$

$$y_1(x) = k + \int_{x_0}^x f[t, y_0(t)] \, dt,$$

we have (subtracting)

$$y_2(x) - y_1(x) = \int_x^{x_0} \{f[t, y_1(t)] - f[t, y_0(t)]\} \, dt.$$

If K is a Lipschitz constant for f, then

$$|f[t, y_1(t)] - f(t, y_0)| < K|y_1(t) - y_0(t)| \le KM|t - x_0|.$$

Consequently, we see that

$$|y_2(x) - y_1(x)| \le KM \left| \int_{x_0}^x |t - x_0| \, dt \right|, \qquad |x - x_0| \le \alpha.$$

By considering the cases $x \ge x_0$ and $x < x_0$ separately, we find that

$$|y_2(x) - y_1(x)| \le \frac{KM|x - x_0|^2}{2}.$$

It can be shown by mathematical induction (Exercise 4) that

$$|y_n(x) - y_{n-1}(x)| \le \frac{MK^{n-1}|x - x_0|^n}{n!} \tag{12.10}$$

for $|x - x_0| \le \alpha$ and $n = 1, 2, 3, \ldots.$ Thus

$$|y_n(x) - y_{n-1}(x)| \le \frac{MK^{n-1}\alpha^n}{n!} \tag{12.11}$$

for $|x - x_0| \le \alpha$ and $n \ge 1$. The series of constants

$$|k| + \sum_{n=1}^{\infty} \frac{MK^{n-1}\alpha^n}{n!}$$

converges (as can be shown by the ratio test). Hence the series (12.9) converges and the sequence $\{y_n\}$ converges. Let us denote the limit function by y. Since $|y_n(x) - k| \le b$ for $|x - x_0| \le \alpha$ we must have $|y(x) - k| \le b$ for $|x - x_0| \le \alpha$.

We must now show that the function y is continuous and is a solution of the integral equation (12.6). The key to the investigation of these matters is the concept of *uniform convergence*. A sequence of functions $\{f_n\}$ is said to converge uniformly to a function f on an interval $\mathscr{I}$ if for every positive number ε there is an integer $N(\varepsilon)$ such that

$$|f_n(x) - f(x)| < \varepsilon \tag{12.12}$$

whenever

$$n \geq N(\varepsilon) \tag{12.13}$$

for all x in $\mathscr{I}$. The integer N may depend on ε but not on the point of the interval. If the sequence of functions $\{f_n\}$ converges uniformly on $\mathscr{I}$, then for each x in $\mathscr{I}$ the sequence of numbers $\{f_n(x)\}$ converges. For any given ε, there is one integer $N(\varepsilon)$ such that satisfaction of condition (12.13) ensures that the criterion (12.12) holds for all x. An infinite series of functions,

$$\sum_{n=1}^{\infty} u_n$$

is said to converge uniformly on an interval if and only if its sequence of partial sums converges uniformly on the interval.

We now state without proof two standard theorems about uniform convergence. Proofs can be found in Taylor [3].

Theorem 12.2   If a sequence or series of continuous functions converges uniformly on an interval, then the limit function is continuous on that interval.

Theorem 12.3   Suppose that each of the functions u_n, $n = 1, 2, 3, \ldots$, is defined on an interval $\mathscr{I}$. If there is a convergent series of nonnegative constants

$$\sum_{n=1}^{\infty} M_n$$

such that

$$|u_n(x)| \leq M_n$$

for $n \geq 1$ and for all x in $\mathscr{I}$, then the series

$$\sum_{n=1}^{\infty} u_n$$

converges uniformly on $\mathscr{I}$.

We now apply these theorems to our problem in differential equations. In view of the comparison (12.11), the series (12.9) converges uniformly on the interval $[x_0 - \alpha, x_0 + \alpha]$, by Theorem 12.3. Hence its sequence of partial sums $\{y_n\}$ converges uniformly on the same interval. Hence the limit function y is continuous, by Theorem 12.2. Next, since

$$y_n(x) - k - \int_{x_0}^{x} f[t, y_{n-1}(t)] \, dt = 0$$

for every positive integer n, we may write

$$y(x) - k - \int_{x_0}^{x} f[t, y(t)] \, dt = y(x) - y_n(x) + \int_{x_0}^{x} \{f[t, y_{n-1}(t)] - f[t, y(t)]\} \, dt .$$

Thus

$$\left| y(x) - k - \int_{x_0}^{x} f[t, y(t)] \, dt \right| \leq |y(x) - y_n(x)| + K \left| \int_{x_0}^{x} |y_{n-1}(t) - y(t)| \, dt \right| .$$

Given $\varepsilon > 0$, there is an integer $N(\varepsilon)$ such that

$$|y(x) - y_k(x)| < \frac{1}{2} \frac{\varepsilon}{1 + \alpha K}$$

whenever $n \geq N$ and $|x - x_0| \leq \alpha$. Chosing $n = N + 1$, we see that

$$\left| y(x) - k - \int_{x_0}^{x} f[t, y(t)] \, dt \right| < \frac{1}{2} \frac{\varepsilon}{1 + \alpha K} + K \left| \int_{x_0}^{x} \frac{1}{2} \frac{\varepsilon}{1 + \alpha K} \, dt \right|$$

$$\leq \frac{1}{2} \frac{\varepsilon}{1 + \alpha K} + \frac{1}{2} \frac{\varepsilon K}{1 + \alpha K} |x - x_0|$$

$$\leq \varepsilon .$$

Since this is true for every positive number ε, we must have

$$y(x) - k - \int_{x_0}^{x} f[t, y(t)] \, dt = 0 ,$$

which we wished to show.

We now prove that the problem (12.5) can have but one solution. Suppose that u and v are both solutions on an interval $\mathcal{I}$ that contains x_0. Then

$$u(x) = k + \int_{x_0}^{x} f[t, u(t)] \, dt ,$$

$$v(x) = k + \int_{x_0}^{x} f[t, v(t)] \, dt ,$$

so that

$$u(x) - v(x) = \int_{x_0}^{x} \{f[t, u(t)] - f[t, v(t)]\} \, dt$$

for x in $\mathscr{J}$. Using the fact that f satisfies a Lipschitz condition, we have

$$|u(x) - v(x)| \le K \left| \int_{x_0}^{x} |u(t) - v(t)| \, dt \right|$$

for x in $\mathscr{J}$. An application of the lemma of Section 2.12 shows that $|u(x) - v(x)| = 0$ or $u(x) = v(x)$ for x in $\mathscr{J}$. Thus u and v must be the same and there is only one solution.

The number α that is described in Theorem 12.1 may be small even when a and b are large. To illustrate this, we consider an example.

Example 1

$$y' = 200xy^2, \qquad y(0) = 1.$$

Here the functions $f(x, y) = 200xy^2$ and $f_y(x, y) = 400xy$ are continuous everywhere, and hence on any rectangle of the form $|x| \le a$, $|y - 1| \le b$. The solution of the initial value problem is given by the formula

$$y = \frac{1}{1 - 100x^2}.$$

This solution exists only on the interval $(-1/10, 1/10)$, so it is clear that $\alpha < 1/10$ no matter how a and b are chosen.

Usually the function f and its partial derivatives will be continuous on a region D that is not a rectangle. The region may consist of the entire plane, as in the preceding example. However, Theorem 12.1 can be applied by considering a rectangle that is contained in D. The theorem then assures the existence of a solution on some interval $[x_0 - \alpha, x_0 + \alpha]$, where α may be small. It may be possible to continue or extend the solution to the right of $x_0 + \alpha$, or to the left of $x_0 - \alpha$. For instance, suppose that y is a solution on the interval $[x_0 - \alpha, x_0 + \alpha]$. If the point $P: (x_0 + \alpha, y(x_0 + \alpha))$ lies in the interior of the region D, then there is a rectangle with center at P and contained in D. According to Theorem 12.1, there is a solution $\tilde{y}$, for which $\tilde{y}(x_0 + \alpha) = y(x_0 + \alpha)$, that exists on some interval $[x_0 + \alpha - \alpha_1, x_0 + \alpha + \alpha_1]$, where $\alpha_1 > 0$. By the uniqueness part of Theorem 12.1, y and $\tilde{y}$ must coincide on the interval where both are defined. Thus the solution y is continued to the right of $x_0 + \alpha$, up to $x_0 + \alpha + \alpha_1$. If the point $(x_0 + \alpha + \alpha_1, y(x_0 + \alpha + \alpha_1))$ is in D, the solution can be continued still farther to the right. It may happen that solution can be continued to the right for all x greater than x_0. If not, it can be shown† that the solution can be continued up to a point x_1 and that as x

----

† See, for example, Hurewicz [2].

approaches x_1 from the left either $y(x)$ becomes infinite or else the point $(x, y(x))$ approaches the boundary of the region D. Similar remarks apply to the continuation of the solution to the left of $x_0 - \alpha$.

If, in Theorem 12.1, we omit the hypothesis that f satisfies a Lipschitz condition and assume only that f is continuous on the rectangle R, it is still possible to prove that a solution exists. A different method of proof must be employed in this case. Also, the solution may not be unique, as the following example shows.

Example 2

$$y' = 3y^{2/3}, \qquad y(0) = 0.$$

Here it may readily be verified that u and v, where $u(x) = 0$ and $v(x) = x^3$ for all x, are both solutions. Also, the function w, where $w(x) = 0$ for $x \le 0$ and $w(x) = x^3$ for $x > 0$, is another solution. If $f(x, y) = 3y^{2/3}$, then f is continuous on every rectangle of the form $|x| \le a$, $|y| \le b$. However, f cannot satisfy a Lipschitz condition on any such rectangle. (See, in this connection, Exercise 5, Section 12.1.)

Exercises for Section 12.2

1. Use Theorem 12.1 to show that the given initial value problem has a unique solution. In parts (a), (b), and (c) find the solution and describe the interval on which it is defined.

   (a) $y' = \frac{2}{3}x^{1/3}y^{-1}$, $y(1) = -2$ (b) $y' = y^2e^x$, $y(0) = 1$

   (c) $y' = \dfrac{x^2 + 2y^2}{xy}$, $y(1) = 2$ (d) $y' = x^2 + y^2$, $y(0) = 1$

   (e) $y' = \sin xy + 2y$, $y(0) = 0$ (f) $y' = \dfrac{1}{x^2 - y^2}$, $y(1) = 0$

2. Find the functions y_0, y_1, and y_2 in the sequence of successive approximations (12.7) and (12.8) for the case of the initial value problem

   $$y' = x + y^2 - 2, \qquad y(0) = 1.$$

3. Work Problem 2 for the initial value problem

   $$y' = \frac{x^2 - y^2}{x}, \qquad y(1) = 0.$$

4. Use mathematical induction to establish the inequality (12.10).

5. Show that the given series of functions converges uniformly on the speci-
    fied interval. Use Theorem 12.3.

(a) $\displaystyle\sum_{n=1}^{\infty} \frac{\sin nx}{n^2}$ for all x

(b) $\displaystyle\sum_{n=1}^{\infty} \frac{1}{n^2 + x^2}$ for all x

(c) $\displaystyle\sum_{n=0}^{\infty} e^{-nx}$, $x \geq a$, $a > 0$

(d) $\displaystyle\sum_{n=0}^{\infty} \frac{x^n}{n!}$, $|x| \leq a$, $a > 0$

6. Find at least two solutions of the given initial value problem.

(a) $y' = \frac{3}{2} y^{1/3}$, $y(0) = 0$

(b) $y' = 3y^{2/3}(y^{1/3} + 1)$, $y(0) = 0$

7. If y_0 were taken to be any continuous function such that $|y_0(x) - k| \leq b$
    for $|x - x_0| \leq a$, would the sequence of functions defined by Eq. (12.8)
    still converge to a solution of the initial value problem? Why?

12.3   VECTOR FUNCTIONS

The study of the theory of systems of differential equations is greatly
facilitated by the use of vector notation. This section is devoted to the basic
definitions and properties of vectors and vector functions that are needed for
such a study.

An *n-dimensional vector* is an ordered set of n real numbers that obeys
certain rules of combination with other vectors and numbers, as explained
below. We denote vectors by boldface symbols, writing

$$\mathbf{a} = (a_1, a_2, \ldots, a_n), \qquad \mathbf{b} = (b_1, b_2, \ldots, b_n),$$

where $\mathbf{a}$ and $\mathbf{b}$ are vectors and the numbers a_i and b_i are the *components* of
$\mathbf{a}$ and $\mathbf{b}$, respectively. The vectors $\mathbf{a}$ and $\mathbf{b}$ are said to be *equal*, written $\mathbf{a} = \mathbf{b}$,
if $a_i = b_i$ for $1 \leq i \leq n$. If c is a number, we define the product $c\mathbf{a}$ as

$$c\mathbf{a} = \mathbf{a}c = (ca_1, ca_2, \ldots, ca_n).$$

The *sum*, $\mathbf{a} + \mathbf{b}$, of two n-dimensional vectors is defined by the relation

$$\mathbf{a} + \mathbf{b} = (a_1 + b_1, a_2 + b_2, \ldots, a_n + b_n).$$

These two rules are the "rules of combination" mentioned earlier. The vector
whose components are all zero is denoted by $\mathbf{0}$. Thus

$$\mathbf{0} = (0, 0, \ldots, 0)$$

and $\mathbf{a} + \mathbf{0} = \mathbf{a}$ for every vector $\mathbf{a}$.

The *norm* of a vector $\mathbf{a}$, written $|\mathbf{a}|$, is defined† as

$$|\mathbf{a}| = \max_{1 \le i \le n} |a_i|.$$

Evidently $|\mathbf{a}| = 0$ if and only if $\mathbf{a} = \mathbf{0}$. We also observe that if c is a number, then

$$|c\mathbf{a}| = |c| \cdot |\mathbf{a}|.$$

A proof of the important *triangle inequality*,

$$|\mathbf{a} + \mathbf{b}| \le |\mathbf{a}| + |\mathbf{b}|,$$

is left as an exercise for the reader.

An *n-dimensional vector function* is a rule that associates with every number of an interval an n-dimensional vector. For example, a three-dimensional vector function $\mathbf{u}$ is defined by the formula

$$\mathbf{u}(t) = (3t, e^t, 1 - t^2) \qquad \text{for all } t.$$

In general, if $u_1, u_2, \ldots, u_n$ are ordinary functions of a real variable defined on a common interval, the formula

$$\mathbf{u}(t) = [u_1(t), u_2(t), \ldots, u_n(t)]$$

defines an n-dimensional vector function $\mathbf{u}$. Two n-dimensional vector functions $\mathbf{u}$ and $\mathbf{v}$ are said to be equal, written $\mathbf{u} = \mathbf{v}$, if they are defined on the same interval and if $\mathbf{u}(t) = \mathbf{v}(t)$ for all t in the interval. The sum, $\mathbf{u} + \mathbf{v}$, and the product, $c\mathbf{u}$, where c is a number, are defined by the rules

$$(\mathbf{u} + \mathbf{v})(t) = \mathbf{u}(t) + \mathbf{v}(t), \qquad (c\mathbf{u})(t) = c\mathbf{u}(t).$$

The derivative $\mathbf{u}'$ of a vector function $\mathbf{u}$ is defined as

$$\mathbf{u}'(t) = [u_1'(t), u_2'(t), \ldots, u_n'(t)].$$

The integral of a vector function $\mathbf{u}$ from a to b is defined as

$$\int_a^b \mathbf{u}(t)\, dt = \left[\int_a^b u_1(t)\, dt, \int_a^b u_2(t)\, dt, \ldots, \int_a^b u_n(t)\, dt \right].$$

For example, if

$$\mathbf{u}(t) = (3t^2, e^{-t}, 2)$$

---

† Other definitions for the norm of a vector are commonly used. Specific examples are $|\mathbf{a}| = (a_1^2 + a_2^2 + \cdots + a_n^2)^{1/2}$ and $|\mathbf{a}| = |a_1| + |a_2| + \cdots + |a_n|$. The symbol $\|\mathbf{a}\|$ is sometimes used instead of $|\mathbf{a}|$.

for all t, then

$$\mathbf{u}'(t) = (6t, -e^{-t}, 0),$$

$$\int_0^1 \mathbf{u}(t)\, dt = (1, 1 - e^{-1}, 2),$$

and

$$\int_0^t \mathbf{u}(s)\, ds = (t^3, 1 - e^{-t}, 2t).$$

If $\mathbf{u}$ is a vector function, we define $|\mathbf{u}|$ to be the scalar function with values

$$|\mathbf{u}|(t) = |\mathbf{u}(t)|.$$

Thus

$$|\mathbf{u}|(t) = \max_{1 \le i \le n} |u_i(t)|.$$

A vector function $\mathbf{u}$ is said to be *continuous* on an interval if each of its components u_i is continuous on the interval. The concept of continuity is involved in each of the next two theorems. The proofs of the theorems are left to the reader.

Theorem 12.4 If $\mathbf{u}$ is continuous on an interval, then $|\mathbf{u}|$ is continuous.

Theorem 12.5 If $\mathbf{u}$ is continuous on the interval $[a, b]$, then

$$\left| \int_a^b \mathbf{u}(t)\, dt \right| \le \int_a^b |\mathbf{u}|(t)\, dt.$$

A sequence of vectors $\{\mathbf{a}^n\}_{n=1}^\infty$ is said to converge to the vector $\mathbf{a}$ if

$$\lim_{n \to \infty} |\mathbf{a}^n - \mathbf{a}| = 0.$$

From this definition, we see that the sequence converges to $\mathbf{a}$ if and only if

$$\lim_{n \to \infty} a_i^n = a_i, \qquad 1 \le i \le n,$$

where a_i^n and a_i are the ith components of $\mathbf{a}^n$ and $\mathbf{a}$, respectively. A sequence of vector functions $\{\mathbf{u}^n\}_{n=1}^\infty$ is said to converge to a vector function $\mathbf{u}$ on an interval if $\{\mathbf{u}^n(t)\}_{n=1}^\infty$ converges to $\mathbf{u}(t)$ for every t in the interval.

In the next section, we shall have occasion to deal with vector functions of several variables. An example of a three-dimensional vector function of two variables is

$$\mathbf{F}(x_1, x_2) = (x_1 - x_2, \sin x_1 x_2, x_2 - 1).$$

In the case of a vector function of m variables, $x_1, x_2, \ldots, x_m$, we write

$$\mathbf{F}(x_1, x_2, \ldots, x_m) = \mathbf{F}(\mathbf{x}),$$

where $\mathbf{x} = (x_1, x_2, \ldots, x_m)$. We shall also be interested in vector functions of the form

$$\mathbf{f}(t, x_1, x_2, \ldots, x_m) = \mathbf{f}(t, \mathbf{x}),$$

where the first variable t plays a special role.

Exercises for Section 12.3

1. If $\mathbf{a}$, $\mathbf{b}$, and $\mathbf{c}$ are n-dimensional vectors, show that
    (a) $\mathbf{b} + \mathbf{a} = \mathbf{a} + \mathbf{b}$ (b) $(\mathbf{a} + \mathbf{b}) + \mathbf{c} = \mathbf{a} + (\mathbf{b} + \mathbf{c})$

2. Verify the following properties of vectors.
    (a) $c(\mathbf{a} + \mathbf{b}) = c\mathbf{a} + c\mathbf{b}$ (b) $(c + d)\mathbf{a} = c\mathbf{a} + d\mathbf{a}$
    (c) $(cd)\mathbf{a} = c(d\mathbf{a})$ (d) $0\mathbf{a} = \mathbf{0}$

3. Prove the triangle inequality $|\mathbf{a} + \mathbf{b}| \le |\mathbf{a}| + |\mathbf{b}|$ for vectors. *Suggestion*: Notice that $|a_i + b_i| \le |a_i| + |b_i|$.

4. Show that $|c\mathbf{a}| = |c| \cdot |\mathbf{a}|$.

5. If $\mathbf{u}(t) = (1, 4t, 3t^2)$, find $\mathbf{u}'(t)$ and $\int_0^2 \mathbf{u}(t)\, dt$.

6. If $\mathbf{u}(t) = (\sin t, \cos t, 2t, 1 - 3t^2)$, find $\mathbf{u}'(t)$ and $\int_0^\pi \mathbf{u}(t)\, dt$.

7. Prove Theorem 12.4. *Suggestion*: Show that $\|\mathbf{u}(t + h)| - |\mathbf{u}(t)\| \le |\mathbf{u}(t + h) - \mathbf{u}(t)|$.

8. Prove Theorem 12.5.

9. Let

$$\mathbf{a}^n = \left(\frac{1}{n}, \frac{n}{n+1}, \frac{2n+1}{n+3} \right)$$

for n a positive integer. Show that the sequence $\{\mathbf{a}^n\}_{n=1}^\infty$ converges, and find its limit.

10. The series of vectors

$$\sum_{n=1}^\infty \mathbf{a}^n$$

is said to converge to the vector $\mathbf{s}$ if the sequence $\{\mathbf{s}^n\}_{n=1}^{\infty}$, where $\mathbf{s}^n = \mathbf{a}^1 + \mathbf{a}^2 + \cdots + \mathbf{a}^n$, converges to $\mathbf{s}$. Show that the series of vectors converges if the series of numbers

$$\sum_{n=1}^{\infty} |\mathbf{a}^n|$$

converges.

12.4   FIRST-ORDER SYSTEMS

We consider an initial value problem for a first-order system,

$$x_i' = f(t, x_1, x_2, \ldots, x_n),$$

$$x_i(t_0) = k_i, \qquad i = 1, 2, \ldots, n,$$

where the functions f_i are defined on some region D of $n + 1$ dimensional space that contains the point $(t_0, k_1, k_2, \ldots, k_n)$. Using vector notation, we may write our problem as

$$\mathbf{x}' = \mathbf{f}(t, \mathbf{x}), \qquad \mathbf{x}(t_0) = \mathbf{k}, \tag{12.14}$$

where

$$\mathbf{x} = (x_1, x_2, \ldots, x_n), \qquad \mathbf{f} = (f_1, f_2, \ldots, f_n), \qquad \mathbf{k} = (k_1, k_2, \ldots, k_n).$$

The vector function $\mathbf{f}$ is said to be continuous in the region D if each of its components f_i is continuous in D. We recall from Section 12.3 the definition of the norm of a vector. If $\mathbf{u} = (u_1, u_2, \ldots, u_n)$, then

$$|\mathbf{u}| = \max_{1 \leq i \leq n} |u_i|.$$

The vector function $\mathbf{f}$ is said to satisfy a Lipschitz condition in D if there is a positive number K such that

$$|\mathbf{f}(t, \mathbf{x}) - \mathbf{f}(t, \mathbf{y})| \leq K|\mathbf{x} - \mathbf{y}|$$

whenever $(t, \mathbf{x})$ and $(t, \mathbf{y})$ are both in D. A real-valued function $g(t, \mathbf{x})$ is said to satisfy a Lipschitz condition in D if there is a positive number L such that

$$|g(t, \mathbf{x}) - g(t, \mathbf{y})| \leq L|\mathbf{x} - \mathbf{y}|$$

whenever $(t, \mathbf{x})$ and $(t, \mathbf{y})$ are in D. We leave it to the reader to show that the vector function $\mathbf{f}$ satisfies a Lipschitz condition if and only if each of its components f_i satisfies a Lipschitz condition. A practical criterion for ascertaining that a function satisfies a Lipschitz condition is as follows.

Lemma Let g be a function of $n + 1$ real variables, with values $g(t, \mathbf{x})$ for $(t, \mathbf{x})$ in a "rectangle" R, where

$$R = \{(t, \mathbf{x}) : |t - t_0| \leq a, |\mathbf{x} - \mathbf{k}| \leq b\}.$$

If g and its partial derivatives with respect to $x_1, x_2, \ldots, x_n$ are continuous in R then g satisfies a Lipschitz condition in R.

The proof, for the case $n = 2$, is left as an exercise.
The main result of this section may be stated as follows.

Theorem 12.6 Let $\mathbf{f}$ be continuous and satisfy a Lipschitz condition on the rectangle

$$R = \{(t, \mathbf{x}) : |t - t_0| \leq a, \quad |\mathbf{x} - \mathbf{k}| \leq b\}.$$

If M is a positive number such that $|\mathbf{f}(t, \mathbf{x})| \leq M$ for $(t, \mathbf{x})$ in R (such a number is guaranteed to exist because of the hypotheses on $\mathbf{f}$) and if

$$\alpha = \min\left(a, \frac{b}{M}\right),$$

then the initial value problem (12.14) has a solution on the interval

$$[t_0 - \alpha, t_0 + \alpha].$$

If $\mathbf{u}$ and $\mathbf{v}$ are both solutions of the problem on an interval $\mathscr{J}$ that contains t_0, then $\mathbf{u}(t) = \mathbf{v}(t)$ for all t in $\mathscr{J}$.

PROOF We first observe that a vector function is a solution of the initial value problem (12.14) if and only if it is a solution of the integral equation

$$\mathbf{x}(t) = \mathbf{k} + \int_{t_0}^{t} \mathbf{f}[s, \mathbf{x}(s)] \, ds. \tag{12.15}$$

Next we define a sequence of successive approximations $\{\mathbf{x}_n\}$ by means of the relations

$$\mathbf{x}_0(t) = \mathbf{k}$$
$$\mathbf{x}_n(t) = \mathbf{k} + \int_{t_0}^{t} \mathbf{f}[s, \mathbf{x}_{n-1}(s)] \, ds, \qquad n \geq 1 \tag{12.16}$$

for $|t - t_0| \leq \alpha$. The proof that this sequence converges to a solution of Eq. (12.15) is similar to the proof of Theorem 12.1. We leave the details as an exercise.

If the functions f_i and their partial derivatives $\partial f_i/\partial x_j$ are continuous in a region D that is not a rectangle, we may apply Theorem 12.6 by considering a rectangle that is contained in D. Then the existence of a solution on an interval $[t_0 - \alpha, t_0 + \alpha]$ is guaranteed. It may be possible to continue the solution to the right of $t_0 + \alpha$ (and to the left of $t_0 - \alpha$). It may be possible to continue the solution to the right for all $t \geq t_0$. If not it can be shown that the solution exists up to a point t_1 and that as t approaches t_1 either $|\mathbf{x}(t)|$ becomes infinite or else the solution curve approaches the boundary of the region D.

As an example, let us consider the initial value problem

$$\frac{dx_1}{dt} = \cos(x_1 x_2 + t) - t^2, \qquad \frac{dx_2}{dt} = \exp(x_1 t) + t^3 x_2^4,$$

$$x_1(0) = 2, \qquad x_2(0) = -1.$$

Here

$$f_1(t, x_1, x_2) = \cos(x_1 x_2 + t) - t^2,$$

$$f_2(t, x_1, x_2) = \exp(x_1 t) + t^3 x_2^4,$$

and

$$\frac{\partial f_1}{\partial x_1} = -x_2 \sin(x_1 x_2 + t), \qquad \frac{\partial f_1}{\partial x_2} = -x_1 \sin(x_1 x_2 + t),$$

$$\frac{\partial f_2}{\partial x_1} = t \exp(x_1 t), \qquad \frac{\partial f_2}{\partial x_2} = 4t^3 x_2^3.$$

Each of these six functions is continuous for all (t, x_1, x_2). On any rectangle of the form

$$|t| \leq a, \qquad |x_1 - 2| \leq b, \qquad |x_2 + 1| \leq b,$$

Theorem 12.6 applies and the existence of a solution is assured on some interval $[-\alpha, \alpha]$. The positive number α may be small.

We now consider the special case of a *linear* system

$$\frac{dx_i}{dt} = \sum_{j=1}^{n} a_{ij} x_j + b_i, \qquad x_i(t_0) = k_i, \qquad i = 1, 2, \ldots, n, \qquad (12.17)$$

where the functions a_{ij} and b_i are continuous on an interval $\mathscr{I}$ that contains t_0. In vector notation we have

$$\mathbf{x}' = \mathbf{f}(t, \mathbf{x}), \qquad \mathbf{x}(t_0) = \mathbf{k},$$

where

$$f_i(t, \mathbf{x}) = \sum_{j=1}^{n} a_{ij}(t)x_j + b_i(t), \qquad 1 \leq i \leq n.$$

Let $\mathscr{J}$ be a closed subinterval of $\mathscr{I}$. There is a number K such that $|a_{ij}(t)| \le K$ for all t in $\mathscr{J}$, where K does not depend on i and j. Then for t in $\mathscr{J}$ we have

$$|f_i(t, \mathbf{x}) - f_i(t, \mathbf{y})| \le \sum_{j=1}^{n} |a_{ij}(t)| \, |x_j - y_j|$$

$$\le K \sum_{j=1}^{n} |x_j - y_j|$$

$$\le nK|\mathbf{x} - \mathbf{y}|$$

for $1 \le i \le n$. Hence

$$|\mathbf{f}(t, \mathbf{x}) - \mathbf{f}(t, \mathbf{y})| \le nK|\mathbf{x} - \mathbf{y}|$$

and $\mathbf{f}$ satisfies a Lipschitz condition. Application of the method of successive approximations, using the scheme (12.16), shows that a solution exists throughout the closed interval $\mathscr{J}$ (Exercise 8). Since any point in $\mathscr{I}$ is contained in such a closed interval, the (unique) solution exists throughout $\mathscr{I}$. We summarize as follows.

Theorem 12.7 The initial value problem (12.17) possesses a solution on the interval $\mathscr{I}$. Any two solutions that both exist on an interval that contains t_0 are identical on that interval.

In the example

$$x_1' = 2tx_1 + e^{-t}x_2 - \sin t,$$

$$x_1' = (\cos t)x_1 + t^3x_2 + (t^2 + 1)^{-1},$$

$$x_1(2) = 5, \qquad x_2(2) = -4,$$

we have $a_{11}(t) = 2t$, $a_{12}(t) = e^{-t}$, $a_{21}(t) = \cos t$, $a_{22}(t) = t^3$, $b_1(t) = -\sin t$, and $b_2(t) = (t^2 + 1)^{-1}$. Since the functions a_{ij} and b_i are continuous everywhere, the initial value problem possesses a solution that exists on the set of all real numbers.

Theorems 12.6 and 12.7 yield important results about single differential equations. An nth-order equation of the form

$$x^{(n)} = f[t, x, x', \ldots, x^{(n-1)}] \tag{12.18}$$

can be rewritten as a first-order system for the quantities

$$x_1 = x, \qquad x_2 = x', \qquad x_3 = x'', \ldots, \qquad x_n = x^{(n-1)}.$$

For a function x is a solution of Eq. (12.18) if and only if the ordered set of functions $(x_1, x_2, \ldots, x_2)$ is a solution of the system

$$
\begin{aligned}
x_1' &= x_2, \\
x_2' &= x_3, \\
&\;\;\vdots \\
x_{n-1}' &= x_n, \\
x_n' &= f(t, x_1, x_2, \ldots, x_n).
\end{aligned}
\tag{12.19}
$$

The derivation of the following theorem is left as an exercise.

Theorem 12.8   Let f be a function of $n+1$ variables that is continuous and satisfies a Lipschitz condition (with respect to its last n arguments) on a rectangle

$$
|t - t_0| \le a, \qquad |x_i - k_i| \le b, \qquad 1 \le i \le n.
$$

Then there exists a positive number α such that on the interval $[t_0 - \alpha, t_0 + \alpha]$ there is a solution of Eq. (12.18) for which

$$
x^{(i-1)}(t_0) = k_i, \qquad 1 \le i \le n.
$$

This solution is unique.

Theorem 12.7 yields a corresponding result for a single linear equation of the form

$$
x^{(n)} + a_1 x^{(n-1)} + \cdots + a_{n-1} x' + a_n x = b.
\tag{12.20}
$$

Theorem 12.9   Let the functions a_i and b be continuous on an interval $\mathscr{I}$ and let t_0 be any point of $\mathscr{I}$. Then there exists on $\mathscr{I}$ a solution of the differential equation (12.20) for which

$$
x^{(i-1)}(t_0) = k_i, \qquad 1 \le i \le n.
$$

This solution is unique.

The proof of this result, using Theorem 12.7, is left as an exercise.

Exercises for Section 12.4

1. Let $\mathbf{f}(t, \mathbf{x})$ be a vector function. Show that $\mathbf{f}$ satisfies a Lipschitz condition in a region if and only if each of its components satisfies a Lipschitz condition in the region.

2. Give a proof of the lemma at the beginning of this section for the case $n = 2$. *Suggestion*: Write

$$f_i(t, x_1, x_2) - f_i(t, y_1, y_2)$$
$$= f_i(t, x_1, x_2) - f_i(t, y_1, x_2) + f_i(t, y_1, x_2) - f_i(t, y_1, y_2)$$

for $i = 1, 2$, and use the mean value theorem.

3. Complete the proof of Theorem 12.6.

4. Given the initial value problem

$$\frac{dx_1}{dt} = -x_1^2, \qquad \frac{dx_2}{dt} = x_1 x_2, \qquad x_1(0) = 1, \qquad x_2(0) = 5:$$

(a) Use Theorem 12.6 to show that the problem has a unique solution on some interval containing $t = 0$.

(b) Find the solution of the problem and indicate the interval on which it exists.

5. Work Exercise 4 for the initial value problem

$$\frac{dx_1}{dt} = -2tx_1 x_2 + x_2^2, \qquad \frac{dx_2}{dt} = -2tx_2^2, \qquad x_1(1) = 0, \qquad x_2(1) = 1.$$

6. Find the vector functions $\mathbf{x}_0$, $\mathbf{x}_1$, and $\mathbf{x}_2$ in the sequence of successive approximations (12.16) in the case of the initial value problem

$$x_1' = tx_1 - x_2^2, \qquad x_2' = x_1 x_2 - 2, \qquad x_1(0) = -2, \qquad x_2(0) = 1.$$

7. Work Exercise 6 for the initial value problem

$$x_1' = x_1^2 - x_2, \qquad x_2' = x_1^2 + x_2^2, \qquad x_1(1) = 0, \qquad x_2(1) = 1.$$

8. Prove Theorem 12.7.

9. Use Theorem 12.7 to justify the claim that the given initial value problem possesses a (unique) solution on the interval $(0, \infty)$:

$$tx_1' = (\cos t + 1)x_1 = t^2 x_2 - 7, \quad x_1(1) = 2,$$
$$tx_2' = (1 - t)x_1 + (\sin t)x_2 + e^t, \quad x_2(1) = 0.$$

10. Prove Theorem 12.8, using Theorem 12.6.

11. Prove Theorem 12.9, using Theorem 12.7.

12. Use Theorem 12.8 to show that the given initial value problem has a (unique) solution. Then find the solution and indicate the interval on which it exists.

(a) $2x \dfrac{d^2x}{dt^2} = \left(\dfrac{dx}{dt}\right)^2 + 1, \quad x(0) = 1, \quad x'(0) = -1$

(b) $x \dfrac{d^2x}{dt^2} = -\left(\dfrac{dx}{dt}\right)^2, \quad x(0) = 1, \quad x'(0) = -1$

13. Use Theorem 12.9 to show that the given initial value problem possesses a (unique) solution on the interval $(-1, \infty)$.

$$x'' - \frac{2}{t+1} x' + t^2 x = t^3 + 1, \qquad x(0) = 1, \quad x'(0) = 7.$$

REFERENCES

1. Coddington, E. A., and Levinson, N., *Theory of Ordinary Differential Equations.* McGraw-Hill, New York, 1955.
2. Hurewicz, W., *Lectures on Ordinary Differential Equations.* MIT Press, Cambridge, Massachusetts, 1958.
3. Taylor, A. E., *Advanced Calculus.* Blaisdell, New York, 1955.

Appendix

A1 DETERMINANTS

This appendix presents some elementary properties of determinants and basic facts about systems of linear equations that are used in the text.

Let m and n be positive integers. A *matrix* of size $m \times n$ is an ordered set of numbers a_{ij}, where $1 \le i \le m$ and $1 \le j \le n$. The numbers a_{ij} are called the *elements* of the matrix. In describing a matrix, it is convenient to place the elements in a rectangular array with m rows and n columns, enclosed in brackets. If the matrix is denoted by A, we write

$$A = \begin{bmatrix} a_{11} & a_{12} & \cdots & a_{1n} \\ a_{21} & a_{22} & \cdots & a_{2n} \\ \vdots & \vdots & & \vdots \\ a_{m1} & a_{m2} & \cdots & a_{mn} \end{bmatrix}.$$

We shall denote matrices by capital letters A, B, C, and so on, and shall denote the elements by corresponding lower-case letters with subscripts. Thus b_{ij} denotes the element in the ith row and jth column of the matrix B.

If A is an $m \times n$ matrix, we define the *transpose* of A, written A^T, to be the $n \times m$ matrix whose elements a_{ij}^T are given by the relation

$$a_{ij}^T = a_{ji}.$$

Thus the elements in the ith row of A^T are those in the ith column of A, and the elements in the jth column of A^T are those of the jth row of A. For example, if

$$A = \begin{bmatrix} 2 & 1 & 0 \\ 3 & -1 & 4 \end{bmatrix},$$

then

$$A^T = \begin{bmatrix} 2 & 3 \\ 1 & -1 \\ 0 & 4 \end{bmatrix}.$$

Our concern is with *square matrices*; that is, with those matrices that have the same number of rows as columns. A square matrix of size $n \times n$ is said to be a matrix of *order n*. Associated with a square matrix A is a number, called the *determinant* of A, and denoted by det A. We write

$$\det A = \begin{vmatrix} a_{11} & a_{12} & \cdots & a_{1n} \\ a_{21} & a_{22} & \cdots & a_{2n} \\ \vdots & \vdots & & \vdots \\ a_{n1} & a_{n2} & \cdots & a_{nn} \end{vmatrix}, \quad\quad (A1)$$

when we wish to display the elements of A. If A is of order n, we say that det A is a determinant of order n.

If A is of order 1, with a single element a_{11}, we define det $A = a_{11}$. If A is of order 2,

$$A = \begin{bmatrix} a_{11} & a_{12} \\ a_{21} & a_{22} \end{bmatrix},$$

we define

$$\det A = a_{11}a_{22} - a_{12}a_{21}.$$

Thus

$$\begin{vmatrix} 2 & -3 \\ 1 & 5 \end{vmatrix} = (2)(5) - (-3)(1) = 13.$$

We shall presently define the determinant of a square matrix of arbitrary order n. First, however, we must develop some preliminary ideas. Consider a set† $\{j_1, j_2, \ldots, j_n\}$ whose distinct elements $j_1, j_2, \ldots, j_n$ are positive integers. Each possible ordering of the elements of the set is called a *permutation* of the set. We use parentheses to denote an *ordered* set. For example, the possible permutations of the set $\{1, 2, 5\}$ are $(1, 2, 5)$, $(1, 5, 2)$, $(2, 1, 5)$, $(2, 5, 1)$, $(5, 1, 2)$, and $(5, 2, 1)$. The number of possible permutations of n integers (or of any n objects) is $n!$.

Let $(j_1, j_2, \ldots, j_n)$ be a permutation of a set of n positive integers. Let α_1 be the number of integers following j_1 that are smaller than j_1, let α_2 be the number of integers following j_2 that are smaller than j_2, and so on. Note that α_n is always zero. The sum $\alpha_1 + \alpha_2 + \cdots + \alpha_{n-1}$ is called the number of *inversions* in the permutation $(j_1, j_2, \ldots, j_n)$. For example, in the permutation $(2, 4, 1, 3)$ of $\{1, 2, 3, 4\}$, we have $\alpha_1 = 1$, $\alpha_2 = 2$, and $\alpha_3 = 0$, so the

---

† One way to describe a set is to list the members of the set, enclosed in braces.

number of inversions is three. A permutation is said to have *even or odd parity* according to whether the number of its inversions is even or odd. We define

$$\delta(j_1, j_2, \ldots, j_n)$$

to be one if the parity of $(j_1, j_2, \ldots, j_n)$ is even and minus one if the parity is odd.

We are now in a position to define the determinant (A1) of an nth-order matrix. We form all possible products of the form

$$a_{1j_1}a_{2j_2}a_{3j_3}\cdots a_{nj_n}, \tag{A2}$$

in which there occurs exactly one element from each row and each column of A. Thus $(j_1, j_2, j_3, \ldots, j_n)$ is a permutation of $\{1, 2, 3, \ldots, n\}$. The determinant of A is defined by the formula

$$\det A = \sum \delta(j_1, j_2, \ldots, j_n)a_{1j_1}a_{2j_2}\cdots a_{nj_n}, \tag{A3}$$

where the sum is taken over all possible permutations $(j_1, j_2, \ldots, j_n)$ of $\{1, 2, \ldots, n\}$.

It can be verified that this definition agrees with those previously given for the cases $n = 1$ and $n = 2$. Let us apply the definition to find the determinant of a 3×3 matrix,

$$A = \begin{bmatrix} a_{11} & a_{12} & a_{13} \\ a_{21} & a_{22} & a_{23} \\ a_{31} & a_{32} & a_{33} \end{bmatrix}.$$

The products of the form (A2) are

$$a_{11}a_{22}a_{33}, \quad a_{11}a_{23}a_{32}, \quad a_{12}a_{21}a_{33}$$
$$a_{12}a_{23}a_{31}, \quad a_{13}a_{21}a_{32}, \quad a_{13}a_{22}a_{31}.$$

Finding the proper signs and summing, we have

$$\det A = a_{11}a_{22}a_{23} + a_{13}a_{21}a_{32} + a_{12}a_{23}a_{31}$$
$$- a_{13}a_{22}a_{31} - a_{12}a_{21}a_{33} - a_{11}a_{23}a_{32}.$$

This formula is not easy to remember. However the device

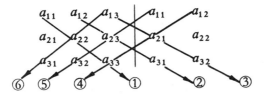

is useful. We have written down the elements of the matrix A in array form and then repeated the first two columns. We form the six products associated with the six arrows, each product having as factors the three elements pierced by that arrow. We assign a plus sign to the products determined by arrows ①, ②, and ③ and a minus sign to the products associated with arrows ④, ⑤, and ⑥. The sum of the six signed products is det A. As an example, we evaluate the determinant

$$\begin{vmatrix} 1 & 2 & 3 \\ -1 & 3 & 0 \\ 2 & -4 & 5 \end{vmatrix}.$$

Forming the array

$$\begin{array}{ccc|cc} 1 & 2 & 3 & 1 & 2 \\ -1 & 3 & 0 & -1 & 3 \\ 2 & -4 & 5 & 2 & -4 \end{array}$$

and using the procedure described above, we find that the value of the determinant is

$$(1)(3)(5) + (2)(0)(2) + (3)(-1)(-4)$$
$$- (2)(-1)(5) - (1)(0)(-4) - (3)(3)(2) = 19 .$$

The reader should be warned that the scheme just described works only for third-order determinants and not for higher order ones. A practical method for evaluating a determinant of any order will be developed in the next section.

A square matrix whose determinant is zero is said to be *singular*. A square matrix that is not singular is called *nonsingular*.

We consider one more topic, the derivative of the determinant of a matrix function. Consider an ordered set of real differentiable functions a_{ij}, $1 \leq i \leq n$, $1 \leq j \leq n$, with a common domain. Associated with each number x in the domain is the matrix

$$A(x) = \begin{bmatrix} a_{11}(x) & a_{12}(x) & \cdots & a_{1n}(x) \\ a_{21}(x) & a_{22}(x) & \cdots & a_{2n}(x) \\ \vdots & \vdots & & \vdots \\ a_{n1}(x) & a_{n2}(x) & \cdots & a_{nn}(x) \end{bmatrix}.$$

For each x we can inquire about (d/dx) det $A(x)$. Recalling that

$$\det A(x) = \sum \pm a_{1j_1}(x) a_{2j_2}(x) \cdots a_{nj_n}(x),$$

we see that

$$(\det A)' = \sum \pm a'_{1j_1} a_{2j_2} \cdots a_{nj_n} + \sum \pm a_{1j_1} a'_{2j_2} \cdots a_{nj_n}$$
$$+ \cdots + \sum \pm a_{1j_1} a_{2j_2} \cdots a'_{nj_n}$$

or

$$
(\det A)' =
\begin{vmatrix}
a'_{11} & a'_{12} & \cdots & a'_{1n} \\
a_{21} & a_{22} & \cdots & a_{2n} \\
\vdots & \vdots & & \vdots \\
a_{n1} & a_{n2} & \cdots & a_{nn}
\end{vmatrix}
+
\begin{vmatrix}
a_{11} & a_{12} & \cdots & a_{1n} \\
a'_{21} & a'_{22} & \cdots & a'_{2n} \\
\vdots & \vdots & & \vdots \\
a_{n1} & a_{n2} & \cdots & a_{nn}
\end{vmatrix}
$$

$$
+ \cdots +
\begin{vmatrix}
a_{11} & a_{12} & \cdots & a_{1n} \\
a_{21} & a_{22} & \cdots & a_{2n} \\
\vdots & \vdots & & \vdots \\
a'_{n1} & a'_{n2} & \cdots & a'_{nn}
\end{vmatrix}.
$$

Thus the derivative of det A is the sum of n determinants that are obtained by successively differentiating the rows of A. As will be shown in the next section the derivative of det A can also be expressed as the sum of n determinants that are obtained by successively differentiating the columns of A.

For purposes of illustration, we observe that

$$
\frac{d}{dx}
\begin{vmatrix}
x & x^2 & x^3 \\
e^x & 1 & 0 \\
\sin x & 0 & 0
\end{vmatrix}
$$

$$
=
\begin{vmatrix}
1 & 2x & 3x^2 \\
e^x & 1 & 0 \\
\sin x & 0 & 0
\end{vmatrix}
+
\begin{vmatrix}
x & x^2 & x^3 \\
e^x & 0 & 0 \\
\sin x & 0 & 0
\end{vmatrix}
+
\begin{vmatrix}
x & x^2 & x^3 \\
e^x & 1 & 0 \\
\cos x & 0 & 0
\end{vmatrix}.
$$

Exercises for Section A1

1. Find all the permutations of the set $\{1, 2, 3, 4\}$.

2. Find the number of inversions in each of the following permutations:
    (a) $(3, 1, 2)$ (b) $(3, 2, 1)$ (c) $(1, 2, 3)$
    (d) $(1, 3, 2, 4)$ (e) $(4, 2, 3, 1)$ (f) $(2, 3, 4, 1)$
    (g) $(1, 3, 5, 2, 4)$ (h) $(4, 1, 5, 3, 2)$

3. With $\delta(j_1, j_2, \ldots, j_n)$ defined as in the text, find the value of each of the following:
    (a) $\delta(2, 1, 3)$ (b) $\delta(1, 2, 3)$ (c) $\delta(2, 4, 1, 3)$
    (d) $\delta(4, 3, 2, 1)$ (e) $\delta(1, 3, 5, 2, 4)$

4. Derive the formula for the value of a second-order determinant from the general formula (A3).

5. Find the value of each of the second-order determinants.

(a) $\begin{vmatrix} 2 & -3 \\ 4 & 5 \end{vmatrix}$

(b) $\begin{vmatrix} 2 & -3 \\ -4 & 6 \end{vmatrix}$

(c) $\begin{vmatrix} -5 & 2 \\ 1 & 3 \end{vmatrix}$

(d) $\begin{vmatrix} 0 & 3 \\ 2 & 4 \end{vmatrix}$

6. Find the value of each of the third-order determinants.

(a) $\begin{vmatrix} 1 & 3 & 2 \\ 3 & 1 & -1 \\ -2 & 4 & 5 \end{vmatrix}$

(b) $\begin{vmatrix} 2 & 0 & -2 \\ 1 & 1 & 5 \\ 3 & 4 & 5 \end{vmatrix}$

(c) $\begin{vmatrix} -4 & -1 & 3 \\ 2 & 2 & 1 \\ 3 & 5 & 0 \end{vmatrix}$

(d) $\begin{vmatrix} 1 & 2 & 3 \\ 3 & 2 & 1 \\ 1 & 1 & 1 \end{vmatrix}$

7. If A is any matrix, the product cA, where c is a number, is defined to be the matrix of the same size as A obtained by multiplying each element of A by c. In particular, we write $-A = (-1)A$.

(a) If A is a square matrix of order n, prove that $\det(-A) = (-1)^n \det A$.

(b) If A is a square matrix of order n and c is a number, prove that $\det(cA) = c^n \det A$.

8. A square matrix D is called a *diagonal matrix* if $d_{ij} = 0$ whenever $i \neq j$. If D is diagonal, show that $\det D = d_{11}d_{22} \cdots d_{nn}$.

9. Evaluate the derivative of the determinant

$$\begin{vmatrix} x^3 + 1 & x^2 \\ x^2 & 2x \end{vmatrix}$$

in two ways: first by evaluating the determinant and then taking the derivative; second, by applying the rule derived at the end of this section.

A2 PROPERTIES OF DETERMINANTS

Listed below are some elementary properties of determinants. Each property is illustrated by an example. A proof of only the first property is given in the text. Proofs of others are left as exercises. The reader who encounters difficulty with these will find proofs in most college algebra texts and in some books on calculus.

Property 1 $\det A^T = \det A$:

$$\begin{vmatrix} 1 & -1 & 2 \\ 3 & 0 & 1 \\ 2 & 1 & 5 \end{vmatrix} = \begin{vmatrix} 1 & 3 & 2 \\ -1 & 0 & 1 \\ 2 & 1 & 5 \end{vmatrix}.$$

Property 2   If every element in a row (column) of A is zero, then $\det A = 0$:

$$\begin{vmatrix} 2 & 0 & 3 \\ 1 & 0 & 1 \\ -1 & 0 & 4 \end{vmatrix} = 0.$$

Property 3   If every element in one row (column) of A is multiplied by the number c, the determinant of the resulting matrix is equal to $c \det A$:

$$\begin{vmatrix} -6 & 3 & -9 \\ 2 & 1 & 0 \\ 1 & 1 & 2 \end{vmatrix} = -3 \begin{vmatrix} 2 & -1 & 3 \\ 2 & 1 & 0 \\ 1 & 1 & 2 \end{vmatrix}.$$

Property 4   If two rows (columns) of A are interchanged, the determinant of the resulting matrix is equal to $-\det A$:

$$\begin{vmatrix} 1 & -1 & 3 \\ 0 & 4 & 1 \\ 2 & 2 & 5 \end{vmatrix} = - \begin{vmatrix} 2 & 2 & 5 \\ 0 & 4 & 1 \\ 1 & -1 & 3 \end{vmatrix}.$$

Property 5   If two rows (columns) of A are identical, then $\det A = 0$:

$$\begin{vmatrix} 2 & 1 & 2 \\ 1 & -4 & 1 \\ 3 & 5 & 3 \end{vmatrix} = 0.$$

Property 6   If every element in the jth column of A is the sum of two numbers so that $a_{ij} = a'_{ij} + a''_{ij}$ for $1 \le i \le n$, then $\det A = \det A' + \det A''$, and A' and A'' are the same as A except that their jth columns consist of the elements a'_{ij} and a''_{ij}, respectively. An analogous property holds for rows:

$$\begin{vmatrix} 1 & 2+3 & 3 \\ 0 & 1-4 & 5 \\ 2 & -2+0 & 6 \end{vmatrix} = \begin{vmatrix} 1 & 2 & 3 \\ 0 & 1 & 5 \\ 2 & -2 & 6 \end{vmatrix} + \begin{vmatrix} 1 & 3 & 3 \\ 0 & -4 & 5 \\ 2 & 0 & 6 \end{vmatrix}.$$

Property 7 If to every element in a row (column) of A is added c times the corresponding element of a different row (column), the determinant of the resulting matrix is equal to det A:

$$\begin{vmatrix} 2 & -1 & 0 \\ 1 & 2 & -3 \\ 4 & 5 & 6 \end{vmatrix} = \begin{vmatrix} 4 & 3 & -6 \\ 1 & 2 & -3 \\ 4 & 5 & 6 \end{vmatrix}.$$

(Here twice the second row has been added to the first row.)

The following lemma is needed in the derivations of some of the properties described above.

Lemma If two adjacent elements in a permutation are interchanged, the parity of the permutation is changed.

PROOF Suppose that j_α and j_β are interchanged in the permutation $(j_1, j_2, \ldots, j_\alpha, j_\beta, \ldots, j_n)$. If $j_\alpha < j_\beta$, the interchange of j_α and j_β introduces one new inversion. If $j_\alpha > j_\beta$, the number of inversions is decreased by one. In each case the parity is changed.

PROOF OF PROPERTY 1 Let a_{ij}^T be the element in the ith row and jth column of A^T. Then $a_{ij}^T = a_{ji}$. The determinant of A^T is the sum of terms of the form

$$\delta(j_1, j_2, \ldots, j_n)a_{1j_1}^T a_{2j_2}^T \cdots a_{nj_n}^T = \delta(j_1, j_2, \ldots, j_n)a_{j_11}a_{j_22} \cdots a_{j_nn}.$$

Now

$$a_{j_11}a_{j_22} \cdots a_{j_nn} = a_{1k_1}a_{2k_2} \cdots a_{nk_n},$$

where $(k_1, k_2, \ldots, k_n)$ is some permutation of $\{1, 2, \ldots, n\}$. We can think of the product on the right-hand side as being formed from the product on the left-hand side by successively interchanging adjacent factors. Each interchange changes the parity of the ordered set of first subscripts and simultaneously changes the parity of the ordered set of second subscripts. Consequently the parity of $(k_1, k_2, \ldots, k_n)$ must be the same as that of $(j_1, j_2, \ldots, j_n)$. Thus $\delta(k_1, k_2, \ldots, k_n) = \delta(j_1, j_2, \ldots, j_n)$, so that

$$\det A^T = \sum \delta(k_1, k_2, \ldots, k_n)a_{1k_1}a_{2k_2} \cdots a_{nk_n} = \det A.$$

The rows of A^T are the same as the columns of A. Consequently, Property 1 allows us to convert theorems about rows of a determinant into corresponding theorems about columns. For example, the derivative of det A can be found by differentiating det A^T by rows; this amounts to differentiating det A by columns.

A square matrix A is said to be *upper triangular* if $a_{ij} = 0$ whenever $i > j$. It is said to be *lower triangular* if $a_{ij} = 0$ whenever $i < j$. For example, the first of the matrices

$$\begin{bmatrix} 2 & 1 & -6 \\ 0 & 0 & 2 \\ 0 & 0 & 5 \end{bmatrix}, \quad \begin{bmatrix} 4 & 0 & 0 \\ 0 & 1 & 0 \\ 2 & 3 & 2 \end{bmatrix}$$

is upper triangular and the second is lower triangular. We shall presently describe a method for evaluating determinants of arbitrary order. This method is based on the following result about the determinant of a triangular matrix.

Theorem A1   If A is an $n \times n$ triangular (upper or lower) matrix, then

$$\det A = a_{11}a_{22} \cdots a_{nn}.$$

PROOF   The determinant of A is the sum of terms of the form

$$\pm a_{1j_1}a_{2j_2} \cdots a_{nj_n}.$$

If one factor, say a_{pj_p}, is such that $p < j_p$, there must be another factor, say a_{qj_q}, such that $q > j_q$, and conversely. This is because

$$1 + 2 + \cdots + n = j_1 + j_2 + \cdots + j_n$$

for every permutation $(j_1, j_2, \ldots, j_n)$. Thus if A is triangular, every term of the sum is zero except the one where $j_1 = 1$, $j_2 = 2$, $\ldots$, $j_n = n$. Hence $\det A$ is equal to the single product.

By using the elementary properties listed at the beginning of this section, we can reduce the problem of evaluating any determinant to one of evaluating the determinant of a triangular matrix. The essential features of the reduction are shown in the following example. Consider the determinant

$$\det A = \begin{vmatrix} 0 & 2 & 1 & -1 \\ 2 & -2 & 4 & 0 \\ -1 & 2 & 0 & 1 \\ -2 & 1 & 1 & 3 \end{vmatrix}.$$

We wish to place a nonzero element in the first row and column. Interchanging the first and third rows, we have

$$\det A = - \begin{vmatrix} -1 & 2 & 0 & 1 \\ 2 & -2 & 4 & 0 \\ 0 & 2 & 1 & -1 \\ -2 & 1 & 1 & 3 \end{vmatrix}.$$

We place zeros in every position of the first column below the first by adding appropriate multiples of the first row to the second and fourth rows. Thus

$$\det A = -\begin{vmatrix} -1 & 2 & 0 & 1 \\ 0 & 2 & 4 & 2 \\ 0 & 2 & 1 & -1 \\ 0 & -3 & 1 & 1 \end{vmatrix} = -2\begin{vmatrix} -1 & 2 & 0 & 1 \\ 0 & 1 & 2 & 1 \\ 0 & 2 & 1 & -1 \\ 0 & -3 & 1 & 1 \end{vmatrix}.$$

We place zeros in every position of the second column below the second by adding appropriate multiples of the second row to the third and fourth rows. We find that

$$\det A = -2\begin{vmatrix} -1 & 2 & 0 & 1 \\ 0 & 1 & 2 & 1 \\ 0 & 0 & -3 & -3 \\ 0 & 0 & 7 & 4 \end{vmatrix} = 6\begin{vmatrix} -1 & 2 & 0 & 1 \\ 0 & 1 & 2 & 1 \\ 0 & 0 & 1 & 1 \\ 0 & 0 & 7 & 4 \end{vmatrix}.$$

We add (-7) times the third row to the fourth to obtain the triangular form

$$\det A = 6\begin{vmatrix} -1 & 2 & 0 & 1 \\ 0 & 1 & 2 & 1 \\ 0 & 0 & 1 & 1 \\ 0 & 0 & 0 & -3 \end{vmatrix}.$$

Using Theorem A1, we have

$$\det A = (6)(-1)(1)(1)(-3) = 18.$$

Exercises for Section A2

1. Derive Properties 2 and 3 of determinants that are given at the beginning of this section.

2. Prove Property 4. (*Suggestion*: Use the lemma of this section.) Then use Property 4 to prove Property 5.

3. Derive Property 6.

4. Derive Property 7.

In Exercises 5–9, evaluate the determinant by using Theorem A1 and elementary properties of determinants.

5. (a) $\begin{vmatrix} 1 & 3 & 2 \\ 2 & -1 & 5 \\ -2 & 4 & -4 \end{vmatrix}$ (b) $\begin{vmatrix} 5 & 2 & 3 \\ 2 & -1 & 0 \\ 3 & 4 & 7 \end{vmatrix}$

6. (a) $\begin{vmatrix} -3 & 5 & 7 \\ -5 & -4 & 3 \\ 2 & 5 & 6 \end{vmatrix}$ (b) $\begin{vmatrix} 6 & 5 & 2 \\ 4 & 3 & 2 \\ 7 & 3 & 7 \end{vmatrix}$

7. (a) $\begin{vmatrix} 2 & 1 & 4 & 7 \\ 3 & 0 & 1 & 5 \\ -4 & -3 & 3 & 4 \\ 2 & 2 & -1 & 0 \end{vmatrix}$ (b) $\begin{vmatrix} -2 & 1 & 4 & 2 \\ -3 & 0 & 1 & 6 \\ 1 & 2 & 3 & 4 \\ -4 & 3 & -2 & 1 \end{vmatrix}$

8. (a) $\begin{vmatrix} 4 & 0 & 2 & 0 \\ 0 & 1 & 0 & 3 \\ 5 & 0 & 7 & 0 \\ 0 & 8 & 0 & 6 \end{vmatrix}$ (b) $\begin{vmatrix} 6 & 2 & 8 & 0 \\ 1 & 3 & 5 & 2 \\ 2 & 1 & 0 & -3 \\ 2 & -5 & -2 & -7 \end{vmatrix}$

9. $\begin{vmatrix} 2 & -1 & 0 & 4 & 1 \\ 1 & 5 & 2 & 0 & -2 \\ -1 & 3 & -3 & 1 & 0 \\ 0 & 1 & 1 & 2 & -2 \\ 2 & 2 & 1 & 0 & -1 \end{vmatrix}$

10. Let $f_1, f_2, \ldots, f_n$ be functions that are defined and possess at least n derivatives on an interval. If

$$
A(x) = \begin{bmatrix} f_1(x) & f_2(x) & \cdots & f_n(x) \\ f_1'(x) & f_2'(x) & \cdots & f_n'(x) \\ \vdots & \vdots & & \vdots \\ f_1^{(n-1)}(x) & f_2^{(n-1)}(x) & \cdots & f_n^{(n-1)}(x) \end{bmatrix},
$$

show that

$$
\frac{d}{dx} \det A(x) = \begin{vmatrix} f_1(x) & f_2(x) & \cdots & f_n(x) \\ f_1'(x) & f_2'(x) & \cdots & f_n'(x) \\ \vdots & \vdots & & \vdots \\ f_1^{(n-2)}(x) & f_2^{(n-2)}(x) & \cdots & f_n^{(n-2)}(x) \\ f_1^{(n)}(x) & f_2^{(n)}(x) & \cdots & f_n^{(n)}(x) \end{vmatrix}.
$$

A3 COFACTORS

Let A be an $m \times n$ matrix. Any matrix that is formed from A by deleting rows of A or columns of A, or both, is called a *submatrix* of A. In addition, it is sometimes convenient to regard A as a submatrix of itself (deletion of no rows and no columns).

We now restrict attention to the case where A is a square $n \times n$ matrix. If we delete the ith row and kth column of A (the row and column containing the element a_{ik}), we obtain a square submatrix of order $n - 1$. The determinant of this submatrix is called the minor of the element a_{ik}; we denote the minor by M_{ik}. We may write

$$M_{ik} = \sum \delta(j_1, \ldots, j_{k-1}, j_{k+1}, \ldots, j_n) a_{1j_1} \cdots a_{k-1, j_{k-1}} a_{k+1, j_{k+1}} \cdots a_{nj_n},$$

where i is excluded from the row subscripts and the sum is over all permutations of $1, 2, \ldots, k - 1, k + 1, \ldots, n$. The quantity

$$A_{ik} = (-1)^{i+k} M_{ik}$$

is called the *cofactor* of the element a_{ik}. For example, if

$$A = \begin{bmatrix} 1 & -2 & 0 \\ 3 & 1 & 4 \\ 2 & 2 & 1 \end{bmatrix}, \tag{A4}$$

then

$$A_{11} = \begin{vmatrix} 1 & 4 \\ 2 & 1 \end{vmatrix} = -7, \qquad A_{12} = - \begin{vmatrix} 3 & 4 \\ 2 & 1 \end{vmatrix} = 5,$$

and so on.

The determinant of a matrix can be expressed in terms of the cofactors of the elements in any one row or column, as is shown by the following theorem.

Theorem A2 If each element in any one row (column) of an $n \times n$ matrix A is multiplied by its cofactor, the sum of the n products so formed is equal to det A. Thus

$$\sum_{j=1}^{n} a_{ij} A_{ij} = \det A, \qquad 1 \le i \le n, \tag{A5}$$

$$\sum_{i=1}^{n} a_{ij} A_{ij} = \det A, \qquad 1 \le j \le n. \tag{A6}$$

PROOF We first establish the relation (A5), starting with the formula

$$\det A = \sum \delta(j_1, j_2, \ldots, j_n) a_{1j_1} a_{2j_2} \cdots a_{nj_n}.$$

For fixed i, we collect the products that involve $a_{i1}, a_{i2}, \ldots, a_{in}$. Then

$$\det A = \sum_{j_i=1}^{n} a_{ij_i} \sum \delta(j_1, \ldots, j_i, \ldots, j_n) a_{1j_1} \cdots a_{i-1, j_{i-1}} a_{i+1, j_{i+1}} \cdots a_{nj_n},$$

where the inner sum is taken over all permutations $(j_1, \ldots, j_i, \ldots, j_n)$ of $\{1, 2, \ldots, n\}$ with j_i fixed. Since j_i is in the ith position,

$$\delta(j_1, \ldots, j_i, \ldots, j_n) = (-1)^{i-1} \delta(j_i, j_1, \ldots, j_{i-1}, j_{i+1}, \ldots, j_n).$$

In the symbol on the right, j_i is followed by $j_i - 1$ smaller terms, so this is equal to

$$(-1)^{i-1}(-1)^{j_i-1}\delta(j_1, \ldots, j_{i-1}, j_{i+1}, \ldots, j_n).$$

Hence

$$\det A = \sum_{j_i=1}^{n} a_{ij_i}(-1)^{i+j_i}M_{ij_i} = \sum_{j_i=1}^{n} a_{ij_i}A_{ij_i}.$$

This establishes Eq. (A5).

Formula (A6) can be derived by expressing $\det A$ in terms of the cofactors of the elements of the jth row of A^T, and observing that the cofactor of a_{ji}^T is the same as the cofactor of a_{ij}. We omit the details.

As an example, we consider the matrix (A4). Applying formula (A5), with $i = 1$, we have

$$\det A = (1)\begin{vmatrix} 1 & 4 \\ 2 & 1 \end{vmatrix} - (-2)\begin{vmatrix} 3 & 4 \\ 2 & 1 \end{vmatrix} + (0)\begin{vmatrix} 3 & 1 \\ 2 & 2 \end{vmatrix}$$

$$= (1)(-7) - (-2)(-5) + 0$$

$$= -17.$$

Theorem A3   If the elements of the ith row (column) of an $n \times n$ matrix A are multiplied by the cofactors of the corresponding elements of the jth row (column), the sum of the products is $\det A$ if $i = j$ and zero if $i \neq j$. In symbols,

$$\sum_{k=1}^{n} a_{ik}A_{jk} = \delta_{ij}\det A, \tag{A7}$$

$$\sum_{k=1}^{n} a_{ki}A_{kj} = \delta_{ij}\det A, \tag{A8}$$

where δ_{ij} is the Kronecker delta.†

PROOF   The validity of the formulas follows from Theorem A2 if $i = j$. For the case $i \neq j$, the sum on the left-hand side in Eq. (A7) can be regarded as the determinant of a matrix whose jth row is the same as its ith row. Hence its value must be zero. Similarly, the left-hand member of Eq. (A8) can be regarded as the determinant of a matrix whose jth column is the same as its ith column.

Theorem A3 will be used to derive some results of theoretical importance in the next section. Although formulas (A5) and (A6) can be used to evaluate determinants, the method described in the previous section requires fewer arithmetic operations to be performed, and is more efficient when the order of the matrix is large.

† That is, $\delta_{ij} = 0$ if $i \neq j$ and $\delta_{ij} = 1$ if $i = j$.

Exercises for Section A3

1. Find the cofactor of each element of the given matrix.

(a) $\begin{bmatrix} 2 & 3 \\ -1 & 0 \end{bmatrix}$ (b) $\begin{bmatrix} a & b \\ c & d \end{bmatrix}$

(c) $\begin{bmatrix} 2 & -1 & 3 \\ 1 & 0 & -2 \\ 3 & 1 & 1 \end{bmatrix}$ (d) $\begin{bmatrix} 4 & 0 & 2 \\ 0 & 2 & -2 \\ 1 & 3 & 1 \end{bmatrix}$

2. Evaluate the given determinant by applying Theorem A2. Use any row or column.

(a) $\begin{vmatrix} 1 & 2 & -1 \\ 4 & 1 & 2 \\ 1 & 1 & -3 \end{vmatrix}$ (b) $\begin{vmatrix} 4 & 3 & -2 \\ -1 & 2 & 0 \\ 1 & -1 & 3 \end{vmatrix}$

3. Find det D if

$$D = \begin{bmatrix} 0 & \cdots & 0 & 0 & 0 & d_1 \\ 0 & \cdots & 0 & 0 & d_2 & 0 \\ 0 & \cdots & 0 & d_3 & 0 & 0 \\ \vdots & & \vdots & \vdots & \vdots & \vdots \\ d_n & \cdots & 0 & 0 & 0 & 0 \end{bmatrix}.$$

4. Let A be a third-order matrix with elements a_{ij}. Verify that the sum

$$a_{11}A_{21} + a_{12}A_{22} + a_{13}A_{23}$$

(whose terms are the products of the elements in the first row of A with the cofactors of the corresponding elements of the second row) is the determinant of the matrix whose first and second rows are identical. (Hence the sum is equal to zero.)

5. Let P_1 and P_2 be distinct points with rectangular coordinates (x_1, y_1) and (x_2, y_2) in a plane. Show that the equation

$$\begin{vmatrix} x & y & 1 \\ x_1 & y_1 & 1 \\ x_2 & y_2 & 1 \end{vmatrix} = 0$$

is that of the straight line through P_1 and P_2.

6. Let $x_1, x_2, \ldots, x_n$ be distinct numbers. Show that the formula

$$P(x) = \begin{vmatrix} 1 & x & x^2 & \cdots & x^n \\ 1 & x_1 & x_1^2 & \cdots & x_1^n \\ 1 & x_2 & x_2^2 & \cdots & x_2^n \\ \vdots & \vdots & \vdots & & \vdots \\ 1 & x_n & x_n^2 & \cdots & x_n^n \end{vmatrix}$$

defines a polynomial P whose zeros are $x_1, x_2, \ldots, x_n$.

A4   CRAMER'S RULE

We consider a system of linear equations

$$\begin{aligned} a_{11}x_1 + a_{12}x_2 + \cdots + a_{1n}x_n &= b_1, \\ a_{21}x_1 + a_{22}x_2 + \cdots + a_{2n}x_n &= b_2, \\ &\vdots \\ a_{n1}x_1 + a_{n2}x_2 + \cdots + a_{nn}x_n &= b_n \end{aligned} \tag{A9}$$

with n equations and n unknowns. The $n \times n$ matrix A with elements a_{ij} is called the *coefficient matrix* of the system.

Theorem A4   If $\det A \neq 0$, the system (A9) possesses exactly one solution.

PROOF   We first write down the $n \times (n + 1)$ matrix

$$\begin{bmatrix} a_{11} & a_{12} & \cdots & a_{1n} & b_1 \\ a_{21} & a_{22} & \cdots & a_{2n} & b_2 \\ \vdots & \vdots & & \vdots & \vdots \\ a_{n1} & a_{n2} & \cdots & a_{nn} & b_n \end{bmatrix}, \tag{A10}$$

which is called the *augmented matrix* of the system (A9). By interchanging two rows of this matrix, or by adding a constant multiple of one row to another, we obtain the augmented matrix of a system that is equivalent† to the system (A9). Furthermore, the determinant of the coefficient matrix of the new system is the same as $\det A$, except possibly for its sign.

Since A is nonsingular, there is at least one element in the first column of the matrix (A10) that is not zero. By interchanging rows, if necessary, we place

† Two systems are said to be equivalent if they have the same solutions.

a nonzero element in the first row and first column. Then by adding appropriate multiples of the first row to the other rows we introduce zeros in all positions of the first column below the first. The result is an augmented matrix

$$\begin{bmatrix} a'_{11} & a'_{12} & \cdots & a'_{1n} & b'_1 \\ 0 & a'_{22} & \cdots & a'_{2n} & b'_2 \\ \vdots & \vdots & & \vdots & \vdots \\ 0 & a'_{n2} & \cdots & a'_{nn} & b'_n \end{bmatrix}$$

of a system that is equivalent to the system (A9). Since the coefficient matrix of this system is nonsingular, at least one element in the second column below the first position must be different from zero. We place a nonzero element in the second position of the second column by interchanging rows if necessary. Then we introduce zeros in all positions of the second column below the second position by adding appropriate multiples of the second row to the lower rows. The result is an augmented matrix of the form

$$\begin{bmatrix} a''_{11} & a''_{12} & a''_{13} & \cdots & a''_{1n} & b''_1 \\ 0 & a''_{22} & a''_{23} & \cdots & a''_{2n} & b''_2 \\ 0 & 0 & a''_{33} & \cdots & a''_{3n} & b''_3 \\ \vdots & \vdots & \vdots & & \vdots & \vdots \\ 0 & 0 & a''_{n3} & \cdots & a''_{nn} & b''_n \end{bmatrix},$$

where a''_{11} and a''_{22} are not zero. Since det $A \neq 0$, at least one element in the third column of this matrix below the second position must be different from zero, so we can continue this process. Finally, we arrive at an augmented matrix of the form

$$\begin{bmatrix} \tilde{a}_{11} & \tilde{a}_{12} & \tilde{a}_{13} & \cdots & \tilde{a}_{1n} & \tilde{b}_1 \\ 0 & \tilde{a}_{22} & \tilde{a}_{23} & \cdots & \tilde{a}_{2n} & \tilde{b}_2 \\ 0 & 0 & \tilde{a}_{33} & \cdots & \tilde{a}_{3n} & \tilde{b}_3 \\ \vdots & \vdots & \vdots & & \vdots & \vdots \\ 0 & 0 & 0 & \cdots & \tilde{a}_{nn} & \tilde{b}_n \end{bmatrix},$$

where none of the elements $\tilde{a}_{11}, \tilde{a}_{22}, \ldots, \tilde{a}_{nn}$ is zero. The last row of this matrix corresponds to the equation $\tilde{a}_{nn} x_n = \tilde{b}_n$, so we can solve for x_n, finding $x_n = \tilde{b}_n / \tilde{a}_{nn}$. The $(n-1)$st row corresponds to the equation

$$\tilde{a}_{n-1,n-1} x_{n-1} + \tilde{a}_{n-1,n} x_n = \tilde{b}_{n-1}$$

and x_{n-1} is now found from this equation. By working upward, we find all the solution components, which are uniquely determined. This concludes our proof.

We have established the existence of a unique solution of the system (A9) by carrying out a *Gauss reduction*. For a specific case, this procedure provides an efficient method for solving the system.

We shall now derive a formula, known as Cramer's rule, for the solution components of the system (A9). The use of this rule to find the solution is less efficient than the Gauss reduction method. Nevertheless, it is important for some theoretical purposes, as we shall illustrate.

Cramer's rule can be stated as follows.

Theorem A5   If det $A \neq 0$, the components of the solution of the system (A9) are given by the formula,

$$x_k = \frac{\det B_k}{\det A}, \qquad 1 \le k \le n, \tag{A11}$$

where the matrix B_k is the same as A except that the elements a_{ik}, $1 \le i \le n$, in the kth column of A have been replaced by the terms b_i, $1 \le i \le n$, respectively.

We shall look at an example before proving the theorem. Consider the system

$$
\begin{aligned}
2x_1 + 2x_2 - x_3 &= 2, \\
-3x_1 - x_2 + 3x_3 &= -2, \\
4x_1 + 2x_2 - 3x_3 &= 0.
\end{aligned}
$$

Calculation shows that the determinant of the coefficient matrix is 2. Since this matrix is nonsingular, Theorem A5 applies. Using formula (A11), we have

$$x_1 = \frac{1}{2}\begin{vmatrix} 2 & 2 & -1 \\ -2 & -1 & 3 \\ 0 & 2 & -3 \end{vmatrix} = \frac{-14}{2} = -7,$$

$$x_2 = \frac{1}{2}\begin{vmatrix} 2 & 2 & -1 \\ -3 & -2 & 3 \\ 4 & 0 & -3 \end{vmatrix} = \frac{10}{2} = 5,$$

$$x_3 = \frac{1}{2}\begin{vmatrix} 2 & 2 & 2 \\ -3 & -1 & -2 \\ 4 & 2 & 0 \end{vmatrix} = \frac{-12}{2} = -6.$$

PROOF OF THEOREM A5   Let $(x_1, x_2, \ldots, x_n)$ be the solution of the system (A9). Then

$$\sum_{j=1}^{n} a_{ij} x_j = b_i, \qquad 1 \le i \le n.$$

Let k be any fixed positive integer such that $1 \leq k \leq n$. Multiplying through in the ith equation by A_{ik} and adding equations, we have

$$\sum_{i=1}^{n} \sum_{j=1}^{n} a_{ij} A_{ik} x_j = \sum_{i=1}^{n} b_i A_{ik}.$$

Interchanging the order of summation on the left-hand side, we have

$$\sum_{j=1}^{n} x_j \sum_{i=1}^{n} a_{ij} A_{ik} = \sum_{i=1}^{n} b_i A_{ik}.$$

But by Theorem A3, the inner sum on the left-hand side is equal to $\delta_{jk} \det A$. Consequently this equation becomes

$$\det A \sum_{j=1}^{n} x_j \delta_{jk} = \sum_{i=1}^{n} b_i A_{ik}$$

or

$$(\det A) x_k = \sum_{i=1}^{n} b_i A_{ik}. \tag{A12}$$

Now $\det A$ can be expressed in terms of the cofactors of the kth column of A as

$$\sum_{i=1}^{n} a_{ik} A_{ik}.$$

Hence the sum on the right-hand side of Eq. (A12) is the determinant of a matrix B_k that is obtained from A by replacing a_{ik} by b_i for $i = 1, 2, \ldots, n$. Since $\det A \neq 0$, we can divide through in Eq. (A12) to obtain the formula (A11).

Notice that the relation (A12), which can be written as

$$(\det A) x_k = \det B_k, \qquad 1 \leq k \leq n,$$

holds regardless whether or not $\det A = 0$. The only place where we used the assumption $\det A \neq 0$ was where we divided both sides of this equation by $\det A$. Thus if $\det A \neq 0$, the system (A9) has a unique solution; if $\det A = 0$, the system can have a solution only if $B_k = 0$ for all k.

The special case when the system (A9) is homogeneous ($b_1 = b_2 = \cdots = b_n = 0$) is of some interest. A homogeneous system always possesses the trivial solution, all of whose components are zero. If A is nonsingular Theorem A4 says that this is the only solution. In order to see what happens when $\det A = 0$ we use the Gauss reduction method of solution. Application of this method shows that the system (A9) is equivalent to a system of the form

$$\tilde{a}_{11}x_{i_1} + \tilde{a}_{12}x_{i_2} + \cdots + \tilde{a}_{1r}x_{i_r} + \cdots + \tilde{a}_{1n}x_{i_n} = 0,$$

$$\tilde{a}_{22}x_{i_2} + \cdots + \tilde{a}_{2r}x_{i_r} + \cdots + \tilde{a}_{2n}x_{i_n} = 0,$$

$$\vdots$$

$$\tilde{a}_{rr}x_{i_r} + \cdots + \tilde{a}_{rn}x_{i_n} = 0,$$

$$0 = 0,$$

$$\vdots$$

$$0 = 0,$$

where $r \leq n$ and $a_{ii} \neq 0$ for $1 \leq i \leq r$. Here $(i_1, i_2, \ldots, i_n)$ is some permutation of $\{1, 2, \ldots, n\}$. Because of the types of operations used in deriving this system, the determinant of its coefficient matrix is also zero. Hence we must have $r < n$ and the system possesses an $n - r$ parameter family of solutions. The last $n - r$ unknowns can be assigned arbitrary values and the remaining r unknowns are then uniquely determined. We summarize as follows.

Theorem A6 The homogeneous system with n equations and n unknowns,

$$a_{11}x_1 + \cdots + a_{1n}x_n = 0,$$

$$\vdots$$

$$a_{n1}x_1 + \cdots + a_{nn}x_n = 0,$$

possesses a nontrivial solution if and only if $\det A = 0$.

As an application of Cramer's rule, let the quantities a_{ij} and b_i, $1 \leq i \leq n$, $1 \leq j \leq n$, be *continuous functions* defined on an interval $\mathcal{I}$. If $\det A(x)$ does not vanish for any x in $\mathcal{I}$, the system

$$a_{11}(x)f_1(x) + \cdots + a_{1n}(x)f_n(x) = b_1(x),$$

$$\vdots$$

$$a_{n1}(x)f_1(x) + \cdots + a_{nn}(x)f_n(x) = b_n(x),$$

determines a set of functions $f_1, f_2, \ldots, f_n$ each defined on $\mathcal{I}$. Cramer's rule allows us to conclude that each of these functions is *continuous*, since each can be expressed as the quotient of quantities that are the sums of products of continuous functions. It is not necessary to actually solve the system to determine this important property of the solution functions.

Exercises for Section A4

1. Let A be of size $m \times n$. Under what conditions can Cramer's rule be used to find the solutions of a system with A as its coefficient matrix?

In Exercises 2–9, solve the system by Cramer's rule if the rule applies. If it does not, find all solutions that exist by another method.

2. $3x_1 - 2x_2 = 1$
    $-2x_1 + 2x_2 = 5$

3. $4x_1 + 5x_2 = 8$
    $2x_1 + x_2 = -7$

4. $2x_1 - 6x_2 = 1$
    $-x_1 + 3x_2 = 4$

5. $-3x_1 + x_2 = 6$
    $9x_1 - 3x_2 = -18$

6. $2x_1 - x_2 + 3x_3 = 1$
    $x_2 + 2x_3 = -3$
    $x_1 + x_3 = 0$

7. $-4x_1 + x_2 = 3$
    $2x_1 + 2x_2 + x_3 = -2$
    $3x_1 + 4x_3 = 2$

8. $3x_1 + x_3 = -2$
    $x_1 + 2x_2 - x_3 = 0$
    $x_1 - 4x_2 + 3x_3 = 1$

9. $-2x_1 - x_2 = 3$
    $x_1 + 3x_2 - x_3 = 0$
    $5x_2 - 2x_3 = 3$

10. Let A be a singular matrix. Show that a system with A as its coefficient matrix is either inconsistent or else possesses infinitely many solutions. (Use the Gauss reduction method.)

11. Consider the system

$$a_{11}x_1 + a_{12}x_2 = b_1, \qquad a_{21}x_1 + a_{22}x_2 = b_2,$$

where neither a_{11} nor a_{21} is zero. Clearly, we can eliminate x_1 from the second equation by multiplying through in the first equation by a_{21}/a_{11} and subtracting the resulting equation from the second equation. Alternatively, we could eliminate x_1 from the first equation by multiplying through in the second equation by a_{11}/a_{21} and subtracting the resulting equation from the first equation. In a practical problem the numbers a_{ij} and b_i would probably be rounded and not exact. If $|a_{11}/a_{21}| < 1$, explain why it would be better to eliminate x_1 from the first equation rather than the second.

Answers to Selected Exercises

CHAPTER I

Section 1.1

1. (a) First order, linear   (c) First order, nonlinear

     (e) Second order, nonlinear   (g) Third order, linear

2. (a) $y = x^2 - 3x + c$ (c) $y = \ln\left|\dfrac{x-4}{x}\right| + c$

     (e) $y = -\ln|\cos x| + c_1 x + c_2$

     (g) $y = x^4 - x^3 + c_1 x^2 + c_2 x + c_3$

3. (a) $y = -5$ (c) $y = 2x^2 - 3x - 17$

     (e) $y = -x + 3$ (g) $y = -\cos x + 1$

5. (a) $y = ce^{-3x}$ (c) $y = ce^{x/3}$

8. $f'(1) = 5, \quad f''(1) = 22, \quad f'''(1) = 140$

Section 1.2

1. $y = \pm(4x^2 + c)^{1/2}, \quad y = -(4x^2 + 5)^{1/2}$

3. $y = \dfrac{1}{c - x^2}$ and $y = 0, \quad y = \dfrac{1}{5 - x^2}$

5. $y = \dfrac{x + c}{1 - cx}, \quad y = \dfrac{7x + 1}{7 - x}$

7. $y = 1 \pm (e^x + c)^{1/2}, \quad y = 1 - (e^x + 8)^{1/2}$

9. $y = (ce^{\sin x} - 1)^{1/3}$

11. $y = \sin^{-1}(x + c) + 2n\pi$ and $y = -\sin^{-1}(x + c) + (2n + 1)\pi$

13. $y = \dfrac{x}{\ln|x| + c}$ and $y = 0$ **15.** $y = \pm x(cx^2 + 1)^{1/2}$

17. $y = x \ln(cx^2 + 1)$ **19.** $\dfrac{1}{2}\left(cx^2 - \dfrac{1}{c}\right)$

22. (a) $y = 2\tan(2x + c) - 4x + 1$

      (c) $y = 3x \pm (12x + c)^{1/2}$

24. (a) $x - 1 = (y + 2)(\ln|y + 2| + c)$

Section 1.3

3. $x^2 y^3 - 2xy^2 = c$ **5.**   Not exact

7. $y = x^2 \pm (2x^4 + c)^{1/2}$ **9.** $y = \pm[x^2 \pm (x^4 + c)^{1/2}]^{1/2}$

11. $y = \ln[x \pm (2x^2 + c)^{1/2}]$ **13.** $y = [\sin x \pm (\sin^2 x + c)^{1/2}]^{-1}$

17. $\rho(x, y) = y^{-3}, \quad y = [x \pm (4x^2 + c)^{1/2}]^{-1}$

19. $\rho(x, y) = xy^{-2}, \quad y = x^{-2}[c \pm (c^2 + x^5)^{1/2}]$

21. $\rho(x, y) = x^{-2}, \quad \dfrac{y}{x} + x^3 - y^4 = c$

23. $\rho(x, y) = y^{-2}, \quad \dfrac{x}{y} + y^2 + x^3 = c$

Section 1.4

1. $y = cx^{-2} + x^2, \quad y = 3x^{-2} + x^2$

3. $y = x^2 e^{-x}(3x + c)$

5. $y = e^{x^2}\left(c + \displaystyle\int e^{-x^2}\, dx\right), \quad y = e^{x^2}\left(be^{-a^2} + \displaystyle\int_a^x e^{-t^2}\, dt\right)$

7. $y = \ln x + \dfrac{c}{\ln x}$ **9.** $y = 1 + ce^{-x^2}$

11. $y = x(x + 1) + \dfrac{cx}{x + 1}$ **17.** $y = e^{3x}(cx^{-2} + x)^{-3}, \quad y = 0$

19. $y = \pm x(c - 2\ln|x|)^{1/2}$

21. $y = \pm\{(x+1)[c+(x-1)^2]\}^{-1/2}, \quad y = 0$

23. $y = \tan(1 + cx^{-2})$

Section 1.5

1. $y = e^{-x} + k$

3. $x^2 + y^2 = k$

5. $y^4 = kx$

7. $y^3 + 3x^2y = k$

9. $x^3 + y^3 = k$

11. $x^2 + 2xy - y^2 = k$

13. $y = x - 2\tan^{-1}x + k$

15. $y = \sqrt{3}x - 2\ln|2x + \sqrt{3}| + k$

19. $r = k\cos\theta$

21. $r^2 = k\sin 2\theta$

Section 1.6

3. 4 gm

5. 20 yr

7. $V = \pi\left(4 - \dfrac{t}{12}\right)^3 \text{ft}^3$

9. 4.77 min

11. $200 \exp\left[-(\frac{1}{50} + k)t\right]$

Section 1.7

1. $N(t) = 2000(\frac{5}{4})^{t/2}$

3. (a) $N(t) = [N_0^{1-\alpha} + (1-\alpha)kt]^{1/(1-\alpha)}$
      (b) If $0 < \alpha < 1$, $N(t) \to \infty$

5. $N(t) = 15000\left[1 + 2\exp\left(-\dfrac{t}{10}\ln\dfrac{16}{7}\right)\right]^{-1}$

Section 1.8

1. $P(t) = \dfrac{a-c}{b+d} + \left(P_0 - \dfrac{a-c}{b+d}\right)e^{-k(b+d)t}$

3. $S(t) = D + (S_0 - D)e^{-kt}$

5. $K(t) = K(0)e^{abt}$

Section 1.9

1. After $10\,\dfrac{\ln 3}{\ln(3/2)} = 27.1$ min

3. $u = 60 + \dfrac{1}{k} - t + \left(140 - \dfrac{1}{k}\right) e^{-kt}, \quad k = \dfrac{1}{10} \ln \dfrac{8}{7}$

5. (a) $x(t) = y(t) = \dfrac{a}{1 + akt}$ (b) $t = \dfrac{1}{ka}$

7. $x = a\left[1 + \dfrac{t}{T}(2^{n-1} - 1)\right]^{-1/(n-1)}, \quad n > 1, \quad x = a2^{-t/T}, \quad n = 1$

Section 1.10

3. $x = \pm \dfrac{2}{3c_1}(c_1 t - 1)^{3/2} + c_2$

5. $x = -t - \dfrac{2}{c_1} \ln|c_1 t - 1| + c_2, \quad x = \pm t + c$

7. $x = \dfrac{t^2}{2} \pm \left\{\dfrac{t}{2}(t^2 + c_1)^{1/2} + \dfrac{c_1}{2} \ln|t + (t^2 + c_1)^{1/2}|\right\} + c_2$

9. $x = \dfrac{c_1}{8} t^4 - \dfrac{1}{2c_1} \ln|t| + c_2$

11. $x = \pm [c_1(t + c_2)^2 - c_1^{-1}]^{1/2}, \quad x = \pm(\pm 2t + c)^{1/2}$

13. $x = \pm(2t + c_2)^{1/2} + c_1, \quad x = c$

15. $x = \ln\left(\dfrac{c_2 e^{c_1 t} - 1}{c_1}\right), \quad x = \ln(t + c), \quad x = c$

17. $x = \dfrac{t + c_2 \pm [(t + c_2)^2 + 4c_1]^{1/2}}{2c_1}, \quad x = -(t + c)^{-1}, \quad x = c$

19. $x = \dfrac{c_2 e^{c_1 t} + 2}{c_1}, \quad x = -2t + c, \quad x = c$

21. $x = (t + c_1) \ln(t + c_1) - t + c_2$

Section 1.11

3. (a) $m\ddot{x} + c\dot{x}|\dot{x}| = -mg$

(b) $t_1 = \left(\dfrac{m}{cg}\right)^{1/2} \tan^{-1}\left[\left(\dfrac{c}{mg}\right)^{1/2} v_0\right], \quad h = \dfrac{m}{2c} \ln \dfrac{cv_0^2 + mg}{mg}$

(c) $v_1 = -v_0\left(\dfrac{mg}{cv_0^2 + mg}\right)^{1/2}$

$$T = \left(\frac{m}{cg}\right)^{1/2} \tanh^{-1}\frac{v_0}{(v^2 + mg/c)^{1/2}}$$

$$= \left(\frac{m}{cg}\right)^{1/2} \cosh^{-1}\left(\frac{cv_0^2 + mg}{mg}\right)^{1/2}$$

5. (a) $m\ddot{x} = -c\dot{x}^n + mg$, where x is the directed distance downward.

   (b) $v = \left(\frac{mg}{c}\right)^{1/n}$

7. (a) $h = \frac{1}{2}\left(\frac{m}{cg}\right)^{1/2} \tan^{-1}\left[\left(\frac{c}{mg}\right)^{1/2} v_0^2\right]$

   (b) $h = \frac{1}{2}\left(\frac{m}{cg}\right)^{1/2} \tanh^{-1}\left[\left(\frac{c}{mg}\right)^{1/2} v_0^2\right]$

CHAPTER II

Section 2.1

1. The zero function is a solution.

2. (a) $2(1 + x)e^{2x}$ (c) 0

3. (a) $3x^2 - 2$ (c) $2x \sin x - 2 \cos x$

5. $L_1 L_2 f(x) = f''(x) + (2x - 1)f'(x) - 2xf(x)$
   $L_2 L_1 f(x) = f''(x) + (2x - 1)f'(x) + 2(1 - x)f(x)$

7. $y(x) = x^4 + 2x^{-2}$

9. The zero function

Section 2.2

1. (a) Independent   (c) Dependent   (e) Independent
   (g) Dependent   (i) Independent

3. It must be the zero function.

7. (a) Yes   (b) No

Section 2.3

1. (a) $W(x) = (b - a)e^{(a+b)x}$; independent
   (c) $W(x) = 2$; independent

(e) $W(x) = -2x^{-6}$; independent

(g) $W(x) = 0$; dependent if m is even, independent if m is odd

2. (a) False   (b) True   (c) True

4. $W(x) = -48e^{5x}$

Section 2.4

1. (a) $(D^2 - 3D + 2)y = 0$ (c) $(D^3 - 3D^2 - D + 1)y = 0$

2. (a) $(D - 1)(D + 2)y = 0$ (c) $(D - 1)^2(D + 2)y = 0$

3. (a) $(D^2 - D - 2)y = 0$ (c) $(D^3 - 4D^2 + 4D)y = 0$

5. $y = c_1 e^{2x} + c_2 e^{3x}$

7. $y = c_1 e^x + c_2 e^{-x} + c_3 e^{-5x}$

9. Not possible

Section 2.5

3. (a) $\cos 3x + i \sin 3x$ (c) $e^{2x}(\cos 3x - i \sin 3x)$

(e) $\frac{1}{2}(e^{2ix} + e^{-2ix})$ (g) $\dfrac{1}{2i}(e^{ix} - e^{-ix})$

7. $e^{-x} \cos 2x, \quad e^{-x} \sin 2x$

8. (a) $\cos 3x, \quad \sin 3x$ (c) $e^{2x} \cos 2x, \quad e^{2x} \sin 2x$

9. $2 \cos 2x - 4 \sin 2x, \quad 4 \cos 2x + 2 \sin 2x$

11. $\cos(2 \ln x), \quad \sin(2 \ln x)$

Section 2.6

1. $y = c_1 e^{-2x} + c_2 e^{3x}$ **3.** $y = c_1 + c_2 e^{-2x}$

5. $y = c_1 + c_2 e^x + c_3 e^{-4x}$ **7.** $y = (c_1 + c_2 x)e^{-x}$

9. $y = (c_1 + c_2 x + c_3 x^2)e^{2x}$ **11.** $y = c_1 + c_2 x + c_3 e^{-x}$

13. $y = c_1 \cos 3x + c_2 \sin 3x$ **15.** $y = e^{3x}(c_1 \cos 2x + c_2 \sin 2x)$

17. $y = (c_1 + c_2 x) \cos x + (c_3 + c_4 x) \sin x$

19. $y = (c_1 + c_2 x)e^{2x} + c_3 \cos \sqrt{2}\,x + c_4 \sin \sqrt{2}\,x$

21. $y = -3e^x + 2e^{3x}$ **23.** $y = \cos 2x - 2 \sin 2x$

25. $y = 3 - e^{-x}$

29. (a) $y'' + 4y' + 4y = 0$ (c) $y'' + 4y = 0$

     (e) $(D^2 + 9)^2 y = 0$

Section 2.7

1. $y = c_1 x^2 + c_2 x^{-1}$ **3.** $y = c_1 + c_2 x^{1/3}$

5. $y = (c_1 + c_2 \ln x)x^{1/2}$ **7.** $y = c_1 + c_2 \ln x + c_3 x$

9. $y = c_1 \cos(2 \ln x) + c_2 \sin(2 \ln x)$

11. $y = c_1 x + c_2 \cos(\ln x) + c_3 \sin(\ln x)$

13. $y = 4x^{-1} - 3x^{-2}$

15. $y - \cos(2 \ln x) + 2 \sin(2 \ln x)$

17. $y = cx$

21. (a) $y = [c_1 + c_2 \ln(x - 3)](x - 3)^{-1}$

22. (a) All zeros must have positive real parts.

Section 2.8

1. $y = c_1 e^x + c_2 e^{-x} + \sin 2x$

3. (a) $y = c_1 e^{2x} + 2e^{5x}$ (c) $y = c_1 \cos x + c_2 \sin x + 2e^x$

7. (a) $y = c_1 e^x + c_2 e^{3x} + 2e^{2x} + e^{-x}$

Section 2.9

1. $y = c_1 e^x + c_2 e^{-3x} + e^{2x}, \quad y = 3e^x + e^{-3x} + e^{2x}$

3. $y = c_1 e^{-x} + c_2 e^{-2x} + (6x - 5)e^x$

5. $y = c_1 e^{-x} + c_2 e^{-2x} - \cos 2x + 3 \sin 2x, \quad y = -\cos 2x + 3 \sin 2x$

7. $y = c_1 e^{3x} + c_2 e^{-2x} - \frac{1}{3}$

9. $y = (c_1 + c_2 x)e^x + c_3 e^{-x} + \frac{2}{5}(\cos 2x - 2 \sin 2x)$

11. $y = c_1 e^{-x} + c_2 e^{-2x} - 5xe^{-2x}$

13. $y = c_1 e^{-x} + c_2 e^{2x} + \left(x^2 + \frac{2x}{3}\right)e^{-x}$

15. $y = c_1 e^{-x} + c_2 e^{-3x} + \left(x^3 - \frac{3x^2}{2} + \frac{3x}{2}\right)e^{-x}$

17. $y = c_1 + c_2 e^{-x} + x^3 - 3x^2 + 6x$

19. $y = e^{-x}(c_1 \cos 2x + c_2 \sin 2x) + xe^{-x} \sin 2x$

22. (a) $y = c_1 e^x + c_2 e^{2x} + e^{-x}$

    (c) $y = c_1 e^{-x} + c_2 e^{2x} - 3 \cos x - \sin x$

    (e) $y = (c_1 + c_2 x)e^x + c_3 e^{-x} + 3e^{2x}$

24. (a) $y = c_1 e^{2x} + c_2 e^{-x} + 2xe^{2x}$

    (c) $y = c_1 \cos x + c_2 \sin x + 2x \sin x$

25. $y = c_1 x^{-2} + c_2 x^3 + x^4$ **27.** $y = c_1 x + c_2 x^3 - 2$

29. $y = c_1 x + c_2 x^{-2} + 2x \ln x$

Section 2.10

1. $y = c_1 e^x + c_2 e^{-x} - 1 + e^x \ln(1 + e^{-x}) - e^{-x} \ln(1 + e^x)$

3. $y = (c_1 + c_2 x)e^{-x} + x^2 e^{-x}(2 \ln|x| - 3)$

5. $y = c_1 \cos x + c_2 \sin x - x \cos x + (\sin x) \ln|\sin x|$

7. $y = e^{-x}(c_1 \cos x + c_2 \sin x - 1 - \cos x + \sin x \ln| \sec x + \tan x|)$

9. $y = (c_1 + c_2 x + c_3 x^2)e^x - 2xe^x \ln|x|$

13. $y = c_1 x + c_2 xe^{1/x}$

15. $y = c_1 e^x + c_2 x^{1/2} e^x + xe^x$

Section 2.11

1. (a) $x = c_1 e^{-\alpha t} + c_2 e^{-\beta t}$ (b) $x = \dfrac{x_0}{\beta - \alpha}(\beta e^{-\alpha t} - \alpha e^{-\beta t})$

    (c) $x = \dfrac{v_0}{\beta - \alpha}(e^{-\alpha t} - e^{-\beta t})$

5. $m > 1$

Section 2.12

1. (a) $I = \dfrac{E_0}{R}(1 - e^{-Rt/L})$

    (b) $E_0(1 - e^{-Rt/L})$ across the resistance, $E_0 e^{-Rt/L}$ across the inductance.

3. $I = \dfrac{A\omega_1}{D} \sin(\omega_1 t + \alpha + \beta), \quad \beta = \sin^{-1} \dfrac{c^{-1} - \omega_1^2 L}{D},$

    $D = [(c^{-1} - \omega_1^2 L)^2 + (\omega_1 R)^2]^{1/2}$

5. $I = -Q_0 \omega \sin \omega t, \quad \omega = (LC)^{-1/2}$

7. (a) $E = \dfrac{AR^2 C\omega}{1 + (RC\omega)^2} e^{-t/(RC)} + \dfrac{AR}{1 + (RC\omega)^2}(\sin \omega t - RC\omega \cos \omega t)$

(b) $\dfrac{A}{1 + (RC\omega)^2}(\sin \omega t - RC\omega \cos \omega t)$

(c) $\dfrac{ARC\omega}{1 + (RC\omega)^2}(\cos \omega t + RC\omega \sin \omega t)$

CHAPTER III

Section 3.1

1. $(0, 2)$ **3.** $(1, 3)$

5. All x **7.** $(-1, 1)$

9. $f(x) + g(x) = \displaystyle\sum_{n=0}^{\infty} (n + 2)(x - 2)^n, \qquad |x - 2| < 1$

$f(x)g(x) = \dfrac{1}{2}\displaystyle\sum_{n=0}^{\infty} (n + 1)(n + 2)(x - 2)^n, \qquad |x - 2| < 1$

11. $f(x) + g(x) = \displaystyle\sum_{n=0}^{\infty} \dfrac{n^2 + 2n + 2}{n + 1} x^n, \qquad |x| < 1$

$f(x)g(x) = \displaystyle\sum_{n=0}^{\infty} \left(\sum_{k=0}^{n} \dfrac{n - k + 1}{k + 1} \right) x^n, \qquad |x| < 1$

13. $\displaystyle\sum_{n=0}^{\infty} (n + 2)(n + 1)x^n$ **15.** $\displaystyle\sum_{n=1}^{\infty} (n^2 - 2n + 3)x^n$

17. $f'(x) = \displaystyle\sum_{n=1}^{\infty} \dfrac{(-1)^n n x^{n-1}}{2^n(n + 1)}, \quad f''(x) = \displaystyle\sum_{n=2}^{\infty} \dfrac{(-1)^n n(n - 1)x^{n-2}}{2^n(n + 1)}, \quad |x| < 2$

Section 3.2

1. $3 + 13(x - 2) + 9(x - 2)^2 + 2(x - 2)^3$

3. $\displaystyle\sum_{n=1}^{\infty} \dfrac{(-1)^{n+1}}{n}(x - 1)^n$

5. $1 + \dfrac{1}{2}x + \displaystyle\sum_{n=2}^{\infty}(-1)^{n+1}\dfrac{1\cdot 3\cdot 5\cdots(2n-3)}{2^n n!}\,x^n$

7. $\displaystyle\sum_{n=0}^{\infty}(-1)^n\left(\dfrac{x}{4}\right)^n, \quad |x| < 4$

9. $\dfrac{2}{3}\displaystyle\sum_{n=0}^{\infty}\left[1-\left(-\dfrac{1}{2}\right)^{n+1}\right]x^n, \quad |x| < 1$

11. $\displaystyle\sum_{n=0}^{\infty}(n+1)x^n, \quad |x| < 1$

13. $\displaystyle\sum_{n=0}^{\infty}\dfrac{x^{2n+1}}{2n+1}, \quad |x| < 1$

15. $x\dfrac{d}{dx}(xe^x) = (x^2 + x)e^x$

17. $\dfrac{d}{dx}\left[x\displaystyle\int_0^x\dfrac{1}{1-t}\,dt\right] = \dfrac{x}{1-x} - \ln(1-x)$

Section 3.3

1. (a) $x = -2, 0, 1$　　　　　　　　　　(c) None

3. $y = A_0\left[1 + \displaystyle\sum_{m=1}^{\infty}\dfrac{x^{2m}}{2^m 1\cdot 3\cdot 5\cdots(2m-1)}\right]$

$\quad + A_1\displaystyle\sum_{m=1}^{\infty}\dfrac{x^{2m-1}}{2^{2m-2}(m-1)!}\qquad$ for all x

5. $y = A_0\left[1 + \displaystyle\sum_{m=1}^{\infty}\dfrac{(-1)^m 2^m m!\,x^{2m}}{1\cdot 3\cdot 5\cdots(2m-1)}\right]$

$\quad + A_1\displaystyle\sum_{m=1}^{\infty}(-1)^{m+1}\dfrac{1\cdot 3\cdot 5\cdots(2m-1)}{2^{m-1}(m-1)!}x^{2m-1}, \qquad |x| < \sqrt{2}$

7. $y = A_0\displaystyle\sum_{m=0}^{\infty}\dfrac{x^{3m}}{3^m m!} + A_1\displaystyle\sum_{m=0}^{\infty}\dfrac{x^{3m+1}}{1\cdot 4\cdot 7\cdots(3m+1)}\qquad$ for all x

9. $y = A_0(1 + \tfrac{1}{2}x^2 - \tfrac{1}{6}x^3 + \tfrac{1}{8}x^4 + \cdots) + A_1(x + \tfrac{1}{6}x^3 - \tfrac{1}{12}x^4 + \cdots)$,
$\qquad\qquad\qquad\qquad\qquad\qquad\qquad\qquad\qquad\qquad |x| < 1$

11. $y = A_0(1 + \tfrac{1}{6}x^3 - \tfrac{1}{120}x^5 + \tfrac{1}{180}x^6 + \cdots)$

$\quad + A_1(x + \tfrac{1}{12}x^4 - \tfrac{1}{180}x^6 + \cdots)\qquad$ for all x

13. $y = A_0[1 - 2(x + 1)^2] + A_1\left[(x + 1) - \frac{1}{2}(x + 1)^3\right.$

$$\left. - \sum_{m=3}^{\infty} \frac{1 \cdot 3 \cdot 5 \cdots (2m - 5)}{2 \cdot 4 \cdot 6 \cdots (2m - 2)}(x + 1)^{2m-1}\right], \qquad |x + 1| < 1$$

15. $y = A_0\left[1 + \sum_{m=1}^{\infty} \frac{(x + 3)^{3m}}{2 \cdot 5 \cdot 8 \cdots (3m - 1)}\right] + A_1 \sum_{m=0}^{\infty} \frac{(x + 3)^{3m+1}}{3^m m!}$ for all x

Section 3.4

1. (a) $0, \ -1$ \qquad\qquad\qquad\qquad (c) $-\frac{1}{2}$

3. $y = c_1 x\left[1 + \sum_{n=1}^{\infty} \frac{x^n}{n! \, 5 \cdot 7 \cdot 9 \cdots (2n + 3)}\right]$

$$+ c_2 x^{-1/2}\left[1 - x - \sum_{n=2}^{\infty} \frac{x^n}{n! \, 1 \cdot 3 \cdot 5 \cdots (2n - 3)}\right]$$

5. $y = c_1 x^{1/3}\left[1 + \sum_{n=1}^{\infty} \frac{(-1)^n x^n}{n! \, 4 \cdot 7 \cdot 10 \cdots (3n + 1)}\right]$

$$+ c_2\left[1 + \sum_{n=1}^{\infty} \frac{(-1)^n x^n}{n! \, 2 \cdot 5 \cdot 8 \cdots (3n - 1)}\right]$$

7. $y = c_1 x^{1/3} \sum_{m=0}^{\infty} 4 \frac{(-1)^m x^{2m}}{2^m m! (6m + 4)} + c_2 x^{-1}$

9. $y = c_1 x^{-1} \sum_{n=0}^{\infty} \frac{(n + 1)! \, x^n}{1 \cdot 3 \cdot 5 \cdots (2n + 1)} + c_2 x^{-3/2} \sum_{n=0}^{\infty} \frac{1 \cdot 3 \cdot 5 \cdots (2n + 1)}{4^n n!} x^n$

11. $y = c_1(x - 1)^{1/3}[1 - \frac{1}{5}(x - 1)]$

$$+ c_2(x - 1)^{-1/3}\left[1 + \sum_{n=1}^{\infty} \frac{(-5)(-2)1 \cdot 4 \cdots (3n - 8)}{3^n n! \, 1 \cdot 4 \cdot 7 \cdots (3n - 2)}(x - 1)^n\right]$$

Section 3.5

1. $y(x) = c_1 y_1(x) + c_2\left[y_1(x) \ln x - x^2 \sum_{n=1}^{\infty} n x^n\right]$

$$y_1(x) = x^2 \sum_{n=0}^{\infty} (n + 1)x^n$$

3. $y(x) = c_1 y_1(x) + c_2 \left[y_1(x) \ln x - 2x \sum\limits_{n=1}^{\infty} \dfrac{\phi(n)}{(n!)^2} x^n \right]$

$y_1(x) = x \sum\limits_{n=0}^{\infty} \dfrac{x^n}{(n!)^2}$

5. $y(x) = c_1 y_1(x) + c_2 \left[y_1(x) \ln x - \sum\limits_{m=1}^{\infty} \dfrac{\phi(m)}{2^m (m!)^2} x^{2m} \right]$

$y_1(x) = \sum\limits_{m=0}^{\infty} \dfrac{x^{2m}}{2^m (m!)^2}$

7. $y(x) = c_1 y_1(x) + c_2 \left[y_1(x) \ln x - 2x^{-2} \sum\limits_{n=1}^{\infty} \dfrac{\phi(n)}{(n!)^2} x^n \right]$

$y_1(x) = x^{-2} \sum\limits_{n=0}^{\infty} \dfrac{x^n}{(n!)^2}$

9. $y(x) = c_1 y_1(x) + c_2 \left[y_1(x) \ln x - 2x^2 + \sum\limits_{n=2}^{\infty} \dfrac{(-1)^{n+1} x^{n+1}}{n(n-1)} \right]$

$y_1(x) = x + x^2$

Section 3.6

The general solution is $y = c_1 y_1 + c_2 y_2$, where y_1 and y_2 are as given.

1. $y_1(x) = x \sum\limits_{n=0}^{\infty} \dfrac{x^n}{n!} = xe^x$

$y_2(x) = y_1(x) \ln x + 1 - \sum\limits_{n=2}^{\infty} \dfrac{\phi(n-1)}{(n-1)!} x^n$

3. $y_1(x) = x^{-1}(1 - 3x^2 + 3x^4 - x^6)$

$y_2(x) = x^{-2} \left[1 + \sum\limits_{m=1}^{\infty} \dfrac{(-7)(-5)(-3) \cdots (2m-9)}{1 \cdot 3 \cdot 5 \cdots (2m-1)} x^{2m} \right]$

5. $y_1(x) = x^2 \sum\limits_{n=0}^{\infty} \dfrac{x^n}{n!(n+1)!}$

$y_2(x) = y_1(x) \ln x + x - x^2 - x \sum\limits_{n=2}^{\infty} \dfrac{\phi(n-1) + \phi(n)}{(n-1)! \, n!} x^n$

7. $y_1(x) = 1 + 2 \sum\limits_{n=1}^{\infty} \dfrac{x^n}{(n+2)!}, \qquad y_2(x) = x^{-2}(1 + x)$

9. $y_1(x) = \displaystyle\sum_{n=0}^{\infty} \frac{x^{n+1}}{n!\,(n+1)!}$

$y_2(x) = y_1(x)\ln x + 1 - x - \displaystyle\sum_{n=2}^{\infty} \frac{\phi(n) + \phi(n-1)}{(n-1)!\,n!} x^n$

11. $y_1(x) = \displaystyle\sum_{n=0}^{\infty} \frac{2^{n+1}x^{n+1}}{n!\,(n+2)!}$

$y_2(x) = -2y_1(x)\ln x$

$\qquad\qquad + x^{-1}\left[1 - 2x + x^2 + \displaystyle\sum_{n=3}^{\infty} \frac{2^n[\phi(n) + \phi(n-2) - 1]}{(n-2)!\,n!} x^n\right]$

13. $y_1(x) = x\displaystyle\sum_{n=0}^{\infty} x^n = \frac{x}{1-x}$, $\qquad y_2(x) = x^{-3}(1 + x + x^2 + x^3)$

Section 3.7

1. (a) 0, ∞ (neither regular) $\qquad\qquad$ (c) 2 (regular), ∞ (not regular)

$\quad$ (e) ∞ (regular), 0 (regular)

3. $y(x) = c_1 \displaystyle\sum_{m=0}^{\infty} \frac{x^{-2m}}{2^m m!} + c_2 \displaystyle\sum_{m=1}^{\infty} \frac{x^{-2m+1}}{1\cdot 3\cdot 5\cdots(2m-1)}$

5. $y(x) = c_1 x^{-1} \displaystyle\sum_{n=0}^{\infty} (-1)^n \frac{2n+3}{3n!} x^{-n} + c_2 x^{-1/2}$

$\qquad\qquad \times \left[1 + \displaystyle\sum_{n=1}^{\infty} \frac{(-1)^n 2^n(n+1)}{1\cdot 3\cdot 5\cdots(2n-1)} x^{-n}\right]$

7. $y(x) = c_1 \displaystyle\sum_{m=0}^{\infty} (m+1)x^{-2m} + c_2\left[y_1(x)\ln x + \frac{1}{2}\displaystyle\sum_{m=1}^{\infty} mx^{-2m}\right]$

Section 3.8

2. (a) $y(x) = c_1 \displaystyle\sum_{m=0}^{\infty} \frac{x^{2m}}{2^m m!} + c_2 \displaystyle\sum_{m=1}^{\infty} \frac{2^m m!}{(2m)!} x^{2m-1}$

$\qquad\qquad + \frac{1}{2}x^2 + \frac{1}{6}x^3 + \frac{1}{6}x^4 + \frac{1}{24}x^5 + \cdots \qquad$ for all x

CHAPTER IV

Section 4.1

1. (a) $\sqrt{\dfrac{\pi}{2}}$ $\qquad\qquad\qquad\qquad\qquad$ (c) $-2\sqrt{\pi}$

8. 1

Section 4.2

3. (a) 0.990   (c) -0.196

4. (a) $y(x) = c_1 J_{1/3}(x) + c_2 J_{-1/3}(x)$

Section 4.3

1. (a) $[2^\alpha \Gamma(\alpha + 1)]^{-1}$

3. (a) $y(x) = c_1 J_1(x) + c_2 Y_1(x)$

Section 4.4

3. $Y_3(x) = \dfrac{8 - x^2}{x^2} Y_1(x) - \dfrac{4}{x} Y_0(x)$

Section 4.6

1. $y(x) = x^{1/2} [c_1 J_{1/4}(\frac{1}{2}x^2) + c_2 J_{-1/4}(\frac{1}{2}x^2)]$

3. $y(x) = x^{-2} [c_1 J_1(2x) + c_2 Y_1(2x)]$

5. $y(x) = x^{1/2} [c_1 I_{1/3}(\frac{2}{3}x^{3/2}) + c_2 I_{-1/3}(\frac{2}{3}x^{3/2})]$

7. $y(x) = x^{-1} [c_1 I_2(2\sqrt{2x}) + c_2 K_2(2\sqrt{2x})]$

9. (a) $\left(\dfrac{2}{\pi x}\right)^{1/2} \left[\dfrac{3 - x^2}{x^2} \sin x - \dfrac{3}{x} \cos x\right]$

   (c) $-\left(\dfrac{2}{\pi x}\right)^{1/2} \cos x$

   (e) $-\left(\dfrac{2}{\pi x}\right)^{1/2} \left(\sinh x + \dfrac{\cosh x}{x}\right)$

CHAPTER V

Section 5.1

1. (a) $\dfrac{2}{5}$ (c) $\dfrac{-\pi}{4}$

2. (a) $\left(\dfrac{2}{7}\right)^{1/2}$ (c) $\dfrac{\pi}{2}$

3. (a) $\|\phi_n\| = \dfrac{1}{\sqrt{2}}$

Section 5.2

1. (a) $\phi_0(x) = 1,\quad \phi_1(x) = x - \frac{1}{2},\quad \phi_2(x) = x^2 - x + \frac{1}{6}$
   (c) $\phi_0(x) = 1,\quad \phi_1(x) = x,\quad \phi_2(x) = x^2 - \frac{1}{2}$
   (e) $\phi_0(x) = 1,\quad \phi_1(x) = x,\quad \phi_2(x) = x^2 - \frac{1}{3}$
   (g) $\phi_0(x) = 1,\quad \phi_1(x) = x - 1,\quad \phi_2(x) = x^2 - 4x + 2$

Section 5.6

1. $0;\quad \pm\dfrac{1}{\sqrt{3}};\quad 0, \pm\sqrt{\dfrac{3}{5}}$

Section 5.8

1. $Q = \frac{8}{3}P_0 + \frac{3}{5}P_1 + \frac{4}{3}P_2 + \frac{2}{5}P_3$

CHAPTER VI

Section 6.1

1. $\lambda_n = \left(\dfrac{2n+1}{2}\right)^2;\quad y_n(x) = \sin\left(\dfrac{2n+1}{2}\right)x,\quad n \geq 0$

3. $\lambda_n = k_n^2$, where k_n is the nth positive root of the equation
   $$\tan k = \frac{1}{k};\quad y_n(x) = \cos k_n x,\quad n \geq 1$$

5. $\lambda_n = n^2;\quad y_n(x) = e^{-x}\sin nx,\quad n \geq 1$

7. $\lambda_n = (n\pi)^4;\quad y_n(x) = \cos n\pi x,\quad n \geq 0$

Section 6.2

1. (a) $(xy')' + (x - x^{-1})y = 0$
   (c) $(e^{2x}y')' + (\lambda + 1)e^{2x}y = 0$
   (e) $(e^{-x^2}y')' + e^{-x^2}y = 0$

Section 6.5

7. $\lambda_n = k_n^2$, where k_n is the nth positive root of the equation

$$J_1\left(\frac{k}{2}\right) + kJ_1'\left(\frac{k}{2}\right) = 0; \quad y_n(x) = x^{1/2}J_1\left(\frac{k_n x}{2}\right); \quad w(x) = 1$$

CHAPTER VII

Section 7.1

1. $\phi_0(x) = c^{-1/2}, \quad \phi_n(x) = \left(\frac{2}{c}\right)^{1/2} \cos\left(\frac{n\pi x}{c}\right), \quad n \geq 1$

3. (a) $\phi_n(x) = \dfrac{H_n(x)}{(2^n n! \sqrt{\pi})}$

5. $\dfrac{1}{2} - \dfrac{4}{\pi^2} \sum_{m=1}^{\infty} \dfrac{\cos(2m-1)\pi x}{(2m-1)^2}$

8. (a) $x^2 = \frac{2}{3}P_2(x) + \frac{1}{3}$

Section 7.2

1. (a) $\dfrac{6}{\pi} \sum_{n=1}^{\infty} \dfrac{1}{n} \sin\dfrac{n\pi x}{3}$

   (c) $\dfrac{8}{\pi^3} \sum_{m=1}^{\infty} \dfrac{\sin(2m-1)\pi x}{(2m-1)^3}$

   (e) $\dfrac{8}{\pi} \sum_{m=1}^{\infty} \dfrac{m \sin 2mx}{4m^2 - 1}$

2. (a) $\dfrac{3}{2} + \dfrac{12}{\pi^2} \sum_{m=1}^{\infty} \dfrac{\cos[(2m-1)\pi x/3]}{(2m-1)^2}$

   (c) $\dfrac{1}{6} - \dfrac{1}{\pi^2} \sum_{m=1}^{\infty} \dfrac{\cos 2m\pi x}{m^2}$

   (e) $\cos x$

3. $\frac{1}{4}P_0 + \frac{1}{2}P_1 + \frac{5}{16}P_2 + \cdots$

5. $\frac{1}{2}L_0 + \frac{1}{4}L_1 + \frac{1}{8}L_2 + \cdots$

7. (a) $2\sum_{n=1}^{\infty} \dfrac{J_1(k_n x)}{k_n J_2(2k_n)}$

Section 7.3

1. (a) Yes   (c) Yes   (e) No

Section 7.4

3. $C_0 = \frac{1}{4}, \quad C_1 = \frac{1}{2}, \quad C_2 = \frac{5}{16}$

4. (a) $A_0 = \frac{1}{2}, \quad A_1 = \frac{1}{4}$

5. $C_0 = \frac{1}{2}, \quad C_1 = \frac{3}{4}, \quad C_2 = 0$

7. (a) $\dfrac{2c}{\pi^2} \sum_{m=1}^{\infty} \dfrac{1}{(2m-1)^2} \le c$

9. Let $f(x) = 0$ when $x < 0$ and $f(x) = 1$ when $x > 0$; apply Theorem 7.3

Section 7.5

9. (a) f is in V (c) h is not in V

10. (a) f is in W (c) h is in W

Section 7.6

1. (a) Piecewise smooth   (c) Not piecewise smooth

2. (a) $\dfrac{1}{2} - \dfrac{2}{\pi} \sum_{m=1}^{\infty} \dfrac{\sin(2m-1)x}{(2m-1)}$

(c) $\dfrac{1}{2} + \dfrac{1}{2}\cos x + \dfrac{1}{\pi}\sum_{n=1}^{\infty}\dfrac{1}{n}\left[(-1)^n \dfrac{2n^2-1}{n^2-1} - 1\right]\sin nx$

3. (a) $\dfrac{1}{2} + \dfrac{2}{\pi}\sum_{m=1}^{\infty}\dfrac{(-1)^{m+1}}{2m-1}\cos\dfrac{2m-1}{c}\pi x$ (c) $\dfrac{2c}{\pi}\sum_{n=1}^{\infty}\dfrac{(-1)^{n+1}}{n}\sin\dfrac{n\pi x}{c}$

7. $\dfrac{1}{2} + \dfrac{2}{\pi}\sum_{m=1}^{\infty}\sin\dfrac{(2m-1)\pi x}{(2m-1)}$

Section 7.7

1. (a) $\dfrac{\pi}{2} - \dfrac{4}{\pi}\sum_{m=1}^{\infty}\cos\dfrac{(2m-1)x}{(2m-1)^2}, \quad 2\sum_{n=1}^{\infty}\dfrac{(-1)^{n+1}\sin nx}{n}$

(c) $\dfrac{2}{\pi} - \dfrac{4}{\pi}\sum_{m=1}^{\infty}\dfrac{\cos 2mx}{(4m^2-1)}, \quad \sin x$

5. (a) $\dfrac{2}{\pi} \displaystyle\sum_{n=1}^{\infty} \dfrac{\cos(n\pi/2) - (-1)^n}{n} \sin \dfrac{n\pi x}{c}$,

$\dfrac{1}{2} + \dfrac{2}{\pi} \displaystyle\sum_{m=1}^{\infty} \dfrac{(-1)^m}{2m-1} \cos \dfrac{(2m-1)\pi x}{c}$

(c) $\dfrac{c}{\pi} \displaystyle\sum_{n=1}^{\infty} \left[\dfrac{2\sin(n\pi/2)}{n^2\pi} - \dfrac{\cos(n\pi/2)}{n} \right] \sin \dfrac{n\pi x}{c}$,

$\dfrac{c}{8} + \dfrac{c}{\pi} \displaystyle\sum_{n=1}^{\infty} \left[\dfrac{2(\cos(n\pi/2) - 1)}{n^2\pi} + \dfrac{\sin(n\pi/2)}{n} \right] \cos \dfrac{n\pi x}{c}$

Section 7.8

1. (a) $\frac{1}{2}P_0(x) + \frac{3}{4}P_1(x) - \frac{7}{16}P_3(x) + \cdots$

(c) $\frac{1}{2}P_0(x) + \frac{5}{8}P_2(x) - \frac{3}{16}P_4(x) + \cdots$

5. (a) $\frac{1}{2}P_0(\cos \phi) - \frac{3}{4}P_1(\cos \phi) + \frac{7}{16}P_3(\cos \phi) + \cdots$

7. (a) $L_0(x) + \frac{1}{2}L_1(x) + \frac{1}{6}L_2(x) + \cdots$

9. (a) $\dfrac{1}{\sqrt{\pi}} [2H_0(x) - \frac{1}{6}H_2(x) + \cdots]$

10. (a) $2c \displaystyle\sum_{n=1}^{\infty} \dfrac{J_2(k_n x)}{k_n J_3(k_n c)}$ (c) $\dfrac{2}{c^3} \displaystyle\sum_{n=1}^{\infty} \dfrac{2k_n c + (4 + c^2 k_n^2)J_3(k_n c)}{k_n^3 [J_3(k_n c)]^2} J_2(k_n x)$

11. (a) $4c^2 \displaystyle\sum_{n=1}^{\infty} \dfrac{J_2(k_n x)}{(c^2 k_n^2 - 4)J_2(k_n c)}$

(c) $\dfrac{4}{c^2} \displaystyle\sum_{n=1}^{\infty} \dfrac{c^2 k_n^2 - 4J_2(k_n c)}{k_n^2(c^2 k_n^2 - 4)[J_2(k_n c)]^2} J_2(k_n x)$

13. $2 \displaystyle\sum_{n=1}^{\infty} \dfrac{k_n J_1(k_n)}{(k_n^2 + h^2)[J_0(k_n)]^2} J_0(k_n x)$, where $hJ_0(k_n) + k_n J_0'(k_n) = 0$

15. (a) $2\pi e^{-x} \displaystyle\sum_{n=1}^{\infty} \dfrac{n[1 - e(-1)^n]}{\pi^2 n^2 + 1} \sin n\pi x$

CHAPTER VIII

Section 8.1

3. Solve the first equation for x_1, then the second for x_2, and then the third for x_3.

5. (a) $x_1' = -k_1 x_1, \quad x_2' = -k_2 x_1 - k_3 x_2$

(b) $x_1(t) = ae^{-k_1 t}, \quad x_2(t) = \left(b - \dfrac{ak_1 k_2}{k_3 - k_1}\right)e^{-k_3 t} + \dfrac{ak_1 k_2}{k_3 - k_1}e^{-k_1 t}$

7. $m_1 \ddot{x}_1 = \dfrac{km_1 m_2}{(x_1 - x_2)^2}, \quad m_2 \ddot{x}_2 = \dfrac{-km_1 m_2}{(x_1 - x_2)^2}$

Section 8.2

1. $x_1' = 4x_1 + \cos t + e^t, \qquad x_1(t_0) = k_1, \quad x_2(t_0) = k_2$
$x_2' = 3x_1 + e^t$

3. $u_1' = u_3 + e^t \qquad\qquad u_1 = x_1, \quad x_1(t_0) = k_1$
$u_2' = u_3 \qquad\qquad\qquad u_2 = x_2, \quad x_2(t_0) = k_2$
$u_3' = u_1 + u_2 + u_3 + \sin t \qquad u_3 = x_2', \quad x_2'(t_0) = k_3$

5. $u_1' = u_2, \qquad\qquad\qquad\quad u_1 = x_1, \quad x_1(t_0) = k_1$
$u_2' = u_3, \qquad\qquad\qquad\quad u_2 = x_1', \quad x_1'(t_0) = k_2$
$u_3' = u_2 - u_1 u_5 + \sin t, \qquad u_3 = x_1'', \quad x_1''(t_0) = k_3$
$u_4' = u_5, \qquad\qquad\qquad\quad u_4 = x_2, \quad x_2(t_0) = k_4$
$u_5' = u_3 - u_4 u_2 - \cos t, \qquad u_5 = x_2', \quad x_2'(t_0) = k_5$

7. $u_1' = u_2, \qquad\qquad\qquad\quad u_2' = tu_2 - u_1^2 + \sin t$

9. $u_1' = u_2, \qquad\qquad\qquad\quad u_2' = u_3, \quad u_3' = u_3 - u_1 + e^t$

Section 8.3

3. $x_1 = -2c_1 e^{-t} - 3c_2 e^{-2t} - 3e^{-3t}, \quad x_1 = -6e^{-2t} - 3e^{-3t}$
$x_2 = c_1 e^{-t} + c_2 e^{-2t} + 2e^{-3t}, \qquad\qquad x_2 = 2e^{-2t} + 2e^{-3t}$

5. $x_1 = c_1 e^{-t} + 3e^{-2t}$
$x_2 = -2c_1 t e^{-t} + c_2 e^{-t} + 12e^{-2t}$

7. $x_1 = 5c_1 \cos t + 5c_2 \sin t + e^{-t}$
$x_2 = (c_1 + 2c_2) \cos t + (-2c_1 + c_2) \sin t + c_3 e^{-2t} + 2e^{-t}$

9. $x_1 = c_1 e^{-t} + 4c_2 e^{-2t} + c_3 \cos t + c_4 \sin t, \quad x_1 = e^{-t} + \sin t$
$x_2 = c_1 e^{-t} + 5c_2 e^{-2t}, \qquad\qquad\qquad\qquad x_2 = e^{-t}$

11. $x_1 = 5c_1 e^{-t} - 2c_2 e^{-2t} + c_3 e^t, \quad x_1 = -2e^{-2t} - e^t$
$x_2 = 2c_1 e^{-t}, \qquad\qquad\qquad\qquad x_2 = 0$
$x_3 = -2c_1 e^{-t} + 3c_2 e^{-2t}, \qquad\quad x_3 = 3e^{-2t}$

13. $x_1 = 2c_1 + c_2 e^{-t} + c_3 e^t + t^2$
$x_2 = c_1 + c_2 e^{-t} - t$
$x_3 = -2c_1 - 2c_2 e^{-t} - c_3 e^t$

15. $x_1 = 7c_1 e^t + c_2 \cos 2t + c_3 \sin 2t$
$x_2 = 2c_1 e^t + c_2 \cos 2t + c_3 \sin 2t$
$x_3 = 3c_1 e^t + (c_2 + c_3) \cos 2t + (-c_2 + c_3) \sin 2t$

17. $x_1 = c_1 e^{-2t} + c_2 e^{-t} + \cos t$
$x_2 = c_1 e^{-2t} + c_3 e^{-t}$
$x_3 = c_1 e^{-2t} + \sin t$

Section 8.4

1. (b) In the equation $P(r) = ar^4 + br^2 + c = 0$,

$$b^2 - 4ac = (m_2 k_1 - m_1 k_2)^2 + m_2 k_2 (m_2 k_2 + 2m_1 k_2 + 2m_2 k_1),$$

which is positive. Hence $-b \pm (b^2 - 4ac)^{1/2}$ is negative.

3. $m_1 \ddot{x}_1 = k_1 x_1 + c(\dot{x}_2 - \dot{x}_1), \quad m_2 \ddot{x}_2 = -k_2 x_2 - c(\dot{x}_2 - \dot{x}_1)$

5. (a) $v_0 \left(\dfrac{2h}{g} \right)^{1/2}$

(b) $y = -\dfrac{\frac{1}{2} g x^2}{v_0^2 + h}$

7. (a) $\dfrac{v_0^2}{g} \sin 2\alpha,$

(b) $y = -\dfrac{g}{2(v_0 \cos \alpha)^2} x^2 + (\tan \alpha) x$

9. $m\ddot{x} = -kx(x^2 + y^2)^{-3/2}, \quad m\ddot{y} = -ky(x^2 + y^2)^{-3/2}$

11. (a) $m_1 \ddot{\mathbf{R}}_1 = (\mathbf{R}_1 - \mathbf{R}_2) \dfrac{m_1 m_2}{r^3}, \quad m_2 \ddot{\mathbf{R}}_2 = (\mathbf{R}_2 - \mathbf{R}_1) \dfrac{m_1 m_2}{r^3}$

(b) $\ddot{\mathbf{U}} = \dfrac{m_1 + m_2}{r^3} \mathbf{U}, \quad \ddot{\mathbf{V}} = 0$

(c) The center of mass of the system moves in a straight lines with constant speed, since $\ddot{\mathbf{V}} = 0$. The motion of the second body relative to the first is as in Exercise 10.

Section 8.5

1. $LI_1'' + R_1 I_1' + \dfrac{1}{C}(I_1 - I_2) = 0, \quad R_2 I_2' + \dfrac{1}{C}(I_2 - I_1) = E'(t),$

$I_1(0) = I_1'(0) = 0, \quad I_2(0) = \dfrac{E(0)}{R_2}$

3. $L(I_1' - I_2') + R_1 I_1 = 0, \quad L(I_2' - I_1') + R_2 I_2 = E, \quad I_1(0) = \dfrac{E}{R_1 + R_2},$

$I_1(t) = 2e^{-t/6}, \quad I_2(t) = 6 - 4e^{-t/6}$

5. $L_1 I_1' + (R_1 + R_2)I_1 - R_2 I_2 = 0,$

$$R_2 I_2' - R_2 I_1' + \left(\frac{1}{C_1} + \frac{1}{C_2}\right)I_2 - \frac{1}{C_2} I_3 = 0,$$

$$R_3 I_3' + \frac{1}{C_2}(I_3 - I_2) = E'(t), \quad I_1(0) = I_2(0) = 0, \quad I_3(0) = \frac{E(0)}{R_3}$$

7. $\left(\frac{1}{R_1} + \frac{1}{R_2}\right)E_1' - \frac{1}{R_2} E_2' + \frac{1}{L} E_1 = 0, \quad \left(\frac{1}{R_2} + \frac{1}{R_3}\right)E_2 - \frac{1}{R_2} E_1 = I(t),$

$$E_1(0) = \frac{R_1 R_3 I(0)}{R_1 + R_2 + R_3}$$

Section 8.6

7. $\dfrac{dH}{dt} = hH(1 - aH - bP), \quad \dfrac{dP}{dt} = k(1 + cH - dP),$

where $h, k, a, b, c,$ and d are positive constants.

CHAPTER IX

Section 9.1

1. (a) $\dfrac{1}{s}$ (c) $\dfrac{2}{s^3}$ (e) $\dfrac{a}{s^2 + a^2}$

(g) $\dfrac{1 - e^{-s}}{s}$ (i) $\dfrac{1 - 2e^{-s} + e^{-2s}}{s^2}$

2. (a) $\dfrac{1}{s + 5}$ (c) $\dfrac{s}{s^2 + 25}$ (e) $\dfrac{3}{s + 2} + \dfrac{4}{s + 1}$

3. (a) e^{-2t} (c) $\cos 2t$ (e) $3e^{2t} - 5e^{-7t}$

5. (a) $\pi^{1/2} 2^{-1} s^{-3/2}$

7. (a) $\dfrac{1}{s} \dfrac{1 - e^{-sT/2}}{1 - e^{-sT}}$

8. (a) $x(t) = -2e^{2t} - 1$

Section 9.3

2. (a) $\dfrac{2}{s+1} - \dfrac{12}{s^2+16}$

(c) $\dfrac{3}{(s-2)^2+9}$

(e) $\dfrac{24}{(s+3)^5}$

(g) $\dfrac{2s^3-6s}{(s^2+1)^3}$

3. (a) $\dfrac{\sqrt{\pi}}{2(s-2)^{3/2}}$

(c) $\dfrac{2}{s(s-1)^3}$

(e) $\dfrac{1}{s}e^{-2s}$

(g) $\left(\dfrac{2}{s^3}+\dfrac{2}{s^2}+\dfrac{1}{s}\right)e^{-s}$

4. (a) $s^2F(s)-s-2$

(c) $s^3F(s)-s^2+s-5$

(e) $s^4F(s)-2s^3$

Section 9.4

1. (a) te^{-t}

(c) $e^{-t}\cosh 2t$

(e) $e^{-t}-e^{-2t}$

2. (a) $2e^t-2e^{-2t}$

(c) $\tfrac{8}{5}e^t+3te^t-\tfrac{8}{5}\cos 3t-\tfrac{6}{5}\sin 3t$

(e) $\dfrac{1}{12}e^{2t}-\dfrac{1}{12}e^{-t}\cos\sqrt{3}\,t-\dfrac{\sqrt{3}}{9}e^{-t}\sin\sqrt{3}\,t$

4. (a) $\dfrac{t^3}{6}$

(c) $e^{2t}-e^t$

5. (a) $f(t)=\begin{cases}0, & 0\le t\le 1,\\(t-1)e^{2(t-1)}, & t>1\end{cases}$

(c) $\left(\dfrac{1}{\sqrt{\pi}}\right)\displaystyle\int_0^t \sqrt{u}\,e^{2u}\cos(t-u)\,du$

(e) $\displaystyle\int_0^t f(t-u)e^{-u}\,du$

Section 9.5

1. (a) $x=e^{-2t}+e^t$

(c) $x=-\tfrac{1}{3}\sin 2t+\tfrac{8}{3}\sin t$

(e) $x=e^{-2t}+\cos t+1$

3. $x=\begin{cases}\cosh t, & 0\le t\le 1,\\\cosh t+(1-t)+\sinh(t-1), & t>1\end{cases}$

5. (a) $x=1+e^{2t}$

6. (a) $x_1 = e^t - \frac{1}{3}e^{-3t} - \frac{2}{3}, \quad x_2 = \frac{3}{2}e^t + \frac{1}{6}e^{-3t} - \frac{2}{3}$

(c) $x_1 = e^{-t}(2 \cos t - \sin t), \quad x_2 = e^{-t}(1 - \cos t + 3 \sin t)$

(e) $x_1 = -\frac{2}{5}e^{-t} \cos 2t + \frac{4}{5}e^{-t} \sin 2t + 2t + \frac{12}{5}$,

$x_2 = \frac{8}{5}e^{-t} \cos 2t + \frac{4}{5}e^{-t} \sin 2t + 2t + \frac{12}{5}$

CHAPTER X

Section 10.1

1. (a) Hyperbolic (c) Parabolic

Section 10.2

1. $u_t(x, t) = ku_{xx}(x, t), \quad 0 < x < 2, \quad t > 0$

$u(0, t) = 0, \quad u(2, t) = 10, \quad t \geq 0$

$u(x, 0) = 5x, \quad 0 \leq x \leq 2$

3. (a) $u(x) = A + \dfrac{B - A}{a} x$ (c) $u(x) = T$

Section 10.3

1. (a) $u(x, t) = 3 \sin\left(\dfrac{\pi x}{a}\right)e^{-(\pi/a)^2 kt} - 5 \sin\left(\dfrac{4\pi x}{a}\right)e^{-(4\pi/a)^2 kt}$

(c) $u(x, t) = \dfrac{4a}{\pi^2} \sum_{m=1}^{\infty} \dfrac{(-1)^{m+1}}{(2m - 1)^2} \sin \dfrac{(2m - 1)\pi x}{a} \exp\left[-\dfrac{(2m - 1)^2\pi^2}{a^2} kt\right]$

3. (a) $u(x, t) = 1 - x$

(c) $u(x, t) = 2x - \dfrac{16}{3\pi} \sin \pi x\, e^{-\pi^2 kt}$

$+ \dfrac{3}{2\pi} \sin 2\pi x\, e^{-4\pi^2 kt} + \dfrac{16}{\pi} \sum_{n=3}^{\infty} \dfrac{(-1)^{n+1}}{n(n^2 - 4)} \sin n\pi x\, e^{-\pi^2 kt}$

5. $u(x, t) = \dfrac{16}{\pi^2} \sum_{n=1}^{\infty} \dfrac{\cos[(2n - 1)\pi x/2]}{(2n - 1)^2} e^{-(2n-1)^2\pi^2 kt/4}$

7. $g_n(t) = e^{-(n\pi/a)^2 kt} \displaystyle\int_0^t f_n(s)e^{(n\pi/a)^2 ks}\, ds$

Section 10.4

1. $u(x, y) = \dfrac{8a^2}{\pi^3} \displaystyle\sum_{m=1}^{\infty} \dfrac{\sin[(2m-1)\pi x/a]\sinh[(2m-1)\pi y/a]}{(2m-1)^3 \sinh[(2m-1)\pi b/a]}$

3. $u(x, y) = \dfrac{8a^2}{\pi^3} \displaystyle\sum_{m=1}^{\infty} \dfrac{\sin[(2m-1)\pi x/a]\{\sinh[(2m-1)\pi y/a]}{}$
$\dfrac{\qquad\qquad\qquad - \sinh[(2m-1)\pi(y-b)/a]\}}{(2m-1)^3\sinh[(2m-1)\pi b/a]}$

5. $u(x, y) = \displaystyle\sum_{n=1}^{\infty} C_n \sin \dfrac{n\pi x}{a} \left[\cosh \dfrac{n\pi y}{a} + \dfrac{ah}{n\pi} \sinh \dfrac{n\pi y}{a} \right],$

$C_n = 2 \left[a \left(\cosh \dfrac{n\pi b}{a} + \dfrac{ah}{n\pi} \sinh \dfrac{n\pi b}{a} \right) \right]^{-1} \displaystyle\int_0^a f(x) \sin \dfrac{n\pi x}{a} \, dx$

7. $u(x, y) = \displaystyle\sum_{n=1}^{\infty} C_n \sin \dfrac{n\pi x}{a} e^{-n\pi y/a}, \quad C_n = \dfrac{2}{a} \displaystyle\int_0^a f(x) \sin \dfrac{n\pi x}{a} \, dx$

Section 10.6

7. $u(x, t) = \sin \dfrac{\pi x}{a} \cos \dfrac{\pi c t}{a} + \dfrac{a}{2\pi c} \sin \dfrac{2\pi x}{a} \sin \dfrac{2\pi c t}{a}$

Section 10.7

3. $u_x = \sin \phi \cos \theta \, u_\rho + \dfrac{\cos \phi \cos \theta}{\rho} u_\phi - \dfrac{u_\theta \sin \theta}{\rho \sin \phi}$

5. $g_x = \dfrac{1}{\sinh^2 u + \sin^2 v} [(\sinh u \cos v)g_u - (\cosh u \sin v)g_v]$

$g_y = \dfrac{1}{\sinh^2 u + \sin^2 v} [(\cosh u \sin v)g_u + (\sinh u \cos v)g_v]$

8. (a) $u(r) = \dfrac{1}{\ln b - \ln a} [A \ln b - B \ln a + (B - A) \ln r]$

9. (a) $u(\rho) = \dfrac{1}{b - a} \left[bB - aA + ab(A - B)\dfrac{1}{\rho} \right]$

Section 10.8

1. $u(r, t) = A_0 + \displaystyle\sum_{n=1}^{\infty} A_n J_0(\lambda_n r)e^{-\lambda_n^2 kt}, \quad$ where $\quad J_0'(\lambda_n c) = 0$ and

$A_n = \dfrac{2}{c^2[J_0(\lambda_n c)]^2} \displaystyle\int_0^c rf(r)J_0(\lambda_n r) \, dr$

3. $u(r, t) = \sum\limits_{n=1}^{\infty} A_n J_0(\lambda_n r)e^{-\lambda_n^2 kt}$,   where $\lambda_n J_0'(\lambda_n c) + hJ_0(\lambda_n c) = 0$

and

$$A_n = \frac{2}{c^2} \frac{\lambda_n^2}{(\lambda_n^2 + h^2)[J_0(\lambda_n c)]^2} \int_0^c rf(r)J_0(\lambda_n r)\, dr.$$

(At the boundary, $u_v(c, t) + Hu(c, t) = 0$, where H is a positive constant.)

5. $u(r, z) = \sum\limits_{n=1}^{\infty} A_n \sinh \lambda_n z J_0(\lambda_n r)$,   where $J_0(\lambda_n c) = 0$ and

$$A_n = \frac{2}{c^2 \sinh \lambda_n h [J_1(\lambda_n c)]^2} \int_0^c rf(r)J_0(\lambda_n r)\, dr.$$

9. $u(r, t) = \sum\limits_{n=1}^{\infty} A_n J_0(\lambda_n r) \cos \lambda_n ct$,   where $J_0(\lambda_n a) = 0$ and

$$A_n = \frac{2}{a^2[J_1(\lambda_n a)]^2} \int_0^a rJ_0(\lambda_n r)f(r)\, dr.$$

Section 10.9

1. $u(\rho, \phi) = \sum\limits_{n=0}^{\infty} A_n \left(\dfrac{c}{\rho}\right)^{n+1} P_n(\cos \phi)$,

$$A_n = \frac{2n + 1}{2} \int_0^{\pi} f(\phi)P_n(\cos \phi) \sin \phi\, d\phi$$

3. $u(\rho, \phi) = \sum\limits_{m=1}^{\infty} A_m \left(\dfrac{\rho}{c}\right)^{2m-1} P_{2m-1}(\cos \phi)$,

$$A_m = (4m - 1) \int_0^{\pi/2} f(\phi)P_{2m-1}(\cos \phi) \sin \phi\, d\phi$$

5. $u(\rho, \theta) = \tfrac{1}{2}A_0 + \sum\limits_{n=1}^{\infty} \rho^{a_n}(A_n \cos n\theta + B_n \sin n\theta)$,

$a_n = \tfrac{1}{2}[-1 + (1 + 4n^2 \csc^2 \alpha)^{1/2}]$,

$A_n = (\pi c^{a_n})^{-1} \int_{-\pi}^{\pi} f(\theta)\, d\theta$, $B_n = (\pi c^{a_n})^{-1} \int_{-\pi}^{\pi} f(\theta) \sin n\theta\, d\theta$

Section 10.10

1. $u(x, y, z) = \sum\limits_{m,n=1}^{\infty} A_{mn} \sin m\pi x \sin n\pi y \sinh(\sqrt{m^2 + n^2}\, \pi z)$,

$$A_{mn} = \frac{4}{\sinh(\sqrt{m^2 + n^2}\, \pi)} \int_0^1 \int_0^1 f(x, y) \sin m\pi x \sin n\pi y\, dy\, dx$$

3. $u(r, z, t) = \frac{1}{2} \sum_{m=0}^{\infty} A_{m0} J_0(\mu_m r) \exp(-\mu_m^2 kt)$

$$+ \sum_{m=0, n=1}^{\infty} A_{mn} J_0(\mu_m r) \cos \frac{n\pi z}{h} \exp\left\{\left[-\mu_m^2 - \left(\frac{n\pi}{h}\right)^2\right] kt\right\},$$

$$A_{mn} = \frac{4}{c^2 h [J_0(\mu_m c)]^2} \int_0^h \int_0^c rf(r, z) J_0(\mu_m r) \sin \frac{n\pi z}{h} \, dr \, dz,$$

where $J_0'(\mu_m c) = 0$.

CHAPTER XI

Section 11.1

1. (a) The solutions are $x(t) = A \cos(2t - \alpha)$, $y(t) = -2A \sin(2t - \alpha)$. The trajectories are the ellipses $x^2/A^2 + y^2/(4A^2) = 1$.

(c) The solutions are $x(t) = c_1 e^{-t}$, $y = 2/(c_1^2 e^{-2t} + c_2)$ and $x(t) = 0$, $y(t) = c$. The trajectories are the curves $y = 2/(x^2 + c_2)$ and the points $(0, c)$.

3. (a) $(3, 7)$ (c) $(-2, 1)$, $(8, -4)$
   (e) $(\pm 2, 0)$

6. $x^2 + y^2 = c$ **8.** $y = cx - 3x^2$

Section 11.2

1. (a) Isolated critical points $(\pm 1, 0)$
   (c) Isolated critical points $(1, 1)$ and $(2, 2)$
   (e) Isolated critical points $(m\pi, \pi/2 + n\pi)$, where m and n are integers

6. (a) Stable, but not asymptotically stable
   (c) Unstable

Section 11.3

1. (a) Positive definite   (c) Negative definite

5. $E(x, y) = x^2 + 2y^2$

7. $E(x, y) = x^4 + 2y^2$

Section 11.4

2. Asymptotically stable   **4.** Unstable

6. $(0, 0)$ asymptotically stable, $(1, -1)$ unstable

9. $a > c$ and $d > b$

CHAPTER XII

Section 12.1

7. (a) $y(x) = 2 + \int_1^x \{ty(t) + [y(t)]^2\} \, dt$

8. (a) $y = (5 + x)e^x$

Section 12.2

1. (a) $y = -(x^{4/3} + 3)^{1/2}$ for all x

(c) $y = x(5x^2 - 1)^{1/2}, \quad x > \dfrac{1}{\sqrt{5}}$

2. $y_0(x) = 1, \quad y_1(x) = 1 - x + \frac{1}{2}x^2,$
$y_2(x) = 1 - x - \frac{1}{2}x^2 + \frac{2}{3}x^3 - \frac{1}{4}x^4 + \frac{1}{20}x^5$

6. (a) $y_1(x) = 0$ for all x_1; $y_2(x) = 0$ for $x \le 0$ and $y_2(x) = x^{3/2}$ for $x > 0$

7. Yes

Section 12.3

5. $(0, 4, 6t), \quad (2, 8, 8)$

9. $(0, 1, 2)$

Section 12.4

4. $x_1(t) = (t + 1)^{-1}, \quad x_2(t) = 5(t + 1), \quad t > -1$

6. $\mathbf{x}_0(t) = (-2, \ 1), \qquad \mathbf{x}_1(t) = (-2 - t - t^2, \ 1 - 4t),$
$\mathbf{x}_2(t) = (-2 - t + 3t^2 - \frac{17}{3}t^3 - \frac{1}{4}t^4, \ 1 - 4t + \frac{7}{2}t^2 + t^3 + t^4$

12. (a) $x(t) = \frac{1}{2}(t^2 - 2t + 2)$ for all t

APPENDIX

Section A1

1. There are $4! = 24$ permutations.

2. (a) 2 (c) 0 (e) 5 (g) 3   **3.** (a) -1 (c) -1 (e) -1

5. (a) 22 (c) -17 **6.** (a) -2 (c) 29

9. $3x^2 + 2$

Section A2

5. (a) -10 **6.** (a) 178

7. (a) -83 **8.** (a) -324

9. 252

Section A3

1. (a) $A_{11} = 0,\quad A_{12} = 1,\qquad A_{21} = -3,\quad A_{22} = 2$

    (c) $A_{11} = 2,\quad A_{12} = -7,\quad A_{13} = 1,$
$\quad\quad A_{21} = 4,\quad A_{22} = -7,\quad A_{23} = -5$
$\quad\quad A_{31} = 2,\quad A_{32} = 7,\qquad A_{33} = 1$

2. (a) 20

3. $(-1)^N d_1 d_2 \cdots d_n,\quad N = \dfrac{n(n-1)}{2}$

Section A4

1. $m = n$ and A nonsingular   **3.** $x_1 = -\frac{43}{6},\quad x_2 = \frac{22}{3}$

5. Solutions $x_1 = c - 2,\quad x_2 = 3c$

7. $x_1 = -\frac{34}{37},\quad x_2 = -\frac{25}{37},\quad x_3 = \frac{44}{37}$

9. Solutions $x_1 = -c - \frac{3}{2},\quad x_2 = 2c,\quad x_3 = 5c - \frac{3}{2}$

11. This way the rounding errors are multiplied by a numerically smaller quantity.

Subject Index

Numbers in parentheses indicate exercises.